D1094511

Statistical Analysis in the

Geological Sciences

STATISTICAL

ANALYSIS IN

THE GEOLOGICAL

SCIENCES

Robert L. Miller

Department of the Geophysical Sciences

University of Chicago

James Steven Kahn

Lawrence Radiation Laboratory

University of California

JOHN WILEY AND SONS, INC.

New York   London

Library of Congress Catalog Card Number: 62–15186
Printed in the United States of America

To Dorothy and Barbara

Preface

The history of application of statistical analysis in the earth sciences can be conveniently divided into three major stages.

The first stage spans the years from roughly 1890 to the early 1930's. In Europe, the prolific and influential writings of Karl Pearson should be mentioned first. The series of essays entitled *Contributions to the mathematical theory of evolution* and published in Series A of the *Philosophical Transactions* contain a great deal of interest to the paleontologist since in many cases the problems dealt with were based on fossil data. The reader interested in detailed references in this early period in the development of paleobiometrics will find detailed bibliography of both Europe and North America in K. Schmid, 1934, Biometrische Untersuchungen au Foraminiferen aus d. Phacen von Ceram., *Ecologol. Geological Helvetiae* 27: 1; 46–128. This paper also contains an early application and discussion of the normal bivariate surface, contoured on a plane as ellipses of equal probability. The earliest work in Russia known to the authors appears to be that of Laevinson-Lessing, who systematically applied statistics to petrology and geochemistry for about twenty years, beginning in 1914. He studied frequency distributions of "magmatic coefficients." These magmatic coefficients are modifications of the parameters of magmatic rocks after Niggli, Shand, Wolf, and others. Laevinson-Lessing attempted to establish bounds by means of statistical analysis of the coefficients typifying the various magmatic rocks, for example, the boundary between dacite and andesite, andesite and basalt, etc. The analysis was based on the simplest form of large sample statistics, including means, variances, and skewness of frequency distributions of the magmatic coefficients.

His papers include:

F. J. Laevinson-Lessing, 1923, On limits and subdivisions of the family of andesites, *Izv. Geol. Kom. T.* 43: 6; 723–735.

———, 1925, On differentiation of basalts and andesites, *Izv. Geol. Kom.* 44: 4; 411–423.

———, 1930, On differentiation of dacite and liporite, *Dokl. Acad. U.S.S.R.*, Ser. A., 8: 179–185.

———, 1930, Statistical characteristics of the Kimizma trachite, *Izv. U.S.S.R.*, 7: 1; 101–111.

A scattering of papers appeared in the 1920's. Examples are H. S. Pearson, 1928, Chinese fossil Suidae, *Paleontologia Sinica V*, fasc. 5, Ser. C., 1–75, including use of $\bar{X}$, V, and the t-test; and R. Brinkmann, 1929, Statistisch-biostratigraphische Untersuchungen an mitteljurassischen Ammoniten, etc., *Abh. Ges. Wiss. Göttingen Math. Phys.* Kl. N.F. 13 Heft 3, pp. 1–249. The latter is a much quoted monograph.

The early 1930's showed a steady but small flow of papers in paleo-biometrics, culminated in 1939 by G. G. Simpson and A. Roe, *Quantitative Zoology*, McGraw-Hill Book Co., New York. This textbook laid the foundation for the activity and expansion of paleobiometrics in the postwar period from 1945 to the present. Examples of early papers include: A. H. Hersh, 1934, Evolutionary relative growth in the Titanotheres, *Am. Nat.* 68: 537–561, R. C. Robb, 1935, and later, A study of mutations in evolution. Part 1. Evolution in the equine skull, *Jour. Genet* 31: 39–46, which includes regression line analysis.

The record in other branches of geology before the middle thirties appears to be very spotty, although occasional papers appeared discussing problems later formalized by statisticians and explored by geologists in the postwar period. For example, C. J. C. Ewing, 1931, A comparison of the methods of heavy mineral separation, *Geol. Mag.*, discusses qualitatively the subject of operator variation.

The second stage spans the years from the middle 1930's to just before the entry of the United States into World War II. In the middle thirties, a considerable expansion of activity in statistical analysis of sediment size data followed the nonstatistical work of Wentworth and others on graphic analysis of size frequency distributions. The names of Krumbein, Otto, and Dryden appear during this period. By far the most prolific and influential was W. C. Krumbein, who has continued his considerable activity in statistical analysis in sedimentation and stratigraphy through the present period. Examples of his early papers are: Size frequency distributions of sediments, *Jour. Sed. Petrol.* 4: 65–77 in 1934, and Application of logrithmic moments to size frequency distributions of sediments, *Jour. Sed. Petrol.* 6: 35–47 in 1936, which includes the widely used log normal transformation.

An important paper by Churchill Eisenhart appeared in 1935 in the context of sedimentological studies entitled: A test for significance of lithological variation, *Jour. Sed. Petrol.* 5: 137–145. Eisenhart is, however, a statistician, and unfortunately, this was the only geological paper he published during the prewar period.

An early application of the methods of quality control appeared in G. Otto, 1937, The use of statistical methods in effecting improvements in a Jones sample splitter, *Jour. Sed. Petrol.* 7: 110–132.

During the second stage, papers in areas of geologic interest other than sedimentology and paleontology were still relatively rare. Examples include: an application of smoothing and subsequent Fourier analysis for periodicity in bed thickness was published by H. Korn, 1938, Schichtung und absolute Zeit, *Neuea. Jahrb. f. Min. Pal. Geol., A.* 74: 1; 51–166. Two papers in 1940 on the statistical distribution of elements appeared in Russian journals. These are: N. K. Rasumovsky, 1940, The character of the distribution of metal content in mine deposits, *Doklad. Acad. Sci., U.S.S.R.*, T 28, No. 9, pp. 815 ff, and N. K. Rasumovsky, 1940(?), *The logrithmic normal probability distribution function and its properties. Notes.* Leningrad State University, XX, pp. 105–121.

The post World War II period from about 1945 to the present showed a considerable expansion of statistical analysis into virtually all fields of geology. A number of papers were devoted all or in part to discussing the possibilities of applied statistical analysis in various branches in geology. Examples of papers include D. M. Shaw and J. D. Bankier, 1954, Statistical methods applied to geochemistry, *Geochim. et Cosmochim. Acta* 5: 111–123; W. C. Krumbein, 1958, Measurement and error in regional stratigraphic analysis, *Jour. Sed. Petrol.* 28: 175–185; A. N. Strahler, 1953, Statistical analysis in geomorphic research, *Jour. Geol.* 62: 1–25; J. E. Prentice, 1949, The statistical method in paleontology, *Brit. Sci. News* 3(25); 17–19; E. Ingerson, 1954, Geochemical work of the geochemistry and petrology branch, U.S. Geol. Survey, *Geochim et Cosmochim. Acta* 5: 20–39; D. Leitch, 1951, Biometrics and systematics in relation to paleontology, *Proc. Linn. Soc. London*, 162(2): 159–170; R. L. Miller, 1953, Introduction to special issues on statistics in geology, *Jour. Geol.* 61: 479–481; J. C. Griffiths, 1960, Aspects of measurement in the geosciences, *Min. Ind. Bull.* 29(4); F. Chayes, 1956, *Petrographic Modal Analysis*, John Wiley and Sons, New York; and W. C. Krumbein, 1954, Applications of statistical methods to sedimentary rocks, *Jour. Amer. Stat. Assoc.* 49: 51–66.

The *Journal of Geology* published two special issues on statistics in geology, Vol. 61(6), 1953, and Vol. 62(1), 1954. An Earth Sciences Panel representing the fields of geology, meteorology, geophysics, and geochemistry was organized at about this time under the auspices of the American Statistical Association's Committee on Statistics in the Physical Sciences. A symposium on statistics in geology was held at the 1954 G.S.A. meetings in Los Angeles with papers presented by investigators from virtually every branch of geology. In 1956, a book utilizing statistical reasoning and methods to a considerable degree was written on modal analysis: Felix Chayes, 1956, *Petrographic Modal analysis*, John Wiley and Sons, New York. In 1959, a second book appeared on evolution and paleontology, in which statistical analysis formed an important part: E. C. Olsen, and R. L. Miller, 1958, *Morphological Integration*, University of Chicago Press, Chicago.

Two general papers discussing problems in application of statistics in geology are: W. C. Krumbein, 1960, Some problems in applying statistics to geology, *Applied Statistics* IX; 2: 82–91, in which he discusses the problem of sampling in geology and the difficulties resulting from too many variables as is often true in geological problems, and W. C. Krumbein, 1960, The geological population as a framework for analysing numerical data in geology, Liverpool and Manchester, *Geol. Jour.*, Vol. 2; Part 3: 341–336, which includes a general discussion of statistics in geology, the nature of the statistical population in geological context, and a discussion of sampling.

The purpose of this book is to present a reasonably general survey of methods of statistical analysis, illustrative applications of these methods to a wide variety of problems in the earth sciences, and finally to survey the literature on statistical analysis within the earth sciences. The literature is treated in two ways: by reference in the text with a footnote for the complete reference, and in the form of an annotated bibliography at the end of a topic in the text. The list of papers is drawn from sources in Europe and Asia as well as the United States. Although extensive, it is by no means complete.

We hope the book will serve as a general reference for research workers in the various branches of the earth sciences, and also as a text for a graduate level survey course on application of statistical method in these fields.

We strongly recommend that the interested student take several courses in statistics, and that the investigator, whenever possible, seek the aid and advice of professional statisticians if he contemplates statistical analysis as a part of the problem at hand. This last comment is particularly pertinent, since the research worker at the present time is often faced with the decision as to which of several techniques to use, rather than looking to see if one exists for a particular problem.

The application of statistics to problems in geophysics is outside the scope of this book, and seems to us to require separate treatment. We do not include tables in this book except when they are in our judgment difficult to obtain. For such easily available and standard tables as the normal, "*t*," "*F*," chi-square, etc., we recommend the purchase of A. Hald 1952, *Statistical Tables and Formulas*, John Wiley and Sons, New York. A more complete set of tables is that of K. Pearson 1930, *Tables for Statisticians and Biometricians*, Cambridge University Press, England, third edition.

This book was begun in 1954 and worked on at intermittent periods to the present time. During this interval we have had helpful suggestions from numerous people. To all of these, our appreciation is given.

To W. C. Kruskal of the Department of Statistics, University of Chicago, we owe a particular debt of gratitude. He has patiently contributed advice throughout the course of the book. Both of us have also profited greatly from attending his lectures.

We are also greatly indebted to John W. Pratt of the Department of Statistics, Harvard University, for a critical reading of the entire manuscript. Paul E. Potter, Illinois State Geological Survey, and John Imbrie, Department of Geology, Columbia University, read and discussed portions of the manuscript. Their suggestions and comments have been most helpful.

We acknowledge with thanks the assistance of E. C. Olson and Ralph G. Johnson of the Department of the Geophysical Sciences, University of Chicago, for discussion and suggestions on the sections on paleobiometrics. Andrew B. Vistellus, Academy of Sciences, U.S.S.R., Leningrad University, kindly supplied information on the Russian literature. Robert Elashoff, Department of Statistics, Harvard University, contributed discussion and advice on the section on the coefficient of variability.

William Bryant, Richard Harkness, and Steven Obrebski aided in checking and proofing the manuscript. The typing was done by Virginia Wilson, Odessa Kellem, Elizabeth Ross, Ann Richardson, and Beverly Johnson.

This book was written with the generous assistance of the Office of Naval Research (Contract N6ori 020(58)). We are grateful to D. M. Gilford of the Office of Naval Research for patience and aid during the long period before the manuscript was completed.

ROBERT L. MILLER
Chicago, Illinois
JAMES S. KAHN
Livermore, California

June 1962

Contents

xiii

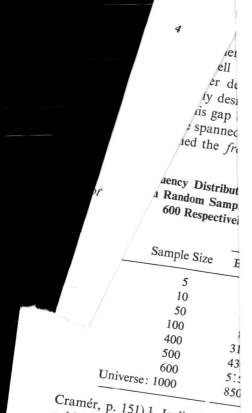

4

...ler
...ell
...er de
...ly desi
...is gap
... spanned
...led the *fr*

...uency Distribut
... Random Samp
600 Respectivel

Sample Size	
5	
10	
50	
100	
400	
500	31
600	43
Universe: 1000	5..
	850

Cramér, p. 151).[1] In light of this
pebbles. Subdivide sample space
500, 600. That is, impartially selec
5 and impartially select 10 pebbles,
an experiment may be summarized
In general, as we increase the sa
brown, black, and green pebbles to
frequency, tends to become more or le
about this constant value. For exa
outcome—a brown pebble—varies fro
varies from one experiment to the ne
variation of the relative frequency of

DEFINITION OF PROBABILITY

The concept of the relative frequency
fixed value leads to a definition of prob
[1] H. Cramér, 1950, *Mathematical methods of*
Princeton, New Jersey.

---

chapter **1**

Probability

SOME COMMENTS ON PROBABILITY

As stated in the preface, this book is a discussion, from an earth science viewpoint, of a tool called statistical inference or statistics. The foundations upon which the theory of statistics rests is the theory of probability. Hence, to facilitate the understanding of statistical inference, even at the level of this book, it is felt that a brief discussion into the realm of probability will be useful. For certain reasons, the authors do not feel that it is appropriate to undertake a lengthy discourse. First, much scholarly and extensive work has been prepared and is already in print. Some of these works are presented in the selected bibliography at the end of this chapter to facilitate investigation of those facets of the problem which interest the reader most. Second, the areas covered by the authors are those which they feel bear directly upon the nature and scope of this book.

SOME CONCEPTS OF PROBABILITY

As an example, consider a group of 1000 pebbles collected at Lake Michigan. Table 1.1 indicates the result of classifying the pebbles on the basis of color.

TABLE 1.1

Classification of 1000 Pebbles on the Basis of Color

Color	Frequency
Brown	852
Black	93
Green	55
Total	1000

1

We shall assume
as far as color is co
bag and decides to s
of selecting a brow
for this answer may
which 852 are brow
selected would be br
and observed. This
called an *outcome* or e
or *sample space*. The
that may result from th
In our example there a
black pebble, and a gre

In arriving at the con
pebble was 0.852, two a
events were mutually exc
pebbles was equally likely
was just as likely to be sele
by assuming we could dil
second assumption we hav
assume it is satisfied. *This
generally called the classic
of an event is the ratio of the
total number of possible even
equally likely.*

An immediate shortcomir
becomes apparent when the
considers the assumption of
gravity may cause the black
differences in the size of the pel
of the bag. The pebbles, on th
mutually exclusive but not nece
tion is of no help when either of t
is not fulfilled. The familiar case
The outcome of flipping a single
Heads can be told from tails. No
probability of heads is $\frac{1}{2}$. In rea
favored on one side or the other.
likely (or not mutually exclusive),
in deducing the desired probabilitie
fiable to employ it.

Geological research presents prot

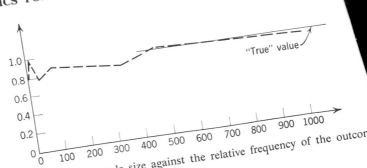

FIG. 1.1. Plot of the sample size against the relative frequency of the outcome
brown pebbles.

Feller (1950),[1] and Doob (1953),[2] e.g., are proponents. That is, *in a series
of random experiments, we should be able to assign a number p to an outcome
such that in many experiments, the relative frequency of the outcome will be
almost equal to p.* In the preceding example, p would be about 0.85. This
is written

$$p \text{ (event = brown pebble)} \cong 0.85 \qquad (1.1)$$

Owing to the nature of geologic problems, the frequency concept of
probability will be adopted in this book. Henceforth, frequency shall refer
to relative frequency, unless otherwise stated. By relative frequency shall
be meant the absolute frequency of an event (or total number of observations of a particular event) divided by the total number of all observations
of all events in the sample. For example, the absolute frequency of black
pebbles for a sample of size 400 was 60 (Table 1.2), whereas the relative
frequency was 0.15 (Table 1.3).

The probability of an event is seen, therefore, to vary between 0 and 1.
It is never negative and never greater than 1, but it may be 1 and it may
be 0. This may be expressed as

$$0 \leq p \leq 1 \qquad (1.2)$$

where $p \leq 1$ means p less than or equal to one and $0 \leq p$ means p greater
than or equal to zero.

When an event is certain to occur, then $p = 1$. For example, the
probability that a single pebble selected from a group of pebbles is going
to be a pebble is certain. Hence the probability of such an event is 1.
However, if $p = 1$, the event is by no means certain. Suppose that instead

[1] W. Feller, 1950, *An introduction to probability theory and its applications*, Vol. I,
John Wiley, New York.
[2] J. L. Doob, 1953, *Stochastic processes*, John Wiley, New York.

of 852 brown pebbles we had 996, the remaining being equally divided among black and green. In repeated experiments the probability of a brown pebble is almost one. However, the selection of a pebble does not presuppose the necessity of it being brown. It could be green or black.

The probability of an impossible event is 0. Hence, the probability of selecting a blue pebble from our collection of 1000 pebbles is 0. However,

TABLE 1.3

Relative Frequency of Brown, Black, and Green Pebbles from Random Samples of Sizes 5, 10, 50, 100, 400, 500, and 600 Respectively, from a Universe of 1000 Pebbles

Relative Frequency of Event

Sample Size	Brown	Black	Green	Total
5	0.80	0.20	0.00	1.00
10	1.00	0.00	0.00	1.00
50	0.76	0.14	0.02	1.00
100	0.86	0.09	0.05	1.00
400	0.80	0.15	0.05	1.00
500	0.86	0.09	0.05	1.00
600	0.86	0.10	0.04	1.00
Universe: 1000	0.85	0.09	0.06	1.00

if the probability of an event is 0 it is by no means impossible. This short discussion points to the notion of how difficult it is to predict single events, whereas groups of events may be predicted and predicted with some measure of reliability. This phase of probability is discussed in a later section of the book.

Finally, it must be emphasized that when we select a pebble from a group of 1000 we talk about the probability *before selection*. After a selection has been made the probability of a particular pebble having been selected is either 0 or 1. The event which has taken place is either a brown (or black or green) or not brown (or not black or not green).

CONDITIONAL AND MARGINAL PROBABILITIES FOR SINGLE EVENTS

A geologist returns from the field and classifies the sedimentary samples he has collected on the basis of two attributes: first, on the basis of the sedimentary rock type (Krynine, 1948)[1] and second, on the basis of the

[1] P. D. Krynine, 1948, The megascopic study and field classification of sedimentary rocks, *Jour. Geol.*, 56, 130–165.

modal size of the sediment. Table 1.4 represents the distribution of the samples.

This sort of representation may be generalized by letting the row attribute (rock type) be represented by R and the column attribute (modal size) be represented by C. Furthermore, the R attribute or *set*, a *collection of items with common attribute*, divides the sample or population into subsets, R_1, R_2, $\cdots R_i$, $\cdots R_r$, where R_i represents the ith subset of the R set. (Table 1.5.) Hence, R_i might represent any of the three rock types.

TABLE 1.4

Distribution of 2000 Samples Classified According to Sedimentary Rock Type and Modal Size

Rock Type	Coarse	Medium	Fine	Very Fine	Totals
		Modal Size			
Arkose	320	150	130	50	650
L.R. graywacke	50	500	450	100	1100
Quartzite	80	100	20	50	250
Totals	450	750	600	200	2000

It is to be thought of as the general subset of the R set. R_r is the last subset of the R set, and in our specific example would be the quartzites. Since R_i is to be considered a general subset of the r possible subsets of R, we may say i varies from 1 to r and in our example in particular, r is 3. Here, R_1 would represent the arkoses, R_2 the low rank graywackes, and $R_3 = R_r$ would represent the quartzites.

Similarly, the column attribute may be represented by the set C which divides the sample or population into subsets C_1, C_2, $\cdots$, C_j, $\cdots C_s$. The modal size of sediments is the set C with four subsets: C_1 or coarse sand, C_2 or medium sand, C_3 or fine sand, and $C_4 = C_s$ or very fine sand. This generalization is illustrated in Table 1.5. Here n_{ij} represents the number of observations in the ith row and jth column.

Any rectangular array such as is illustrated in Tables 1.4 and 1.5 is called a *matrix*. The size of the matrix is determined by the number of rows and columns it contains. The matrix represented in Table 1.5 is said to be an r by s matrix, $r \times s$. Thus the matrix in Table 1.4 is a 3×4 matrix and is generalized in Table 1.6. The first subscript will always refer to the row location, whereas the second subscript will always refer to the column location.

Thus n_{12} is understood to mean the number of observations in the first row and second column, or the number of samples which were medium

TABLE 1.5

Distribution of N Events Classified According to R and C

$$C$$

	C_1	C_2	C_3	C_4	$\cdots$	C_j	$\cdots$	C_s	Totals
R_1	n_{11}	n_{12}	n_{13}	n_{14}	$\cdots$	n_{1j}	$\cdots$	n_{1s}	$n_{1.}$
R_2	n_{21}	n_{22}	n_{23}	n_{24}	$\cdots$	n_{2j}	$\cdots$	n_{2s}	$n_{2.}$
R_3	n_{31}	n_{32}	n_{33}	n_{34}	$\cdots$	n_{3j}	$\cdots$	n_{3s}	$n_{3.}$
.	.	.	.	.		.		.	.
.	.	.	.	.		.		.	.
R_i	n_{i1}	n_{i2}	n_{i3}	n_{i4}	$\cdots$	n_{ij}	$\cdots$	n_{is}	$n_{i.}$
.	.	.	.	.		.		.	.
.	.	.	.	.		.		.	.
R_r	n_{r1}	n_{r2}	n_{r3}	n_{r4}	$\cdots$	n_{rj}	$\cdots$	n_{rs}	$n_{r.}$

R brackets the rows R_1 through R_r.

| Totals | $n.1$ | $n.2$ | $n.3$ | $n.4$ | $\cdots$ | $n.j$ | $\cdots$ | $n.s$ | $N = n..$ |

TABLE 1.6

Generalization of the Distribution of $N = 2000$ Samples Classified According to Sedimentary Rock Type $= R$ and Modal Size $= C$

$$C$$

		C_1	C_2	C_3	C_4	Totals
R	R_1	n_{11}	n_{12}	n_{13}	n_{14}	$n_{1.}$
	R_2	n_{21}	n_{22}	n_{23}	n_{24}	$n_{2.}$
	R_3	n_{31}	n_{32}	n_{33}	n_{34}	$n_{3.}$
	Totals	$n.1$	$n.2$	$n.3$	$n.4$	$N = n..$

arkoses. Here, n_{12} is 150, n_{34}, representing the number of very fine grained quartzites, is 50.

The total number of arkoses is obtained by adding together all arkoses which are coarse, medium, fine, and very fine. This total is called the *marginal absolute frequency of arkoses*. The marginal frequency of arkoses is 650. This is expressed symbolically as

$$\sum_{j=1}^{4} n_{1j} \tag{1.3}$$

Σ is the greek letter for capital sigma and $\sum\limits_{j=1}^{4} n_{1j}$ means the sum on those

n's with a constant row subscript, namely 1, and where j may take on all integral values from 1 up to and including 4. We know that j represents any of the column subsets. In this example, j represents any of the size subsets. Furthermore, we know we are dealing with only 4 subsets, namely, coarse, medium, fine, and very fine sand. Hence $\sum_{j=1}^{4} n_{1j}$ indicates a sum on the R_1 classification or arkoses, where j is 1, coarse arkoses; 2, medium

TABLE 1.7

	C_1	C_2	C_3	$\cdots$	C_j	$\cdots$	C_s	Totals
R_1	p_{11}	p_{12}	p_{13}	$\cdots$	p_{1j}	$\cdots$	p_{1s}	$p_{1.}$
R_2	p_{21}	p_{22}	p_{23}	$\cdots$	p_{2j}	$\cdots$	p_{2s}	$p_{2.}$
R_3	p_{31}	p_{32}	p_{33}	$\cdots$	p_{3j}	$\cdots$	p_{3s}	$p_{3.}$
$\cdot$	$\cdot$	$\cdot$	$\cdot$		$\cdot$		$\cdot$	$\cdot$
$\cdot$	$\cdot$	$\cdot$	$\cdot$		$\cdot$		$\cdot$	$\cdot$
R_i	p_{i1}	p_{i2}	p_{i3}	$\cdots$	p_{ij}	$\cdots$	p_{is}	$p_{i.}$
$\cdot$	$\cdot$	$\cdot$	$\cdot$		$\cdot$		$\cdot$	$\cdot$
$\cdot$	$\cdot$	$\cdot$	$\cdot$		$\cdot$		$\cdot$	$\cdot$
R_r	p_{r1}	p_{r2}	p_{r3}	$\cdots$	p_{rj}	$\cdots$	p_{rs}	$p_{r.}$
Totals	$p_{.1}$	$p_{.2}$	$p_{.3}$	$\cdots$	$p_{.j}$	$\cdots$	$p_{.s}$	$p_{..} = 1$

arkoses; 3, fine arkoses; and 4, very fine arkoses. Finally we represent (1.3) by $n_{1.}$. (Spoken n one dot.) $n_{2.}$, for example, means sum over j (over columns for the second row, i.e., the absolute marginal frequency of the low-rank graywackes. Similarly, the absolute marginal frequency of very fine-grained sands, $n_{.4}$, is 200. The sum of all observations may be represented by N or equivalently by n. (See Tables 1.5 and 1.6.)

If the cells of the $r \times s$ matrix and the absolute marginal frequencies are divided by N, Table 1.7 results, where

$$\frac{n_{ij}}{N} \cong p_{ij} \tag{1.4}$$

By our definition of probability, the probability of an event having both attribute R_1 and C_3, e.g., is $P\{R_1 C_3\} = p_{13}$. In general, the probability of an event having both attributes R_i and C_j is

$$P\{R_i C_j\} = p_{ij} \cong \frac{n_{ij}}{N} \tag{1.5}$$

Performing the preceding operation on Table 1.4, we immediately obtain Table 1.8.

Hence, the probability that a specimen is a very fine-grained arkose is $P\{R_1C_4\} \simeq 50/2000 \simeq 0.025$.

$P\{R_iC_j\}$ is called the *joint probability* of R_i and C_j. If we were interested in but an R or C subset, i.e., R_i for example, we would then speak of the *marginal probability* of R_i as being defined as

$$P\{R_i\} = \sum_{j=1}^{s} p_{ij} = p_i. \tag{1.6}$$

TABLE 1.8
Modal Size

		C_1	C_2	C_3	C_4	Totals
Rock Types	R_1	0.060	0.075	0.065	0.025	0.325
	R_2	0.025	0.250	0.225	0.050	0.550
	R_9	0.040	0.050	0.010	0.025	0.125
	Total	0.225	0.375	0.300	0.100	1.000

Similarly, the marginal probability of C_j is

$$P\{C_j\} = \sum_{i=1}^{r} p_{ij} = p_{.j} \tag{1.7}$$

Hence the marginal probability of coarse-grained sandstones is

$$P\{C_1\} = \sum_{i=1}^{3} p_{i1} = p_{11} + p_{21} + p_{31} = P\{R_1C_1\} + P\{R_2C_1\} + P\{R_3C_1\}$$

$$= \sum_{i=1}^{3} P\{R_iC_1\} = 0.062 + 0.025 + 0.040 = 0.225 = p_{.1} \tag{1.8}$$

Hence, the marginal probability of quartzites is 0.125; of medium-grained sand is 0.375.

Note that

$$p_{.1} \simeq \sum_{i=1}^{3} \frac{n_{i1}}{N} = \frac{n_{.1}}{N} \tag{1.9}$$

and

$$P\{C_1\} \simeq \frac{n_{.1}}{N} \tag{1.10}$$

In general,

$$P\{C_j\} \simeq \frac{n_{.j}}{N} \tag{1.11}$$

and

$$P\{R_i\} \cong \frac{n_{i.}}{N} \tag{1.12}$$

The concept of marginal probabilities ignores all classifications or sub-sets but those in which one is interested. It is equivalent to collapsing the two-way classification table and dealing but with one attribute. For example, if Table 1.8 were collapsed and just the rock types were considered we obtain Table 1.9. This table completely ignores the size classification. Perhaps it is now more apparent that $P\{R_3\} \cong 0.125$.

TABLE 1.9

R_1	0.325
R_2	0.550
R_3	0.125
Total	1.000

Suppose a sample of quartzite is selected from the group of 2000 speci-mens. What is the probability that it is coarse-grained? That is, what is the probability of obtaining a coarse-grained sample conditional on the knowledge that it is a quartzite? This may be written as

$$P\{c_1 \mid R_3\} \tag{1.13}$$

and is read the probability of C_1 given R_3. It is called the *conditional probability* of C_1 given R_3. We know we are dealing with a quartzite and we also are aware from Table 1.4 that of the 250 observed quartzites, 80 were coarse-grained. Hence, the probability of obtaining a coarse-grained specimen knowing it is a quartzite is 80/250. This is written

$$P\{C_1 \mid R_3\} = \frac{P\{C_1 R_3\}}{P\{R_3\}} \tag{1.14}$$

The conditional probability of the event C_1 given R_3 is the probability of the event C_1 and R_3, i.e., the joint probability of $\{C_1 R_3\}$, divided by the marginal probability of R_3. In general,

$$P\{C_j \mid R_i\} = \frac{P\{C_j R_i\}}{P\{R_i\}} \tag{1.15}$$

Similarly,

$$P\{R_i \mid C_j\} = \frac{P\{C_j R_i\}}{P\{C_j\}} \tag{1.16}$$

Now

$$P\{R_i C_j\} \cong \frac{n_{ij}}{N} \tag{1.17}$$

and

$$P\{C_j\} \cong \frac{n_{.j}}{N} \tag{1.18}$$

and

$$P\{R_i\} \cong \frac{n_{i.}}{N} \tag{1.19}$$

then

$$P\{R_i \mid C_j\} \cong \frac{n_{ij}}{n_{.j}} \tag{1.20}$$

and

$$P\{C_j \mid R_i\} \cong \frac{n_{ij}}{n_{i.}} \tag{1.21}$$

From (1.6) and (1.7)

$$P\{R_i \mid C_j\} = \frac{p_{ij}}{p_{.j}} \tag{1.22}$$

and

$$P\{C_j \mid R_i\} = \frac{p_{ij}}{p_{i.}} \tag{1.23}$$

VENN DIAGRAMMATIC REPRESENTATION OF SETS

The foregoing discussion may be approached in another, perhaps in a more illuminating manner. If we sketch the subsets R_2, R_3, C_1 we obtain a graphical representation such as is illustrated in Fig. 1.2. The probability of an event being either R_3 or C_1 is

$$P\{R_3 \text{ or } C_1\} = P\{R_3\} + P\{C_1\} - P\{C_1 R_3\} \tag{1.24}$$

Hence the probability of obtaining a coarse-grained rock or a quartzite is

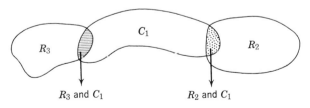

FIG. 1.2. R_3 = the subset of R known as quartzites. R_2 = the subset of R known as low rank graywacks. C_1 = the subset of C known as coarse-grained sands. The region represented by parallel lines is the region or intersection of R_3 and C_1 and is the region common to both. Similarly, the stipled area represents the intersection of R_2 and C_1. Thus the lined region represents coarse-grained quartzites, and the stipled region coarse-grained graywacks.

seen to be the sum of the marginal probabilities of the quartzites and the coarse-grained rocks, minus the joint probability of the event-coarse grained quartzites. This is illustrated in Fig. 1.2. The entire space within the bounds of the shapes represents the marginal probabilities of R_2, R_3, and C_1. These are isolated and sketched in Fig. 1.3.

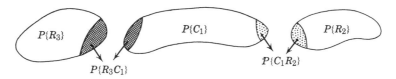

$P\{R_3\}$ $P\{C_1\}$ $P\{R_2\}$

$P\{R_3C_1\}$ $P\{C_1R_2\}$

FIG. 1.3

It is now apparent heuristically why (1.24) is a correct statement. When the marginal probabilities are added, $P(R_3C_1)$ is added in twice, once from $P(R_3)$ and once from $P(C_1)$. To correct this we subtract it once. In general, then

$$P\{R_i \text{ or } C_i\} = P\{R_i\} + P\{C_j\} - P\{R_iC_j\} \qquad (1.25)$$

and it is known as the *addition formula of probability*.

What is the probability of the event $\{R_2 \text{ or } R_3\}$? From Table 1.8, $P\{R_3\}$ is 0.125 and $P(R_2)$ is 0.550. However, by virtue of the fact R_3 and R_2 are mutually exclusive, i.e., a graywacke is not a quartzite, $P\{R_3R_2\}$ is an impossible event, and hence $P\{R_2R_3\}$ is 0. This is illustrated in Fig. 1.2. Here it is seen that there is no common space, intersection, between R_2 and R_3. Thus

$$P\{R_2 \text{ or } R_3\} = P\{R_2\} + P\{R_3\} - P\{R_2R_3\}$$
$$= P\{R_2\} + P\{R_3\} - 0$$
$$= 0.675$$

This leads at once to the following generalization. When two events are mutually exclusive, the probability of one or the other is simply the sum of their marginal probabilities. Thus

$$P\{R_i \text{ or } R_j\} = P\{R_i\} + P\{R_j\} \qquad (1.26)$$

Hence $P(C_2 \text{ or } C_4)$ is 0.475.

What is $P\{R_1 \text{ or } R_2 \text{ or } R_3\}$? Since

$$P\{R_iR_j\} = 0 \quad \text{and} \quad P\{R_iR_jR_k\} = 0$$

$$P\{R_1 \text{ or } R_2 \text{ or } R_3\} = \sum_{i=1}^{3} P\{R_i\} = 1$$

We can obtain this answer by relying on the following Venn diagram.

Here, each area represents R_1, R_2, and R_3, respectively. By definition of the R classification, we know that any R must fall in but one of the subsets and not two or three. Hence the event $\{R_i R_j\}$ is an impossible event for $i \neq j$. Hence any combination of the R's, i.e., $\{R_1 R_2\}$, $\{R_1 R_3\}$, $\{R_2 R_3\}$, is an impossible event. Hence, the probability of such an event is 0. Thus

$$P\{R_1 \text{ or } R_2 \text{ or } R_3\} = P\{R_1\} + P\{R_2\} + P\{R_3\}$$

PROBABILISTIC INDEPENDENCE

Larsen and Berman (1934)[1] have tabled the distribution of anisotropic minerals with respect to biaxial or uniaxial characters and with respect to their optic sign, i.e., plus ($+$) or minus ($-$). (Table 1.10) Let the occurrence of a uniaxial mineral be represented by U and its nonoccurrence by

TABLE 1.10
Frequency Distribution of Minerals Classified
by Optical Characters
(After Larsen and Berman, modified by authors)

		U Uniaxial	$\bar{U}$ Biaxial	Total
Optic sign	$S\ +$	0.082	0.366	0.448
	$\bar{S}\ -$	0.167	0.385	0.552
	Total	0.249	0.751	1.000

$\bar{U}$. $\bar{U}$ then represents the occurrence of a biaxial mineral. U and $\bar{U}$ are said to be *complementary events*. The selection of an anisotropic mineral necessitates it being either uniaxial or biaxial (nonuniaxial). Hence,

$$P(U) + P(\bar{U}) = 1 \tag{1.27}$$

That is, the probability of an event and its complement is one. Similarly, let the occurrence of a positive anisotropic mineral be denoted by S and let $\bar{S}$ represent the occurrence of a negative anisotropic mineral.

[1] Esper S. Larsen and Harry Berman, 1934, The microscopic determinations of the nonopaque minerals, *U.S. Dept. Interior, Bulletin* 848, 266 pp.

Now by (1.13) and (1.14) the conditional probability of the event—a uniaxial mineral given that it is positive—is $P\{U\,|\,S\} = P\{US\}/P\{S\} = \dfrac{0.082}{0.448} = 0.183$. Note that $P(U\,|\,S) \neq P(U\,|\,\bar{S})$. That is, the probability that a mineral be uniaxial, conditional on the fact that it is positive, is not the same as the probability of a mineral being uniaxial, conditional on the knowledge that it is negative. Furthermore, $P(U\,|\,\bar{S}) \neq P(U)$. The conditional probability of a uniaxial mineral, given that it is negative, is not equal to the marginal probability of a uniaxial mineral.

When the probability of an event R_i, conditional on another event C_j, is equal to the conditional probability of the event R_i, conditional on the complement of the other, $\bar{C}_j$, then the events, C_j, R_i are said to be *independent in the probability or statistical sense*. This may be written

$$P\{R_i\,|\,C_j\} = P\{R_i\,|\,\bar{C}_j\} \qquad (1.28)$$

From (1.27) we know in general that

$$P\{R_i\} + P\{\bar{R}_i\} = 1$$

and likewise

$$P\{C_i\} + P\{\bar{C}_i\} = 1$$

Hence if (1.28) is true, then

$$P\{R_i\,|\,C_j\} = P\{R_i\} \qquad (1.29)$$

PROOF. Since

$$P\{R_i\} = P\{R_iC_j\} + P\{R_i\bar{C}_j\}$$

(See 1.7)

$$= P\{R_i\,|\,C_j\}P\{C_j\} + P\{R_i\,|\,\bar{C}_j\}P\{\bar{C}_j\}$$

But by (1.28) we know $P\{R_i\,|\,C_j\} = P\{R_i\,|\,\bar{C}_j\}$
Therefore

$$P\{R_i\} = P\{R_i\,|\,C_j\}[P\{C_j\} + P\{\bar{C}_j\}] \qquad (1.30)$$

and

$$P\{R_i\} = P\{R_i\,|\,C_j\} \qquad (1.31)$$

Also since

$$P\{R_i\,|\,C_j\} = \frac{P\{R_iC_j\}}{P\{C_j\}}$$

then by (1.31)

$$P\{R_iC_j\} = P\{R_i\}P\{C_j\} \qquad (1.32)$$

Equation 1.32 is a statement denoting statistical independence. The outcomes R_i and C_i are considered independent if it can be shown that their joint probability is the product of their marginal probabilities.

The preceding is known as the *law of multipication* for independent events. When two events are independent in the probabilistic or statistical sense, their joint probability is the product of their marginal probabilities.

EXAMPLE

A die is a cube with each face being numbered from 1 to 6. To illustrate independence in the probability sense consider a toss with the subsequent result of a four on the uppermost face. The die is to be tossed again and we ask: what is the probability of the event, a two, conditional upon the knowledge that we had first tossed a four? That is,

$$P(2 \mid 4) = ?$$

Clearly the knowledge of obtaining a four on the first toss has not, or will not, help us in determining the result on the second toss. That is, the results are independent. The probability of tossing the die a second time and obtaining a two is $\frac{1}{6}$ and this is also the conditional probability of tossing a two. Hence,

$$P(2 \mid 4) = P(2) = \frac{1}{6}.$$

The probability of tossing a two and then a four is

$$P(2, 4) = P(2)\,P(4) = \frac{1}{36}.$$

By independence of events the joint probability of a two and then a four is

$$P(2, 4) = P(2)\,P(4)$$

i.e., the product of their marginal probabilities.

SUGGESTED READINGS ON THE SUBJECT OF PROBABILITY

William Feller, 1950, *An introduction to probability theory and its applications*, Vol. I, John Wiley, New York. Chapters 1–7 are recommended. Later chapters require stronger mathematical background.

M. E. Munroe, 1951, *Theory of probability*, McGraw-Hill Book Co., New York. The whole text is recommended.

R. Von Mises, 1939, *Probability statistics and truth*, The Macmillan Co., New York. A series of lectures from which the reader can choose in his area of interest.

W. A. Whitworth, 1942, *Choice and chance*, G. E. Stechert, New York and *DCC exercises*, 1945, reprinted G. E. Stechert, New York. Recommended for detailed discussion of problems in the context of this chapter. Includes problems and solutions. The authors have found these two volumes very helpful.

H. Cramér, 1951, *Mathematical Methods of Statistics*, Princeton University Press, Princeton, New Jersey. Very widely used. Pertinent discussion found throughout the book.

The following papers involve the use of probability applied to areas of interest within the scope of this chapter:

A. N. Kolmogorov, 1951, *Mechanism of stratification*, Transl. 53, Office Naval Research. Translation by The American Mathematical Society. The mechanism of stratification over long periods of geological time is approached through the solution of a problem in probability.

F. E. Wickman, 1954, The total amount of sediments and the composition of the average igneous rock, *Geochim. et Cosmochim. Acta.* 5: 97–110. A system of four linear equations based on tables of average chemical composition, are given for estimating average Al, Fe, Na, and K in igneous rocks. The limits of error are considered in terms of the gaussian error equation for several independent variables.

$$E = \pm \left[\left(\epsilon_1 \frac{\partial f}{\partial x_1} \right)^2 + \left(\epsilon_2 \frac{\partial f}{\partial x_2} \right)^2 + \cdots + \left(\epsilon_n \frac{\partial f}{\partial x_n} \right)^2 \right]^{1/2}$$

where E is the error of $F = f(x_1, x_2, \cdots x_n)$ and $\epsilon_1 \epsilon_2 \cdots \epsilon_n$ are the errors of the n independent variables. The similarity is pointed out between calculations of this type and a problem much studied in recent years in econometrics.

G. W. Boguslavsky, 1956, Statistical estimation of the size of a small population, *Science* 124: 317–318, presents a simple model for estimating population size of very small magnitude, e.g., $n = 15$ is large because of the computational labor involved. It is possible, however, that high speed computor methods would relieve this difficulty.

The model involves drawing an individual, tagging it, and replacing it. For example, if only one individual is tagged on the first draw, and it keeps reappearing on subsequent draws, the hypothesis is tested that there is only *one* in the population versus the alternative that there is two. The probability of the alternative hypothesis is $p = (\frac{1}{2})^{r_1 - 1}$ after r_1 drawings. Setting $(\frac{1}{2})^{r_1 - 1} = 0.10$ will give the number of drawings r_1 necessary for 0.90 confidence $(1.00 - 0.10)$ that the null hypothesis is correct. He points out that an application of Markov processes (see W. Feller, 1950, *An introduction to probability theory and its applications*, John Wiley, New York) will facilitate computation where populations are considerably higher than 1.

chapter 2

Probability Density Functions

DISCRETE DISTRIBUTIONS

Our discussion on probability has dealt essentially with probabilities of single events. We now turn to the problem of compound events. Consider as an example the heavy mineral residue of a sedimentary rock. The petrologist undertaking this investigation decides that the important attributes to consider are those of opaqueness versus nonopaqueness. From past experience the petrologist knows that for every twenty grains examined under a microscope he usually obtains two opaque grains. Hence, we shall say the probability of an opaque mineral grain is 1/10. *Let x represent the number of times an opaque mineral appears in a field of n mineral grains.* Since x will vary from field to field, it is a random variable. Furthermore, let $p = 1/10$ represent the probability of obtaining an opaque mineral in a single observation. Hence, $(1 - p) = 9/10$ represents the probability of the complementary event, $\bar{Q}$ the nonoccurrence of an opaque mineral. Let us further assume that our observations are independent in the statistical sense.

If the microscope field contained but three grains, i.e., $n = 3$, then the probability that all three grains are opaque is, by the multiplication theorem (1.32) and the assumption of stochastic independence,

$$P(x = 3) = p \cdot p \cdot p = p^3 = \left(\frac{1}{10}\right)^3$$

In a like manner, the probability that all three grains are nonopaque is

$$P(x = 0) = (1 - p)^3 = \left(\frac{9}{10}\right)^3$$

We know that we have not exhausted our sample points. One grain may be opaque and the two remaining ones nonopaque. Or two grains might be opaque and the third nonopaque. In the former, then, the opaque grain

17

might have been the first observed and the nonopaques the last; or the first observation might have been nonopaque, the second opaque, and the third nonopaque; or the first two might have been nonopaque and the last opaque. Hence, the probability that of a field of three grains one is opaque is

$$P(x = 1) = P(Q\bar{Q}\bar{Q} \text{ or } \bar{Q}Q\bar{Q} \text{ or } \bar{Q}\bar{Q}Q)$$

$$= P(Q\bar{Q}\bar{Q}) + P(\bar{Q}Q\bar{Q}) + P(\bar{Q}\bar{Q}Q)$$

$$= p(1 - p)(1 - p) + (1 - p)(p)(1 - p) + (1 - p)(1 - p)(p)$$

$$= 3p(1 - p)^2 = 3 \cdot (1/10) \cdot (9/10)^2$$

In a like manner it is easily shown (and the reader is invited to substantiate this statement by arguing as above) that

$$P(x = 2) = 3 (1/10)^2 (9/10)$$

It is now seen that if x is the number of opaque minerals in a field of $n = 3$ minerals, then the probability of obtaining three, two, one, or no opaque minerals, where the probability of obtaining an opaque mineral in a single trial is $p = 1/10$, is

$$P(x = 3) = (1/10)^3 \qquad = p^3$$

$$P(x = 2) = 3(1/10)^2(9/10) = 3p^2(1 - p)$$

$$P(x = 1) = 3(1/10)(9/10)^2 = 3p(1 - p)^2$$

$$P(x = 0) = (9/10)^3 \qquad = (1 - p)^3$$

One of the events $x = 3, 2, 1,$ or 0 must occur; hence, $\sum_{x=0}^{3} P(x)$ must equal one. This is easily verified as follows:

$$= p^3 + 3p^2(1 - p) + 3p(1 - p)^2 + (1 - p)^3$$

$$= p^3 + 3p^2 - 3p^3 + 3p - 6p^2 + 3p^3 + 1 - p^3 - 3p + 3p^2 = 1$$

It can be readily shown that the probabilities associated with the occurrence of an opaque mineral can be obtained by expanding $(p + (1 - p))^3$. This expansion gives us the probability of any event x in samples of size $n = 3$. That is, $(p + (1 - p))^3 = P(x = 3) + P(x = 2) + P(x = 1) + P(x = 0) = 1$. In general, the expansion of $(p + (1 - p))^n$ gives the probability of an event of x, where $x = 0, 1, 2, 3, \cdots, n$.

EXAMPLE

Compute the probability of the event x opaque minerals and $(n - x)$ non-opaque minerals. This statement asks for the probability of the event $(x)Q$'s and $(n - x)\bar{Q}$'s. By independence the probability that the event Q will occur x times is the probability of the single event $P(Q) = p$ multiplied by itself x times. Likewise, the probability of the complementary event occurring $(n - x)$ times is $(1 - p)^{n-x}$. Now we must not forget that events may occur in many different ways. In general, the number of ways x items may be selected from n is

$$\binom{n}{x} = \frac{n!}{x!\,(n - x)!} \qquad x = 0, 1, 2, \cdots, n$$

where $n!$ (read, n factorial) is defined to be

$$n! = n(n - 1)(n - 2) \cdots 5 \cdot 4 \cdot 3 \cdot 2 \cdot 1,$$

e.g., $4! = (4)(3)(2)(1) = 24$, $5! = 120$, and $0!$ is defined to be 1. Returning now to our problem at hand we find then that

$$P\{Q\bar{Q}\bar{Q}Q \cdots \bar{Q}Q\} \text{ is } \binom{n}{x} p^x(1 - p)^{n-x} \qquad \text{for } x = 0, 1. \cdots, n$$

The probability that the random variable x will be equal to a particular value x_0 in n independent trials when p is the probability of success in a single trial is

$$P\{x = x_0\} = \binom{n}{x_0} p^{x_0}(1 - p)^{n - x_0} \qquad x = 0, 1, \cdots, n$$

The random variable x is permitted to take on any integral value from 0 to n. In our initial example above, x ranged from 0 to 3. *A sample space in which the random variable may assume only isolated values is said to be discrete.* Discrete spaces may be finite as in the case of the heavy minerals (or infinite as the case of all positive integers or all integers greater than 21, 458).

If we can define a function of the discrete random variable $x, f(x)$, such that for every value of $x = x_0$, $f(x_0) = P(x_0)$, then $f(x)$ is said to be the *probability density function of the random variable x.* If the sample space is discrete, $f(x)$ is said to be a discrete probability density function.

In general, then, if S represents a discrete sample space of x and $f(x)$ is a function over S and $f(x) \geq 0$ (read greater or equal to zero) for $x \in S$, read for all x belonging to S, and if $\sum_{x \in S} f(x) = 1$, then $f(x)$ is said to be a discrete probability density function.

We are now in the position to decide if

$$f(x) = \binom{n}{x} p^x(1 - p)^{n - x}$$

where $x = 0, 1, \cdots, n$ is indeed a discrete probability density function (pdf). $f(x)$ is a function over a discrete space, $f(x) \geq 0$ and

$$\sum_{x=0}^{n} f(x) = [p + (1 - p)]^n = 1$$

Hence,

$$f(x) = \binom{n}{x} p^x (1 - p)^{n-x} \tag{2.1}$$

is the discrete pdf of the random variable x, and x is said to have the *binomial distribution. This distribution may be used as the theoretical model for those situations or experiments where there are but two outcomes, viz., heads or tails, life or death, garnet or not garnet, grain-to-grain contact or not, success or failure.*

p, the probability of success in a single trial and n, the number of trials, will vary from one binomial distribution to another. For example, the probability of the success of obtaining a head when a balanced coin is tossed once is $\frac{1}{2}$, whereas the probability of a grain-to-grain contact in an arkose is $6/10$. (Kahn, 1956.)[1] In the former case n might be thirty, whereas in the latter n might be in the hundreds. n and p are therefore fixed characteristics of a particular binomial distribution. They are called *parameters*, and may too, be considered variables in the sense that they change from binomial distribution to binomial distribution. Hence to ascertain a particular binomial distribution it is necessary to know n and p exactly. When they are not known exactly, we would like a means of at least obtaining some estimate of them.

Once the parameters and the distribution function of a variate are known then the probabilities of any events in sample space become matters of routine.

We mentioned that the probability of obtaining a grain-to-grain contact in a thin section analysis of packing in a group of akoses was found to be 0.6. In a subsequent discussion of packing with a group of geologists it was asked that if one examined a traverse of twenty grains, "would it be "probable" to observe exactly three grain-to-grain contacts?" The replies were "absolutely not," "yes," "maybe," "sometimes," "why not?". This cross section of answers points to the need for a common reference system from which all concerned can react. The answer to this question is exact. A probability statement can be made concerning the event in question, i.e., what is the probability of obtaining three grain-to-grain

[1] J. S. Kahn, 1956, The analysis and distribution of the properties of packing in sand size sediments. 2. The distribution of the packing measurements and an example of packing analysis, *Jour. Geol.* 64: 578–606.

contacts in a traverse of twenty grains of an arkose when the probability of obtaining a grain-to-grain contact on a single grain (trial) is 0.6? There is no need to be vague or ambiguous. We shall now discuss the means at arriving at the answer.

TABLE 2.1
Probabilities Associated with the Binomial
Distribution When $p = 0.6$, $n = 20$

Event	Probability of Event $= P\{x\} = f(x)$
$x =$	
0	~0
1	~0
2	~0
3	~0
4	~0
5	0.001
6	0.005
7	0.015
8	0.036
9	0.071
10	0.117
11	0.160
12	0.180
13	0.166
14	0.124
15	0.075
16	0.035
17	0.012
18	0.003
19	~0
20	~0

The number of grain-to-grain contacts in an arkose is distributed as

$$f(x) = \binom{n}{x} 0.6^x 0.4^{n-x} \qquad x = 0, 1, \ldots, n$$
$$= 0 \qquad\qquad\qquad\qquad \text{otherwise}$$

where x, the random variable, represents the number of grain-to-grain contacts, and n represents the size of the sample or the number of grains under consideration. Knowing the distribution function of the random variable x and also the parameters n and p we can compute the probability of any event in sample space. Table 2.1 lists the probability of the events $x = 0, 1, 2, \cdots, 19, 20$, where $n = 20$, and $p = 0.6$.

Now let us compute the probability of some compound events. (1) The probability that the number of grain-to-grain contacts are between 7 and 19 inclusive is

$$P\{7 \leq x \leq 19\} = \sum_{x=7}^{19} f(x) = f(7) + f(8) + \cdots + f(19) = 0.994$$

(2) The probability that the number of grain-to-grain contacts are 12, given that the number of contacts is less than 18, is

$$P\{x = 12 \mid x < 18\} = \frac{P\{x = 12\}}{P\{x < 18\}}$$

$$= \frac{f(12)}{\displaystyle\sum_{x=0}^{17} f(x)} = \frac{0.180}{0.997} = 0.1805$$

(3) The probability that the number of grain-to-grain contacts are less than 10, given they are less than 14, is

$$P\{x < 10 \mid x < 14\} = \frac{P\{x < 10\}}{P\{x < 14\}}$$

$$= \frac{0.128}{0.751} = 0.1705$$

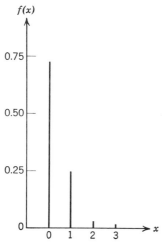

FIG. 2.1. Binomial distribution when $n = 3$, $p = 0.1$.

Finally, with the aid of Table 2.1 we may now return to our problem of deciding whether three contacts in a traverse of twenty grains are rare or not. The probability of three contacts is approximately zero. The event, it seems fair to conclude, is indeed improbable!

The binomial distribution just discussed, i.e., $n = 20$, $p = 0.6$, and the binomial distribution discussed earlier in this section i.e., $n = 3$, $p = 0.1$, are illustrated graphically in Figs. 2.1, 2.2. The probability of any event $x = x_0$ is obtained by reading across the abscissa or x or independent axis, and then estimating the length of the line above it on the dependent or $f(x) = f(x_0)$ or ordinate axis.

When working with discrete distributions, it is imperative that strict attention be paid to the inequality signs, since in general the expressions

$$P\{x \leq b\}, P\{x < b\}$$

are not equivalent.

For example, if $n = 20$ and $p = 0.6$ then

$$P\{x \leq 9\} = 0.128$$

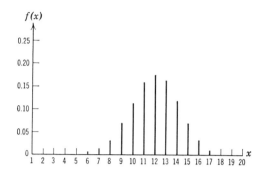

FIG. 2.2. Binomial distribution when $n = 20$, $p = 0.6$.

whereas

$$P\{x < 9\} = 0.057$$

The former is equivalent to

$$\sum_{x=0}^{9} f(x)$$

whereas the latter is

$$\sum_{x=0}^{8} f(x)$$

CUMULATIVE DISCRETE DISTRIBUTIONS

We know that if $f(x)$ is a discrete probability density function for $a_1 \leq x \leq a_n$, then $P\{a_i \leq x \leq a_j\}$ where $a_1 < a_i < a_j, < a_n$, is

$$\sum_{x=a_i}^{a_i} f(x) = f(a_i) + f(a_{i+1}) + \cdots + f(a_{j-1}) + f(a_j). \qquad (2.1)$$

Now

$$\sum_{x=a_1}^{a_{i-1}} f(x) = f(a_1) + f(a_2) + \cdots + f(a_{i-2}) + f(a_{i-1})$$

and

$$\sum_{x=a_1}^{a_j} f(x) = f(a_1) + f(a_2) + \cdots + f(a_{i-2}) + f(a_{i-1}) + f(a_i)$$
$$+ \cdots + f(a_{j-1}) + f(a_j)$$

Hence

$$\sum_{x=a_1}^{a_j} f(x) - \sum_{x=a_1}^{a_{i-1}} f(x) = f(a_i) + \cdots + f(a_{j-1}) + f(a_j) = \sum_{x=a_i}^{aj} f(x)$$

But this is clearly

$$P\{a_i \leq x \leq a_j\}.$$

Hence

$$P\{a_i \leq x \leq a_j\} = P\{x \leq a_j\} - P\{x \leq a_{i-1}\}.$$

Thus (2.1) could be solved if we had computed (1) the probability of x being less than or equal to the upper bound, a_j, and (2) the probability of x being less the lower bound, and (3) subtracted the two probabilities. A function which directly gives the probability of a random variable x, being equal to or less than some particular value $x = a_k$, is called the *cumulative probability density function* of the random variable x and is

TABLE 2.2

Cumulative Distribution for the Binomial Probability Density Function with Parameters $n = 3$ and $p = 0.1$

Event $= x$	Probability of Being $\leq x = F(x)$
0	0.729
1	0.243
2	0.027
3	0.001

TABLE 2.3

Cumulative Distribution for Binomial Distribution When $n = 20$, $p = 0.6$

x	Probability of Being $\leq x = F(x)$
0	~0
1	~0
2	~0
3	~0
4	~0
5	0.001
6	0.006
7	0.021
8	0.057
9	0.128
10	0.245
11	0.405
12	0.585
13	0.751
14	0.875
15	0.950
16	0.985
17	0.997
18	~1.000
19	~1.000
20	1.000

denoted by $F(x)$. Henceforth we shall denote cumulative probability density function by $F(x)$, and the probability density function by $f(x)$. Hence

$$F(x = a_k) = F(a_k) = P(x \leq a_k) = \sum_{x=a_1}^{a_k} f(x)$$

and

$$a_1 \leq a_2 \leq a_3 \leq \cdots \leq a_k \leq \cdots a_n$$

where $x = a_1, \cdots, a_k$.

Now

$$0 = F(a_1) \leq F(a_2) \leq F(a_3) \leq \cdots \leq F(a_k) \leq \cdots \leq F(a_n) = 1$$

Hence $F(x)$ is said to be a nondecreasing positive function. The cumulative distributions for the binomial distributions illustrated in Figs. 2.1 and 2.2 are tabulated in Tables 2.2, 2.3, and illustrated in Figs. 2.3, 2.4. Hence

$$P\{7 \leq x \leq 19\} = F\{19\} = F\{6\} = 0.994$$

$$P\{10 \leq x \leq 12\} = F\{12\} - F\{9\} = 0.457$$

$$P\{9 < x < 13\} = P\{9 < x \leq 12\} = F\{12\} - F\{9\} = 0.457$$

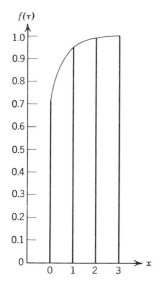

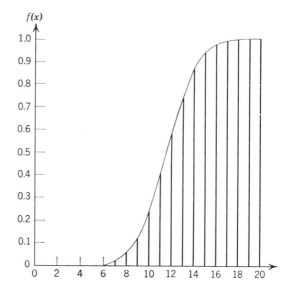

FIG. 2.3. Cumulative frequency distribution for binomial distribution when $n = 3, p = 0.1$.

FIG. 2.4. Cumulative frequency distribution for binomial distribution when $n = 3, p = 0.1$.

MULTINOMIAL DISTRIBUTION

If an experiment can result in r possible outcomes, then to each of these outcomes can be assigned a probability p_i, where $i = 1, 2, 3, \cdots, r$.

The experiment may consist, e.g., of determining the presence of some trace elements, $t_1, t_2, t_3, \cdots, t_t$. Here the outcomes of an experiment may be t_1, t_2, or t_t with probabilities p_1, p_2, or p_t respectively.

A company preparing ceramic powders inspects its product and rejects it if 0.5% or more of the material is greater than a specified size and also rejects the batch if 3% or more of the material is less than a specified size. Here the possible outcomes are: (1) reject because material is too coarse with probability p_1; (2) reject because material is too fine with probability p_2; and (3) accept, with probability p_3. It will be assumed that a sample cannot be both too fine and too coarse.

If we assume independence in the probability sense then the probability of rejecting x_1 items for being too coarse and x_2 items for being too fine in a sample of size n is

$$p_1^{x_1} p_2^{x_2} p_3^{x_3} = p_1^{x_1} p_2^{x_2} (1 - p_1 - p_2)^{n - x_1 - x_2}$$

multiplied by the total number of ways, x_1, x_2, and $(n - x_1 - x_2)$ items, may be selected from n samples. Now x_1 items may be selected from the n items in $\binom{n}{x_1}$ ways. x_2 items may be selected from the remaining $(n - x_1)$ items in $\binom{n - x_1}{x_2}$ ways, whereas x_3 may be selected in but one way from $n - x_1 - x_2$. Hence x_1, x_2, and x_3 may be selected together from n items in $\binom{n}{x_1}\binom{n - x_1}{x_2}$ different ways. But

$$\binom{n}{x_1}\binom{n - x_1}{x_2} = \frac{n!}{x_1!(n - x)!} \cdot \frac{(n - x)!}{x_2!(n - x_1 - x_2)!}$$

$$= \frac{n!}{x_1!\, x_2!\, x_3!}$$

and therefore the probability of x_1 items being too coarse, x_2 items being too fine, and x_3 items being satisfactory is

$$P\{x_1 x_2 x_3\} = \frac{n!}{x_1!\, x_2!\, x_3!}\, p_1^{x_1} p_2^{x_2} p_3^{x_3}$$

If we let π, the Greek letter pi, represent the product notation, then

$$P\{x_1 x_2 x_3\} = n! \prod_{i=1}^{3} \frac{p_i^{x_i}}{x_i!} = f(x_1 x_2 x_3)$$

Hence, the probability that five samples would be rejected because they were too coarse and three rejected for being fine when a sample of $n = 200$ were examined, when $p_1 = 0.005$, $p_2 = 0.03$ is

$$\frac{200!}{5!\,3!\,192!}\,(0.005)^5(0.03)^3(0.965)^{192}$$

In general, if an experiment may result in r possible outcomes with the probability of each outcome being $p_1, p_2, \cdots, p_r$ respectively, then the probability that the first outcome occurs x_1 times, the second $x_2 \cdots$, the rth x_r times is

$$f(x_1 x_2 \cdots x_r) = n! \prod_{i=1}^{r} \left(\frac{p_i^{x_i}}{x_i!}\right)$$

where $n = \sum_{i=1}^{r} x_i$.

This distribution is called the *multinomial distribution*.

Since $\sum_{i-1} x_i = n$, then $(r - 1)$ of the variables may vary at will. Once they are fixed the rth variable is automatically fixed. Hence $f(x_1, x_2, \cdots, x_r)$ might also be written as $g(x_1, x_2, \cdots, x_{r-1})$. Hence, when $r = 2$,

$$f(x_1, \cdots, x_r) = g(x_1) = \frac{n!}{x_1!\,(n - x_1)!}\,p_1^{x_1}(1 - p)^{n-x_1} = \binom{n}{x_1}p_1^{x_1}(1 - p^{n-x_1}),$$

which we at once recognize as the binomial distribution, a special case of the multinomial distribution.

Geological Example of the Use of a Discrete Probability Density Function

Krumbein and Slack (1955)[1] have shown that x, the number of α particles emitted per 1.5-in. diameter circular surface of powdered material, is distributed as

$$f(x) = \frac{\exp(-np)(np)^x}{x!} \qquad x = 0, 1, 2, \cdots, n$$

$$= 0 \qquad\qquad\qquad \text{otherwise}$$

Here n represents the sample size or number of observations, whereas p represents the probability of the outcome—the emission of an α particle in a single trial. $f(x)$ is known as the Poisson distribution. If we let $\lambda = np$, then

$$f(x) = \frac{(\exp -\lambda)\lambda^x}{x!}$$

[1] H. Slack and W. C. Krumbein, 1955, Measurement and statistical evaluation of low level radioactivity in rocks, *Trans. A.G.U.* 36: 460–464. See also W. C. Krumbein and H. A. Slack, 1956, Statistical analysis of low-level radio-activity in Pennsylvanian black fissile shale in Illinois, *Bull. G.S.A.* 67:739 ff.

Thus the theoretical discrete probability density function has served adequately as a model for geological experimentation. The use of the Poisson model is further discussed in Chapter 16.

Chayes (1956)[1] derives a standard deviation from a binomial model in application to petrographic modal analysis.

EXAMPLES OF DISCRETE FREQUENCY DISTRIBUTION ANALYSIS AND USE

J. Small, 1950, Quantitative evolution XVI. Increase of species in diatoms, *Ann. Bot.* XIV: 91–113. Utilizing frequency distributions of generic size.

J. Small, 1949, Quantitative evolution XVII. The shape and pattern of evolution, *Phyton* 1: 269–281. Analyzes discrete frequency distributions in a qualitative way interpreting "skewness," and "troughs" of genus number against time, in evolutionary context.

J. Small, 1948, Evolution IX–XIII. Details of the history of diatoms, *Proc. Roy. Irish Acad.* 51: 261–346.

W. D. Pye, 1943, Rapid methods of making sedimentational analyses of arenaceous sediments, *Jour. Sed. Petrol.* 13: 85–104.

A. W. Marschner, 1953, A method for the size analysis of sand on a number frequency basis, *Jour. Sed. Petrol.* 23: 49–59. Proposes a method by which number frequency instead of weight may be used in the size analysis of sand.

CONTINUOUS DISTRIBUTIONS

The *pH* of a solution may vary from 0 to 14 with any value within these limits or *range* being theoretically feasible. The velocity of a particular river may range from 0 to 20 ft/sec or more. Depending on the gauge in question, the velocities may be any value greater than zero. The index of refraction of minerals ranges from 1.40 to 3.22, with the minerals assuming values within this band (Rogers and Kerr, 1959, p. 157).[2] Although we could not speak of a $1\frac{1}{4}$ of a grain of hematite as being opaque, or $3\frac{1}{2}\alpha$ emissions in the first second of observation, we can speak of a car traveling at 97.6 mph; a mineral with a refractive index of 1.546; the percentage of $CaCO_3$ in a sample as 33.25%; the modulus of rupture of a rock as 25,020.9 psi. When a variate (variates) may assume any value, integral or not, within a given range we say it is a *continuous variate*. As with discrete variates, so, too, with continuous variates can distribution functions be defined.

If $f(x)$ is defined over some region R, i.e., $f(x)$ is defined from 0 to 123,990 or from $-\pi/2$ to -27π, etc., and if

$$f(x) \geq 0$$

[1] F. Chayes, 1956, *Petrographic modal analyses*, John Wiley, New York.

[2] A. F. Rogers and P. F. Kerr, 1959, *Optical mineralogy*, McGraw-Hill Book Co., New York.

for all x belonging to R written $\forall x \in R$ and if

$$\int_{-\infty}^{\infty} f(x)\, dx = 1$$

then $f(x)$ is said to be a *continuous probability density function*, or simply a density function of the continuous random variable x.

The probability of the random variable x being less than a specific value $x = t$ may be written

$$P\{x \le t\} = \int_{-\infty}^{t} f(x)\, dx \tag{1.33}$$

Let $P\{t \le x\} = F(x)$. $F(x)$ is called the cumulative distribution of the random variable x. If $F(x)$ is a continuous function with a continuous first derivative (except perhaps at a finite number of points, say 2,657), then x and its density function are continuous. Some properties of the cumulative distribution function are worth noting.

1. $F(-\infty) = 0$; i.e., the limiting value of $F(x)$, as x becomes very large in a negative sense, is zero, i.e., $\lim\limits_{x \to -\infty} F(x) = 0$.

2. $F(\infty) = 1$, i.e., $\lim\limits_{x \to \infty} F(x) = 1$.

3. $F(-\infty) \le F(x_1) \le F(x_2) \le \cdots \le F(\infty)$, where $-\infty \le x_1 \le x_2 \cdots \le \infty$.

4. At any time, the rate of change of the cumulative probability density function of x, with respect to x itself, is equivalent to the probability density function of x, $f(x)$. That is, the first derivation of $F(x)$ with respect to x is $f(x)$. Thus $dF(x)/dx = f(x)$ and there is a density function of which $F(x)$ is the cumulative density function.

Now, since

$$\int_{a}^{a} f(x)\, dx = 0$$

the probability of the event $x = a$ is zero. Hence, to obtain probability statements involving continuous variates we deal with intervals rather than points as was the case with discrete variates. In this respect it is unimportant whether we heed strictly to our inequality signs since

$$P\{c \le x \le b\} = P\{c \le x \le b\} = P\{c < x < b\} = \int_{c}^{b} f(x)\, dx$$

For a continuous variate, probabilities may be considered areas under $f(x)$ bounded by the x axis. Hence, *most* functions can be made into a density function by a suitable selection of constants. To select these constants merely compute $\int_{-\infty}^{\infty} g(x)\, dx$. If this value is not 1, or 0, then the

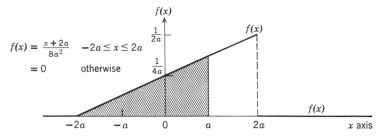

$f(x) = \dfrac{x + 2a}{8a^2}$ $-2a \le x \le 2a$

$= 0$ otherwise

FIG. 2.5. Graph of density $f(x) = (x + 2a)/8a^2$. To ascertain that the total probability under the curve $f(x) = (x + 2a)/8a^2$ is *one*, one may merely compute the area under the triangle bounded by $f(x)$, the x axis, and the line $x = 2a$. Here area $= \dfrac{1}{2} \cdot 4a \cdot \dfrac{1}{2a} = 1.$

probability density function of the random variable x is

$$\frac{g(x)}{\displaystyle\int_{-\infty}^{\infty} g(x)\,dx}$$

For example,

$$g(x) = \frac{1}{2a}\left(\frac{x}{2a} + 1\right) = \frac{x + 2a}{4a^2} \qquad \text{for } -2a \le x \le 2a$$
$$= 0 \qquad\qquad\qquad \text{otherwise}$$

is not a density function since

$$\int_{-\infty}^{\infty} g(x)\,dx = \int_{-\infty}^{-2a} g(x)\,dx + \int_{-2a}^{2a} g(x)\,dx + \int_{2a}^{\infty} g(x)\,dx$$

$$= \int_{-\infty}^{-2a} 0\,dx + \int_{-2a}^{2a} \frac{x + 2a}{4a^2}\,dx + \int_{2a}^{\infty} 0\,dx = \frac{1}{4a^2}\left(\frac{x^2}{2} + 2ax\right)\Big|_{-2a}^{2a}$$

$$= \frac{1}{4a^2}\left[(2a^2 + 4a^2) - (2a^2 - 4a^2)\right] = 2$$

But

$$f(x) = \frac{1}{2} \cdot \frac{1}{2a}\left(\frac{x}{2a} + 1\right) = \frac{x + 2a}{8a^2} \qquad -2a \le x \le 2a$$
$$= 0 \qquad\qquad\qquad\qquad \text{otherwise}$$

is a density function of x.

This density function is plotted in Fig. 2.5. The heavy dark lines represent the density function.

Hence, for example, $P(-2a \le x \le a)$ may be computed in two ways: the first by evaluating

$$\frac{1}{8a^2}\int_{-2a}^{a} (x + 2a)\,dx$$

as

$$\frac{1}{8a^2}\left(\frac{x^2}{2} + 2ax\right)\Bigg|_{-2a}^{a} = \frac{1}{8a^2}\left[\left(\frac{a^2}{2} + 2a^2\right) - (2a^2 - 4a^2)\right] = \frac{9}{16}$$

and the second by computing the area enclosed by the cross hatches in Fig. 2.6.

Examples of Continuous Density Functions

Uniform Distribution

If the random variable x is distributed such that

$$f(x) = \frac{1}{\beta - \alpha} \qquad \alpha \leq x \leq \beta$$

$$= 0 \qquad \text{elsewhere}$$

then x is said to be uniformly distributed and has a uniform or rectangular distribution.

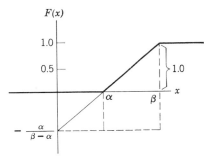

FIG. 2.6. Graph of the cumulative distribution of the uniform distribution $\frac{1}{\beta - \alpha}$. Here $F(x) = \frac{x - \alpha}{\beta - \alpha}$ $R: \alpha \leq x \leq \beta$, $F(x) = 1$ for $x \geq \beta$, $F(x) = 0$ for $x \leq \alpha$.

$$P\{x \leq c\} = \frac{1}{\beta - \alpha} \int_{\alpha}^{c} dx = \frac{c - \alpha}{\beta - \alpha} \qquad \text{where } \alpha \leq c \leq \beta$$

$$P\{c < x < d\} = \frac{d - c}{\beta - \alpha} \qquad \text{where } \alpha \leq c \leq d \leq \beta$$

from equation 1.33 (see Fig. 2.6)

$$F(x) = \int_{\alpha}^{x} f(x)\,dx$$

$$F(x) = \frac{x - \alpha}{\beta - \alpha}$$

Hence, if x is uniformly distributed, the probability of x falling within a subset of the permissible range of the variate is the ratio of the absolute length of the subset divided by the absolute length of the permissible range of the variate.

The graph of the particular uniform distribution

$$f(x) = \frac{1}{\beta - \alpha} \qquad \alpha \leq x \leq \beta$$

$$= 0 \qquad \text{otherwise}$$

where $\alpha = 0$, $\beta = e$, is plotted in Fig. 2.7.

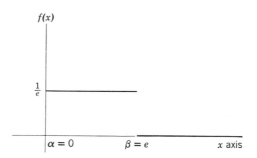

FIG. 2.7. The graph of the uniform distribution $f(x) = \dfrac{1}{\beta - \alpha} = \dfrac{1}{e}, 0 \le x \le e = 0$ otherwise.

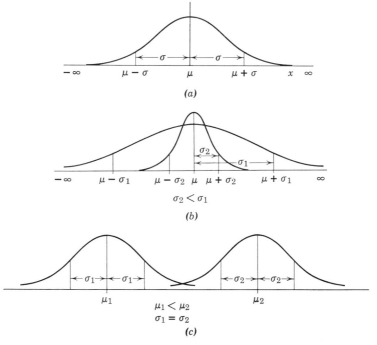

FIG. 2.8. (a) Typical normal distribution with parameters μ and σ. (b) Variation in shape of normal curve due to a change in σ. In both cases $\mu_1 = \mu_2$. (c) Variation in the shape of normal curve due to change in μ. Here σ is the same in both cases.

Normal Distribution

If a variable x is distributed as $f(x) = 1/\sqrt{2\pi\sigma^2}\, e^{-(x-\mu)^2/2\sigma^2}$, i.e., $N(\mu, \sigma^2)$, x is said to have the normal distribution, where μ and σ represent the parameters in this two parameter family of distributions. Figure 2.8 illustrates some different forms or shapes of the normal distribution. The differences in shape and position on the x axis are explained as functions of changes in the parameters μ and σ.

From the preceding figures it is evident that changes in μ, with constant σ, merely shift the curve or displaces the curve along the x axis. The curve is moved entirely. A change in σ with constant μ changes the flatness and peakedness of the distribution. Tables for the normal distribution are readily available; for example, A. Hald, 1952, *Statistical tables and formulas*, John Wiley, New York, Table I, Normal Distribution Function, and Table II, Cumulative Normal Distribution.

PAPERS THAT INCLUDE A DISCUSSION OR ANALYSIS OF CONTINUOUS PROBABILITY DISTRIBUTION FUNCTIONS

E. C. Olson, 1957, Size frequency distributions in samples of extinct organisms, *Jour. Geol.* 65: 309–330, in which theoretical size frequency distributions for death assemblages of fossils are derived and developed. Comparison is made with empirical data.

R. L. Miller, and E. D. Goldberg, 1955, The normal distribution in geochemistry. *Geochim. et Cosmochim.* Acta 8: 53–62. Includes a critical examination of the proposed log normal geochemical law of Ahrens 1954a, *ibid.* A general discussion of several theoretical models which may lead to the formulation of frequency distributions of elements in geochemistry is given; in particular the derivation from geochemical data of a normal distribution.

L. H. Ahrens, 1954a, The lognormal distribution of the elements. (A fundamental law of geochemistry and its subsidiary.) *Geochim. et Cosmochim. Acta.* 5: 49–73. Frequency distributions of a number of elements in diabases and granites are examined. It is proposed that these are distributed as log-normal, and hence a law concerning the nature of the distribution of element concentrations in specific igneous rocks is proposed.

L. H. Ahrens, 1954b, The lognormal distribution of the elements (II), *Geochim. et Cosmochim. Acta.* 6: 121–131. Further examples of distributions which closely approach log-normality are given, and the suggested law is discussed. The magnitude of distortion which can arise when predictions and comparisons are made on the basis of assumed normality is illustrated by examining the distribution of Rb in Ontario diabase and Sn in mica.

F. Chayes, 1954, The log-normal distribution of the elements; a discussion, *Geochim. et Cosmochim. Acta.* 6: 119–120. A critical discussion of Ahrens, 1954a, *ibid.* paper on the log-normal distributions of elements. Chayes stresses that consideration of class width should be made when interest is focused on the form of an empirical frequency distribution. The suggestion is made that for purpose of estimating or comparing goodness of fit, the class width should not exceed $\frac{1}{4}$ to $\frac{1}{2}$ the standard deviation in accord with standard statistical tests.

L. H. Ahrens, 1957, Lognormal distributions III, *Geochim. et Cosmochim. Acta.* 11: 205–212. Defends earlier papers in response to discussions by Chayes, 1954, *ibid.*, and Miller and Goldberg, 1955, *ibid.* Presents further evidence to show that log-normal distributions are common in nature.

S. Durovic, 1959, Contribution to the lognormal distribution of elements, *Geochim. et Cosmochim. Acta.* 15: 330–336. Suggests that the frequency distribution of the elements is properly treated as continuous rather than discrete. Concludes that the geometric mean is not representative for evaluation of elements in a deposit, but the arithmetic mean is.

Z. V. Jizba, 1959, Frequency distribution of elements in rocks, *Geochim. et Cosmochim, Acta.* 16: 79–82. Discusses two models which may generate frequency distributions corresponding to those found for elements in nature.

1. One due to K. Pearson, 1894, Contributions to the mathematical theory of evolution, *Phil. Trans. Roy. Soc. London* 185: 71ff, based on a differential equation derived from the binomial distribution.

2. A second described by J. C. Kapteyn, 1903, Skew frequency curves in biology and statistics. Noordhoff, Groningen (see also Miller and Goldberg, 1955, *ibid.* for discussion of Kapteyn's model), based on a derivation of the central limit theorem. This model as projected by Jizba leads to a log-normal distribution for trace elements but not for major elements.

A. B. Vistelius, 1948, On the roundness of quartz sand of the Great Bank (delta of the Volga), *Dokl. Akad Nayk, Trans.* 63: 1. Frequency distributions of Wadell's coefficients of roundness are studied by using the truncated normal function. See A. Hald 1952, *Statistical theory with engineering applications*, John Wiley, New York, for discussion of the truncated normal distribution and applications.

Cumulative curves are used to varying degree in the following papers:

W. C. Krumbein, 1934, Size frequency distributions of sediments, *Jour. Sed. Petrol.* 4: 65–77, discusses cumulative curves as contrasted with frequency distributions or histograms. The advantages are: (1) independent of scale, (2) medians, quartiles, percentiles in general are easily read from the cumulative curve.

A. B. Vistelius 1958, Volume frequency analysis of sediments from thin section data: a discussion, *Jour. Geol.* 66: 224–226. A discussion of Packham's 1955, *ibid.* paper including an analytical discussion of the cumulative probability distribution function for intercept diameters of grains in thin section.

F. Chayes, 1954, The theory of thin section analysis, *Jour. Geol.*; 62: 92–101. A general discussion of the Delesse, 1848 and Rosiwal, 1898 models for micrometric analysis. For a given probability distribution function, expected values in several regions are computed. Also considers bias.

K. O. Emery, 1955, Grain size of marine beach gravels. *Jour. Geol.* 63: 39–49. Included are cumulative size frequency curves of gravels from Pacific coast and Japan.

S. A. Harris, 1958a, Probability curves and the recognition of adjustment to depositional environment, *Jour. Sed. Petrol.* 28: 151–163. Discusses analysis of cumulative curves of sediment particle size. Considers the size cumulative curve as actually composed of contributions of one or more Gaussian curves, each corresponding to a particular type of environment. See also S. A. Harris, 1958b, Differentiation of various Egyptian Aolian micro-environments by mechanical composition, *Jour. Sed. Petrol.* 28: 164–174 for application of analytic method referred to above.

W. C. Krumbein, 1938, Size frequency distributions of sediments and the normal Phi curve, *Jour. Sed. Petrol.* Discussion of the log_2 transformation to induce symmetry in percent by weight particle size frequency distributions.

E. A. Lohse, 1955, A theoretical curve for statistical analysis of sediments, *Jour. Sed. Petrol.* 25: 293–296. Suggests a graphic method for comparing empirical sediment size cumulative curves with a "theoretical perfect grade size distribution."

DISTRIBUTIONS INVOLVING MORE THAN ONE VARIABLE

Problems in the physical world are such that in order to analyze behavior or causality it often becomes necessary to consider groups of variables or at least more than one independent variable. The examples we have given have dealt with one independent variable and one dependent variable in the mathematical sense.

If we observe a single attribute of an object, i.e., perform an experiment and record or observe one event, we can then plot each observation as a point on the x axis or abscissa. In the event of duplications of observations some points would in fact represent more than one observation. We can assign the value $1/n$ to each observation, where n represent the total number of observations. Hence, each observation or event can be described by a single value, positioned somewhere on the one-dimensional x axis.

Suppose another attribute of the object is placed under observation and recorded. Each observation or event is characterized by two factors, and each event may be characterized for convenience by first drawing two mutually perpendicular axes, calling one an x_1 axis and the other x_2 axis. An event may hence be characterized by a point in two-space. This discussion may easily be extended so that $3, 4, 5, 6, \cdots, k$ factors or attributes may be observed on each of n objects. Here, each observation would be represented as a point in $3, 4, 5, 6, \cdots, k$-space. We would then be concerned with $3, 4, 5, 6, \cdots, k$ mathematically independent variables or variates.

An example of a two-dimensional graph is illustrated in Fig. 2.9a. Here each point is represented by two values. The first subscript indicates the attribute under consideration, whereas the second indicates the number of the observation. Hence (x_{17}, x_{27}) indicates the seventh observed object for attributes 1 and 2.

A line drawn from the origin ($x_{1i} = x_{2i} = 0$) to any point in two-space

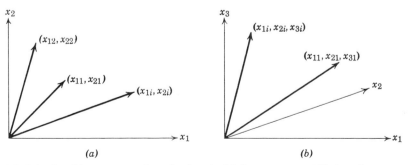

(a)   (b)

FIG. 2.9. Graphic representation of points in (a) $k =$ two-space, (b) $k =$ three-space.

will describe a directed line segment or vector, whose magnitude and direction are determined entirely by a point in two-space.

Similarly a three-dimensional graph can represent the events in three-space.

Here, too, any line connecting a point in three-space with the origin would be a vector determined completely by the reference set of axis and the point in question. Here our observations can be thought of as vectors in three-space.

This discussion may now be generalized to k-dimensional space, where each point may be thought of as a vector in k-dimensional space.

In Fig. 2.6 for example, each event x_0 is plotted on the x axis along with its associated value $F(x_0)$; this plots as a one-dimensional surface in two-dimensional space.

If one plots the events (x_{1i}, x_{2i}) as well as the value of $f(x_1, x_2)$ at x_{1i}, x_{2i}, one obtains a surface in three-dimensional space.

In a similar manner, k variates, when plotted with their pdf's, will plot as a k-dimensional surface in $k + 1$-dimensional space, although the points themselves can be plotted in k-space.

If we denote the variables $(x_1, x_2, x_3, \cdots, x_k)$ by X_k, then $f(X_k)$ is said to be a probability density function if

$$f(X_k) \geq 0 \qquad X_k \in R$$

$$f(X_k)$$

is continuous, and

$$\int_R f(X_k) \, dX_k = 1$$

where $dX_k = dx_1, dx_2, dx_3 \cdots, dx_k$.

If $f(X_k)$ fulfills the above, then it is said to be the joint probability function of the variables $(x_1, x_2, \cdots, x_k) = X_k$.

The concepts of marginal and conditional probabilities are easily extended to k-dimensions.

Consider the function

$$g(x_1, x_2) = 3 - x_1 + x_2 \quad \text{for} \quad R \begin{cases} -3 \leq x_1 \leq 0 \\ 0 \leq x_2 \leq 3 \end{cases}$$

This function can be made to be a density function in the following manner. First integrate $g(x_1, x_2)$ over the region R.

$$\int_0^3 \int_{-3}^0 (3 - x_1 + x_2) \, dx_1 \, dx_2 = \int_0^3 \left(\frac{27}{2} + 3x_2 \right) dx_2 = 54$$

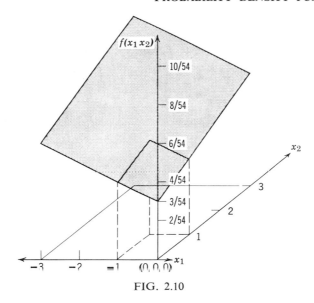

FIG. 2.10

Hence

$$f(x_1, x_2) = \frac{1}{54}(3 - x_1 + x_2) \quad \text{for} \quad R\begin{vmatrix} -3 \le x_1 \le 0 \\ 0 \le x_2 \le 3 \end{vmatrix} \qquad (2.2)$$

$$= 0 \qquad\qquad\qquad\qquad \text{otherwise}$$

is a density function. Its graph is plotted in Fig. 2.10.

With the knowledge of the pdf, then

$$P\{-1 \le x_1 \le 0, 1 < x_2 < 2\}$$

for example, is

$$= \frac{1}{54} \int_1^2 \int_{-1}^0 (3 - x_1 + x_2)\, dx_1\, dx_2$$

$$= \frac{1}{54} \int_1^2 \left(\frac{7}{2} + x_2\right) dx_2 = \frac{1}{54}\left[\left(\frac{7}{2} - 2 + 2\right) - \left(\frac{7}{2} + \frac{1}{2}\right)\right]$$

$$= \frac{5}{54}$$

In some instances we may become interested in working with only one of a set of k variables. That is to say, we shall ignore all variables but x_i. This suggests finding a function of x_i so that we may find $P\{b \le x_i \le a\}$. This function is denoted as $f_i(x_i)$. It is called the marginal distribution of x_i or simply the distribution of x_i, and may be obtained by integrating out all variables but x_i from the joint distribution function $f(X_k)$. That is,

$$f_i(x_i) = \int_{-\infty}^{\infty} \cdots \int_{-\infty}^{\infty} f(X_k) \, dx_1 \, dx_2 \cdots dx_{i-1} \, dx_{i+1} \cdots dx_k$$

The probability distribution of x_1 when

$$f(x_1, x_2) = \frac{1}{54}(3 - x_1 + x_2)$$

is

$$f_1(x_1) = \frac{1}{54} \int_0^3 (3 - x_1 + x_2) \, dx_2$$

$$= \frac{1}{54}\left(-3x_1 + \frac{27}{2}\right)$$

$$= -\frac{x_1}{18} + \frac{1}{4}$$

Hence

$$P\{a \le x_1 \le b\} = \int_a^b \left(-\frac{x_1}{18} + \frac{1}{4}\right) dx_1 = \frac{(a - b)(a + b - 9)}{36}$$

If $f(x_1, x_2, \cdots, x_k)$ is a k dimensional surface in $(k + 1)$ dimensional space, then the joint marginal distribution of x_i, x_j, x_k is

$$f_{ijk}(x_i x_j x_k)$$
$$= \int_{-\infty}^{\infty} \cdots \int_{-\infty}^{\infty} f(X_k) \, dx_1 \cdots dx_{i-1} \, dx_{i+1} \cdots dx_{j-1} \, dx_{j+1} \cdots d_{k-1}$$

The joint cumulative distribution is

$$F(X_k) = \int_{-\infty}^{x_1} \int_{-\infty}^{x_2} \cdots \int_{-\infty}^{x_k} f(X_k) \, dX_k$$

and the joint cumulative distribution of x_{ijk} is

$$F_{ijk}(x_i x_j x_k) = \int_{-\infty}^{\infty} \cdots \int_{-\infty}^{\infty} \int_{-\infty}^{x_i} \cdots \int_{-\infty}^{x_j} \cdots \int_{-\infty}^{\infty} \int_{-\infty}^{x_k} f(X_k) \, dx_k$$

From our definition of conditional probability (1.14)

$$P\{a \le x_i \le b \mid c \le x_j \le d\} = \frac{\displaystyle\int_c^d \int_a^b f_{ij}(x_i x_j) \, dx_i \, dx_j}{\displaystyle\int_c^d f_j(x_j) \, dx_j}$$

The conditional density $f(x_i \mid x_j)$ is

$$\frac{f_{ij}(x_i x_j)}{f_j(x_j)}$$

Hence the conditional distributions of one set of variables, given another, is the joint distribution of the variables divided by the distribution of the given set.

Bivariate Normal Or Two-Dimensional Normal Distribution

(1) x_1 is $N(\mu_1, \sigma_1^2)$, x_2 is $N(\mu_2, \sigma_2^2)$; x_1 and x_2 are random variables, independent in the statistical sense (see Chapter 1).

Let the pdf of x_1 be $g(x_1)$ and that of x_2 be $g(x_2)$; then by the assumption of independence, the joint pdf of x_1 and x_2 is

$$f(x_1, x_2) = g(x_1)g(x_2)$$

$$= \frac{1}{2\pi\sigma_1\sigma_2} \exp -\frac{1}{2}\left[\left(\frac{x_1 - \mu_1}{\sigma_1}\right)^2 + \left(\frac{x_2 - \mu_2}{\sigma_2}\right)^2\right]$$

(2) x_1 is $N(\mu_1, \sigma_1^2)$, x_2 is $N(\mu_2, \sigma_2^2)$; x_1 and x_2 are nonindependent random variables with covariance $= \sigma_{12}$. (See Chapter 3 for amplification of these concepts.)

Under the restrictions listed here, the joint probability distribution of x_1, x_2 is

$$f(x_1, x_2) = \frac{1}{2\pi\sigma_1\sigma_2\left(\dfrac{\sigma_1^2\sigma_2^2 - \sigma_{12}}{\sigma_1^2\sigma_2^2}\right)^{1/2}}$$

$$\times \exp -\frac{1}{2}\left[\frac{\left(\dfrac{x_1 - \mu_1}{\sigma_1}\right)^2 + \left(\dfrac{x_2 - \mu_2}{\sigma_2}\right)^2 - 2\dfrac{\sigma_{12}}{\sigma_1\sigma_2}\dfrac{(x_1 - \mu_1)}{\sigma_1}\dfrac{(x_2 - \mu_2)}{\sigma_2}}{\dfrac{\sigma_1^2\sigma_2^2 - \sigma_{12}^2}{\sigma_1^2\sigma_2^2}}\right]$$

Let $\rho = \sigma_{12}/\sigma_1\sigma_2$; then

$$f(x_1, x_2) = \frac{1}{2\pi\sigma_1\sigma_2(1 - \rho^2)^{1/2}}$$

$$\times \exp -\left[\frac{\left(\dfrac{x_1 - \mu_1}{\sigma_1}\right)^2 + \left(\dfrac{x_2 - \mu_2}{\sigma_2}\right)^2 - 2\rho\left(\dfrac{x_1 - \mu_1}{\sigma_1}\right)\left(\dfrac{x_2 - \mu_2}{\sigma_2}\right)}{2(1 - \rho^2)}\right]$$

ρ, a unitless parameter, is the *correlation coefficient* of the variable x_1 and x_2 and measures the degree of association between x_1 and x_2.

EXERCISES

1. (a) Define a density function from the function $6 - 2x_1 - x_2$ when

$$R\begin{cases} 0 \leq x_1 \leq 2 \\ -1 \leq x_2 \leq 2 \end{cases} \quad \text{and} \quad 0 \text{ elsewhere} \quad Ans. \quad \frac{1}{21}(6 - 2x_1 - x_2)$$

Find: (b) $f(x_1, x_2)$
      (c) $f_2(x_2)$

      (d) $f_1(x_1)$ Ans. $\dfrac{1}{21}(33 - 12x_1)$

      (e) $F_2(x_2)$
      (f) $F(x_1, x_2)$

      (g) $F_1(x_2)$ Ans. $\dfrac{1}{21}(6x_1 - x_1{}^2 - 2x_1x_2)$

Compute: (h) $P\{-\tfrac{1}{2} \le x_1 \le 1, 0 \le x_2 \le 2\}$ Ans. $\dfrac{1}{6}$

           (i) $P\{0 \le x_2 \le 2\}$

           (j) $P\{\tfrac{1}{2} \le x_1 \le 1\}$

           (k) $P\{\tfrac{1}{2} \le x_1 \le 1 \mid 0 \le x_2 \le 2\}$ Ans. $\dfrac{7}{24}$

           (l) $P\{0 \le x_2 \le 2 \mid \tfrac{1}{2} \le x_1 \le 1\}$

2.   (a) Define a density function for $g(x_1, x_2, x_3) = 2x_1x_2x_3$

where $R \begin{cases} 0 \le x_1 < 2 \\ 0 \le x_2 \le 2 \\ 0 \le x_3 \le 2 \end{cases}$

Find: (b) $f_i(x_i)$ $i = 1, 2, 3$
      (c) $f_{ij}(x_i, x_j)$ Ans. $x_i x_j / 4$
      (d) $f(x_1 \mid x_2x_3)$
      (e) $f(x_1x_2 \mid x_3)$ Ans. $x_1x_2 / 4$

3. In Problem 2 are x_1, x_2, and x_3 independent in the probability sense?
                                               Ans. Yes.

4. If $f(x) = \tfrac{3}{8}x^2$ $R:$ $0 \le x \le 2$
                    $= 0$ otherwise

    (a) Find the number a such that
$$P\{x \ge a\} = 0.9$$
Hint: $P\{x \ge a\} = 1 - P\{x \le a\}$
    (b) Find the number b such that
$$P\{x \le b\} = 0.95$$

    (c) Draw the density and cumulative distributions and indicate a, b.
    (d) Find the number c such that
$$P\{x \le c\} = 0.5$$

c is called the median of the distribution and is that value of the variate which has $\tfrac{1}{2}$ of the distribution above and below it.

5. If $f(x)$ is distributed as

$$\frac{3x^2 - 6x + 9}{20} \qquad R: \quad 1 \le x \le 3$$

Find: (a) $P\{x \geq 1\}$
      (b) $P\{x \geq 2\}$
      (c) $P\{x \geq 3\}$

(d) What is the probability of three values of x satisfying simultaneously: (a), (b), and (c) above?   *Ans.* $1, \left(\dfrac{13}{20}\right)^3, 0.$

(e) What is the probability that at least one value of four observed values is less than 2?

Hint: $P(\text{at least one} > 2) = P(1 \text{ or } 2 \text{ or } 3 \text{ or } 4 \text{ greater than } 2) = 1 - P \text{ (none of 4 is greater than 2)} = 1 - \left(\dfrac{13}{20}\right)^4.$

6. (a) Show that if $\dfrac{1}{54}(3 - x_1 + x_2)$ is defined over the region $\begin{Bmatrix} -3 \leq x_1 \leq 0 \\ 0 \leq x_2 \leq 3 \end{Bmatrix}$

then

$$f(x_1 \mid x_2) = \frac{6 - 2x_1 + 2x_2}{27 + 6x_2}$$

(b) Find $P\{-2 \leq x_1 \leq -1 \mid 0 \leq x_2 < 1\}$ *Ans.* $\dfrac{1}{3}$

7. x_1 is $N(\mu_1, \sigma_1^2)$ and x_2 is $N(\mu_2, \sigma_2^2)$ with covariance σ_{12}. Find the correlation coefficient of $(x_1 - \mu_1)/\sigma$ and $(x_2 - \mu_2)/\sigma_2$.

chapter 3

Moments and Expectations

The term "moment" is familiar to us from our experience with elementary physics. There we spoke of the center of gravity as being a moment and also of the moment of inertia of a body. Moments were defined as integrals or sums, depending on whether the variables in question were continuous or discrete. If some force F is applied to a rod of length r, attached to a point or axis about which it can move, and if the total mass of the body is considered to consist of very small particles of mass Δm_i at a distance r_i from the point or axis of rotation, the moment of inertia of the rod is defined as $\int r^2 \, dm$.

The expectation of a function of a random variable, or of the random variable itself, is defined as the weighted average value of the function or variable, averaged over all possible values of the function or the variable.

The moments of a random variable are the expectations of the powers of the random variable.

For example, a discrete variable takes the values of $x = 2, 4, 6, 8, 10$ with probabilities values $1/20, 2/20, 4/20, 6/20, 7/20$, respectively. Hence, the expectation of the random variable x, written $E(x)$, is $E(x) = 2/20 + 8/20 + 24/20 + 48/20 + 70/20 = 152/20 = 7.6$. Similarly, the first moment of x is

$$E(x') = E(x) = 7.6$$

In general, if $f(x)$ is the discrete probability density function of a discrete random variable x, then

$$E(x) = \sum_{x=a_1}^{a_n} x f(x) \qquad (3.1)$$

where $x = a_1, a_2, \cdots, a_n$.

If $f(x)$ is the density function for a continuous random variable x, then the expectation of x is defined as

$$E(x) = \int_R x f(x) \, dx \qquad \text{for all } x \in R \qquad (3.2)$$

The moments about an arbitrary point x_0 are defined as

$$E[(x - x_0)^r] = \int_R (x - x_0)^r f(x) \, dx \qquad \text{for } x \in R \qquad (3.3)$$

The moments about the point $x_0 = 0$ are defined as

$$\mu_k' = E[(x)^k] = \int_R x^k f(x) \, dx \qquad \text{for } x \in R \qquad (3.4)$$

Henceforth the superscript indicates moments about zero. Hence, $\mu_1' = E(x) = \int_R x f(x) \, dx$. The first moment about zero is called the *mean* of the distribution $f(x)$.

The moments about the point $x_0 = \mu_1' = E(x)$ or the mean of the distribution are denoted by μ_k and defined as

$$\mu_k = E[x - E(x)]^k = E[(x - \mu_1')^k] = \int_R (x - \mu_1')^k f(x) \, dx \quad \text{for all } x \in R$$

$$\qquad (3.5)$$

or

$$\sum_{x=a_1}^{a_n} (x - \mu_1')^k f(x)$$

when x is discrete.

The third moment about the mean $\mu_3 = E[x - E(x)]^3$ is called the "skewness," and the fourth moment about the mean $\mu_4 = E[x - E(x)]^4$ is called "kurtosis." Sample estimates and tests of significance for these higher moments are given in G. W. Snedecor, *Statistical methods*, 1953, Iowa State College Press, Ames, Iowa, pp. 174–177.

SOME GENERALIZATIONS AND SOME PROPERTIES OF EXPECTATIONS

If $f(x_1, x_2, \cdots, x_k)$ is the joint probability density function of the random variable $X_k = (x_1, x_2, \cdots, x_k)$ and $g = g(X_k)$ is a properly defined function, then

$$E(g) = E[g(X_k)] = \int_R \cdots \int g(X_k) f(X_k) \, dX_k \qquad (3.6)$$

Furthermore

$$E[g + a] = \int_R \cdots \int (g + a) f(X_k) \, dX_k$$

where a is some constant. Now

$$\int_R \cdots \int (g + a)f(X_k)\,dX_k$$

$$= \int_R \cdots \int gf(X_k)\,dX_k + a\int_R \cdots \int f(X_k)\,dX_k \qquad (3.7)$$

$$= E(g) + a$$

since

$$\int_R \cdots \int f(X_k)\,dX_k = 1$$

by hypothesis that $f(X_k)$ is a density function.

$$Ega = a\int_R \cdots \int gf(X_k)\,dX_k = aE(g) \qquad (3.8)$$

$$E[g - E(g)] = \int_R [g - E(g)]f(X_k)\,dX_k = \int_R gf(X_k)\,dX_k - E(g)$$

Therefore
$$E[g - E(g)] = 0 \qquad (3.9)$$

If $h = h(X_k)$ is a random variable too, then

$$E(h + g) = \int_R \cdots \int (h + g)f(X_k)\,dX_k$$

$$= \int_R \cdots \int hf(X_k)\,dX_k + \int_R \cdots \int gf(X_k)\,dX_k$$

Therefore
$$E(h + g) = E(h) + E(g). \qquad (3.10)$$

If x_i and x_j are two stochastically independent variables, distributed as $f_{ij}(x_i x_j)$, then

$$f_{ij}(x_i x_j) = f_i(x_i)f_j(x_j)$$

and hence,

$$E(x_i x_j) = \iint x_i f_i(x_i) x_j f_j(x_j)\,dx_i\,dx_j$$

$$= E(x_i)E(x_j) \qquad (3.11)$$

Variance

The second moment of the random variable, taken about its mean, is called the variance of the random variable and is denoted as

$$\begin{aligned}
\text{var}(x) &= E[x - E(x)]^2 \\
&= E\{x^2 - 2xE(x) + [E(x)]^2\} \\
&= Ex^2 - 2E(x)E(x) + [E(x)^2] \\
&= Ex^2 - (Ex)^2 \\
&= \mu_2 = (\mu_2' - \mu_1'^2) \qquad (3.12)
\end{aligned}$$

Variance (x) is often designated by the square of the small greek letter sigma, σ^2; $\sqrt{\sigma^2} = \sqrt{\text{var}(x)}$ is called the standard deviation.

SOME PROPERTIES OF THE VARIANCE

If a is a constant, then

$$\text{var}(x + a) = E[(x + a) - E(x + a)]^2$$

where

$$E(x + a) = E(x) + E(a) = \mu_1' + a$$

Hence

$$\text{var}(x + a) = E(x + a - \mu_1' - a)^2 = E(x - \mu_1')^2 = \mu_2 = \text{var}\, x \quad (3.13)$$

$$\text{var}(xa) = E[ax - E(ax)]^2 = E[ax - a\mu_1']^2$$

$$= E(a^2x^2) - 2a^2\mu_1'E(x) + a^2\mu_1'^2$$

$$= a^2Ex^2 - a^2\mu_1'^2 = a^2E[x^2 - \mu_1'^2]$$

$$= a^2\mu_2 = a^2\,\text{var}\, x \quad (3.14)$$

COVARIANCE AND CORRELATION

The covariance of two random variables x_1 and x_2 is defined as

$$\text{cov}(x_1, x_2) = E\{[x_1 - E(x_1)][x_2 - E(x_2)]\} \quad (3.15)$$

Rewriting (3.15) as

then[1]

$$Ex_1x_2 - E(x_2)E(x_1) - E(x_1)(x_2) + E(x_1)E(x_2)$$

$$\text{cov}(x_1, x_2) = E(x_1x_2) - E(x_1)E(x_2)$$

This is designated by σ_{12}.

The linear correlation coefficient ρ between two variables x_1, x_2 is defined as

$$\rho_{x_1x_2} = \rho_{12} = \frac{\text{cov}(x_1, x_2)}{[\text{var}(x_1)\,\text{var}(x_2)]^{1/2}} = \frac{\sigma_{x_1x_2}}{\sigma_{x_1}\sigma_{x_2}}$$

and

$$\rho_{12}^2 = \frac{\sigma_{x_1x_2}^2}{\sigma_{x_1}^2\sigma_{x_2}^2} \quad (3.16)$$

[1] $E[E(x_1)\,x_2] = E(x_1)E(x_2)$ since $E(x_1)$ is a constant, i.e., $E(ax) = aE(x)$.

If x_1 and x_2 are independent in the statistical sense, then from (3.11)

$$E(x_1, x_2) = E(x_1)E(x_2)$$

Hence

$$\sigma_{x_1 x_2} = 0$$

and therefore from (3.15)

$$\rho_{12} = 0$$

The converse of this statement is not necessarily true. That is, if $\rho_{12} = 0$, it does not necessarily follow that x_1 and x_2 are statistically independent. We may now define var $(x + y)$, where x and y are random variables, as var (x) + var (y) + 2 cov (xy).

SCHWARZ' INEQUALITY AND THE UPPER BOUND OF THE LINEAR CORRELATION COEFFICIENT

It can be shown that[1]

$$E(x_1{}^2)E(x_1{}^2) \geq [E(x_1 x_2)]^2 \qquad (3.17)$$

Formula 3.17 is generally called Schwarz' inequality. We can now show that ρ_{12}, the linear correlation coefficient between any two random variables x_1 and x_2, is never greater than one.[2]

For a particular pair of variables x_1 and x_2 we translate the origin of the distributions to $E(x_1)$ and $E(x_2)$ respectively. This defines a new pair of variables $x_1 - E(x)$ and $x_2 - E(x_2)$. When we substitute these variables in (3.17) we obtain

$$E[x_1 - E(x_1)]^2 E[x_2 - E(x_1)]^2 \geq E\{[x_1 - E(x_1)][x_2 - E(x_2)]\}^2$$

We now divide both sides of the inequality by $E[x_1 - E(x_1)]^2 E[x_2 - E(x_2)]^2$ which is nonzero.

Hence

$$\frac{\{E[x_1 - E(x_1)]E[x_2 - E(x_2)]\}^2}{E[x_1 - E(x_1)]^2 E[x_2 - E(x_2)]^2} \leq 1 \qquad (3.18)$$

However, the left side of (3.18) is identical with (3.16) and hence

$$\rho_{12}^2 \leq 1$$

and therefore

$$|\rho_{12}| \leq 1$$

and

$$-1 \leq \rho_{12} \leq 1$$

[1] See for example, M. E. Munroe, 1951, *Theory of probability*, p. 115, McGraw-Hill Book Co., New York.

[2] Based on M. E. Munroe, 1951, *ibid.*

MEANS AND VARIANCES OF SOME PARTICULAR DISTRIBUTIONS

Uniform or Rectangular Distribution[1]

$$f(x) = \frac{1}{\beta - \alpha} \qquad R: \alpha \le x \le \beta$$

$$= 0 \qquad \text{otherwise}$$

$$\mu_1' = E(x) = \frac{1}{\beta - \alpha} \int_\alpha^\beta x \, dx = \frac{\beta^2 - \alpha^2}{2(\beta - \alpha)} = \frac{\beta + \alpha}{2}$$

$$\mu_2' = E(x^2) = \frac{1}{\beta - \alpha} \int_\alpha^\beta x^2 \, dx = \frac{\beta^3 - \alpha^3}{3(\beta - \alpha)} = \frac{\beta^2 + \alpha^2 + \alpha\beta}{3}$$

$$\text{var } x = \mu_2' - (\mu_1')^2 = \frac{4(\alpha^2 + \beta^2 + \alpha\beta) - 3(\beta^2 + \alpha^2 + 2\alpha\beta)}{12}$$

$$= \frac{\alpha^2 + \beta^2 - 2\alpha\beta}{12} = \frac{(\beta - \alpha)^2}{12}$$

Binomial Distribution

$$f(x) = \binom{n}{x} p^x (1 - p)^{n-x} \qquad R: x = 0, 1, 2, \cdots, n$$

$$= 0 \qquad \text{otherwise}$$

$$\mu_1' = E(x) = \sum_{x=0}^n x f(x) = \sum_{x=0}^n x \binom{n}{x} p^x (1 - p)^{n-x}$$

We now rewrite this as

$$0 + \sum_{x=1}^n x \frac{n(n-1)!}{(n-x)! \, x(x-1)!} p \cdot p^{x-1} (1-p)^{n-x}$$

Factoring, we obtain

$$np \sum_{x=1}^n \frac{(n-1)!}{(n-x)! \, (x-1)!} p^{x-1} (1-p)^{n-x}$$

but

$$\sum_{x=1}^n \binom{n-1}{x-1} p^{x-1} (1-p)^{n-x}$$

[1] See Griffiths and Rosenfeld, 1953, A further test of dimensional orientation of quartz grain in Bradford sand, *Amer. J. Sci.* 251: 192–214.

is a binomial density function with parameters p and $n - 1$ and hence must sum to unity. Therefore

$$\mu_1' = Ex = np$$

Now

$$\text{var } x = E(x^2) - (\mu_1')^2.$$

This can be rewritten as

$$E[x(x - 1) + x] - (\mu_1')^2 = E[x(x - 1)] + E(x) - (\mu_1')^2$$

where

$$E[x(x - 1)]$$

$$= 0 + 0 + \sum_{x=2}^{n} x(x - 1) \frac{n(n - 1)(n - 2)!}{(n - x)! \, x(x - 1)(x - 2)!} p^2 p^{x-2} (1 - p)^{n-x}$$

$$= n(n - 1)p^2$$

Hence

$$\mu_2 = \text{var } x = n(n - 1)p^2 + np - n^2 p^2 = np(1 - p)$$

EXERCISES

1. If the number of grain-to-grain contacts in an arkose is binomially distributed with $p = 0.60$, (a) what is the expected number of grain-to-grain contacts in a slide of 2000 grains? (b) What is the variance of the number of grain-to-grain contacts? (c) The standard deviation? *Ans.* (a) 1200; (b) 480; (c) 21.8.

2. If $h(x) = e^{xt}$, and x is distributed as $f(x)$ for $x \in R$ find $E(e^{xt})$.

$$\text{Ans. } \int_R e^{xt} f(x) \, dx$$

3. Let $g(t) = E(e^{xt})$. Find:

(a) $\dfrac{dg(t)}{dt}$

$$\text{Ans. } \int_R x e^{xt} f(x) \, dx$$

(b) $\dfrac{dg(t)}{dt}\bigg|_{t=0}$ [that is, the first derivative of $g(t)$ with respect to t, evaluated at $(t = 0)$].

$$\text{Ans. } \int_R x f(x) \, dx$$

(c) $\dfrac{d^2 g(t)}{dt^2}\bigg|_{t=0}$

$$\text{Ans. } \int_R x^2 f(x) \, dx$$

(d) $\dfrac{d^r g(t)}{dt^r}\bigg|_{t=0}$

$$\text{Ans. } \int_R x^r f(x) \, dx$$

(e) What is the functional relation between $g(t)$ and the moments about zero of $f(x)$? *Ans.* The rth derivative of $g(t)$ with respect to t evaluated at $t = 0$ is u_r'. $g(t)$, for obvious reasons, is called the moment generating function of $f(x)$.

4. Find: (*a*) the moment generating function, (*b*) mean, (*c*) variance, and (*d*) standard deviation of the following distributions.

4(1) $f(x) = \dfrac{1}{\sqrt{2\pi\sigma^2}} e^{-(x-\mu)^2/2\sigma^2}$ *Ans.* (*a*) $\exp\left(\dfrac{2t\mu + \sigma^2 t^2}{2}\right)$

(*b*) μ

(*c*) σ^2

(*d*) σ

4(2) $f(x) = \dfrac{x^\gamma e^{-x/\lambda}}{\gamma!\ \lambda^{\gamma+1}}$ for $x > 0$ *Ans.* (*a*) $(1 - \lambda\epsilon)^{-(\gamma+1)}$

$\quad = 0$ otherwise   (*b*) $\lambda(\gamma + 1)$

(*c*) $\lambda^2(\gamma + 1)$

(*d*) $\lambda(\gamma + 1)_{1/2}$

A variate distributed as 4(2) is said to have the gamma distribution.

5. Find the mean and variance of the beta distribution

$f(x) = \dfrac{(\alpha + \beta + 1)}{\alpha!\ \beta!} x^\alpha (1 - x)^\beta$ R: $\ 0 < x < 1$

$\quad = 0$ otherwise

Ans. (*a*) $\dfrac{(\alpha + \beta + 1)!\,(\alpha + 1)!}{(\alpha + \beta + 2)!\,\alpha!} = \dfrac{\alpha + 1}{\alpha + \beta + 2}$

(*b*) $\dfrac{(\alpha + 1)(\beta - 1)}{(\alpha + \beta + 2)^2(\alpha + \beta + 3)}$

6. Find μ_r' of the beta distribution.   *Ans.* $\dfrac{(\alpha + \beta + 1)!\,(\alpha + r)!}{(\alpha + \beta + r + 1)!\,\alpha!}$

7. Show that the mean and variance of the Poisson distribution, Chapter 2, p. 27 is λ.

8. Write the discrete analogues of (3.6) to (3.11).

EXAMPLES OF COMPUTATION AND USE OF MOMENTS IN EARTH SCIENCE

Karl Pearson, 1894, Contributions to the mathematical theory of evolution, *Phil. Trans. Ser. A* 185: 71–110. A method is described for dissecting an assymetrical frequency curve into two normal curves. He obtains expressions for the first five moments of the curve, which he solves after algebraic manipulation. A similar procedure, the solution of moment equations, may be applied to the dissection into *three* normal curves. See H. S. Pollard, 1934, *On the relative stability of the median and arithmetic mean, etc., Annals Math. Stat.* 5: 239ff.

W. C. Krumbein, 1935, Thin-section mechanical analysis of indurated sediments, *Jour. Geol.* 43: 482–496, includes a discussion of the computation of moments through the fourth moment in some detail. He also considers the range of error of average grain size in thin section.

W. C. Krumbein, 1936, Application of logarithmic moments to size frequency distributions of sediments, *Jour. Sed. Petrol.* 6: 35–47. By inducing a symmetry to sediment size frequency distributions "normal" statistical analysis is facilitated.

H. L. Alling, 1944, Grain analysis of minerals of sand size in Ball Mills, *Jour. Sed. Petrol.* 14: 103–114, uses the second and third moments (sorting and skewness).

N. N. Greenman, 1951, The mechanical analyses of sediments from thin section data, *Jour. Geol.* 59: 447–462. In this paper, Krumbein's 1935 (*ibid.*) method is extended to achieve the total size frequency distribution as well as the moments.

G. H. Packham, 1955, Volume, weight and number frequency analysis of sediments from thin section data, *Jour. Geol.* 63: 50–58. Calculation of moments from a probability distribution function for distribution of intercepts in thin section size analysis. This is followed by a new method of number frequency analysis.

George V. Cohee, 1938, Sediments of the submarine canyons off the California coast, *Jour. Sed. Petrol.* 8: 19–33. Gives data with percentiles and third moments.

W. J. Plumley, 1948, Black Hills terrace gravels: a study in sediment transport. *Jour. Geol.* 56: 526–577. Relates size shape and roundness to the third moment (skewness).

I. I. Cheboterov, 1955, Metamorphism of natural waters in the crust, etc. *Geochim. et Cosmochim. Acta.* 8: 22–48. Describes a method for forming frequency distributions from empirical data in geochemistry. Utilizes first and second moments and coefficient of skewness.

E. D. Sneed and R. L. Folk, 1958, Pebbles in the lower Colorado river, Texas; a study in particle morphogenesis, *Jour. Geol.* 66: 114–150. Applies first four moments including some standard errors. A graphic method for computing the third and fourth moments is given in R. Folk, and D. Ward, 1957, *Jour. Sed. Petrol.* (*ibid.*).

F. Chayes, 1956, *Petrographic modal analysis*, John Wiley, New York. Calculates expected values, and moments, e.g., of a rectangular distribution in analysis of banded rocks.

V. E. McKelvey, 1940, Beach sediments of Trout Lake, Wisconsin, *Jour. Sed. Petrol.* 10: 65–77. Tests the accuracy of field sampling by replication and simultaneous sampling. Contains data condensed as first three moments.

H. E. Wright, Jr., 1956, Origin of the Chuska sandstone Arizona-New Mexico, etc., *Bull. G. S. A.* 413–434. Includes estimation of first three parameters for postulating depositional environment.

W J. Plumley and D. H. Davis, 1956, Estimation of recent sediment size parameters from a triangular diagram, *Jour. Sed. Petrol.* 26: 140–155. Describes a graphic method for estimating sediment size parameters including the first three moments.

J. C. Griffiths, 1958, Petrography and Porosity of the Cow Run Sand, St. Marys, West Virginia, *Jour. Sed. Petrol.* 28: 15–30. Considers the first four moments, including skewness and kurtosis.

R. Folk and W. C. Ward, 1957, Brazos River bar: A study in the significance of grain size parameters, *Jour. Sed. Petrol.* 27: 3–26. A detailed discussion and interpretation of the first four moments of both normal and non-normal curves. The trends of the moments are schematically linked in a helix, as a unifying device for environment analysis.

A book of general interest in this context, is W. P. Elderton, 1938, *Frequency curves and correlation*, third edition, Cambridge University Press. He discusses the inverse problem of: given the data, what is the proper theoretical frequency curve? The method of moments and the "Pearson frequency curves" for generating population frequency distributions are given in detail.

READINGS ON THE SPECIFIC USE OF THE MEAN AND VARIANCE (OR STANDARD DEVIATION)

There is a very numerous literature in areas of study within the context of this book. The following are a few examples.

P. L. Carpenter, 1939, Bacterial counts in the muds of Crystal Lake, etc., *Jour. Sed. Petrol.* 9: 3–7. Uses geometric mean[1] instead of arithmetic mean for bacterial counts.

T. J. H. Van Andel, 1954, Roundness and shape of marine gravels from Urk (Netherlands) a comparison of several methods of investigation. *Jour. Sed. Petrol.* 24: 100–116.

K. O. Emery, 1954, Some characteristics of Southern California Sediments, *Jour. Sed. Petrol.* 24: 50–59. Uses the median and a "sorting coefficient," Trask's $\sqrt{P_{75}/P_{25}}$ instead of mean and standard deviation. See Chapter 4, for discussion of percentile estimates of μ and σ.

[1] See Chapter 4 for discussion of geometric mean and kinds of averages other than the arithmetic mean.

4

Statistical Inference: The Estimation of Parameters and Their Probability Density Functions

The problems in the experimental sciences are such that one rarely knows exactly the distribution functions governing the variables under study. Many examples exist where a theoretical model will serve as the basis for sampling as well as for obtaining an idea as to the values the parameters in the model may attain. At times these models are successful and appropriate (Krumbein and Slack, *op. cit.* p. 27); in other instances they are not (Miller and Goldberg, 1955). Furthermore, most experimentation is concerned with drawing conclusions not about the sample examined but about the populations from which the samples have come. The scientific method thus draws inferences from the sample to the population. Statistical inference is the means by which one draws objective inference from the samples to the populations. What sort of inference can be drawn? The experimenter may wish to estimate the parameters in the probability distributions governing his variables; or he may wish to test hypotheses concerning the material he is working with. Statistical inference may thus be broken into two not necessarily mutually independent groups, namely, (1) statistical inference concerning the estimation of parameters, and (2) statistical inference concerning the testing of hypotheses concerning these parameters.

METHOD OF MAXIMUM LIKELIHOOD

One method of obtaining estimators of parameters is the maximum likelihood one introduced and developed by R. A. Fisher. We shall discuss the theory of maximum likelihood with the help of the continuous probability density function. The application of the maximum likelihood theory to the discrete variable will be self-evident.

Consider a sample of size n taken from a population governed by a continuous pdf $f(x_i, \theta)$, i.e., distributed as $f(x_i)$ with parameters $\theta = \theta_1$, $\theta_2, \cdots, \theta_k$. Henceforth, pdf will denote continuous pdf's unless otherwise stated. The likelihood function is a joint function of the sample points, and is defined as

$$L = L(x_1, x_2, \cdots, x_n, \theta) = f(x_1, \theta)f(x_2, \theta) \cdots f(x_n, \theta)$$
$$= \prod_{i=1}^{n} f(x_i, \theta) \tag{4.1}$$

Often, the natural logarithm of L is preferred to L for simplicity.

Hence, once the sampling has been done and the values $x_1, x_2, \cdots, x_n$ are known, L is just a function of the unknown parameters $\theta = \theta_1, \theta_2$, $\theta_3, \cdots, \theta_k$. The concept of maximum likelihood consists in selecting those values

$$\hat{\theta}_1, \hat{\theta}_2, \hat{\theta}_3, \cdots, \hat{\theta}_k$$

which maximize (4.1). Therefore we desire to select values for the θ_i's, out of possible values of θ_i which maximize (4.1). Thus our maximum likelihood function is such that

$$\prod_{i=1}^{n} f(x_i, \hat{\theta}) > \prod_{i=1}^{n} f(x_i, \hat{\hat{\theta}})$$

where $\hat{\theta} = \hat{\theta}_1, \hat{\theta}_2, \cdots, \hat{\theta}_k$ is one set of possible estimates of the parameters and $\hat{\hat{\theta}} = \hat{\hat{\theta}}_1, \hat{\hat{\theta}}_2, \hat{\hat{\theta}}_3, \cdots, \hat{\hat{\theta}}_k$ is another.

Maximizing the Likelihood Function

We are now ready to maximize the likelihood function. This is ordinarily done in the standard manner with the aid of the calculus. We first differentiate L with respect to the parameter and equate the derivative or when there is more than one parameter, the partial derivatives to zero. We then solve for the parameter and obtain a function which will maximize or minimize the L parameter. To establish the value as either a maximum or minimum is imperative, for we are interested in the maximum values and not the minimum. To summarize:

(1)
$$\frac{\partial L}{\partial \theta_i} = \frac{\partial \prod_{i=1}^{n} f(x_i, \theta)}{\partial \theta_i} = 0$$

(2)
$$\hat{\theta}_i = g_i(x_1, x_2, \cdots x_n)$$

and then test to see that $\hat{\theta}_i$ is a maximum.

THE MEAN AND VARIANCE OF A
NORMAL DISTRIBUTION

Let us consider as an example the problem of estimating the parameters μ and σ^2 in a normal distribution. Here any x_i is distributed as

$$f(x_i; \theta = \mu, \sigma^2) = \frac{1}{\sqrt{2\pi\sigma^2}} \exp\left[\frac{-(x_i - \mu)^2}{2\sigma^2}\right]$$

If a random sample of size n has been taken from such a population, then by virtue of independence from sample to sample, the likelihood function is

$$L = \prod_{i=1}^{n} f(x_i; \mu, \sigma^2) = \frac{1}{(2\pi\sigma^2)^{n/2}} \exp\left[\frac{-\sum_{i=1}^{n}(x_i - \mu)^2}{2\sigma^2}\right]$$

Let us consider obtaining an estimator of the parameter μ. We therefore find $\partial L/\partial \mu$ and equate to zero.

Since $\ln L$ will be at a maximum at the same time as L, we can just as conveniently discuss $\ln L = -\frac{n}{2}\ln 2\pi - \frac{n}{2}\ln \sigma^2 - \frac{1}{2\sigma^2}\sum_{i=1}^{n}(x_i - \mu)^2$ as L. We proceed, therefore, and obtain

$$\frac{\partial \ln L}{\partial \mu} = \frac{\sum_{i=1}^{n}(x_i - \mu)}{\sigma^2} = 0$$

Therefore
$$\sum_{i=1}^{n}(x_i - \mu) = 0, \qquad \sum_{i=1}^{n}x_i = n\mu$$

$$\sum_{i=1}^{n}\frac{x_i}{n} = \hat{\mu}$$

Hence, the maximum likelihood estimator of the unknown parameter μ is the sample statistic, $\hat{\mu}$, the first moment around zero, the sample mean, most often referred to as $\bar{x}$.

To obtain the maximum likelihood estimator of the parameter σ^2 we proceed as follows:

$$\frac{\partial \ln L}{\partial \sigma^2} = \frac{\partial}{\partial \sigma^2}\left[-\frac{n}{2}\ln \sigma^2 - \frac{1}{2\sigma^2}\sum_{i=1}^{n}(x_i - \mu)^2\right]$$

$$\frac{\partial \ln L}{\partial \sigma^2} = -\frac{n}{2\sigma^2} + \frac{1}{2\sigma^4}\sum_{i=1}^{n}(x_i - \mu)^2$$

Now replace σ^2 and μ by $\hat{\sigma}^2$ and $\bar{x}$. Then

$$\frac{\partial \ln L}{\partial \sigma^2} = -\frac{n}{2\hat{\sigma}^2} + \frac{1}{2\hat{\sigma}^4} \sum_{i=1}^{n} (x_i - \bar{x})^2 = 0$$

$$n\hat{\sigma}^2 = \sum_{i=1}^{n} (x_i - \bar{x})^2$$

$$\hat{s}^2 = \hat{\sigma}^2 = \frac{\sum_{i=1}^{n} (x_i - \bar{x})^2}{n}$$

Thus the maximum likelihood estimator of σ^2 is the second sample moment about the mean, or the sample variance $\hat{s}^2$.[1]

METHOD OF MOMENTS

Another method which can and has been used for obtaining estimates of parameters is the method of moments developed by Karl Pearson.

In general, the method of moments works as follows. Suppose one has a random sample of n from a population where each random variable is distributed as $f(x_i, \theta)$, where $\theta = \theta_1, \theta_2, \cdots, \theta_k$. Furthermore, let us assume that the moments about zero for the pdf of x exist and are functions of the parameters $\theta = \theta_1, \theta_2, \cdots, \theta_k$. Hence $\mu_i' = E(x)^i$ and

$$\mu_1' = g_1(\theta_1, \theta_2, \cdots, \theta_k)$$
$$\mu_2' = g_2(\theta_1, \theta_2, \cdots, \theta_k)$$
$$\cdot$$
$$\cdot \qquad\qquad\qquad\qquad (4.2)$$
$$\cdot$$
$$\mu_k' = g_k(\theta_1, \theta_2, \cdots, \theta_k)$$

The method of moments says that we substitute the estimates of the θ_i's in (4.2), i.e., substitute $\hat{\theta}_i$ for θ_i. When this has been done, we replace the population moments μ_i' by the sample moments m_i'. Hence, we obtain a series of equations in terms of the unknown estimates and the known sample moments, the number of equations being strictly a function of the

---

[1] The sample moments are defined analogously to the population moments. Thus in a sample of size n

$$m_r' = \sum_{i=1}^{n} \frac{x_i^r}{n} \quad \text{and}$$

$$m_r = \sum_{i=1}^{n} \frac{(x_i - \bar{x})^r}{n}$$

number of unknown parameters. The final equations are as follows:

$$m_1' = g_1(\hat{\theta}_1, \hat{\theta}_2, \cdots \hat{\theta}_k) = g_1(x_1, x_2, \cdots, x_n)$$

$$m_2' = g_2(\hat{\theta}_1, \hat{\theta}_2, \cdots \hat{\theta}_k) = g_2(x_1, x_2, \cdots, x_n)$$

$$\vdots \qquad\qquad\qquad \vdots$$

$$m_k' = g_k(\hat{\theta}_1, \hat{\theta}_2, \cdots \hat{\theta}_k) = g_k(x_1, x_2, \cdots, x_n)$$

THE MEAN AND VARIANCE OF THE NORMAL DISTRIBUTION

To illustrate this method let us consider obtaining estimates of the parameters μ and σ^2 of the normal distribution.

Let $\theta_1 = \mu$ and $\theta_2 = \sigma^2$. We know

$$\mu_1' = \theta_1$$

and

$$\mu_2' = \theta_1^2 + \theta_2$$

Therefore

$$m_1' = \hat{\theta}_1$$

and

$$m_2' = \hat{\theta}_1^2 + \hat{\theta}_2 \qquad\qquad (4.3)$$

Thus $\hat{\theta}_1$ is simply

$$\bar{x} = m_1' = \frac{\sum\limits_{i=1}^{n} x_i}{n}$$

and substituting for $\hat{\theta}_1$ in (4.3) we obtain

$$m_2' - (m_1')^2 = \hat{\theta}_2$$

$$\frac{\sum\limits_{i=1}^{n} x_i^2}{n} - \frac{\sum\limits_{i=1}^{n} x_i \sum\limits_{i=1}^{n} x_i}{n \quad n} = \frac{1}{n}\left[\sum\limits_{i=1}^{n} x_i^2 - \frac{(\sum\limits_{i=1}^{n} x_i)^2}{n}\right] = s^2$$

Hence, in this case at least, the method of moments gives estimates which are identical with those suggested by the method of maximum likelihood.

In general, then, the method of moments gives estimates as functions of the sample moments. These estimates can be sometimes improved by examining the properties of these estimators and deciding if they have the properties generally considered "good."

CRITERIA FOR JUDGING ESTIMATORS

As was stated earlier, it may happen that there exists one, two, none, or many estimators of a particular parameter. Let θ represent the parameter in question. Let the function of our random variables (our observations) which is to estimate θ be $\Phi(X_k = x_1, x_2, \cdots, x_k)$. We shall now define some properties which, on an intuitive basis, seem reasonable for an estimator to have; then we will show that estimators are themselves similar in many respects to the random variables which go to make them up. In this manner we will discuss the necessity of examining the probability density functions of some of the estimators and of some functions of the estimators.

Unbiased Estimators

DEFINITION. $\Phi(X_k)$ is an unbiased estimator of θ if,

$$E[\Phi(X_k)] = \theta$$

where k is constant.

If $E[\Phi(X_k)] > \theta$, then $\Phi(X_k)$ is said to be positively biased; if

$$E[\Phi(X_k)] < \theta$$

then $\Phi(X_k)$ is said to be negatively biased. θ could conceivably be at times positively biased and at other times negatively biased.

Relying upon the concept of expectations, we may therefore interpret unbiasedness as meaning that over a period, when $\Phi(X_k)$ has made many, many estimates of θ, that the average value of all such estimates will be θ. At any one time, i.e., for any one sample of size k, we need not have $\Phi(X_k) \equiv \theta$. However, when many such estimates have been made they will average out to θ. Hence, the justification for the prerequisite of unbiasedness seems well substantiated, for indeed it would be absurd to consider an estimator which, e.g. gave

$$E[\Phi(X_k)] = \pi e^3$$

when indeed, θ, for example, was ϵ/π. In this case, we could, however, easily correct such a glaring discrepancy by merely considering a new estimator of θ, namely, $\xi(X_k) = \dfrac{1}{\pi^2 e^2} \Phi(X_k)$, for here

$$E[\xi(X_k)] = \frac{\pi e^3}{\pi^2 e^2} = \frac{\epsilon}{\pi}$$

which indeed is θ. Hence, in an example as trivial as the preceding, when we knew the direction of bias, it is easy to correct it. This, however, need not be so at all times.

EXAMPLE

If $E[\eta(X_k)] = \theta + \epsilon$, describe a new estimator which corrects this bias; show that the new estimator is unbiased. Ans. $\eta(X_k) - \epsilon$. Is the bias positive or negative? *Positive.*

Consistent Estimators

Consider a sequence of random samples of sizes $X_1 = x_1$; $X_2 = x_1$, x_2; $\cdots$; $X_k = x_1, \cdots, x_k$. For each sample consider the estimator of θ, namely, $\Phi(X_j)$, where $j = 1, 2, \cdots, k$.

DEFINITION. The sequence of estimators

$$\Phi(X_1), \Phi(X_2), \cdots, \qquad \Phi(X_k) = \{\Phi(X_j)\}$$

is a consistent sequence of estimators if the probability, that the sequence of estimators is within an arbitrarily small distance of θ, approaches one, as j gets very, very large. In shorthand, this may be written as

$$P\{\{\Phi(x_j)\} \text{ is with a small distance } \Delta \text{ from } \theta\} \to 1 \quad \text{for } j \to \infty$$

where the symbol $\to$ is understood to mean approaches or converges toward.

Efficient Estimators

DEFINITION. $\Phi(X_j)$ is an efficient estimator = minimum variance estimator of θ and is to be preferred to any other unbiased estimator $\xi(X_j)$ if

(1) $\Phi(X_j)$ is unbiased.

(2) The variance of $\Phi(X_j) \leq$ variance $\xi(X_j)$.

The desirability of an attribute such as efficiency can be illustrated by considering the graph in Fig. 4.1.

Here the variance of the estimators is plotted against the possible values of θ. It is clear from this graph that $\Phi(X_j)$ is to be preferred to $\xi(X_j)$ since for any value of θ, the variance of the estimating function, $\Phi(X_j)$, is always less than the variance of the estimator $\xi(X_j)$. That is, the deviation of the estimator $\Phi(X_j)$ from its mean value, in this case, by the assumption of unbiasedness θ, is less than any other unbiased estimator. This once

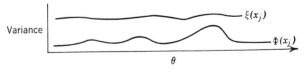

FIG. 4.1

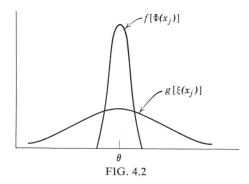

FIG. 4.2

again may be seen if one examines Fig. 4.2. Here the probability density function of the estimating function is compared with that of another unbiased estimator. Here we see that the pdf of $\Phi(X_j)$, $f[\Phi(X_j)]$ is clustered more about θ than the pdf of $\xi(X_j)$, $g[\xi(X_j)]$.

Sufficient Estimators

The estimator $\Phi(X_j)$ is said to be a sufficient estimator of θ if the maximum likelihood function of the sample is equal to the distribution of the estimating function times a function of the sample points which is independent of θ. This may be written as

$$\prod_{j=1}^{n} f(x_i, \theta) = L = g[\Phi(X_j)]h(X_j)$$

where L is the likelihood function for a sample of size n, $g[\Phi(X_j)]$ is the probability density function of $\Phi(X_j)$, and $h(X_j)$ is a function independent of $\Phi(X_j)$. Thus a sufficient estimator tells all there is to know about an unknown parameter through a sample of size n.

SAMPLING DISTRIBUTIONS: THEIR NEED AND USE

The estimator or the estimating function consists of combinations of random variables. Estimators are therefore functions of the sample values and since the estimator will change from sample to sample, however slightly, it too is a random variable, for this is how a random variable was defined (Chapter 1). Hence, as we could not predict individual values of the random variables we have dealt with before, here too we cannot predict isolated events. Thus to talk about the reliability or accuracy of an estimator, or about properties of an estimator in general, it is once again necessary to examine the probability density function of our random variable, in this case, the estimating function. The distributions of estimators as well as any function of the sample are known as sampling distributions. We will be interested in the sampling distribution of certain estimators and also in the sampling distribution of functions of estimators. Here too we will examine, as we did with other pdf's, their properties, for example, their means, variances, and covariances. With the aid of the sampling distributions we will be able to make probability statements concerning the outcome of certain events of interest.

CHI-SQUARE DISTRIBUTION

The probability density function of the random variable x, which is normally distributed with mean $\mu = 0$, and vaiance $\sigma^2 = 1$, ($N(0, 1)$) is

$$f(x) = \frac{1}{(2\pi)^{1/2}} e^{-x^2/2} \qquad -\infty < x < \infty$$

It can be shown[1] that the distribution of the random variable $z = x^2$, where x is defined as above, is

$$\frac{1}{(2\pi)^{1/2}} \frac{e^{-z/2}}{\sqrt{z}} \qquad 0 \le z < \infty$$

The distribution of $\sum\limits_{i=1}^{n} z$ is

$$\frac{1}{\left(\dfrac{n-2}{2}\right)!} \frac{1}{z^{n/2}} (\chi_n^2)^{(n-2)/2} e^{-\chi_n^2/2} \qquad \chi_n^2 > 0 \qquad (4.3)$$

where $\chi_n^2 = \sum\limits_{i=1}^{n} z_i$. This distribution is known as the chi-square distribution with n degrees of freedom.

Mean and Variance of χ_n^2

When we utilize the moment generating function, for example, the mean of χ_n^2 is n and the variance is $2n$. The chi-square distributions for varying degrees of freedom are in Tables F–IV, H–V.[2]

CUMULATIVE CHI-SQUARE DISTRIBUTION

The cumulative chi-square distribution is written as

$$F(\chi_n^2) = \int_0^{\chi^2} \frac{1}{\left(\dfrac{n-2}{2}\right)! \, 2^{n/2}} (\chi_n^2)^{(n-2)/2} e^{-(\chi_n^2/2)} \, d\chi_n^2$$

---

[1] See proof in appendix.

[2] Tables indicated by F and H are to be found in R. A. Fisher and F. Yates *Statistical Tables*, Hafner Publishing Co., New York, 1953 and A. Hald *Statistical Tables and Formula*, John Wiley and Sons, New York, 1952. The Roman numerals refer to the tables in these references.

Here $F(\chi_n^2)$ is a function of n, the degrees of freedom. Thus for a given n

$$P\{b \leq \chi_n^2 \leq a\} = \alpha \qquad 0 < b \leq a \leq \infty$$
$$= F[a] - F[b] = \alpha$$
$$= P\{\chi_n^2 \leq a\} - P\{\chi_n^2 \leq b\}$$

Hence to compute the probability of any random variable distributed as $\chi_{(n)}^2$ we must know a, b, and n. Conveniently enough, the chi-square cumulative distribution has been tabulated in many places. (See Tables F–IV, H–V.) Here any probability value of χ_n^2 may be obtained by entering the tables at the appropriate number of degrees of freedom. On the other hand, if a desired chi-square value is needed, one enters the table for the respective degrees of freedom, then proceeds to obtain a particular chi-square for the desired probability. Caution must be taken before entering the chi-square, or for that matter, any tables of the cumulative function to see what values have been entered in the tables, i.e.,

$$\int_0^{\chi_n^2} \frac{1}{\left(\dfrac{n-2}{2}\right)!} \frac{1}{2^{n/2}} (\chi_n^2)^{(n-2)/2} e^{-\chi_n^2/2} \, d\chi_n^2 = F(\chi_n^2)$$

or

$$1 - \int_0^{\chi_n^2} f(\chi_n^2) \, d\chi_n^2 = \int_{\chi_n^2}^{\infty} f(\chi_n^2) \, d\chi_n^2$$

the latter being $1 - F(\chi_n^2)$ and the former being $F(\chi_n^2)$.

The Addition Theorem for the Chi-Square Distribution

The property of the addition of chi-square distributed variables will become extremely useful when we subsequently deal with the analysis of variance technique (see Chapter 8). With this brief motivation let us examine the probability density function of the variable

$$v = \chi_{n_1}^2 + \chi_{n_2}^2$$

where

$$\chi_{n_2}^2 = \sum_{i=1}^{n_1} z_i = \sum_{i=1}^{n_1} x_i^2$$

$$\chi_{n_2}^2 = \sum_{i=1}^{n_2} z_i = \sum_{i=1}^{n_2} x_i^2$$

and where the x_i are each $N(0, 1)$, and $\chi_{n_1}^2$, $\chi_{n_2}^2$ are independent in the statistical sense. Since $\sum_{i=1}^{n_1} z_i + \sum_{i=1}^{n_2} z_i = \sum_{i=1}^{n_1+n_2} z_i$ which itself is a sum of $n_1 + n_2 = nx_i^2$s, $\sum_{i=1}^{n_1+n_2} z_i$ is equivalent to a chi-square variate with $n_1 + n_2$

degrees of freedom. Thus the sum of any two chi-square distributed variates is itself distributed as chi-square with the number of degrees of freedom equal to the sum of the degrees of freedom of the independent chi-squares contributing to the new chi-square.

PARTITION THEOREM OR COCHRAN'S THEOREM

If the sum of squares, $x_1^2 + x_2^2 + x_3^2 \cdots$, of n independent variables, each $N(0, 1)$, are partitioned into a sum of squares, $S_1^2, S_2^2, S_3^3, \cdots, S_m^2$, with $n_1, n_2, \cdots, n_m$ linearly independent observations or degrees of freedom respectively; i.e., if

$$\chi^2 = \sum_{i=1}^{n} \chi_i^2 = S_1^2 + S_2^2 + S_3^2 + S_4^2 + \cdots + S_m^2$$

then the necessary and sufficient condition that $S_1^2, S_2^2, S_3^2, \cdots, S_m^2$ are independent in the probability sense and also distributed as chi-square with $n_1, n_2, n_3, \cdots, n_m$ degrees of freedom is that

$$\sum_{j=1}^{m} n_j = n$$

"F" OR FISHER DISTRIBUTION

The distribution of the ratio[1]

$$z = \frac{x_1/n_1}{x_2/n_2}$$

where x_1 and x_2 are independent and distributed as chi-square with n_1 and n_2 degrees of freedom respectively, is

$$g(z) = \frac{n_1^{n_1/2} \, n_2^{n_2/2} \, z^{n_1/2-1} \left(\dfrac{n_1 + n_2 - 2}{2}\right)!}{\left(\dfrac{n_1 - 2}{2}\right)! \left(\dfrac{n_2 - 2}{2}\right)! \, (n_2 + n_1 z)^{(n_1+n_2)/2}}$$

$$z > 0$$

Any variable distributed as $g(z)$ is said to have the F distribution, with degrees of freedom equal to the degrees of freedom of the numerator and denominator; in this case, z is said to be distributed as F with n_1 and n_2 degrees of freedom, i.e., z is $F\begin{bmatrix} n_1 \\ n_2 \end{bmatrix}$ (Tables F–V, H–VII).

[1] See appendix for proof.

SAMPLING DISTRIBUTION OF THE SAMPLE MEAN

The sample mean is contained in many summary statistic sheets and is, of course, the estimating function for the parameter μ of a normal distribution. We shall consider two cases in discussing the sampling distribution of $\bar{x}$.

$X_1, X_2, X_3, \cdots, X_n$ is a sample of size n from a population governed by a normal distribution whose mean is μ and variance σ^2. $\bar{x}$ is the sample estimate of μ.

Before we develop this any further, the following theorem, generally called an addition theorem, will be stated without proof.[1]

Addition Theorem for n Random and Independent Normal Variates

If the random variable x_i's are independent and $N(\mu_i, \sigma_i^2)$, where $i = 1, \cdots, n$, then any linear combination of the x's, say

$$l(x) = \tau_0 + \tau_1 x_1 + \cdots + \tau_n x_n$$

is itself normally distributed with mean

$$E[l(x)] = \tau_0 + \tau_1 \mu_1 + \tau_2 \mu_2 + \cdots + \tau_n \mu_n$$

and variance

$$\text{var}\,[l(x)] = \tau_1^2 \sigma_1^2 + \tau_2^2 \sigma_2^2 + \tau_3^2 \sigma_3^2 + \cdots + \tau_n^2 \sigma_n^2 = \sum_{i=1}^{n} \tau_i^2 \sigma_i^2$$

Returning to the problem at hand, namely, determining the distribution of a mean of a sample obtained from a normal distribution, one proceeds in the following manner.

If

$$\tau_0 = 0, \tau_1 = \tau_2 = \cdots = \tau_n = \frac{1}{n}, \mu_i = \mu \quad \text{and} \quad \sigma_i^2 = \sigma^2$$

then

$$l(x) = \bar{x} = \frac{x_1}{n} + \frac{x_2}{n} + \cdots + \frac{x_n}{n}$$

By the addition theorem above, and its assumptions, this is a linear combination of normally distributed variables and is itself normally distributed with mean

$$E[l(x)] = \sum_{i=1}^{n} \tau_i \mu_i = \sum_{i=1}^{n} \frac{1}{n} \mu = n \cdot \frac{1}{n} \cdot \mu = \mu$$

and variance

$$\text{var}\,[l(x)] = \sum_{i=1}^{n} \tau_i^2 \sigma_i^2 = \sum_{i=1}^{n} \frac{1}{n^2} \sigma^2 = n \cdot \frac{1}{n^2} \sigma^2 = \frac{\sigma^2}{n}$$

Thus under the restrictions established above, $\bar{x}$ is $N(\mu_1, \sigma^2/n)$.

[1] For a proof of this, see A. Hald, 1952, pp. 215–216.

EXERCISES

Using the addition theorem for normal variates, determine the distribution of the variable $(x - \mu)/\sigma$ when x is $N(\mu, \sigma^2)$.

Hint: Let $\tau_0 = \mu/\sigma$, $\tau_1 = 1/\sigma$ and $\tau_2 = \cdots \tau_n = 0$, then $l(x) = (x - \mu)/\sigma$. Now apply the addition theorem and see that $l(x)$ is by definition normally distributed with mean

$$E[l(x)] = E\left(\frac{x - \mu}{\sigma}\right) = 0 \tag{4.5}$$

and variance

$$\text{var } [l(x)] = \text{var } \left(\frac{x - \mu}{\sigma}\right) = \frac{1}{\sigma^2} \sigma^2 = 1 \tag{4.6}$$

Thus $(x - \mu)/\sigma$ is $N(0, 1)$ and is known as the *standarized normal or unit normal deviate*. Any normal variate x can be transformed to the unit variate normal variate by the transformation

$$\frac{x - \mu}{\sigma}$$

where μ and σ are the mean standard deviation of x.

The cumulative unit normal distribution $\Phi[(x - \mu)/\sigma]$ for various values is found in Tables F–VIII, H–II.

1. Find the mean and variance of $\sum_{i=1}^{m} ix_i$ if x_i is $N(i\mu_i, i^2\sigma^2)$

$$\text{Ans. } N\left[\sum_{i=1}^{m} i^2\mu_i, \quad \sigma^2 \sum_{i=1}^{m} i^4\right]$$

2. Find the mean and variance of $\dfrac{\sum_{i=1}^{m} ix_i}{m}$ if x_i is $N(i\mu_i, i^2\sigma^2)$

$$\text{Ans. } N\left[\frac{\sum_{i=1}^{m} i^2\mu_i}{m}, \quad \frac{\sigma^2 \sum_{i=1}^{m} i^4}{m^2}\right]$$

3. If x is $N(0, 1)$, then the probability that $x < 0$ may be found in the following manner.

$$P\{x < 0\} = P\left\{\frac{x - \mu}{\sigma} < \frac{0 - \mu}{\sigma}\right\} = P\left\{\frac{x - \mu}{\sigma} < 0\right\} = \Phi\left[\frac{x - \mu}{\sigma} = 0\right]$$

Examination of Table H–II indicated that for $(x - \mu)/\sigma = 0$,

$$\Phi\left[\frac{x - \mu}{\sigma} = 0\right] = 0.5$$

Thus $P\{x < 0\} = 0.5$.

4. If x is $N(0, 1)$ find $P\{x < 1\}$ *Ans.* 0.8413

5. If x is $N(0, 9)$ find $P\{x^2 - 1\}$ *Ans.* 0.3707

6. If x is $N(16, 36)$ find $P\{x < 2\sigma\}$ *Ans.* 0.3514

$x_1, x_2, x_3, \cdots, x_n$ is set of random independent variables, each with a mean μ_i and variance σ_i^2 and each governed by some probability density function g_i.

CASE I.

All χ's have the identical probability density function, g, with mean μ and variance σ^2. If the common variance exists and is finite, then, as n, the sample size increases, the sum

$$\chi_1 + \chi_2 + \chi_3 + \cdots + \chi_n = \sum_{i=1}^{n} x_i$$

will tend to be normally distributed with mean

$$E\left[\sum_{i=1}^{n} x_i\right] = n\mu$$

and variance

$$\mathrm{var}\left[\sum_{i=1}^{n} x_i\right] = n\sigma^2$$

Thus the distribution of a sample mean $\bar{x}$, constructed of independent and random variates each distributed with some common probability density function g, whose mean is μ and whose finite variance is σ^2, is asymptotically normally distributed with a mean

$$E\left[\frac{\sum_{i=1}^{n} x_i}{n}\right] = \mu$$

and variance

$$\mathrm{var}\left[\frac{\sum x_i}{n}\right] = \frac{1}{n^2} \times n\sigma^2 = \frac{\sigma^2}{n}$$

CASE II.

All x's are independent and random, but they do not have the identical probability density function.

Under this more general condition the sum

$$\sum_{i=1}^{n} x_i \quad \text{and the mean} \quad \frac{\sum_{i=1}^{n} x_i}{n}$$

are both essentially normally distributed with means and variances $n\mu$, μ, $n\sigma^2$ and σ^2/n respectively. In this case, however, Cramér[1] reminds the reader that whereas the assumption of a finite variance was sufficient where each x has the same distribution, it is not sufficient in the case of different distributions. Here one must assume the existence of a finite third absolute moment for each variate x and further that the cube root of the sum of these moments, divided by σ, tends to 0 as n gets very big.

These two remarkable and powerful results are known as the *central limit theorems* for independent variables. For a more comprehensive

[1] H Cramér, 1951, *Mathematical Methods of Statistics*, pp. 215–217, Princeton Univ. Press, Princeton, N. J.

treatment of this problem, the reader is encouraged to study Cramér's chapter on the "Normal Distribution," Chapter 17, and in particular pp. 213–227.

THE DISTRIBUTION OF THE SAMPLE VARIANCE

If $x_1, x_2, \cdots, x_n$ is a random sample of n independent observations from a normal population with a known mean μ and an unknown variance σ^2, then a satisfactory estimate of σ^2 is

$$\sum_{i=1}^{n} \frac{(x_i - \mu)^2}{n} = \hat{s}^2 \tag{4.7}$$

The distribution of this variable may be determined from the following considerations. It has been shown (4.5, 4.6) that the variable $[(x_i - \mu)/\sigma]$ is $N(0, 1)$ and that the variable

$$\chi_n^2 = \sum_{i=1}^{n} \left(\frac{x_i - \mu}{\sigma} \right)^2$$

is distributed as chi-square with n degrees of freedom, since there are no linear restraints among the $[(x_i - \mu)/\sigma]$'s. Thus by substitution, the relationship between $\hat{s}^2$ and χ_n^2 becomes apparent, namely,

$$\hat{s}^2 = \frac{\sigma^2}{n} \chi_n^2$$

(See Table H–VI.)

The exact distribution of $\hat{s}^2$ can be obtained by substituting for χ^2 in (4.3) and recalling that

$$d\hat{s}^2 = \frac{\sigma^2}{n} d\chi_n^2$$

Thus the distribution of $\hat{s}^2$ is

$$\frac{1}{\left(\frac{n-2}{2} \right)!} \frac{1}{2^{n/2}} \left(\frac{n\hat{s}^2}{\sigma^2} \right)^{(n-2)/2} \frac{\sigma^2}{n} \exp \left[-\frac{n}{2} \left(\frac{\hat{s}^2}{\sigma^2} \right) \right] \qquad \text{for } \hat{s}^2 > 0$$

Since the mean and variance of a chi-square distributed variate with n degrees of freedom are n and $2n$ respectively, the mean and variance of s^2 with n degrees of freedom are

$$E\hat{s}^2 = E \left[\frac{\sigma^2}{n} \cdot \chi_n^2 \right] = \sigma^2$$

and

$$\text{var } \hat{s}^2 = \text{var } \frac{\sigma^2}{n} \chi_n^2 = \frac{\sigma^4}{n^2} \cdot 2n = \frac{2\sigma^4}{n}$$

The more realistic condition exists when the parameter μ is unknown and is estimated by $\bar{x}$. In this case, by analogy, a function of the random variable $\sum_{i=1}^{n} (x_i - \bar{x})^2$ would be a desirable estimator of σ^2. As a matter of fact one of the estimates employed is

$$\frac{\sum_{i=1}^{n} (x_i - \bar{x})^2}{n - 1} = s^2$$

The distribution of this variable is not determined in as straightforward manner as was the distribution of $\hat{s}^2$. Here use will be made of the partition theorem for chi-square distributed variates.

The chi-square distributed variate $\sum_{i=1}^{n} \left(\dfrac{x_i - \mu}{\sigma}\right)^2$ may be partitioned as follows:

$$\sum_{i=1}^{n} \left(\frac{x_i - \mu}{\sigma}\right)^2 = \sum_{i=1}^{n} \left[\frac{(x_i - \bar{x})}{\sigma} + \frac{(\bar{x} - \mu)}{\sigma}\right]^2$$

$$= \sum_{i=1}^{n} \left(\frac{x_i - \bar{x}}{\sigma}\right)^2 + n\left(\frac{\bar{x} - \mu}{\sigma}\right)^2$$

The first term has one restraint imposed upon it by virtue of the single linear relationship between the random variables x_i and the sample mean $\bar{x}$. Thus, this sum of squares has $(n - 1)$ degrees of freedom, i.e., the number of variables minus the linear relationships between the x_i and $\bar{x}$. The second sum of squares, reduced to but one square, has but one random variable, $\bar{x}$, and no linear relation between $\bar{x}$ and the constants μ, σ, and n. The number of degrees of freedom for this term is but 1. Thus, $\sum_{i=1}^{n} \left(\dfrac{x_i - \mu}{\sigma}\right)^2$ with n degrees of freedom has been partitioned into two sums of squares with $(n - 1)$ and 1 degree of freedom respectively. Thus, by application of the partition theorem of chi-square distributed variates:

(1) $\sum_{i=1}^{n} \left(\dfrac{x_i - \bar{x}}{\sigma}\right)^2$ is independent of $n[(\bar{x} - \mu)/\sigma]^2$, i.e., *the sample variance determined from the normal population is independent of sample means from that population and* (2) $\sum_{i=1}^{n} \left(\dfrac{x_i - \bar{x}}{\sigma}\right)^2$ *is distributed as χ^2 with $(n - 1)$ degrees of freedom.*

The variable $s^2 = \dfrac{\sum (x_i - \bar{x})^2}{n - 1}$ may now be written as

$$s^2 = \frac{\sigma^2 \chi^2}{n - 1}$$

and the distribution of s^2 is thus found to be

$$g(s^2) = \frac{1}{\left(\dfrac{n-3}{2}\right)!} \frac{1}{2^{(n-1)/2}} \left(\frac{n-1}{\sigma^2} s^2\right)^{(n-3)/2} \frac{\sigma^2}{n-1}$$
$$\exp\left(-\frac{(n-1)s^2}{2\sigma^2}\right) \qquad \text{for } s^2 > 0$$

$$= 0 \qquad \text{otherwise}$$

and where

$$Es^2 = \sigma^2$$

and

$$\operatorname{var} s^2 = \frac{2\sigma^4}{n-1}$$

It is to be noted that $E(s) \neq \sigma$.

OTHER ESTIMATORS OF μ AND σ

1. Estimates of the central value of a distribution other than $\bar{x}$, useful for samples of 10 or less.

   (a) *Median value* (*M*). Defined as the middle value in a size-ordered sequence of values. If the number of values is odd, the median is the middle value; if the number values is even, the median lies midway between the two middle values.

   (b) *Midrange* (*M_r*). Defined as the average of the largest and smallest observation. In a sample of, say 6, this would be

$$M_r = \frac{x_1 + x_6}{2}$$

where x_1 is the smallest in a size-ordered sequence.

2. Estimates of the population standard deviation, σ, other than the sample statistic s.

   (a) *The range ω* (*for samples of* 10 *or less*)

   The range is not only an inefficient estimate of σ, it also is biased. See this chapter for further discussion of biased estimates. The bias is corrected for by a coefficient, and it is found that for samples up to 10 the efficiency of the range is rather high.[1] Tables

[1] G. G. Simpson, 1941, Range as a zoological character, *Am. Jour. Sci.* 239: 11; 785–804, discusses some of the properties of the range as a useful estimator of variation from the point of view of the biologist. The inadequacy of the direct use of range for small samples is stressed and a "standard range" based on sample size of 1000 is proposed. This article is at the present time misleading (through no fault of Simpson) in that subsequent statistical investigation has shown that with the use of a suitable coefficient, the range is a rather efficient estimator of the standard deviation for samples of 10 or less. The standard range was subsequently applied by H. S. Cooke, 1947, Variation in the molars of the living African elephant and a critical revision of fossil Proboscidea of South Africa, *Am. Jour. Sci.* 245: 434—457.

for the range as an estimate of σ include the correction coefficient, and efficiency for sample sizes from 2 to 10; these are found in Dixon and Massey, 1957, *Introduction to statistical analysis.*

(*b*) Several other estimates of σ are given in Dixon and Massey, 1957, *ibid.*, pp. 273–274, for samples of 10 or less. (See also Table H–VIII.)

PERCENTILE ESTIMATES

Percentile estimates of the mean and standard deviation are often useful in processing data where for various reasons the sample frequency distribution is plotted as a cumulative curve. This is particularly important in sediment size analyses, since the cumulative curve is by far the most common method of presenting and recording the data. A general discussion is given by W. C. Krumbein, 1936, The use of quartile measures in describing and comparing sediments, *Am. Jour. Sci.* 32: 98–111.

Estimates of μ, the Population Mean

1. The median or fiftieth percentile. For symmetric populations a short discussion of the efficiency of the median is given in Dixon and Massey, 1957, *ibid.*, p. 265.

2. Combinations of several percentile values, for example, $(P_{25} + P_{75})/2$. A table of efficiencies for various combinations of percentiles as an estimate of μ is given in Dixon and Massey, 1957, *ibid.* [Table A-8a(1)].

Estimates of σ

A general discussion of combinations of percentiles with suitable coefficients and the relevant efficiencies is given in Dixon and Massey, pp. 265–266 and Table A-8a(2).

SUGGESTED READINGS ON SEDIMENT SIZE ANALYSES

D. L. Inman, 1952, Measures for describing the size distribution of sediments, *Jour. Sed. Petrol.* 22: 125–145, proposes an estimate of σ in the form of $0.5\,(P_{84} - P_{16})$, as does W. C. Krumbein, 1938, Size frequency distributions of sediments and the normal phi curve, *Jour. Sed. Petrol.* 8: 84–90. J. C. Griffiths, 1951, Size versus sorting in some Caribbean sediments, *Jour. Geol.* 59: 211–243 uses $0.5\,(P_{90} - P_{10})$. P. D. Trask, 1932, *Origin and environment of source sediments of petroleum*, Gulf Publ. Co., Houston, uses $P_{75} - P_{25}$. Trask also utilizes the ratio of P_{75} to P_{25} in the widely used "Trask sorting coefficient" So. $= \sqrt{P_{75}/P_{25}}$. R. L. Miller, and J. M. Zeigler, 1958, A model relating dynamics and sediments patterns .... etc., *Jour. Geol.* 66: 417–441, use $(P_{80} - P_{20})/P_{50}$ as a dimensionless estimate. W. F. Tanner, 1958, Comparison of phi percentile deviations, *Jour. Sed. Petrol.* 28: 203–204, discusses the general case of sorting (measures of variation) in sediments. He proposes that a coefficient equivalent to 1 over the number of standard deviations covered by the percentile difference should precede the difference.

Thus, the percentile estimate $P_{95} - P_{05}$ should be written as $1/3.29\,(D_{95} - D_{05})$, where 3.29 is the number of standard deviations covered under a normal curve. He suggests that for normal distributions good approximation to σ is achieved.

It appears from the number of different estimates of σ now in the literature relevant to size analysis that a generally satisfactory estimator which is suitably convenient and sensitive to differences between size frequency distributions, and at the same time a good estimator of σ, has yet to be found. The bias and efficiency of the estimator have not as yet been given formal consideration.

A difficulty which underlies the problem is that sediment size analysis is usually recorded in percent by weight per size class for obvious practical reasons. Very little has been done with actual grain counts. The very large numbers in the smaller size classes appear to lead to J-shaped frequency distributions. Unfortunately, percent by weight analysis fixes the sample size for an individual analysis at $N = 100$, so that the usual tests of hypotheses regarding the parameters of individual analyses cannot be made. The tendency in percent by weight analysis for skewness toward the smaller size classes, common to many types of sediments, has been overcome by a $\log_2$ transformation called the ϕ transformation. (W. C. Krumbein, 1936, *ibid.*) This transformation is satisfactory provided the tails (extremes) of the distribution are not regarded as important. However, there is some evidence (D. J. Doeglas, 1946, Interpretation of results of mechanical analyses, *Jour. Sed. Petrol.* 16: 19–40, and others) that the tails are very sensitive to environmental changes and hence important in the analysis.

It seems that there remains considerable room for further work in this area of study.

ESTIMATES OF CENTRAL TENDENCY OTHER THAN THE ARITHMETIC MEAN

Geometric Mean

For n entries it is defined as

$$\text{G.M} = n\sqrt{x_1 \cdot x_2 \cdots x_n}$$

Harmonic Mean

$$H = \frac{1}{\dfrac{1}{n}\left(\dfrac{1}{x_1} + \dfrac{1}{x_2} + \cdots + \dfrac{1}{x_n}\right)}$$

Root Mean Square

$$R = \sqrt{\frac{x_1^2 + x_2^2 + \cdots + x_n^2}{n}}$$

Exponential Mean

$$E = \log_b \left(\frac{b^{x_1} + b^{x_2} + \cdots + b^{x_n}}{n} \right)$$

for example, for log to the base 10

$$E = \log_{10} \left(\frac{10^2 + 10^3 + 10^9 + 10^{11}}{4} \right)$$

for a sample of $n =$ with entries $X_1 = 2$, $X_2 = 3$, $X_3 = 9$, and $X_4 = 11$.

The geometric mean is sometimes advantageous for asymmetrical frequency distribution analysis as an alternative to a symmetry inducing transformation. The log of the geometric mean is equivalent to the arithmetic mean of the logs of the entries, a useful point to remember when log data are used.

M. C. Powers, 1953, A new roundness scale for sedimentary particles *Jour. Sed. Petrol.* 23: 117–119, applies the geometric mean to class intervals on the roundness scale.

The harmonic mean is often written as $\frac{1}{H} = \frac{1}{n} \sum_{i=1}^{n} \frac{1}{x_i}$. It is useful in rate problems in which averages of time rates are required.

For example, suppose a core 200 cm long is taken in the delta area of the Gulf of Mexico and that the rate of sedimentation is estimated to be 10 cm per year for the first 100 cm and 5 cm per year for the second 100 cm. The total time involved is thus $10 + 20 = 30$ years. The arithmetic mean of $\frac{1}{2}(10 + 5) = 7.5$ cm per year would be misleading, i.e., (30 years)(7.5 cm/year) + 225 cm. The harmonic mean, however, gives the following results:

$$\frac{1}{H} = \frac{1}{n} \sum_{i=1}^{n} \frac{1}{x_i} = \frac{1}{2}\left(\frac{1}{10} + \frac{1}{5} \right) = 6.666 \text{ cm/year}$$

Here (30 years)(6.66 cm/year) $\simeq$ 200 cm. In this connection, it may be useful to define the harmonic mean in terms of its application to rates as

$$\frac{1}{H} = \frac{\dfrac{1}{r_1} + \dfrac{1}{r_2} + \cdots + \dfrac{1}{r_n}}{n}$$

where the r's are rates.

A general discussion of the structure and properties of averages with particular interest in applications to economics is given by E. L. Dodd, 1945, *Lectures on probability and statistics*, University of Texas Press, Austin, Texas.

PAPERS IN THE CONTEXT OF THIS CHAPTER

F. Chayes, The theory of thin section analysis, *Jour. Geol.* 62: 92–101, J. D. Bankier, 1955, The theory of thin section analysis; a discussion, *Jour. Geol.* 63: 287–288. F. Chayes, 1955, The theory of thin section analysis: a reply, *Jour. Geol.* 63: 288–290, in which bias and consistency are discussed. A more detailed discussion applied to petrographic modal analysis is found in F. Chayes, 1956, *Petrographic modal analysis*, John Wiley and Sons, New York (especially Chapters 1 and 4).

H. Brown, and C. Patterson, 1947, The composition of meteoritic matter. I The composition of the silicate of stony meteorites, *Jour. Geol.* 55: 405ff. Utilizes the standard error of the mean to analyze accuracy of the average composition of the silicate phase of stony meteorites and for a fixed standard error of the mean estimates the number of analyses required to satisfy this criterion.

"Standard errors" are also used by W. G. Schlect, 1949, Probable error of a geochemical analysis, *Bull.* 992. *Contributions to geochemistry, U.S.G.S.*, and by W. Schwarzacher, 1953, Cross-bedding and grain size in the lower K. sands of East Anglia, *Geol. Mag.* XC, 322–329, who uses the standard error of the median.

H. W. Fairbairn, 1953, Precision and accuracy of chemical analysis in silicate rocks, *Geochim. et Cosmochim. Acta* 4: 143–156. Discusses the statistical analysis of replicate analysis of a granite and a diabase, including means and standard deviations useful for calibration purposes. He shows that the relative error varies inversely with concentration of the constituent, where the relative error is defined as $S\bar{x}/\bar{x}\%$, which is the standard error of the mean in percent.

J. S. Olson, 1958, Lake Michigan dune development: I wind velocity profiles, *Jour. Geol.* 66: 254–263. Includes standard deviations, pooled standard deviations, and confidence limits for wind velocity profiles.

F. Chayes, 1956, *Petrographic modal analysis*, John Wiley and Sons, New York, derives statistics for estimation of error in modal analysis.

chapter 5

Statistical Inference: Tests of Hypotheses Concerning the Parameters of Probability Density Functions

TESTS OF HYPOTHESES

Among the many concepts discussed in this work, statistical inference is one of the most important. The computation and reporting of means and variances in general are sterile numbers if done merely for lack of space and summary purposes. Is this all that can be said about our samples? What can be said about the population from which this sample (or samples) came? What can be *inferred* from the sample to the population? With our inference must also come a statement of assurance or reliability.

The practice of observing a series of experimental results and pronouncing some conclusions based on intuition or experience alone motivates the need for objective criteria for examining and drawing inferences and conclusions from a series of data. Hence, we goad ourselves by the desire to enter an endeavor which has as its outcome contributions to science and industry; and which is governed by a set of rules which, if adopted by all concerned, will minimize the errors of interpretation. We therefore proceed to embark upon a discussion of the testing of hypotheses which, needless to say, is not a panacea. It is a frame of reference from which ambiguity is at a minimum.

Informal Hypothesis Testing: A Heuristic Approach to the Probable History of the Testing of Hypotheses

Consider for a moment the apprehension of a man suspected of a crime and his subsequent trial. The jury must decide, on the basis of the evidence

True Position
of Defendant

Jury Decision	Not Guilty	Guilty
Guilty	α	$1 - \beta$
Not Guilty	$1 - \alpha$	β

FIG. 5.1. Possible outcomes of events under varying jury decisions and true positions of defendant. α, β represent probability of these events when null hypotheses is true.

presented, whether the defendant did indeed commit the crime. On the basis of this evidence the jury will decide: guilty or not guilty. The processes of arriving at and asserting the innocence or guilt of an individual will not be discussed at all. We do know that the jury makes known its decision after it has seen and heard evidence pro and con. A juror rarely deliberates—this man is guilty (not guilty)—for he originally formulated a question which does not have this as a possible answer.

The original question was somewhat as follows: Did this man commit the crime of which he is accused? A hypothesis could rather formally be stated as: Mr. X did not commit the crime of which he is accused.

Evidence is presented to show that he did and that he did not. The juror will then vote on the basis of the evidence presented. This man is guilty (not guilty) of the crime. On this decision the court will acquit or sentence.

Whatever the decision of the jury, they might have erred. That is, voted guilty when indeed the defendant was not guilty, or voted not guilty when indeed he was guilty.

Let us establish a *null hypothesis*,[1] namely, H_1—the defendant is not guilty. With this hypothesis let us consider the possible outcomes of jury deliberation depending upon whether the defendant is really guilty or not guilty. (See Fig. 5.1.)

The defendant is either not guilty or guilty. The two decisions the jury can reach are also not guilty, and hence accept H_1, or guilty, and hence reject H_1. This is illustrated in Fig. 5.1, where the rows represent the possible jury decisions and the columns the true position of the defendant. Let us assume that the defendant is really not guilty, column 1. The jury, of course, does not know this. We, as objective observers, would desire that the decision be: not guilty. The jury can, however, err. They can return a verdict of: guilty. That is, they have rejected the hypothesis, when it was true. This error is called an *error of the first kind* or equivalently the α error. We do not want this to happen too often; hence we want the probability of making this error to be small. On the other hand,

[1] A hypotheses of no differences.

we would like the complementary event, that of accepting the man's innocence, when he is innocent, to be large. This is $1 - \alpha$.

Consider the true position of Mr. X as being guilty. Once again the jury has two possible decisions to make, either not guilty or guilty. In this case, as objective observers, we desire the decision to be: guilty. Here, too, the jury can err. They can decide: not guilty. That is, they are accepting H_1, which is still: Mr. X is not guilty—when it is false. This error is called *an error of the second kind*, the β error. We certainly wish to keep this error at a minimum; hence we want the probability of accepting the hypothesis, when indeed it is wrong, to be small. On the other hand, we would like to decide guilty, when H_1 is false. Hence, we would like the complement of β, $1 - \beta$, called the *power of the test*, to be large.

BALANCE OF ERRORS: A PRELUDE TO DECISION MAKING

Both errors above are serious to a society, let alone the defendant. Which error is more deleterious will not be discussed at all. What is evident is that we must attempt to control them. We must minimize the possibility of making them. In some cases one is more serious than the other. We shall now proceed to discuss in more general terms the concept of hypothesis testing and too the concept of "errors." The rather simple example given merely illustrated the manner in which we intend to go. A problem is presented, some hypothesis concerning it is established. We then wish to test the hypothesis. We perform an experiment or we are shown evidence which will help us decide upon a course of action concerning the hypothesis, i.e., accept or reject? We shall discuss further the types of errors in terms of probability statements, and how we can minimize them as much as possible.

Hypothesis Testing: Single Alternative—General Approach

Consider a population of individuals characterized in k different ways. Let

$$X = X_i = x_{i1}, x_{i2}, \cdots, x_{ij}, \cdots, x_{ik}$$

where

$$1 \leq i \leq \infty$$
$$k \geq 1$$

and

$$-\infty < x_{ij} < \infty$$

That is, any individual, say the ith, X_i, has associated with n characteristics. The first being x_{i1}, the second x_{i2}, $\cdots$. The population, for example, might be that of all 1953 well cuttings in Oklahoma. Here x_{i1} might be the color of the cutting, x_{i2} might be percent of $CaCO_3$, $\cdots$.

When $x_{ij} = 0$ for all $j > 1$ we have the one-dimensional case of a population with but one characteristic of interest.

$$X_i = x_{i1}$$

Let us assume we are interested in the pdf of X, namely, $f(X)$. Further assume that we know *a priori* that $f(X) = g(X)$ or $f(X) = h(X)$. Let us establish as our *null* hypothesis, the distribution of X is

$$H_1 : f(X) = g(X)$$

with the alternative

$$H_2 : f(X) = h(X)$$

As criteria for making a decision, i.e., to determine H_1 or H_2 we shall select but one sample point

$$X_i = x_{i1}, x_{i2}, \cdots, x_{ik}$$

observe it, and on the basis of it decide to reject or accept H_1. The merit of such a size of sample will not be discussed.

The procedure thus far has been to establish a hypothesis about a certain population and to make a decision based on a single observation. The decision will be to accept or reject our null hypothesis. There are many possible outcomes to this sampling procedure. How are we to make a decision? A good procedure would be to look at *all possible outcomes of sampling if the null hypothesis were indeed true*, and decide upon those values of X which make H_1 plausible. For indeed, if X were distributed as $g(X)$, then there are values of X which more likely fit $g(X)$ than $h(X)$. After looking at all possible outcomes we could then arbitrarily state that if X_i fell within a certain set of values or within a certain region we would accept H_1, whereas if it fell within another set of values or region we would reject H_1.

Let R_1 represent the region containing those values of X which necessitate acceptance of H_1, and R_2 represent the region containing those values of X whose observance necessitates rejection of H_1; R_1 is called the acceptance region under the null hypothesis and R_2 the rejection region under the null hypothesis. This is illustrated in Fig. 5.2.

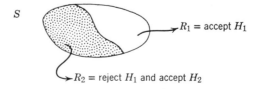

FIG. 5.2. Rejection and acceptance regions under null hypothesis. S = sample space of all possible outcomes of sampling a population with individuals X_i.

Now we would like to (1) accept H_1 when it is true, and (2) reject H_1 when it is false. That is, we would desire our sample point, X_i, to fall in (1) R_1 when H_1 is true, and (2) R_2 when H_1 is not true.

Alternatively, we would not like to (3) reject H_1 when it is true, or (4) accept H_1 when it is false. That is, we do not want our sample point X_i to (3) fall in R_2 when H_1 is true, or (4) fall in R_1 when H_1 is false.

These events and their respective probabilities are summarized in the accompanying table, where the Greek letter $\in$ represents shorthand for belongs to or falls in.

TABLE 5.1

	Event		Probability
(1)	$X \in R_1$	under H_1	$P_{H_1}\{X \in R_1\} = \int_{R_1} g(X)\,dX = 1 - \alpha$
(2)	$X \in R_2$	under H_2	$P_{H_2}\{X \in R_2\} = \int_{R_2} h(X)\,dX = 1 - \beta$
(3)	$X \in R_2$	under H_1	$P_{H_1}\{X \in R_2\} = \int_{R_2} g(X)\,dX = \alpha$
(4)	$X \in R_1$	under H_2	$P_{H_2}\{X \in R_1\} = \int_{R_1} h(X)\,dX = \beta$

With the preceding as motivation it is easily understood why we desire $1 - \alpha$, and $1 - \beta$ to be relatively large and α, and β to be, by necessity, small.

Consider event (1). Under H_1, X is distributed as $g(X)$ and by definition of a pdf

$$\int_{-\infty}^{\infty} g(X)\,dX = 1$$

To find the probability of an event, say,

$$a < x \le b$$

we merely evaluate

$$\int_a^b g(X)\,dX$$

Thus for *any* region we can find the probability of X falling within it or belonging to it. Hence, if we define, as we have, $X \in R$, to mean X falling in some defined region, say R_1 then

$$\int_{R_1} g(X)\,dX$$

has meaning.

Thus, if we define the acceptance region, under H_1, to be R_1 the probability of this event is

$$P\{x \in R_1\} = \int_{R_1} g(X)\, dX$$

This we defined as $1 - \alpha$.

Likewise, if X *were* distributed as $h(X)$, then the probability of X belonging to R_1 is

$$\int_{R_1} h(X)\, dX$$

which we arbitrarily defined as β. In this manner we arrived at Table 5.1.

α AND β RISK: TYPE OF ERRORS

Error of the First Kind

Under the null hypothesis, there will be values of X which, although distributed as $g(X)$, will be less probable than others. Indeed, these rather improbable values under H_1 might be very probable values under alternate H_2. These values could, for example, be $|X| > k$ or $X > k$ or $k > X$.

We thus consider those values of X which occur relatively frequently, say, $(1 - \alpha)\%$ of the time, where α is relatively small and the region R_1 is such that

$$\int_{R_1} g(X)\, dX = 1 - \alpha$$

This is the probability of the desirable event $X \in R_1$ when H_1 is true. By virtue of this model we have not considered those values of X which are, of course, distributed as $g(X)$ but whose probability of occurrence is small, in fact, as small as α. The probability of such an event is

$$P_{H_1}\{X \in R_2\} = \int_{R_2} g(X)\, dX = \alpha \tag{5.1}$$

If H_1 were true and the event $X \in R_2$ occurred, we must reject H_1 by previous decision agreement. *We are thus rejecting the null hypothesis when it is true.* This is the error of the first kind. We would not like to make this error too often. Hence, we must predetermine how small we wish α to be. If we first establish α, then R_1 is a function of α. If we establish R_1, then we cannot control α; it is a function of R_1.

Error of the Second Kind and Power of a Test

Thus far we have considered the position of the sample point X if X were distributed as $g(X)$. Consider the alternative position, namely, X is distributed as $h(X)$, i.e., H_1 is false. The event $X \in R_1$ has, under these conditions, the probability

$$\int_{R_1} h(X)\,dX \tag{5.2}$$

And if this event did occur we must accept H_1. However, we would be doing so when H_1 is false. *Thus we would be accepting the null hypothesis when it is false.* This is certainly an undesirable action to take under the circumstances. We must minimize the possibility of this event, when H_1 is false. If we let (5.2) be a small value, say β, then we must make β as small as we are able to. β is called the error of the second kind, i.e., the error of accepting a hypothesis when it is false.

If β is made small, we thus increase the probability of its complement, namely, $1 - \beta$, which is the probability of the event $X \in R_2$ when H_1 is false. This event is indeed very desirable when H_1 is false. The probability of this event is

$$P_{H_2}\{X \in R_2\} = \int_{R_2} h(X)\,dX = 1 - \beta$$

and is the power of the test under the alternative hypothesis.

In any testing procedure, it thus seems natural to minimize α and maximize the power of the test under the alternative hypothesis (hypotheses).

LEVEL OF SIGNIFICANCE, POWER OF THE TEST, AND CRITICAL REGIONS

Our discussion concerning the variable X has been with respect to n characteristics. X is thus n dimensional. Obviously, it is difficult to sketch such a distribution curve. Let us simplify matters by considering the one-dimensional case, namely,

$$X_i = x_{i1} = x_i$$

and

$$f(X) = f(x)$$

Here

$$H_1 : f(X) = g(x)$$

with the alternative

$$H_2 : f(X) = h(x)$$

Under H_1, x is distributed as $g(x)$ and under H_2, x is distributed as $h(x)$. These distributions are illustrated in Fig. 5.3.

Having thus far established a null hypothesis with an alternative we must next define acceptance and critical regions, the level of significance, and the power of the test, although not necessarily in that order. A

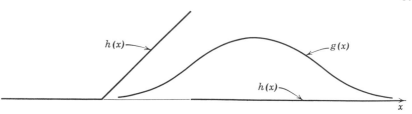

FIG. 5.3. Distributions of x under H_1 and H_2.

procedure is to define either the level of significance, or α-error, or the power of the test. When either is fixed, possible values of the other are reduced, since either determines R_1 and R_2, which in turn defines the other error.

As before, we shall make a single observation and reject or accept H_1 on the basis of this observation. We must know select a critical region. This is a function of our chosen level of significance. Since

$$\int_{R_2} g(x)\, dx = \alpha$$

we are motivated to select α such that it is small. A seemingly natural position for R_2 would thus be on the left side of $g(x)$, say, to the left of some point $x = k$, such that

$$\int_{R_2} g(x)\, dx = \alpha = \int_{-\infty}^{k} g(x)\, dx$$

and

$$G(k) = \alpha$$

See Fig. 5.4. Thus we can solve for k, as a function of α.

To find β we solve as follows:

$$\int_{k=\text{ some function of }\alpha}^{\infty} h(x)\, dx = \beta$$

But integrating we obtain

$$1 - h(k = \text{ some function of }\alpha) = \beta$$

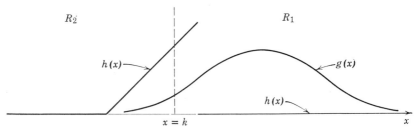

FIG. 5.4. Critical region, R_2, and acceptance region, R_1, under H_1.

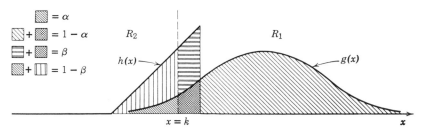

FIG. 5.5. Areas representing α, β error and their complements.

The areas of the curves representing α, β, and their complements are indicated in Fig. 5.5.

Establishing a Boundary Between R_1 and R_2

The criteria for selecting $x = k$ are relatively arbitrary, for there are many values of x which could be utilized to establish R_2 as long as

$$\int_{R_2} g(x)\, dx = \alpha$$

For example, consider some other values of x, k', k'', k''', and k^{IV}. We shall accept H_1, if

$$x < k'$$

or

$$x > k^{\text{IV}}$$

or

$$k'' \leq x \leq k'''$$

These points define another critical region. Let R_2' be that region containing all values of x less than k'' but greater than k'. Let R_2'' be that region containing all values of x less than k^{IV} but greater than k'''. Thus,

$$\left[\int_{R_2'} g(x)\, dx = \int_{k'}^{k''} g(x)\, dx\right] + \left[\int_{R_2''} g(x)\, dx = \int_{k'''}^{k^{\text{IV}}} g(x)\, dx\right] = \alpha$$

and if $R_2' + R_2'' = R_2$, then

$$\int_{R_2} g(x)\, dx = \alpha$$

Hence, our new critical regions do satisfy our criteria for the error of the first kind, namely, that it be α. Which critical region shall we thus select? The answer lies in examining the error of the second kind, β.

Figure 5.6 indicates the areas representing α and β. Comparison of Fig. 5.5 with Fig. 5.6 indicates the greater desirability of the critical region

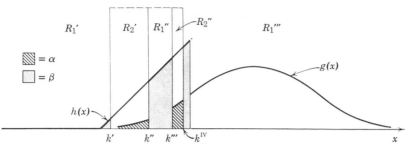

FIG. 5.6. α, β error as a function of critical regions. Here, $R_1{}'$, $R_1{}''$, and $R_1{}'''$ are acceptance regions, $R_2{}'$, $R_2{}''$ are rejection regions under the null hypothesis.

illustrated in Fig. 5.5 since the error of the second kind is much smaller in this instance.

Thus the superior critical region is the one which satisfies the conditions of minimum α and maximum power.

THE NEYMAN-PEARSON LEMMA AND THE SELECTION OF CRITICAL REGIONS

Sample of Size $n = 1$

We have so far presented a heuristic approach to the problem of testing hypotheses. Indeed there is an even more general procedure for obtaining tests and critical regions. Furthermore, this procedure is easily extended from a single observation, as in the preceding examples, to n observations, where n observations may even be regarded as one multivariate observation.

Consider once again the problem stated above, namely,

$$H_1 : f(X) = g(x)$$
$$H_2 : f(X) = h(x)$$

The left-hand tail of $g(x)$ and the right-hand tail of $h(x)$ are illustrated in Fig. 5.7. The ordinate markings are one unit each. We have discussed the procedure of preselecting an arbitrary portion on the abscissa, say the area to the left of k, which will govern our decision. We defined

$$\int_{R_2} g(x)\, dx = \int_{-\infty}^{k} g(x)\, dx \tag{5.3}$$

Thus the ratio

$$\frac{h(k)}{g(k)}$$

is some number, in this case greater than one, i.e.,

$$\frac{h(k)}{g(k)} \cong \frac{16}{4.5} \cong 3.6$$

Clearly for all x less than k this ratio is greater than 3.6, i.e.,

$$\forall x < k \rightarrow \forall x \in R_2 \rightarrow \frac{h(k)}{g(k)} > 3.6$$

This is indeed what we desire, for if this ratio is greater than 3.6, then more of $h(x)$ will be contained in R_2. Hence, the more likely will we reject H_1 when it is false.

In general, then, to establish a critical region for a given α, we should select those values of x such that

$$\frac{h(x)}{g(x)} > \text{constant} = c$$

Samples of Size $n = n$

This discussion is immediately extended to n observations of our one-dimensional variable

$$X = x_i$$

Each x_i is distributed as $g(x)$. We may thus write our hypotheses as follows:

$$H_1 : f(X) = g(x_1)g(x_2) \cdots g(x_n) = g(x) \tag{5.4}$$

$$H_2 : f(X) = h(x_1)h(x_2) \cdots h(x_n) = h(x) \tag{5.5}$$

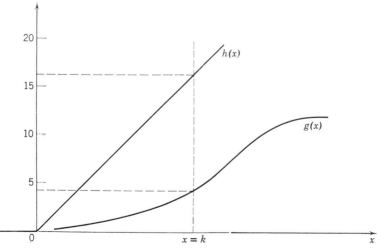

FIG. 5.7. Tails of $g(x)$, $h(x)$ about the critical boundary $x = k$.

If we let $\prod_{i=1}^{n} g(x_i)$ represent (5.4) and $\prod_{i=1}^{n} h(x_i)$ represent (5.5) then we may form the ratio

$$\frac{\prod\limits_{i=1}^{n} h(x_i)}{\prod\limits_{i=1}^{n} g(x_i)} \geq c$$

Neyman-Pearson Lemma

We may now state as follows, without proof, the Neyman-Pearson lemma: If the critical region R_2 is such that (1)

$$\int_{R_2} \prod_{i=1}^{n} g(x_i) \, dx_i = \alpha = \int_{R_2} g(x) \, dx$$

and (2) there exists a constant c such that

$$h(x) \geq cg(x) \qquad \text{for all } x \in R_2, \text{ and}$$
$$h(x) \leq cg(x) \qquad \text{for all } x \in R_1$$

then, there exists no more powerful critical region R_2 at level α.

This theorem is easily illustrated in Fig. 5.7; here

$$g(X) = g(x)$$
$$h(X) = h(x)$$

We assumed

$$\int_{R_2} f(x) \, dx = \alpha$$

and, too, a number c existed such that for all x belonging to the critical region

$$h(x) \geq cg(x)$$

and for all x belonging to R_1

$$h(x) \leq cg(x)$$

This is easily verified by substituting in $g(x)$ and $h(x)$ their ordinate values for various values of x.

The general theory of hypothesis testing was unified by J. Neyman and E. S. Pearson in the following papers:

(1928) On the use and interpretation of certain test criteria for purposes of statistical inference Parts I, II, *Biometrika*, 20 A, pp. 175–240, 263–294.

(1933) On the problem of the most efficient tests of statistical hypotheses, *Phil. Trans. Roy. Soc.* A, 231, pp. 289–337.

(1936) Contributions to the theory of testing statistical hypotheses, *Stat. Res. Mem.* 1, pp. 1–37;

(1936) Sufficient statistics and uniformly most powerful tests of statistical hypotheses, *Stat. Res. Mem.* 1, pp. 113–137

(1938) Contributions to the theory of testing statistical hypotheses, *Stat. Res. Mem.* 2, pp. 25–57.

chapter 6

Statistical Inference: Tests of Specific Hypotheses

TESTS CONCERNING THE MEAN OF A NORMAL DISTRIBUTION

An extremely important group of problems is the one concerned with testing hypotheses of data which are distributed in a normal distribution. The following are a series of hypotheses frequently tested.

Assume a sample point X of size n has been obtained from a normal population with mean μ unknown, and variance σ^2 known. The hypothesis in question is

$$H_1: \mu = \mu_1$$

with the alternative hypothesis

$$H_2: \mu = \mu_2$$

Here we wish to test the hypothesis that the mean of a normal population has some particular value, namely, μ_1. If we reject this hypothesis, we will assume the mean to be some other value, namely, μ_2.

Let the error of the first kind be α, that of the second kind β, and the power $1 - \beta$. Let R_1 represent the acceptance region and R_2 the rejection region.

Applying the Neyman-Pearson lemma, we wish to find some general constant c, such that

$$\prod_{i=1}^{n} h(x) \geq c \prod_{i=1}^{n} g(x) \qquad \text{for all } x \in R_2$$

and

$$\prod_{i=1}^{n} h(x) \leq c \prod_{i=1}^{n} g(x) \qquad \text{for all } x \in R_1$$

In this particular problem

$$h(x) = N[\mu_2, \sigma^2]$$
$$g(x) = N[\mu_1, \sigma^2]$$

and therefore

$$\left(\frac{1}{\sqrt{2\pi\sigma^2}}\right)^n \exp\left[-\frac{1}{2}\sum_{i=1}^{n}\left(\frac{x_i - \mu_2}{\sigma}\right)^2\right]$$

$$\geq c\left(\frac{1}{\sqrt{2\pi\sigma^2}}\right)^n \exp\left[-\frac{1}{2}\sum_{i=1}^{n}\left(\frac{x_i - \mu_1}{\sigma}\right)^2\right]$$

This reduces to

$$\exp\left[-\frac{1}{2}\sum_{i=1}^{n}\left(\frac{x_i - \mu_2}{\sigma}\right)^2\right] \geq c\exp\left[-\frac{1}{2}\sum_{i=1}^{n}\left(\frac{x_i - \mu_1}{\sigma}\right)^2\right]$$

and therefore

$$\frac{\exp\left[-\frac{1}{2\sigma^2}\sum_{i=1}^{n}(x_i - \mu_2)^2\right]}{\exp\left[-\frac{1}{2\sigma^2}\sum_{i=1}^{n}(x_i - \mu_1)^2\right]} \geq c$$

$$= \exp\left\{-\frac{1}{2\sigma^2}\left[\sum_{i=1}^{n}(x_i - \mu_2)^2 - \sum(x_i - \mu_1)^2\right]\right\} \geq c$$

and

$$-\frac{1}{2\sigma^2}\left[\sum_{i=1}^{n}(x_i - \mu_2)^2 - \sum_{i=1}^{n}(x_i - \mu_1)^2\right] \geq \ln c$$

If we let

$$-2\sigma^2 \ln c = c'$$

then

$$\sum_{i=1}^{n}(x_i - \mu_2)^2 - \sum_{i=1}^{n}(x_i - \mu_1)^2 \geq c'$$

$$= \sum_{i=1}^{n}x_i^2 - 2\mu_2\sum_{i=1}^{n}x_i + \mu_2^2 - \sum_{i=1}^{n}x_i^2 + 2\mu_1\sum_{i=1}^{n}x_i - \mu_1^2 > c'$$

$$= \sum_{i=1}^{n}x_i(-2\mu_2 + 2\mu_1) > c' + \mu_1^2 - \mu_2^2$$

Letting

$$c'' = c' + \mu_1^2 - \mu_2^2$$

then

$$\sum_{i=1}^{n}x_i > \frac{c''}{2\mu_1 - 2\mu_2}$$

If we further let

$$nc''' = \frac{c''}{2\mu_1 - 2\mu_2}$$

then

$$\sum_{i=1}^{n} x_i > nc'''$$

and

$$\sum_{i=1}^{n} \frac{x_i}{n} = \bar{x} > c'''$$

Hence, our test criterion is such that if $\bar{x}$ is greater than some constant c''', we will reject H_1, whereas if it is not, we will accept H_1.

The next problem is to find c''', such that

$$P\{\bar{x} \geq c'''\} = \alpha$$

We have shown that the sampling distribution of means drawn from a normal population with mean μ and variance σ^2 is itself normally distributed with mean μ and variance σ^2/n, where n is sample size. Thus, if our null hypothesis is true, $\bar{x} = \sum_{i=1}^{n} x_i/n$ is distributed as $N(\mu_1, \sigma^2/n)$ and the variable $(\bar{x} - \mu_1)/\sqrt{\sigma^2/n}$ is normally distributed with mean 0 and variance 1. Thus

$$P_{H_1}\{\bar{x} \geq c'''\} = \alpha = P_{H_1}\left\{\frac{\bar{x} - \mu_1}{(\sigma^2/n)^{\frac{1}{2}}} \geq \frac{c''' - \mu_1}{(\sigma^2/n)^{\frac{1}{2}}}\right\} = \alpha$$

Examination of the standardized normal table (see Tables F-VIII$_4$, H-II) will help solve for c'''. [See exercises (c) to (f), Chapter 4.]

The power of the above is defined as

$$1 - \beta = P_{H_2}\{\bar{x} \geq c'''\}$$

$$1 - \beta = P_{H_2}\left\{\frac{\bar{x} - \mu_2}{(\sigma^2/n)^{\frac{1}{2}}} \geq \frac{c''' - \mu_2}{(\sigma^2/n)^{\frac{1}{2}}}\right\}$$

EXAMPLE 1

General. x_i is $N[\mu, \sigma^2]$. H_1: $\mu = \mu_1$; H_2: $\mu = \mu_2$.

Specific. Assume that the average absolute minimum difference between strike readings in azimuth of a joint system has been shown to be normally distributed with a mean μ and variance σ^2. If $\sigma^2 = 100$ and a sample of size 105 differences is considered, test the hypothesis that $\mu = \mu_1 = 30$, when $\bar{x} = 36$. The alternative hypothesis is H_2: $\mu = \mu_2 = 38$. Let $\alpha = 0.01$.

Our problem now is to establish a decision criterion. What value shall determine acceptance or rejection of H_1? To illustrate the relationship of the null hypothesis to the alternative hypothesis and the sample mean, $\bar{x}$, consider Fig. 6.1. Here the distributions of $\bar{x}$ under H_1 and H_2 are drawn. The sample mean, $\bar{x}$, is also indicated. It is apparent from this diagram why our rejection region is an area to the right of μ_1. Let us find that region.

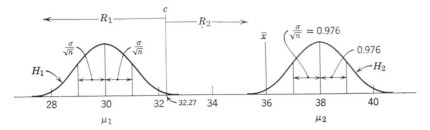

FIG. 6.1. Distribution of x under H_1 and H_2.

We know that

$$P_{H_1}\left\{\frac{\bar{x} - 30}{\sqrt{100/105}} \geq \frac{c - 30}{\sqrt{100/105}}\right\} = \alpha = 0.01$$

If Φ represents the cumulative unit normal distribution function (see Chapter 4), then

$$1 - \Phi\left[\frac{c - 30}{\sqrt{100/105}}\right] = 0.01$$

and

$$\Phi\left[\frac{c - 30}{0.976}\right] = 0.99$$

Looking up this value in the tabulated normal cumulative curves, Tables F-VIII$_4$, H-II, we find that the value of $(c - 30)/0.976$ which has 99% of the area of the normal curve less than it, or to its left, is 2.33. Thus

$$\frac{c - 30}{0.976} = 2.33$$

and

$$c = (2.33)(0.976) + 30 = 32.27$$

If the position of c is examined in Fig. 6.1, it is seen that the sample statistic we had agreed upon to aid us in making our decision, namely, $\bar{x}$, is well within the critical region, necessitating rejection of H_1.

The power of this test under the alternative hypothesis is

$$1 - \beta = P_{H_2}\{\bar{x} \in R_2\}$$

$$= P_{H_2}\left\{\frac{\bar{x} - 38}{0.976} > \frac{32.27 - 38}{0.976}\right\}$$

$$= P_{H_2}\left\{\frac{\bar{x} - 38}{0.976} > -5.87\right\}$$

$$= 1 - \Phi[-5.87] = \Phi[5.87]$$

$$\cong 0.9999$$

That is, the probability of rejecting the null hypothesis when it is false, a definitely desirable action, is very high, namely, 0.999. Since $1 - \beta$ is so high, we might have been wiser to have taken α even smaller than 0.01.

EXAMPLE 2

General. x_i is $N[\mu, \sigma^2]$, σ^2 is known.

$$H_1: \mu = \mu_1$$
$$H_2: \mu > \mu_1$$

Specific. Using the specific data in Example 1, we find as before that we reject H_1 and accept H_2. Let us carefully look at the power of the test.

The power function of the test was defined as $1 - \beta = P_{H_2}\{\bar{x} \in R_2\}$ and is obviously a function of the alternative hypothesis and its parameters. Considering that $H_2: \mu > \mu_1$, the power function of the test in this example, is

$$P_{H_2}\{\bar{x} > c\} = 1 - \beta = P_{H_2}\left\{ \frac{\bar{x} - \mu}{0.976} \geq \frac{32.27 - \mu}{0.976} \right\}$$

$$\text{Power function} = 1 - \Phi\left[\frac{32.27 - \mu}{0.976} \right].$$

Thus it is seen that the power function is purely determined by the parameter μ. Thus to obtain a graphical representation of the relationship between the power function and the alternative values of μ, under H_2, we compute the power for different values of $\mu > \mu_1$. That is, we wish to compute

$$1 - \Phi\left[\frac{32.27 - \mu}{0.978} \right] \qquad \text{for} \qquad \mu > \mu_1$$

Table 6.1 lists the values of the power of the test for different values of μ and Fig. 6.2 represents this graphically. Since we consider values of $\mu > \mu_1$ this is termed a one-tailed problem. It is a one-tailed test due to the selection of our critical region R.

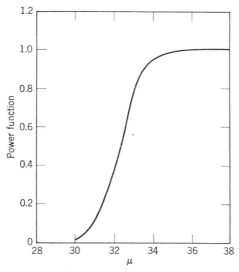

FIG. 6.2. Power function—one-tail unit-normal test.

TABLE 6.1
Values of the Power Function

Alternative Hypotheses	$1 - \Phi$ = Power
μ	
30	$1 - \Phi(2.32) = 0.01$
31	$1 - \Phi(1.30) = 0.0985$
32	$1 - \Phi(0.28) = 0.3930$
33	$1 - \Phi(-0.75) = 0.7734$
34	$1 - \Phi(-1.77) = 0.9616$
35	$1 - \Phi(-2.79) = 0.9974$
36	$1 - \Phi(-3.81) = 0.9999$
37	$1 - \Phi(-4.84) = 0.99999$

EXAMPLE 3

General. x_i is $N[\mu, \sigma^2]$. σ^2 is known.

$$H_1: \mu = \mu_1$$

Error of first kind $= \alpha$

$$H_2: \mu \neq \mu_1$$

The alternative hypothesis in this example forces us to look to the right as well as to the left of μ, if we are to consider rejecting H_1. Let us define our region of rejection. We wish R_2 to be such that

$$\int_{R_2} f(x) = \alpha$$

where $f(x)$ is the distribution of our test statistic; in this case the distribution of $\bar{x}$, when H_1 is true. R_2 may be satisfactorily defined partially to the left of μ_1, and partially to the right. Thus we will reject H_1 if $\bar{x} > c_2$ or $\bar{x} < c_1$, where $c_1 < c_2$.

c_1 and c_2 may be determined from the following relation, namely,

$$P_{H_1}\{\bar{x} \in R_2\} = P_{H_1}\{\bar{x} > c_2\} + P_{H_1}\{\bar{x} < c_1\} = \alpha$$

Therefore,

$$P_{H_1}\left\{\frac{\bar{x} - \mu_1}{\sqrt{\sigma^2/n}} > \frac{c_2 - \mu_1}{\sqrt{\sigma^2/n}}\right\} + P_{H_1}\left\{\frac{\bar{x} - \mu_1}{\sqrt{\sigma^2/n}} < \frac{c_1 - \mu_1}{\sqrt{\sigma^2/n}}\right\} = \alpha$$

or equivalently

$$1 - \Phi\left[\frac{c_2 - \mu_1}{\sqrt{\sigma^2/n}}\right] + \Phi\left[\frac{c_1 - \mu_1}{\sqrt{\sigma^2/n}}\right] = \alpha$$

The critical region will be defined as two regions such that

$$\int_{-\infty}^{c_1} f(x)\, dx + \int_{c_2}^{\infty} f(x)\, dx = \alpha \tag{6.1}$$

where $f(x)$ is the distribution of $\bar{x}$, assuming H_1 true.

It is easily seen that many combinations of c_1 and c_2 will satisfy (6.1). Certainly, the region defined by $\bar{x} > c_1$, and $\bar{x} < -c_1$ will. To decide which critical region is the "better" one, an examination of the power functions under the alternative hypotheses and the different values of c_1 and c_2 is helpful. For example purposes, let us assume that

$$\frac{\sigma^2}{n} = \frac{1}{25}, \mu_1 = 0 \quad \text{and} \quad \alpha = 0.05 \tag{6.2}$$

Our test criterion has been selected as

$$\bar{x} > c_1 \qquad \bar{x} < c_2$$

We shall consider three specific cases, each of which satisfies (6.1) but whose power functions are different. In all three of the examples the power is

$$P(\mu) = 1 - \Phi\left[\frac{c_2 - \mu}{\sqrt{\sigma^2/n}}\right] + \Phi\left[\frac{c_1 - \mu}{\sqrt{\sigma^2/n}}\right] \qquad |\mu| > \mu_1$$

and in particular at $\mu = \mu_1$

$$1 - \Phi\left[\frac{c_2 - \mu_1}{\sqrt{\sigma^2/n}}\right] + \Phi\left[\frac{c_1 - \mu_1}{\sqrt{\sigma^2/n}}\right] = 0.05 = \alpha$$

CASE I

$$\left(1 - \Phi\left[\frac{c_2 - \mu_1}{\sqrt{\sigma^2/n}}\right]\right) + \Phi\left[\frac{c_1 - \mu_1}{\sqrt{\sigma^2/n}}\right] = 0.05$$

By (6.2) this reduces to

$$(1 - \Phi[5c_2]) + \Phi[5c_1] = 0.05$$
$$(1 - 0.96) + 0.01 = 0.05$$

and therefore

$$5c_2 = 1.75$$
$$c_2 = 0.35$$

and

$$5c_1 = -2.326$$
$$c_1 = -0.466$$

The power function under these restrictions is

$$P(\mu) = 1 - \Phi[1.75 - 5\mu] + \Phi[-2.326 - 5\mu]$$

and is plotted in Fig. 6.3a.

CASE II

$$(1 - \Phi[5c_2]) + (\Phi[5c_1]) = 0.05$$
$$(1 - 0.98) + 0.03 = 0.05$$

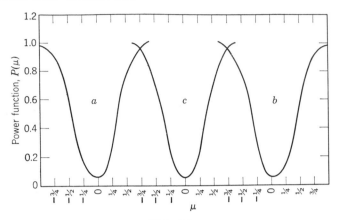

FIG. 6.3

Therefore

$$5c_2 = 2.06$$
$$c_2 = 0.412$$

and

$$5c_1 = -1.88$$
$$c_1 = -0.376$$

The power function under this critical region is

$$P(\mu) = 1 - \Phi[2.06 - 5\mu] + \Phi[-1.88 - 5\mu]$$

This is plotted in Fig. 6.3b.

CASE III

$$(1 - \Phi[5c_2]) + \Phi[5c_1] = 0.05$$
$$(1 - 0.975) + (0.025) = 0.05$$

Here

$$5c_2 = 1.960$$
$$c_2 = 0.392$$
$$5c_1 = -1.96$$
$$c_1 = -0.392$$

Thus $c_1 = -c_2$. Under these circumstances the critical region is said to be symmetrical. The power function is defined as

$$P(\mu) = 1 - \Phi[1.96 - 5\mu] + \Phi[-1.96 - 5\mu]$$

Here

$$P(\mu) = P(-\mu)$$

This is plotted in Fig. 6.3c.

Table 6.2 lists some values of the power functions of these three cases for identical values of μ. It can be seen from this table that for certain alternatives different critical regions may be more desirable. For example, for the alternative $\mu > \mu_1$, the critical region of I is more desirable than that of II or III. Thus the selection of a critical region is a function of the specific problem under consideration and there really is no "better" region. The experimenter alone, or in consultation with a statistician, is the best judge of the critical region. Unless

TABLE 6.2

Values of the Power Function[1] for Varying Values of μ and Three Different Critical Regions

The null hypothesis H_1 is $\mu = 0$, and the alternative hypothesis H_2 is $\mu \neq 0$. $\sigma^2/n = \frac{1}{25}$ and $\alpha = 0.05$. Critical regions: I. $c_1 = -0.466$, $c_2 = 0.35$; II. $c_1 = -0.376$, $c_2 = 0.412$; III. $c_1 = -0.392$, $c_2 = 0.392$

	Power		
μ	I	II	III
-1.00	0.9962	0.9991	0.9988
-0.75	0.9222	0.9693	0.9633
-0.50	0.5675	0.7324	0.7054
-0.25	0.1414	0.2648	0.2396
0.00	0.0500	0.0500	0.0500
0.25	0.3085	0.2099	0.2396
0.50	0.7774	0.6772	0.7054
0.75	0.9772	0.9545	0.9633
1.00	0.9994	0.9984	0.9988

[1] (I) $P(\mu) = 1 - \Phi(1.75 - 5.0\mu) + \Phi(-2.33 - 5.0\mu)$
   (II) $P(\mu) = 1 - \Phi(2.06 - 5.0\mu) + \Phi(-1.88 - 5.0\mu)$
   (III) $P(\mu) = 1 - \Phi(1.96 - 5.0\mu) + \Phi(-1.96 - 5.0\mu)$

stated otherwise, we shall, under an alternative of $\mu \neq \mu_1$, a *two-tail test*, use a symmetrical critical region.

Specific. x_i is $N[\mu, 100]$

$$H_1: \mu = 30$$
$$H_2: \mu \neq 30$$
$$\bar{x} = 31, n = 10, \alpha = 0.05$$

Now

$$\int_{-\infty}^{c_1} f(x)\, dx = P_{H_1}\{\bar{x} < c_1\} = P_{H_1}\{\bar{x} - 30 < c_1 - 30\} = \Phi[c_1 - 30]$$

$$= \frac{\alpha}{2} = 0.025$$

Thus

$$c_1 - 30 = -1.96$$
$$c_1 = 28.04$$

Similarly,

$$\int_{c_2}^{\infty} f(x)\, dx = P_{H_1}\{\bar{x} > c_2\} = \frac{\alpha}{2} = 0.025$$

Thus

$$\Phi[c_2 - 30] = 0.975$$
$$c_2 - 30 = 1.96$$
$$c_2 = 31.96$$

Therefore the region of rejection will be the regions defined as

$$\bar{x} > 31.96, \quad \bar{x} < 28.04$$

Since $\bar{x} = 31$, we accept H_1.

We examined areas to the left and right of μ, i.e., we had a *composite* and not a *single* alternative hypothesis. Furthermore, we have performed a *two-tail test*.

The power function is defined as

$$1 - \beta = P_{H_2}\{\bar{x} \in R_2\}$$
$$= P_{H_2}\{\bar{x} - \mu > 31.96 - \mu\} + P_{H_2}\{\bar{x} - \mu < 28.04 - \mu\}$$
$$= 1 - P_{H_2}\{\bar{x} - \mu < 31.96 - \mu\} + P_{H_2}\{\bar{x} - \mu < 28.04 - \mu\}$$

At $\mu = 30$,

$$\text{Power} = 1 - P_{H_2}\{\bar{x} - 30 < 1.96\} + P_{H_2}\{\bar{x} - 30 < -1.96\} = 0.05 = \alpha$$

Some values of this power function, for specific alternative values of μ, are listed in Table 6.3. The function is plotted in Fig. 6.4. The reader should satisfy himself that the power function in Fig. 6.4 is the power function for any two-tail unit normal test at $\alpha = 0.05$. No matter what the specific value of μ_1, the standardized variate $(c_1 - \mu)/\sqrt{\sigma^2/n}$ will always be the same.

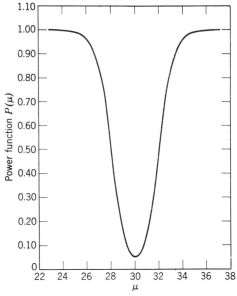

$$\text{Power} = 1 - P[\bar{x} - \mu < 31.96 - \mu] +$$
$$P\{\bar{x} - \mu < 28.04 - \mu\}$$

FIG. 6.4

The foregoing problems have been concerned with testing hypotheses about the means of normal distributions when the variance σ^2 is known. This at times is an unrealistic approach since σ^2 is very frequently unknown. In such cases we can consider an estimate of σ^2, namely,

$$\frac{\sum_{i=1}^{n}(x_i - \bar{x})^2}{n - 1} = s^2$$

where, since x_i is normal, s^2 is independent of $\bar{x}$.

TABLE 6.3
Values of the Power Function
$$1 - P\{\bar{x} - \mu < 31.96 \ -\mu\} + P\{\bar{x} - \mu < 28.04 - \mu\}$$

μ	Power
22	0.99999
24	0.99998
26	0.9793
27	0.8508
28	0.5160
29	0.1701
30	0.0500
31	0.1701
32	0.5160
33	0.8508
34	0.9793
36	0.99998
38	0.99999

Thus a likely substitute for testing means of a normal distribution with a one-tail test with a null hypothesis $\mu = \mu_1$, with the alternative of $\mu > \mu_1$, would be a statistic of the form

$$\frac{\bar{x} - \mu}{\sqrt{s^2/n}} \tag{6.3}$$

such that

$$P_{H_2}\left\{\frac{\bar{x} - \mu_1}{\sqrt{s^2/n}} > \frac{c_1 - \mu_1}{\sqrt{s^2/n}}\right\} = \alpha$$

If we divide numerator and denominator in (6.3) by $\sigma \neq 0$, we obtain

$$\frac{(\bar{x} - \mu)/\sigma}{\sqrt{\dfrac{\sum_{i=1}^{n}(x_i - \bar{x})^2}{\sigma^2 n(n - 1)}}} = \frac{\dfrac{\bar{x} - \mu}{\sigma/\sqrt{n}}}{\sqrt{s^2/\sigma^2}} \tag{6.3a}$$

If H_1 is true, the second numerator is independently distributed as $N(0, 1)$, whereas the denominator is equivalent to

$$\sqrt{\frac{\chi^2_{(n-1)}}{n-1}} = \text{degrees of freedom}$$

The ratio of a unit normal variate to the square root of a χ^2 distributed variate with $n - 1$ degrees of freedom has a known distribution attributed to "Student." It is the "t" distribution and is tabled in F-III, H-IV. Thus

$$t = \frac{\bar{x} - \mu_1}{s/\sqrt{n}}$$

with $n - 1$ degrees of freedom (t_{n-1})

and

$$P_{H_1}\left\{\frac{\bar{x} - \mu_1}{s/\sqrt{n}} > \frac{c_1 - \mu_1}{s/\sqrt{n}}\right\} = \alpha$$

$$= P_{H_1}\left\{t > \frac{c_1 - \mu_1}{s/\sqrt{n}}\right\} = \alpha$$

$$= \int_{t_{n-1}}^{\infty} f(t)\, dt = \alpha$$

If H_2 is $\mu < \mu_1$, then the critical region for α is such that $(\bar{x} - \mu_1)/(s/\sqrt{n}) \leq t_{(n-1)}$ where

$$\int_{-\infty}^{t_{(n-1)}} f(t)\, dt = \alpha$$

If H_2 is $\mu \neq \mu_1$, a two-tail test is appropriate where the regions are determined by the values of t'_{n-1} and t''_{n-1} such that

$$\int_{-\infty}^{t'_{n-1}} f(t)\, dt + \int_{t''_{n-1}}^{\infty} f(t)\, dt = \alpha$$

If the regions are selected symmetrically, then we will reject H_1 and accept H_2: $\mu \neq \mu_1$, if

$$\frac{\bar{x} - \mu_1}{s/\sqrt{n}} > t_{(n-1)}$$

or if

$$\frac{\bar{x} - \mu_1}{s/\sqrt{n}} < -t_{(n-1)}$$

i.e., we reject if

$$\left|\frac{\bar{x} - \mu}{s/\sqrt{n}}\right| > t_{(n-1)}$$

The power function in this case is

$$P(\mu) = P_{H_2}\left\{\frac{\bar{x} - \mu}{s/\sqrt{n}} > t_{(n-1)}\right\} + P_{H_2}\left\{\frac{\bar{x} - \mu}{s/\sqrt{n}} < -t_{(n-1)}\right\}$$

and at $\mu = \mu_1$, $P(\mu_1) = \alpha$

EXAMPLE 4

General. x_i is $N[\mu, \sigma^2]$ and σ^2 is unknown.

$$H_1: \mu = \mu_1$$
$$H_2: \mu < \mu_1$$

Specific. x_i is $N[\mu, \sigma^2]$ and σ^2 is unknown, but

$$s^2 = 100$$
$$\bar{x} = 26$$
$$n = 25$$
$$H_1: \mu = 30$$
$$H_2: \mu < 30$$

Let $\alpha = 0.05$.

Here our critical region is the value $t_{(n-1)=24}$ for $\alpha = 0.05$, such that

$$P_{H_1}\{t \in R_2\} = \alpha = 0.05$$

In this case the critical region is to the left of μ and hence

$$P_{H_1}\{t < -t_{24,0.05}\} = \alpha$$

where $t_{24,0.05}$ is understood to mean a "t" distributed variate with 24 degrees of freedom and at $\alpha = 0.05$.

Examining the "t" table we find that $-t_{24,0.05} = -1.711$. Thus our calculated $t = (x - \mu_1)/(s/\sqrt{n}) = -6/2 = -3 > -1.711$ and therefore we reject H_1.

EXAMPLE 5.

General. x_i is $N[\mu, \sigma^2]$. σ^2 is unknown.

$$H_1: \mu = \mu_1$$
$$H_2: \mu \neq \mu_1$$

s^2 and $\bar{x}$ are obtained from a sample size n.

Specific. The sum of five pressure readings in dynes/cm² for a 40-cycle sound wave was recorded at the Narragansett Marine Laboratory of the University of Rhode Island as 3200 dynes/cm². $\sum_{i=1}^{5}(x_i - \bar{x})^2 = 12,400$ (dynes/cm²)². Data reported by Dietz and Kahn[1] in 1962 indicate that the pressure readings are $N[485, \sigma^2]$. Do these more recent experimental results conflict with the generally accepted ones? Let $\alpha = 0.05$. Here

$$H_1: \mu = 485$$
$$H_2: \mu \neq 485$$

[1] F. T. Dietz and J. S. Kahn, Application of the theoretical model for the seasonal analysis of shallow water ambient sound. Submitted to *Jour. Amer. Acoustial Society.*

We must select that value of t such that

$$\int_{t_{(n-1)}}^{\infty} f(t)\,dt = \frac{\alpha}{2} = \int_{-\infty}^{-t_{(n-1)}} f(t)\,dt$$

Thus our critical regions are such that we reject if

$$\left| t = \frac{\bar{x} - \mu_1}{s/\sqrt{n}} \right| > 2.776$$

Here

$$\left| t = \frac{640 - 485}{\sqrt{3100/5}} \right| = 6.22 > 2.776$$

Therefore, the hypothesis is rejected.

EXAMPLE 6.

General. x_i is $N[\mu, \sigma_1^2]$, y_i is $N[\mu_2, \sigma_2^2]$ and x_i and y_i are independent. $\sigma_1^2 \neq \sigma_2^2$ but both are known

$$H_1: \mu_1 = \mu_2$$
$$(1)\ H_2: \mu_1 < \mu_2$$
$$(2)\ H_3: \mu_1 > \mu_2$$
$$(3)\ H_4: \mu_1 \neq \mu_2$$

Level of significance $= \alpha$, $\bar{x}$ is obtained from sample of size n_1, $\bar{y}$ is obtained from sample of size n_2.

Since x_i, and y_i, are independent and normally distributed, then the variate $(\bar{x} - \bar{y})$ has expectation $\mu_1 - \mu_2$ and variance $\sigma_1^2/n_1 + \sigma_2^2/n_2$. Therefore the variate

$$\frac{(\bar{x} - \bar{y}) - E(\bar{x} - \bar{y})}{\sqrt{\sigma_1^2/n_1 + \sigma_2^2/n_2}} = \frac{(\bar{x} - \bar{y}) - (\mu_1 - \mu_2)}{\sqrt{\sigma_1^2/n_1 + \sigma_2^2/n_2}} \qquad (6.4)$$

is a unit normal variate. Under the null hypothesis $(\mu_1 - \mu_2) = 0$ and (6.4) reduces to

$$\frac{\bar{x} - \bar{y}}{\sqrt{\sigma_1^2/n_1 + \sigma_2^2/n_2}}$$

which, since its distribution is known, can be used effectively as a test statistic. (1) Our critical region, with the alternative hypothesis of $\mu_1 < \mu_2$, is determined by that value of c such that $\bar{x} - \bar{y} < c$ and

$$P_{H_1}\left\{ \frac{\bar{x} - \bar{y}}{\sqrt{\sigma_1^2/n_1 + \sigma_2^2/n_2}} < \frac{c}{\sqrt{\sigma_1^2/n_1 + \sigma_2^2/n_2}} \right\} = \alpha$$

and therefore

$$\Phi\left[\frac{c}{\sqrt{\sigma_1^2/n_1 + \sigma_2^2/n_2}} \right] = \alpha$$

or, since $c/\sqrt{\sigma^2/n_1 + \sigma_2^2/n_2}$ is another constant, say k, this may be written $\Phi[k] = \alpha$. (2) The critical region for this alternative hypothesis is found similarly, since under this alternative

$$P_{H_1}\left\{\frac{\bar{x} - \bar{y}}{\sqrt{\sigma_1^2/n_1 + \sigma_2^2/n_2}} > \frac{c}{\sqrt{\sigma_1^2/n_1 + \sigma_2^2/n_2}}\right\} = \alpha$$

and

$$\Phi\left[\frac{c}{\sqrt{\sigma_1^2/n_1 + \sigma_2^2/n_2}}\right] = 1 - \alpha$$

(3) The test here is a two-tailed test with the critical region defined by c such that

$$P_{H_1}\left\{\left|\frac{\bar{x} - \bar{y}}{\sqrt{\sigma_1^2/n_1 + \sigma_2^2/n_2}}\right| > \frac{c}{\sqrt{\sigma_1^2/n_1 + \sigma_2^2/n_2}}\right\} = \alpha$$

EXERCISES

1. Obtain the test statistic if, in the above problem: (a) $\sigma_1^2 = \sigma_2^2$ but $n_1 \neq n_2$. (b) $\sigma_1^2 = \sigma_2^2$ and $n_1 = n_2$.

2. Prepare examples from your specific area of study in which H_1: $\mu_1 = \mu_2$ and (a) H_2: $\mu_1 > \mu_2$. (b) H_2: $\mu_1 \neq \mu_2$.

EXAMPLE 7

General. x_i and y_i are normal independent variates distributed as $N[\mu_1, \sigma_1^2]$ and $N[\mu_2, \sigma_2^2]$ where σ_1^2 and σ_2^2 are unknown and are estimated by s_1^2 and s_2^2.

$$H_1: \mu_1 = \mu_2$$
$$(1)\ H_2: \mu_1 < \mu_2$$
$$(2)\ H_3: \mu_1 > \mu_2$$
$$(3)\ H_4: \mu_1 \neq \mu_2$$

Now under H_1 $E(\bar{x} - \bar{y}) = \mu_1 - \mu_2 = 0$

and $\text{Var}\,(\bar{x} - \bar{y}) = \dfrac{\sigma_1^2}{n_1} + \dfrac{\sigma_2^2}{n_2}$

Thus

$$\frac{\bar{x} - \bar{y}}{\sqrt{\sigma_1^2/n_1 + \sigma_2^2/n_2}}$$

is $N[0, 1]$.
This would be an excellent test statistic if σ_1^2, σ_2^2 were known, but they are not. We use instead their estimates, i.e., s_1^2 and s_2^2 respectively. Thus we substitute in the preceding equation and obtain

$$\frac{\bar{x} - \bar{y}}{\sqrt{s_1^2/n_1 + s_2^2/n_2}} \tag{6.5}$$

To utilize this statistic in finding our critical region and making a decision for the three alternative hypotheses above, we must know the distribution of the statistic if H_1 were true. It can be shown that this statistic is not distributed as a t variate since the radicand $(s_1^2/n_1 + s_2^2/n_2)^{1/2}$ is not distributed as

$$\frac{\sigma^2 \chi^2}{\text{(degree of freedom)}}$$

If, however, n_1 and n_2 are large, then (6.5) is approximately normally distributed. Under the circumstances, critical regions are obtained as in Example 6.

Thus we change our assumptions above in the following manner:

$$H_1: \mu_1 = \mu_2 \quad \text{and} \quad \sigma_1^2 = \sigma_2^2 = \sigma^2$$

the alternatives remaining as before. Formula (6.5) reduces to

$$\frac{\bar{x} - \bar{y}}{\sqrt{\sigma_1^2/n_1 + \sigma_2^2/n_2}} = \frac{\bar{x} - \bar{y}}{\sigma\sqrt{(n_1 + n_2)/n_1 n_2}}$$

We must now obtain an estimate of σ^2.

Since $\sigma_1^2 = \sigma_2^2 = \sigma^2$ we can obtain a "pooled" estimate of σ^2 by using s_1^2 and s_2^2.

We have shown that if x_i is $N[\mu, \sigma^2]$ then s^2, computed from such a population, may be expressed as a function of χ^2 such that

$$\chi^2 = \frac{(n - 1)s^2}{\sigma^2}$$

If we selected many samples of different sizes from the same population, then each is related to χ^2 in a similar manner. That is,

$$\chi_1^2 = \frac{(n_1 - 1)s_1^2}{\sigma_1^2}$$

$$\chi_2^2 = \frac{(n_2 - 1)s_2^2}{\sigma_2^2}$$

.
.
.

$$\chi_m^2 = \frac{(n_m - 1)s_m^2}{\sigma_m^2}$$

Now

$$\sum_{i=1}^{m} \chi_i^2 = \sum \frac{(n_i - 1)s_i^2}{\sigma_i^2} \tag{6.6}$$

has a χ^2 distribution with $\sum_{i=1}^{m}(n_i - 1)$ degrees of freedom. Hence, if

$$\sigma_1^2 = \sigma_2^2 = \sigma_3^2 = \cdots = \sigma_m^2 = \sigma^2$$

$$\sum_{i=1}^{m} \chi_i^2 = \frac{\sum_{i=1}^{m}(n_i - 1)s_i^2}{\sigma^2} = \chi^2$$

and therefore

$$\frac{\sigma^2\chi^2}{\sum\limits_{i=1}^{n}(n_i - 1)} = \frac{\sum\limits_{i=1}^{m}(n_i - 1)s_i^2}{\sum\limits_{i=1}^{m}(n_i - 1)}$$

Thus

$$\frac{\sigma^2\chi^2}{\sum\limits_{i=1}^{n}(n_i - 1)}$$

is equal to some weighted estimate of σ^2. If we let

$$s_p^2 = \frac{\sum\limits_{i=1}^{m}(n_i - 1)s_i^2}{\sum\limits_{i=1}^{m}(n_i - 1)}$$

then to obtain a pooled estimate of $\sigma_1^2 = \sigma_2^2 = \sigma^2$ we compute

$$s_p^2 = \frac{\sum\limits_{i=1}^{2}(n_i - 1)s_i^2}{\sum\limits_{i=1}^{2}(n_i - 1)} = \frac{(n_1 - 1)s_1^2 + (n_2 - 1)s_2^2}{n_1 + n_2 - 2}$$

Thus the test statistic under H_1 assumes the form

$$\frac{\bar{x} - \bar{y}}{s_p\sqrt{(n_1 + n_2)/n_1 n_2}}$$

And this is a t-distributed variate with $n_1 + n_2 - 2$ degrees of freedom. Critical values for the above alternatives are

Alternative (1) $\mu_1 < \mu_2$—rejection region is the value of $t_{n_1+n_2-2,\alpha}$ such that

$$t = \frac{\bar{x} - \bar{y}}{s_p\sqrt{(n_1 + n_2)/n_1 n_2}} < t_{n_1+n_2-2,\alpha}$$

Here $t_{n_1+n_2-2,\alpha}$ is negative.
    Alternative (2) $\mu_1 > \mu_2$—reject H_1 if

$$t = \frac{\bar{x} - \bar{y}}{s_p\sqrt{(n_1 + n_2)/n_1 n_2}} > t_{n_1+n_2-2,1-\alpha}$$

Alternative (3) $\mu_1 \neq \mu_2$—reject H_1 if

$$|t| > t_{n_1+n_2-2,1-\alpha/2}$$

Specific. Smith and Flanagan (1956)[1] undertook a study of the changes in radioactivity, as a function of weathering, in the Conway Granite of New Hampshire. The radioactivity was measured by means of β-γ counts. Their results are summarized in Table 6.4.

[1] W. L. Smith and F. J. Flanagan, 1956, Use of statisical methods to detect radioactivity change due to weathering of a granite, *Amer. Jour. Sci.* 254: 316–324.

TABLE 6.4

Radioactivity of Redstone Quarry Samples

Green Phase				Red Phase			
Weathered		Fresh		Weathered		Fresh	
Sample	Counts*	Sample	Counts*	Sample	Counts*	Sample	Counts*
135	907	113	710	123	836	101	942
136	(1418)**	114	754	124	768	102	887
137	799	115	712	125	904	103	1041
138	831	116	750	126	1044	104	933
139	742	117	713	127	1143	105	969
140	716	118	767	128	953	106	1023
141	801	119	715	129	1030	107	1126
142	760	120	700	130	924	108	776
143	806	121	724	131	996	109	980
144	821	122	716	132	893	110	1051
				133	1100	111	1081
				134	873	112	1060
Number	9		10		12		12
Mean	798.1		726.1		955.3		989.1
Variance	3109.0		507.0		12260.0		9234.0
Standard deviation	55.8		22.5		110.7		96.1

* Net β-γ counts in five minutes.
** This value omitted from calculations.

One of the problems of interest was to see if there were any significant differences among the average radioactivity of the weathered and fresh portions of two color phases of the granite, namely, a red phase and a green phase. Thus, with respect to the red phase a hypothesis was established that there was no significant difference between the weathered and fresh rock, and the radioactivity was the same. The alternative hypothesis, the hypothesis the writers were more interested in, was that the radioactivity in the fresh rock was greater. Thus formally these hypotheses are H_1: $\mu_f = \mu_w$ with the alternative

$$H_2: \mu_w < \mu_f$$

Here μ_f represents the true population mean for the radioactivity of the fresh red rock, and μ_w represents the true population mean for the weathered red rock. Estimates of μ_f and μ_w are 989.1 and 955.3 respectively. $n_f = n_w = 12$. Applying the test procedure outlined above, and assuming the necessary conditions for its use are at present satisfactory, we find that

$$s_p = \left[\frac{(11)(12,260) + (11)(9234)}{22}\right]^{\frac{1}{2}} = (10,747)^{\frac{1}{2}} = 103.7$$

and $t = -33.8/17.3 = -1.96$. The critical region are those points less than $-2.06 = t_{22,0.05}$. The computed value of t is greater than -2.06 and the null hypothesis is accepted. We conclude that the radioactivity of the fresh and weathered red granite is the same.

ADDITIONAL PAPERS IN WHICH THE *t*-TEST
HAVE BEEN APPLIED

R. A. Cadigan, 1954, Testing graphical methods of grain-size analysis of sandstones and siltstones, *Jour. Sed. Petrol.* 24: 123–127. Suggests a test based on Students *t*-distribution for comparing standard deviation or other parameters of grain size frequency distributions with those obtained by graphical analysis.

A. N. Strahler, 1952, Hypsometric (area-altitude) analysis of erosional topography, *Bull. G.S.A.* 63: 1117–1142.

E. D. Sneed and F. L. Folk, 1958, Pebbles in the lower Colorado River, Texas, a study in particle morphogenesis, *Jour. Geol.* 66: 114–150.

J. J. Donner and Björn Kurtén, 1958, The floral and faunal succession of "Cueva de Toll" Spain, *Eiszeitalter u. gegenwart.* Band 9, pp. 72–82. Uses the *t*-test comparison of mean lengths of cheek teeth in *Ursus spelaeus*.

SUBSTITUTE *t*-TESTS

τ_d for Very Small Samples

A substitute *t*-test ratio for the significance of difference between means is available, involving the use of $\bar{x}$ and the range ω. It is not recommended for samples much larger than $n = 10$ and in any case serves best as a quick estimate when tables are available. The statistic τ_d is defined as $\tau_d = (\bar{x}_1 - \bar{x}_2)/(\omega_1 + \omega_2)$ for samples of equal size and is tabled in Dixon and Massey, 1951, *ibid.*, p. 409 [Table A-8C(2)]. For example, two collections of rock specimens are made in the field, with each collection from a different locality. A rough visual estimate is made of the amount of quartz in units of area for each specimen, and the null hypothesis that the means do not differ significantly is tested as follows:

Collection A	*Collection B*
3	6
5	8
6	11
7	12
9	13
$\omega_A = 9 - 3 = 6$	$\omega_B = 13 - 6 = 7$
$\bar{x}_A = 6$	$\bar{x}_B = 10$
$n_A = 5$	$n_B = 5$

$$\tau_d = \frac{\bar{x}_A - \bar{x}_B}{\omega_A + \omega_B} = \frac{6 - 10}{6 + 7} = 0.308$$

For sample size $n_1 = n_2 = 5$ the critical value at the 95th percentile level is 0.246. The null hypothesis of equal means is rejected.

SUGGESTING READING

D. Krinsley, 1960, Magnesium, strontium and aragonite in the shells of certain littoral gastropods, *Jour. Paleon.* 34: 744–755. The author used the substitute *t*-test for comparison between means in strontium and in magnesium content in samples from a number of localities on the West Coast of the United States.

The Mann-Whitney U Test: a Nonparametric Alternative to the t-Test

This is a nonparametric test for comparing two independent samples. It may be considered as an alternative to the *t*-test when the required assumptions are not satisfied for application of the *t*-test. The test may be applied whenever the data can be ordered.

The statistic U is formed as follows:

1. Rank the data by size into a single ordered sequence, but retaining the identity of each entry.

2. Denote the smaller of the samples by N_1, and the larger by N_2.

3. Choose either sample, say N_1, for a counting procedure described in the next step.

4. Proceed from smallest to largest in the ordered sequence. When the first member of N_1 is reached, count all members of N_2 which precede it. When the second member of N_1 is reached, count all members of N_2 which precede it, beginning again at the beginning of the sequence. Continue until all such counts are made. U is the sum of these counts.

The following example illustrates the method. An investigator is interested in pleochroic halos as indicators of relative age in rocks. The diameters of pleochroic halos around biotite inclusions are measured in two thin sections from specimens collected from different localities. Locality A is stratigraphically older than locality B. Table 6.5 records the diameters in units from a micrometer ocular.

TABLE 6.5

A	B
8	7
14	5
11	10
9	

The investigator wishes a preliminary test to verify that values in A are drawn from a population which on the whole is larger than the one from which sample B was drawn. We now proceed with the test.

Step 1. The combined data are arranged in a size-ordered sequence with each diameter identified as to locality A or B. $N_1 = 3$ and denotes the smallest sample. $N_2 = 4$. See Table 6.6.

TABLE 6.6

5	7	8	9	10	11	14
B	B	A	A	B	A	A

Step 2. U is calculated by counting the total number of B's which precede each successive A, $U = 2 + 2 + 3 + 3 = 10$.

Step 3. Proceed to Table J, pp. 271–273 in S. Siegal, (1956, *ibid.*) for a one-tailed test of the null hypothesis, H_0, that sample A is drawn from the same population as sample B, with the alternative hypothesis, H_1, that sample A is stochastically larger than sample B. For $N_2 = 4$ and $N_1 = 3$ we find that the calculated value of U is larger than the largest U value tabled, which is 8. We recompute U as follows:

$$U(\text{recomputed}) = N_1 N_2 - U = (3)(4) - U = 2$$

Had we entered Table 6.6 the other way, counting the total number of A's which precede each successive B, we would have had the same result.

For $N_2 = 4$, $N_1 = 3$, and $U(\text{recomputed}) = 2$ we find that the probability associated with a value of U as small as 2 is 0.114. If we set α at 0.05, the region of rejection of H_0 includes all values of U which are less than or equal to 0.05. Since in this case the probability associated with $U = 2$ exceeds 0.05, the null hypothesis is accepted. On the basis of these data alone the investigator has no reason to conclude that the older sample was drawn from a population of larger pleochroic haloes around biotite inclusions.

Had the alternative hypothesis H_1 been simply that the two samples differed rather than specifying that A was larger than B, a two-tailed test would have been involved and a different set of tables used. For a general discussion of the test, including situations where N_1 and N_2 are large, see S. Siegal, pp. 116–127. The derivation of the test and the tables are given in H. B. Mann, and D. R. Whitney, 1947, On a test of whether one of two random variables is stochastically larger than the other, *Ann. Math. Stats.* 18: 52–54.

Tests Concerning the Variance of a Normal Distribution

The foregoing tests of very frequent application represent tests concerned with but one of the parameters of the normal distribution, namely, the n μ. The variance, σ^2 is the second parameter. Tests concerning nces of normal distributions will now be considered.

LE 8

ral. x_i is $N(\mu, \sigma^2)$. $\bar{x}$ and s^2 are determined from a sample of size n.

$$H_1: \sigma^2 = \sigma_1{}^2$$
$$H_2: \sigma^2 < \sigma_1{}^2$$
$$H_3: \sigma^2 > \sigma_1{}^2$$
$$H_4: \sigma^2 \neq \sigma_1{}^2$$

We have shown that

$$\chi^2_{(n-1)} = \frac{\sum\limits_{i=1}^{n}(x_i - \bar{x})^2}{\sigma^2}$$

where x_i is $N(\mu, \sigma^2)$ may be rewritten as

$$\chi^2_{(n-1)} = \frac{s^2(n-1)}{\sigma^2}$$

If H_1 above is true, then

$$\chi^2_{(n-1)} = \frac{s^2(n-1)}{\sigma_1{}^2}$$

Thus critical regions may be determined by those values of $\chi^2_{(n-1)}$ such that we reject H_1 and accept the alternative hypotheses (2), (3), and (4) if

$$\frac{s^2(n-1)}{\sigma_1{}^2} < \chi^2_{(n-1),\alpha}$$

and

$$\frac{s^2(n-1)}{\sigma_1{}^2} > \chi^2_{(n-1),1-\alpha}$$

and

$$\frac{s^2(n-1)}{\sigma_1{}^2} < \chi^2_{(n-1),\alpha/2}$$

or

$$\frac{s^2(n-1)}{\sigma_1{}^2} > \chi^2_{(n-1),1-(\alpha/2)}$$

POWER FUNCTIONS FOR TESTS CONCERNING σ^2 FROM A NORMAL POPULATION

The critical value for alternative (2) was $\chi^2_{(n-1),\alpha}$ and H_1 was rejected if

$$\frac{s^2(n-1)}{\sigma_1{}^2} < \chi^2_{(n-1),\alpha} \tag{6.7}$$

Consider the alternative $\sigma^2 < \sigma_1^2$, where $\sigma^2 \neq 0$. Then (6.7) may be rewritten as

$$\frac{s^2(n-1)}{\sigma^2} < \frac{\sigma_1^2}{\sigma^2} \chi^2_{(n-1),\alpha}$$

Thus the power function, $P(\sigma^2)$ may be written as

$$P(\sigma^2) = 1 - \beta = P_{H_2}\left\{\frac{s^2(n-1)}{\sigma^2} < \frac{\sigma_1^2}{\sigma^2} \chi^2_{(n-1),\alpha}\right\}$$

If we let $\lambda = \sigma_1^2/\sigma^2$, then this reduces to

$$P\left\{\chi^2 = \frac{s^2(n-1)}{\sigma^2} < \lambda\chi^2_{(n-1),\alpha}\right\}$$

For the other alternative hypotheses

$$P(\sigma^2) = P_{H_3}\left\{\frac{s^2(n-1)}{\sigma^2} > \lambda\chi^2_{(n-1),1-\alpha}\right\}$$

$$P\{\sigma^2\} = P_{H_4}\left\{\frac{s^2(n-1)}{\sigma^2} > \lambda\chi^2_{(n-1),1-(\alpha/2)}\right\} + P_{H_4}\left\{\frac{s^2(n-1)}{\sigma^2} < \lambda\chi^2_{(n-1),\alpha/2}\right\}$$

EXAMPLE 9

General. x_i is $N[\mu_1; \sigma_1^2]$, y_i is $N[\mu_2, \sigma_2^2]$. x_i and y_i are independent and s_1^2, s_2^2 are obtained from samples of size n_1 and n_2, respectively.

$$H_1: \sigma_1^2 = \sigma_2^2$$
$$H_2: \sigma_1^2 < \sigma_2^2$$
$$H_3: \sigma_1^2 > \sigma_2^2$$
$$H_4: \sigma_1^2 \neq \sigma_2^2$$

This problem frequently arises in research. Here we wish to test to see if two samples drawn from normal populations, with the same or different means, have the same variance, i.e., exhibit homogeneous variability. The reader will recall that in general Example 7, where interest was concentrated on the hypothesis $\mu_1 = \mu_2$ where σ_1^2 and σ_2^2 were unknown, we came to the conclusion that to obtain a critical region depending on a t statistic we had to assume $\sigma_1^2 = \sigma_2^2$. The hypothesis being considered now is this one. It is suggested that this hypothesis be tested before a t test for testing for difference between means of normal populations be made.

Both

$$\frac{\sum_{i=1}^{n}(x_i - \bar{x})^2}{\sigma_1^2} = \frac{s_1^2(n_1 - 1)}{\sigma_1^2} \quad \text{and} \quad \frac{\sum_{i=1}^{n}(y_i - \bar{y})^2}{\sigma_2^2} = \frac{s_2^2(n_2 - 1)}{\sigma_2^2}$$

are independent and distributed as χ^2 with $(n_1 - 1)$ and $(n_2 - 1)$ degrees of freedom respectively.

We have shown that the ratio of any two independent χ^2 distributed variates has a distribution, dependent only on n_1 and n_2, known as the "F" distribution. Thus

$$F_{(n_1-1,n_2-1)} = \frac{\dfrac{s_1{}^2(n_1 - 1)}{\sigma_1{}^2(n_1 - 1)}}{\dfrac{s_2{}^2(n_2 - 1)}{\sigma_2{}^2(n_2 - 1)}} = \frac{s_1{}^2\sigma_2{}^2}{s_2{}^2\sigma_1{}^2}$$

If H_1: $\sigma_1{}^2 = \sigma_2{}^2$ is true, then

$$F_{(n_1-1,n_2-1)} = \frac{s_1{}^2}{s_2{}^2}$$

and this can be used as a test criterion.

The rejection criteria at the α level of significance for the preceding alternatives are:

$$F = \frac{s_1{}^2}{s_2{}^2} < F_{(n_1-1,n_2-1),\alpha}$$

$$F = \frac{s_1{}^2}{s_2{}^2} > F_{(n_1-1,n_2-1),1-\alpha}$$

$$F = \frac{s_1{}^2}{s_2{}^2} > F_{(n_1-1,n_2-1),1-(\alpha/2)}$$

or

$$= \frac{s_1{}^2}{s_2{}^2} < F_{(n_1-1,n_2-1),\alpha/2}$$

Utilizing the data of Smith and Flanagan,[1] let us examine the hypothesis that the variability of the fresh and weathered red sample are the same, an assumption made previously. Were we justified in doing so? The null hypothesis is as follows:

$$H_1: \sigma_w{}^2 = \sigma_f{}^2$$

with the alternative

$$H_2: \sigma_w{}^2 > \sigma_f{}^2$$

Here the sample estimates of $\sigma_w{}^2$ and $\sigma_f{}^2$ are obtained from Table 6.4, $s_w{}^2 = 12,260$ and $s_f{}^2 = 923.4$. If H_1 is true, then

$$F\binom{11}{11} = \frac{s_w{}^2}{s_f{}^2}$$

[1] W. L. Smith and F. J. Flanagan, *ibid.*

The rejection area are those values of s_w^2/s_f^2 greater than 2.82, at $\alpha = 0.05$, Tables F–V, H–VII. Here, $s_w^2/s_f^2 = 1.33$. The null hypothesis is therefore accepted and we conclude that we were justified in testing, by means of the t test, the hypothesis $\mu_w = \mu_f$.

What of the hypothesis that the means of the weathered red granite and fresh green granite are the same? Are these samples from the same population, as far as radioactivity is concerned? Before testing this specific hypothesis, let us first examine the hypotheses that the variances of these are the same. Here

$$H_1: \xi_w^2 = \xi_f^2$$

with the alternative

$$H_2: \xi_w^2 > \xi_f^2$$

ξ_w^2 represents the population variance of the weathered green granite, and is estimated by $s_w^2 = 3109$; ξ_f^2 represents the population variance of the fresh green granite and is estimated by $s_f^2 = 507$. The alternative hypothesis is that the variability in radioactivity in the weathered green granite is greater than that of the fresh green granite. Our critical region is defined as all points greater than 3.23.

Thus one computes

$$F = \frac{3109}{507} = 6.13 > 3.23$$

The null hypothesis is rejected and the alternative hypothesis is accepted. These populations do differ. The variability of the radioactivity in weathered green granite is greater than the variability in the fresh granite. There is no need to test to see if the samples come from a single population. They do not.

SUGGESTED READING

A. N. Strahler, 1950, Equilibrium theory of erosional slopes approached by frequency distribution analysis II, *Am. Jour. Sci.* 248: 800–814. Examines three field localities in the San Gabriel and Verdugo Mountains. Two of the areas are underlain by the same rock type, the third by a different rock type, the Wilson diorite. Comparisons of slope means and standard deviations are made, the latter by the *F*-test.

D. Krinsley, 1960, *ibid.*, applied the *F*-test as a preliminary to analysis of variance in strontium and magnesium content in shell samples.

Test of the Equivalence of More Than Two Variances

For the test of the equivalence of more than two variances, we shall introduce one further test criterion known as the maximum likelihood criterion, or likelihood ratio. This function was introduced, in part, at the beginning of this section. The likelihood, L, of a sample has already been defined. The likelihood function will attain some value out of all possible values which could be obtained by considering all possible values of the parameters. Of these possible parameter values which could be introduced into L there will be some which maximize L. When these maximizing values are introduced into L, let $L = L_2$. Furthermore, under H_1, there are values of the parameters which maximize L. Let L in this case be L_1. The ratio of L_1 to L_2, λ, is known as the likelihood ratio. By virtue of the definition of λ, $0 \leq \lambda \leq 1$.

EXAMPLE 10

   General. Consider the null hypothesis H_1: $\sigma_1^2 = \sigma_2^2 = \cdots = \sigma_m^2 = \sigma^2$, where the σ_i^2's have been obtained from samples of sizes $n_1, n_2, \cdots, n_m$ with means $\bar{x}_1, \bar{x}_2, \cdots, \bar{x}_m$ and variances $s_1^2, s_2^2, \cdots, s_m^2$.
   The likelihood, L, is of the form

$$\frac{1}{\sqrt[n_1]{2\pi\sigma_1^2}} \exp\left[-\frac{1}{2}\sum_{j=1}^{n_1}(x_{1j} - \mu_1)^2/\sigma_1^2\right]\frac{1}{\sqrt[n_1]{2\pi\sigma_2^2}} \exp\left[-\frac{1}{2}\sum_{j=1}^{n_2}(x_{2j} - \mu_2)^2/\sigma_2^2\right] \cdots$$

The values of μ_i and σ_i^2 which maximize this function are

$$\bar{x}_{i.} = \frac{\sum_{j=1}^{n_i} x_{ij}}{n_i} = \bar{x}_i \quad \text{and} \quad s_i^2 = \frac{\sum_{j=1}^{n_i}(x_{ij} - \bar{x}_i)^2}{n_i}$$

respectively. L_2 becomes

$$\left[\frac{1}{\dfrac{2\pi\sum_{j=1}^{n}(x_{1j} - \bar{x}_1)^2}{n_1}}\right]^{n_1/2}\left[\frac{1}{\dfrac{2\pi\sum_{j=1}^{n_2}(x_{2j} - \bar{x}_2)^2}{n_2}}\right]^{n_2/2} \cdots$$

$$\times \exp\left\{-\frac{1}{2}\left[\frac{\sum_{j=1}^{n_1}(x_{1j} - \bar{x}_1)^2}{\sum_{j=1}^{n_1}(x_{1j} - \bar{x}_1)^2/n_1} + \frac{\sum_{j=1}^{n_2}(x_{2j} - \bar{x}_2)^2}{\sum_{j=1}^{n_2}(x_{2j} - \bar{x}_2)^2/n_2}\right]\right\} \cdots$$

   Under H_1, $\sigma_1^2 = \sigma_2^2 = \cdots = \sigma^2$ and if we let $\hat{\sigma}^2$ be our *sample estimate* of *any* $\sigma_i^2 = \sigma^2$, L_1 becomes

$$\left[\frac{1}{2\pi\hat{\sigma}^2}\right]^{\frac{1}{2}\left(\sum_{i=1}^{m} n_i\right)} \exp\left\{-\frac{1}{2}\left[\frac{\sum_{i=1}^{m}\sum_{j=1}^{n_i}(x_{ij} - \bar{x}_i)^2}{\hat{\sigma}^2}\right]\right\}$$

The maximum likelihood estimate of the common variance is

$$\hat{\sigma}^2 = \sum_{i=1}^{m}\sum_{j=1}^{n_i}(x_{ij} - \bar{x}_i)^2 \bigg/ \sum_{i=1}^{m} n_i$$

$\lambda = \dfrac{L_1}{L_2}$ is therefore

$$\dfrac{\left[\dfrac{1}{2\pi \sum\limits_{i,j}(x_{ij}-\bar{x}_i)^2 \Big/ \sum\limits_{i=1}^{m} n_i}\right]^{\frac{1}{2}\left(\sum\limits_{i=1}^{m} n_i\right)} \exp\left\{-\dfrac{1}{2}\left[\sum\limits_{i=1}^{m} n_i\right]\right\}}{\prod\limits_{i=1}^{m}\left[\dfrac{1}{2\pi \sum\limits_{j=1}^{n_i}(x_{ij}-\bar{x}_i)^2 / n_i}\right]^{n_i/2} \exp\left\{-\dfrac{1}{2}\left[\dfrac{\sum\limits_{i,j}(x_{ij}-\bar{x}_i)^2}{\sum\limits_{i,j}(x_{ij}-\bar{x}_i)^2 \Big/ \sum\limits_{i=1}^{m} n_i}\right]\right\}}$$

$$= \dfrac{\prod\limits_{i=1}^{m}\left[\dfrac{\sum\limits_{j=1}^{n_i}(x_{ij}-\bar{x}_i)^2}{n_i}\right]^{n_i/2}}{\left[\dfrac{\sum\limits_{j=1}^{n_i}\sum\limits_{i=1}^{m}(x_{ij}-\bar{x}_i)^2}{\sum\limits_{i=1}^{m} n_i}\right]^{\frac{1}{2}\left(\sum\limits_{i=1}^{m} n_i\right)}}$$

To use this as a test criterion we must know the distribution of λ under H_1.

Bartlett (1937, p. 158) has shown that

$$\sum_{i=1}^{m}(n_i-1)\ln \sum_{i=1}^{m}\sum_{j=1}^{n_i}\dfrac{(x_{ij}-\bar{x}_i)^2}{\sum\limits_{i=1}^{m}(n-1)} - \sum_{i=1}^{m}(n_i-1)\ln \dfrac{\sum\limits_{i=1}^{m}(x_{ij}-\bar{x}_i)^2}{n_i-1}$$

$$= \lambda' = \sum_{i=1}^{m}(n_i-1)\ln (s_p^2) - \sum_{i=1}^{m}(n_i-1)\ln s_i^2$$

$$= 2.3026\left[\sum_{i=1}^{m}(n_i-1)\ln_{10} s_p^2 - \sum_{i=1}^{m}(n_i-1)\ln_{10} s_i^2\right] \quad (6.8)$$

is distributed as χ^2 with $(m-1)$ degrees of freedom. This would be identical with $-2\ln \lambda$ if n_i were replaced by (n_i-1). Thus $\lambda' > \chi^2_{(m-1,1-\alpha)}$ would necessitate rejection of H_1. Bartlett further states that if this calculated value of χ^2 appears significant, i.e., if we are forced to accept H_1, then it is advisable to compute a corrected chi square by dividing by

$$C = 1 + \dfrac{1}{3(m-1)}\left[\sum_{i=1}^{m}\dfrac{1}{(n_i-1)} - \dfrac{1}{\sum\limits_{i=1}^{m}(n_i-1)}\right]$$

If $n_i = n$, (6.8) reduces to

$$m(n-1) \ln (s_p^2) - (n-1) \sum_{i=1}^{m} \ln s_i^2 = (n-1)\left(m \ln s_p^2 - \sum_{i=1}^{m} \ln s_i^2\right)$$

$$= 2.3026(n-1)\left(m \ln_{10} s_p^2 - \sum_{i=1}^{m} \ln_{10} s_i^2\right)$$

EXAMPLE 11

General. If x_1 and x_2 are jointly normally distributed random variables distributed as $N(\mu_1, \sigma_1^2)$ and $N(\mu_2, \sigma_2^2)$ respectively with $\rho = \sigma_{12}/\sigma_1\sigma_2$, consider the test of the hypothesis that $\rho = 0$. $\mu_1, \mu_2, \sigma_1^2, \sigma_2^2$, are estimated by $\bar{x}_1, \bar{x}_2, s_1^2$, and s_2^2 respectively.

Here

$$H_1: \rho = 0$$

with the alternative

$$H_2: \rho > 0$$

To begin with, an estimate of ρ must be obtained. Let

$$r = \frac{\sum\limits_{i=1}^{n} (x_{i1} - \bar{x}_{.1})(x_{i2} - \bar{x}_{.2})}{\left[\sum\limits_{i}^{n}(x_{i1} - \bar{x}_{.1})^2 \sum\limits_{i}^{n}(x_{i2} - \bar{x}_{.2})^2\right]^{1/2}} \tag{6.9}$$

be just such an estimate.

By expansion, (6.9) may be simplified to

$$r = \frac{\sum\limits_{i=1}^{n} x_{i1} x_{i2} - \dfrac{\sum\limits_{i=1}^{n} x_{i1} \sum\limits_{i=1}^{n} x_{i2}}{n}}{\left[\left(\sum\limits_{i=1}^{n} x_{i1} - \dfrac{\left(\sum\limits_{i=1}^{n} x_{i1}\right)^2}{n}\right)\left(\sum\limits_{i=1}^{n} x_{i2} - \dfrac{\left(\sum\limits_{i=1}^{n} x_{i2}\right)^2}{n}\right)\right]^{1/2}}$$

or to

$$r = \frac{n\sum\limits_{i=1}^{n} x_{i1} x_{i2} - \sum\limits_{i=1}^{n} x_{i1} \sum\limits_{i=1}^{n} x_{i2}}{\left[\left(n\sum\limits_{i=1}^{n} x_{i1}^2 - \left(\sum\limits_{i=1}^{n} x_{i1}\right)^2\right)\left(n\sum\limits_{i=1}^{n} x_{i2}^2 - \left(\sum\limits_{i=1}^{n} x_{i2}\right)^2\right)\right]^{1/2}}$$

The distribution of r when $\rho = 0$ is complicated. When the hypothesis is true, however, Fisher (1954)[1] states that the variable

$$\frac{r}{(1 - r^2)^{1/2}} (n-2)^{1/2}$$

where n is the number of pairs of data upon which r is based, is distributed as a "t" variate, with $(n-2)$ degrees of freedom.

[1] R. A. Fisher, 1954, *Statistical methods for research workers*, Hafner Publishing Co., New York, pp. 193–194.

TABLE 6.7

Orientation Indices and Uranium Content of Fifty-Eight Samples of Core YB-19

Sample No.	O.I.	%U	Sample No.	O.I.	%U
152.1	1.645	0.0091	167.2	1.747	0.0005
152.4	2.317	0.0076	167.8	2.769	0.0021
152.7	2.003	0.0115	168.0	3.392	0.0016
153.1	2.295	0.0108	168.5	1.667	0.0010
153.8	3.421	0.0086	169.0	2.495	0.0009
154.0	1.615	0.0073	169.5	2.342	0.0010
154.5	2.071	0.0087	170.1	2.336	0.0000
155.1	1.686	0.0089	170.5	1.445	0.0002
155.7	2.872	0.0097	171.1	2.101	0.0007
156.4	2.182	0.0044	171.3	2.729	0.0001
157.3	1.549	0.0036	171.9	2.296	0.0006
158.1	2.011	0.0022	172.1	2.307	0.0010
158.5	0.600	0.0023	172.8	1.878	0.0007
159.0	2.466	0.0040	173.4	2.533	0.0008
159.2	2.688	0.0055	173.9	1.717	0.0003
159.5	1.283	0.0056	174.2	1.651	0.0007
159.9	1.413	0.0057	174.5	1.507	0.0009
160.2	1.714	0.0037	174.8	1.395	0.0002
161.5	2.075	0.0051	175.2	1.833	0.0014
162.1	1.399	0.0071	175.8	1.921	0.0012
162.6	1.550	0.0068	176.1	2.408	0.0020
163.2	2.882	0.0047	176.7	3.188	0.0019
164.1	2.006	0.0071	177.0	2.572	0.0038
164.4	2.104	0.0063	177.3	2.084	0.0032
165.0	2.468	0.0070	177.7	2.699	0.0055
165.3	3.224	0.0071	179.0	2.687	0.0046
166.0	1.993	0.0057	179.9	2.089	0.0027
166.2	3.603	0.0039	180.7	2.137	0.0017
166.8	1.755	0.0014	181.5	0.015	0.0005

From E. N. Silverman and T. F. Bates, *ibid.*, p. 67.

Thus, our region of rejection is of the form

$$t = \frac{r}{(1 - r^2)^{1/2}} (n - 2)^{1/2} > t_{n-2}$$

where t_{n-2} is the upper α level of the t table.

Fisher and Yates[1] have tabled directly values of the correlation coefficient for different levels of significance. If a computed correlation

[1] R. A. Fisher and F. Yates, 1953, *Statistical Tables*, Hafner Publishing Co., New York, Table 6, p. 54 (Table F–6).

coefficient for $(n - 2)$ degrees of freedom at the α level of significance is greater than the value, tabulated in the table, one rejects H_1.

Specific. Silverman and Bates[1] (1960), in attempting to establish a textural control of the uranium content of the Chattanooga shale, tested the hypothesis of zero correlation between the degrees of orientation of the micas and illites, as measured by an orientation index O.I., and the percentage of uranium. They used 58 samples from one core of shale. The data are summarized in Table 6.7.

The estimated correlation coefficient was computed as $r = 0.143$ with $(n - 2) = 56$ degrees of freedom. Examination of Table F-6 indicates that for 56 degrees of freedom and $\alpha = 0.05$ the computed r must exceed approximately 0.26 to reject H_1. Here $r = 0.143 < 0.26$, and the hypothesis $\rho = 0$ is accepted. Thus they rightly concluded there is no association between the mica and illite orientation and the percentage of uranium.

TESTING THE HYPOTHESIS THAT A SAMPLE DISTRIBUTION APPROXIMATES SOME KNOWN THEORETICAL PROBABILITY DENSITY FUNCTION

Parameters Are Known

Consider the experimenter who has designed an experiment to test certain hypotheses which lead to a *t*-test. One of the assumptions that he must rationalize or test is the assumption of normality. Utilizing his data, how should the experimenter proceed? This problem has motivated some workers to consider some variates which would measure the deviation of an observed frequency distribution from a theoretical frequency distribution. Karl Pearson is generally given credit for introducing the χ^2 variate as a suitable measure of departure. In general, if in a sample of size $n = \sum_{i=1}^{m} f_i$, where each group appears f_i times with theoretical probability p_i, and $i = 1, \cdots, m$, a suitable measure of departure of the observed or sampled distribution from the theoretical distribution would be some function of $(f_i - np_i)$. In particular, it has been shown that as $n \to \infty$ and H_1 is assumed true that

$$\sum_{i=1}^{m} \frac{(f_i - np_i)^2}{np_i}$$

is distributed as χ^2 with $(m - 1)$ degrees of freedom.

Note that in this case p_i is known *a priori*; it is not estimated from our

[1] E. N. Silverman and T. F. Bates, 1960, X-ray diffraction study of orientation in the Chattanooga shale, *Amer. Mineralogist*, 45: 60–68.

sample. Thus, to obtain a critical region we enter the χ^2 tables and select a value of χ^2 for our level of significance and particular degrees of freedom. This value is used as a criterion for rejecting our null hypothesis, i.e., if

$$\chi^2 = \sum_{i=1}^{m} \frac{(f_i - np_i)^2}{np_i} \geq \chi^2_{m-1, 1-\alpha}$$

we reject our null hypothesis.

Parameters of the theoretical distributions are estimated from the sample

Many times the parameters which had been assumed in the previous set of examples are not known and therefore must be estimated in advance. As Cramér (pp. 424 to 441) points out, the properties of the sampling distribution of χ^2 will depend, in general, on the estimating functions of the parameters. Since there are many possible estimating functions for one particular parameter, the problem of the distribution of our test statistic arises.

If we assume, as before, m groups of frequency f_i where $i = 1, \cdots, m$, but we now introduce k unknown parameters $(\theta_1, \theta_2, \cdots, \theta_k)$ which are to be estimated from our sample, then it develops that a suitable test criterion is once again χ^2 distributed, this time with $(m - k - 1)$ degrees of freedom. Essentially one degree of freedom is lost for every parameter estimated, e.g., $(m - 1) - k$

The test statistic is

$$\sum_{i=1}^{m} \frac{(f_i - c_i)^2}{e_i} \tag{6.10}$$

where e_i is the expectation of f_i given estimates of the unknown parameters, i.e., $E(f_i \mid$ estimates of certain parameters). Frequently (6.10) is written

$$\sum_{i=1}^{m} \frac{(O - E)^2}{E}$$

where $O = f_i$ represents the observed frequency and where E is the expected or theoretical frequency.

As an example of this test consider as motivation the desire to accept the normality assumption basic to the analysis of variance technique.

Kahn (1956)[1] reported the following distribution of packing as obtained

[1] J. S. Kahn, 1956, The analysis and distribution of packing in sand-size sediments. 2. The distribution of the packing measurements and an example of packing analysis. *Jour. Geol.* 64: 6; 578–606.

from six rock samples from each of three sedimentary rock types, where five traverses were run on each thin section.

Packing Class in percent	f_i
90–100	11
80–90	23
70–80	23
60–70	21
50–60	9
40–50	3
	90

$m = 6$

$\bar{x} = 74.67$

$s = 12.95$

The procedure to test the goodness-of-fit of these data to a normal curve is as follows: since we do not know the parameters μ and σ^2, we estimate them by means of $\bar{x}$ and s. Our null hypothesis is then that our sample is obtained from a normal population with mean $\mu = 74.67$ and $\sigma^2 = (12.95)^2$. If the null hypothesis is true, then the variate

$$\frac{x - 74.67}{12.95}$$

is a unit normal deviate. Here x represents any observation of the 90. Since the data are grouped, we can look at the class limits and compute the proportion of the theoretical distribution which is either greater than or less than the upper or lower class limits.

Thus $\Phi[(x - 74.67)/12.95] =$ proportion of individuals in the parent population less than or equal to $(x - 74.67)/12.95$.

If this procedure is followed for all classes using the lower limit of each class for convenience, and if the cumulative proportions are subtracted (the lower class limit cumulative percentage for one class from the lower class cumulative proportion of the class next above), then the percentage or relative number of individuals or observations per class is determined. If this relative proportion is then multiplied by the sample size, $n = \sum_{i=1}^{m} f_i$, then the expected frequency, e_i, per class, is obtained.

Finally, if we compute

$$\chi^2_{m-k-1} = \sum_{i=1}^{m} \frac{(f_i - e_i)^2}{e_i} \tag{6.11}$$

we have our test statistic.

The example mentioned earlier is worked in detail in Table 6.8. In this case, $k = 2$, since we computed $\bar{x}$ and s^2 from our sample to obtain estimates of the population parameters μ and σ^2 respectively, i.e., there were two linear restraints.

TABLE 6.8
Computation of Test of Goodness-of-Fit to a Normal Curve

i	Class	$\dfrac{x_i - \bar{x}}{s}$	$\Phi\left(\dfrac{x_i - \bar{x}}{s}\right) = \Phi_i$	$\Phi_{i-1} - \Phi_i$ (for $i > 0$)
0	>100	—	1.0000	—
1	90–100	1.184	0.8810	0.1190
2	80–90	0.412	0.6591	0.2219
3	70–80	−0.361	0.3594	0.2997
4	60–70	−1.133	0.1292	0.2302
5	50–60	−1.905	0.0281	0.1011
6	50	−2.736	0.0031	0.0250

$\left(\sum\limits_{i=1}^{n} f_i\right)(\Phi_{i-1} - \Phi_i) = e_i$	f_i	$f_i - e_i$	$\dfrac{(f_i - e_i)^2}{e_i}$
10.71	11	0.29	0.0079
19.97	23	3.03	0.4597
26.97	23	3.97	0.5844
20.72	21	0.28	0.0038
$\left.\begin{array}{c} 9.097 \\ 2.25 \end{array}\right\} 11.35^{1}$	12	0.65	0.0372

Calculated $\chi^2 = 1.093$
Tabled $\chi^2_{2,0.05} = 5.991$

[1] Note pooled frequency.

The reader will note that the observations in the classes 40 to 50 and 50 to 60 were pooled to give an observed frequency of 12. This was done to conform to the generally accepted practice.[1,2] Generally, if the expected frequencies are less than 5, one pools the observed frequency data so that the expected values will be greater than 5.

Since $\chi^2 = \sum\limits_{i=1}^{5} \dfrac{(f_i - e_i)^2}{e_i} = 1.093$ does not fall beyond the critical value of $\chi^2_{2,0.05} = 5.99$, the null hypothesis is accepted.

[1] H. Cramér, 1950, *Mathematical methods of statistics*, Princeton Univ. Press, Princeton, New Jersey.

[2] For a discussion of this with particular reference to the Poisson distribution see Chapter 16, p. 366, *et seq.*

SEVERAL REFERENCES INVOLVING FIT-TO-FREQUENCY
DISTRIBUTIONS

J. C. Griffiths, 1960, Frequency distributions in accessory mineral analysis, *Jour. Geol.* 68: 353–365. By χ^2 tests of goodness of fit, frequency distributions of accessory minerals, i.e., zircon, are assigned to one of several suitable distribution functions. These include the Poisson, mixed Poisson, and binomial and negative binomial. Geological reasons are given for choice of a particular function before testing for fit, and the properties of each of the functions are discussed in some detail.

Björn Kurtén, 1960, Chronology and faunal evolution of the earlier European glaciations, *Societas Sci. Fennica Comm. Biol.* XXI, 5. χ^2 test of normality is used for distribution of tooth row length in Pleistocene hamsters of Hungary.

D. H. Davis, 1954, Estimating porosity of sedimentary rocks from bulk density, *Jour. Geol.* 62: 102–107, uses statistical analysis to evaluate the error in estimating the dependent variable porosity in percent as related to bulk density. The error determination is made by fitting observed errors to the parameters of the normal frequency distribution.

A. Kahma and T. Mikkola, 1946, A statistical method for the quantitative refractive index analysis of minerals in rocks, *Comptes Rendus de la Societe geologique de Finlande*, No. XIX. The purpose is to obtain with a high degree of accuracy, a curve which gives percent distribution of indices of refraction of a mixture of minerals, as a function of the index of refraction; where K is percent by volume of grains with an index of refraction greater than n in the function $K = K(n)$. Two sources of error are considered, the first is accounted for by an estimate of "error of mean square" μ. $\mu = \sqrt{K(100 - K)/v}$ where K is defined above, and v is number of grains (sample size). The second source of error is controlled by analyzing by size classes, where size deviation is relatively small, and can be neglected.

PRACTICAL RELATIONSHIPS BETWEEN α, β, $1 - \beta$,
AND SAMPLE SIZE

In planning experiments it is often desirable to set the risk the investigator is willing to assume well in advance. Too often this is overlooked, and when it does become realized, much unnecessary time, energy, and money have been spent. The level of error is a function of the experiment. The α error, the reader will recall, is the probability of rejecting the null hypothesis when it is true, whereas the β error is the probability of accepting the null hypothesis when it is false. The power, $1 - \beta$, is therefore the probability of rejecting the null hypothesis when it is false. Many investigators consider only the α error—the level of significance—and pay little or no attention to β error. This may be a dangerous oversight, for there are problems where the β error plays an important role. Consider the following two examples.

Recently there has been controversy over the relationship between cigarette smoking and cancer. Let us establish as our null hypothesis that the number of deaths, over some fixed period of time, due to lung cancer associated with cigarette smokers, is equivalent to the number of deaths, in the same period of time, due to lung cancer in noncigarette smokers, i.e.,

$$H_1: \Delta_S = \Delta_N$$

As an alternative hypothesis consider

$$H_2: \Delta_S > \Delta_N$$

Assume further that each group of investigators studying this problem attempts to test this particular hypothesis. The investigators in question might be of two types: one, a research team sponsored by the tobacco industry; the other, some independent research laboratory not affiliated with the tobacco industry.

This type of approach certainly should lead to a clear-cut answer to the problem. However, it did not. The independent research group rejected the null hypothesis, whereas the tobacco industry's group accepted the null hypothesis. *If we assume the data were essentially the same in both studies*, why the discrepancy? Let us look at the α and β errors.

It is apparent that the tobacco industry's group would desire an α error which was extremely small. That is, they certainly would not wish to reject the null hypothesis when it was true. The independent research group, on the other hand, might pay less attention to the α error and be more interested in the power of the test and in making it as large as possible. That is, they might have been more strongly interested in accepting the alternative hypothesis when it was true. Hence, they would be concerned that the probability of rejecting the null hypothesis when it was false was very large. Thus two groups working on the identical problem may obtain different rejection regions due to differences in their evaluation of the *more* important error.

As another example of the importance of α and β error, consider the following possible, although hypothetical, illustration. Let us assume that an oil exploration team has carefully surveyed a potential drilling area. After much deliberation the decision to drill is not recommended. Up to this time the cost to just arrive at this recommendation has been $x'000$, in terms of manpower and time. It is possible that although the recommendation was, do not drill the well, the well would be a producer. Formally, the null hypothesis could be stated in somewhat the following manner: H_1: the oil potential characteristics of this area do not differ significantly from the known oil characteristics of known oil fields, with an alternative hypothesis that they do. Now if the recommendation is do not drill, when there is oil, an α error has been made, i.e., we have rejected the null hypothesis when it was true. On the other hand, suppose the recommendation is to drill, and there is no oil. Here we would be accepting the null hypothesis when it was false, i.e., we have committed a β error.

Which error is more costly? This is undoubtedly a problem for an economist. What must be balanced are not the academic errors, α and β alone, but the α and β errors with respect to cost in terms of dollars and cents.

α, β, $1 - \beta$, and n

Let us assume a series of modulus of rupture determinations will be made on a new solid fuel to see if indeed the strength of the new fuel is the same or greater than that of an older but reliable fuel whose average strength is $\mu = 2.5 \times 10^4$ psi. Find the sample size necessary if we desire $\alpha = 0.05$ and $1 - \beta = 0.99$ when $\mu = 3.5 \times 10^4$ psi. Assume σ^2 is approximately 2.0×10^4 psi and that the measure is a normal variate; then by definition of the power function for a normal variate (Chapter 6),

$$P(\mu) = 1 - \Phi\left[\frac{c - \mu}{\sqrt{\sigma^2/n}}\right]$$

When

$$\mu = 3.5$$

$$P(\mu) = 1 - \Phi\left[\frac{\sqrt{n}(c - 3.5)}{2}\right] = 0.99$$

$$= \Phi\left[\frac{\sqrt{n}(c - 3.5)}{2}\right] = 0.01$$

Thus

$$\frac{\sqrt{n}(c - 3.5)}{2} = -2.33$$

and $\sqrt{n}c - \sqrt{n}\,3.5 = -6.99$. Now the α error is

$$\Phi\left[\frac{\sqrt{n}(c - 2.5)}{2}\right] = 0.95$$

and therefore

$$\frac{\sqrt{n}(c - 2.5)}{2} = 1.645$$

Thus the two equations to be solved simultaneously are

$$\sqrt{n}c - 3.5\sqrt{n} = -4.66$$
$$\sqrt{n}c - 2.5\sqrt{n} = 3.29$$

where it is found that n is approximately 63, i.e., 63 pieces of the new solid fuel should be tested.

Find the sample size needed to obtain a power of 85% when the porosity of the Salt Wash member of the Morrison formation is 22%. The null hypothesis, at a 5% level of significance, is a porosity of 25%. Use a symmetrical two-tailed test and assume a standard deviation of approximately 10.0%.

Thus

$$1 - \Phi\left[\frac{\sqrt{n}c_2 - 25\sqrt{n}}{10}\right] + \Phi\left[\frac{\sqrt{n}c_1 - 25\sqrt{n}}{10}\right] = 0.05$$

and therefore

$$\Phi\left[\frac{\sqrt{n}c_1 - 25\sqrt{n}}{10}\right] = 0.025$$

$$\sqrt{n}c_1 - 25\sqrt{n} = -1.96 \times 10$$

thus

$$\sqrt{n}c_1 = 25\sqrt{n} - 1.96 \times 10$$

and   (6.12)

$$\sqrt{n}c_2 = 25\sqrt{n} + 1.96 \times 10$$

The power $P(\mu)$ at $\mu = 22$ is 0.85; therefore

$$1 - \Phi\left[\frac{\sqrt{n}c_2 - 22\sqrt{n}}{10}\right] + \Phi\left[\frac{\sqrt{n}c_1 - 22\sqrt{n}}{10}\right] = 0.85 \quad (6.13)$$

Substituting the relations of (6.12) in (6.13) we obtain

$$1 - \Phi\left[\frac{19.6 + 3\sqrt{n}}{10}\right] + \Phi\left[\frac{-19.6 + 3\sqrt{n}}{10}\right] = 0.85$$

Substituting in (6.13) various values of n we find that an n of approximately 100 will satisfy our needs.

GENERAL REFERENCES

A general treatment of statistical inference and hypothesis testing including confidence intervals and acceptance sampling is given by J. C. Manning, 1953, Application of statistical estimation and hypothesis testing to geologic data, *Jour. Geol.* 62: 544–556.

The method of sequential analysis has been applied to paleontological data by B. H. Burma, 1953, Studies in quantitative paleontology, III An application of sequential analysis to the comparison of growth stages and growth series, *Jour. Geol.* 61: 533–543. Relevant references to the subject include A. Hald, 1952, *Statistical theory with engineering applications*, John Wiley, New York, Chapter 24, A. Wald, 1947, *Sequential analysis*, John Wiley, New York, and *Statistical Research Group*, 1945, *Sequential analysis of statistical data: applications*, Columbia Univ. Press, and *Techniques of statistical analysis* (also by Statistical Research Group) 1947, Chapter 17, *Elements of statistical analysis*, by W. Allen Wallis, McGraw-Hill Book Co., New York, pp. 417–429.

THE COEFFICIENT OF VARIABILITY

When we consider comparing the variability of a measured attribute in a random sample of n individuals from one population with the variability of that attribute from a second population, we are constrained to look at the respective scales of measurement. For example, in comparing the variance of weight in mice and elephants, it would be absurd to use the F-ratio using a scale in pounds, grams, etc. In geological work it is rather usual for a direct proportional relationship between the mean and standard deviation to manifest itself. A natural scale in which to compare the two groups is suggested by the log scale. Thus, we may rephrase our problem and look for a transformation that has various stabilizing effects. Then we may want to compare the group means, since in many cases the log transformation, for example, induces approximate normality into the distribution of measurements.[1] This may be of value in those cases not as extreme as the mice, elephant example, and in multigroup situations where we can get a much better estimate for the underlying variability than by remaining with the original scale. Such a transformation is valuable if we are interested in analysis of variance situations.

Cases will arise in which no transformation suggests itself to get equal variances. If we are interested in means, we can use the Scheffé (1953) method as a test. However, we may ask ourselves about the relative variability between two groups as we have been unsuccessful in equalizing the absolute variation. Let us see how we can find an acceptable procedure for this question.

The dimensionless measure $s/\bar{x} = v$, called the coefficient of variation, is an adequate measure for relative variability when the distribution sampled from is approximately normal. A useful discussion of this measure is given by Simpson and Roe (1939).[2] We may test the null hypothesis that the population $V = V_0$ say, by several different methods.

It can be shown, e.g., Hald (1952), that $\mu(v) = \sigma/\mu = V$ and

$$\text{var}(v) = \frac{V^2(1 + 2V^2)}{2(n - 1)},\qquad (6.14)$$

where n is large and V is small. Thus an approximate test of significance is

$$Z = \frac{v - V_0}{\sqrt{V_0^2(1 + 2V_0^2)/[2(n - 1)]}}\qquad (6.15)$$

where Z is a $N(0, 1)$ variable. Not much seems known about the robustness of this test. Another method given by Hald (1952) suggests the use of the

[1] For example, the ϕ (log$_2$) transformation in sediment size analysis.

[2] *The discussion on coefficient of variability* pp. 121 to 126 was based on correspondence with Robert Elashoff, Dept. of Statistics, Harvard University, and on G. G. Simpson, and A. Roe, 1939, *Quantitative zoology*, McGraw-Hill Book Co., New York, A. Hald, 1952, *Statistical theory with engineering applications*, John Wiley, New York, pp. 301–303.

H. Scheffe, 1953, A method for judging all contrasts in the analysis of variance, *Biometrika*. 40: 87–104.

statistic $u = s - \bar{x}C_p$, where $P\{s/\bar{x} < C_p\} = p$. It can be shown that u is approximately normally distributed with $E[u] = \sigma - \mu C_p$ and

$$\text{var}(u) = \sigma^2 \left[\frac{1}{2(n-1)} + \frac{C_p}{n} \right] \tag{6.16}$$

This is a better approximation than the Z distribution to normality. By means of the statistic u we can find a test for the H_1: $V = V_0$ as follows. Suppose we are interested in distinguishing $V = V_0$ from $V > V_0$ as the alternative and suppose we let $\alpha = 0.05$. Then compute

$$C_{0.95} = \frac{1 + Z_{0.95}\sqrt{\left[\dfrac{1}{2(n-1)} \right] \left[1 - \dfrac{V_0^2 Z_{0.95}}{n} + \dfrac{V_0^2}{n} \right]}}{1 - \dfrac{V_0^2 Z_{0.95}^2}{n}} \tag{6.17}$$

where $Z_{0.95}$ is the 95th percentile of the standard normal deviate. If $s/\bar{x} < C_{0.95}$ we accept H_1: otherwise, reject.

Still another procedure may be employed to test H_1: $V = V_0$. This method requires tables of the noncentral t-distribution which are not as generally available as those for the normal or χ^2 distribution. The interested reader may refer to the paper by Johnson and Welch, 1940, in the bibliography for details. Lastly, there is a very excellent approximation derived by McKay, 1932, who shows that $\dfrac{nv^2(1/V^2 + 1)}{1 + v^2}$ has an approximate χ^2_{n-1} distribution. McKay's approximation may be used where the underlying distribution is not too skewed and where the population $V \leq \frac{1}{3}$. We carry out the test of hypothesis H_1: $V = V_0$, H_2: $V > V_0$ in the following way. We find $\chi_0^2 = \dfrac{nv^2(1/V_0^2 + 1)}{1 + v^2}$. If $\chi_0^2 > \chi^2_{(n-1)0.05}$, we reject the null hypothesis. This test may be used with very small sample sizes (about 10), provided the conditions mentioned above hold. It appears that the u or χ_0^2 test gives the least disturbance in significance levels.

If our problem is to estimate the unknown V in the population, then it is more accurate to use $v' = (1 + 1/4n)v$, as our estimator to correct for bias (Haldane, 1955, 1956). However, if we are interested in describing the sample only, the estimator v is appropriate. On occasion, we may want an interval estimate of our parameter V or V^2. We may do this in more than one way. Suppose we are employing the χ_0^2 method given above. Then we obtain the 95% confidence interval given by

$$\frac{nv^2}{\chi^2_{n-1,\,0.025}[1 + v^2] - nv^2} < V^2 < \frac{nv^2}{\chi^2_{n-1,\,0.975}[1 + v^2] - nv^2} \tag{6.18}$$

SUGGESTED READINGS

Johnson and Welch, 1940, Application of the non-central t-distribution, *Biometrika* 31: 362ff. However, use of their tables requires a laborious series of computations and for samples greater than 9, a two-way interpolation.

A. T. McKay, 1932, Distribution of the coefficient of variation and the extended "t" distribution, *Jour. Roy. Stat. Soc.* 95: 695ff.

J. B. S. Haldane, 1955, The measurement of variation, *Evolution* IX, p. 484.

J. B. S. Haldane, The distribution of some powers and ratios of cumulant estimates, *Sankhyā* (in press).

A confidence interval for V may be obtained from tables of the non-central t-distribution employing the techniques of Johnson and Welch. Using Hald's u-test given above we may find $C_{0.025}$ and $C_{0.975}$ so that the interval can be written as $C_{0.025} < s/\bar{x} < C_{0.975}$ with confidence coefficient 95%. The Z-test referred to previously gives a confidence interval in the usual manner.

There are many times in which we want to compare the coefficient of variability between two independent groups as samples. If our samples are large, we may use the two-sample Z-test

$$Z = \frac{v_1 - v_2}{\sqrt{\text{st. error}_{v_1} + \text{st. error}_{v_2}}}$$

where the st. error$_v$ is given as above [see var(v) (6.15)]. This test would seem to be acceptable only in very large samples since the one-sample Z-test only holds for large samples. Thus, even more so than in the one-sample case, the use of McKay's distribution would be recommended. It will be recalled that even for very small sample sizes (between 6 and 10) and for $V = \frac{1}{3}$, the distribution of $\dfrac{nv^2}{1+v^2}\left(\dfrac{1}{V^2}+1\right)$ is χ^2_{n-1}. Thus, it seems reasonable that for sample sizes not very much larger than 10, we may use the two-sample version given below. This should be subject to a sampling experiment for verification, however. Since $\dfrac{n_1 v_1^2}{1+v_1^2}\left(1+\dfrac{1}{V_1^2}\right)$ has a χ^2_{n-1} independent of $\dfrac{n_2 v_2^2}{1+v_2^2}\left(1+\dfrac{1}{V_2^2}\right)$, under the H_0: $V_1^2 = V_2^2$, we have

$$F\left[\begin{smallmatrix}n_1-1\\n_2-1\end{smallmatrix}\right] = \frac{\dfrac{v_1^2}{1+v_1^2}\left(\dfrac{n_1}{n_1-1}\right)}{\dfrac{v_2^2}{1+v_2^2}\left(\dfrac{n_2}{n_2-1}\right)} \tag{6.19}$$

where F is Fisher's F-distribution with $(n_1 - 1)$ and $(n_2 - 1)$ d.f. If, as a general rule, we put in the denominator the smallest of the expressions $[v^2/(1 + v^2) \cdot n/(n - 1)]$ we would reject for values of

$$[F_{n_2-1}^{n_1-1}] > F_{[n_2-1,0.95]}^{[n_1-1,0.95]}$$

and would be using a 10% significance level. Thus, for a 5% significance level we use $F_{[n_2-1,0.975]}^{[n_1-1,0.975]}$ and carry out the test as above. A confidence interval for V_1^2/V_2^2 cannot be found easily so as to be immediately interpretable. Another possible way to compare two independent V^2's is by looking at the overlap in their 95% confidence intervals. There does not seem to be much literature available on this method.

When we consider comparing KV's, it seems clear that we will run into at least the difficulties incurred by Bartlett, *ibid.* in finding a test for homogeneity of variances. His test for that problem is very sensitive to the form of the underlying distribution. Thus, comparing KV's is an extremely difficult unsolved problem. One may recommend preparing F-tests as given above and using the significance level for each comparison as $\dfrac{\alpha}{[K(k - 1)]/2}$ which is certainly an extremely conservative test.

APPLICATIONS AND ADDITIONAL RELEVANT REFERENCES

H. S. Pearson, 1928, *Chinese fossil Suidae, Paleontologia Simca Series C*, Vol. V., Fasc. 5, p. 38–41 in an early paper discusses the use of V in conjunction with a standard error of V.

L. H. C. Tippet, 1945, *Methods of Statistics*, Williams and Norgate, Ltd., London, pp. 87–88, gives a deviation for and approximate standard error of V. He describes an approximation technique for the standard error of a function of several statistical constants by treating the standard errors as differentials. By a Taylor expansion, he is then able to set up a generalized expression for an approximate standard error of a combination of any number of statistical constants whose individual standard errors are known. However, implicit in the use of the Taylor expansion is the assumption that the standard errors of the known statistical constants are small. This implies very large samples which unfortunately limits application where earth science problems are concerned.

G. G. Simpson, 1937, The Fort Union of the Crazy Mountain field, Montana, and its mammalian faunas, *U. S. Natural Museum Bull.* 169: 287. Uses both range and coefficient of variability.

G. G. Simpson, 1935, The Tiffany fauna, Upper Paleocene, III, *Amer. Mus. Novit.* 817: 28 pp.

F. B. Phleger, Jr., 1940, Relative growth and vertebrate phylogeny, *Am. Jour. Sci.* 238: 643–662.

G. Rittenhouse and M. P. Connaughton, 1944, Errors of sampling sands for mechanical analysis, *Jour. Sed. Petrol.* 14: 20–25.

G. G. Simpson, 1947, Note on the measurement of variability and on relative variability of fossil mammals, *Am. Jour. Sci.* 245: 522–525. Detailed discussion of V in paleontology.

F. Chayes and H. W. Fairbairn, 1951, A test of the precision of thin section analysis by point counter, *Am. Mineral.* 36: 704–712. Use is made of a coefficient of variability osed of the ratio of the standard deviation of the binomial $\sqrt{np(1-p)}$, to the np. Then if p is percentage of the constituent in a traverse count, and n is the

nt length, then the ratio is $\dfrac{\sqrt{np(1-p)}}{np}$. This reduces to $\sqrt{(1-p)/np} = C$

al coefficient of variation. It is useful as an index of relative error, whenever ed pdf is appropriate.

1955, Variability and evolutionary rate in the Oreodonts *Evolution* IX, 2: coefficient of variation is used extensively. He also uses a test for comparison of two sample v's by forming the ratio of the difference between the two v's to the standard error of the difference, as described in F. E. Croxton, and D. J. Cowden, 1941, *Applied general statistics*, Prentice-Hall, Englewood Cliffs, New Jersey, and applied in Simpson and Roe, 1939, *ibid.* However, his samples are small, and the differences between v's are not large. As pointed out on p. 124, this test is inappropriate for small samples.

I. F. Chebotarev, 1955, Metamorphism of natural water in the crust of weathering. 1, *Geochim. et Cosmochim. Acta.* 8: 22–48. He describes a method for forming frequency distributions from empirical data in geochemistry. Utilizes first three moments and coefficient of variation.

J. J. Hutta and J. C. Griffiths, 1955, Directional permeability of sandstones; a test of technique, *Producers Monthly* 19, 11: 26–34 and 19, 12: 24–31. Coefficient of variation used as a measure of experimental control.

A. Swineford, J. C. Frye, and A. B. Leonard, 1955, Petrography of the late Tertiary volcanic ash fall in the Central Great Plains, *J. Sed. Petrol.* 25: 243–261. V is employed in analysis of the chemical constituents of volcanic ash of the late Tertiary with bentonite.

R. L. Miller and J. M. Zeigler, 1958, A model relating dynamics and sediment pattern in equilibrium, in the region of shoaling waves, breaker zone and foreshore, *Jour. Geol.* 66: 417–441. V is used as a dimensionless measure of sorting of marine sediments, numerically independent of sediment size.

Björn Kurtén, 1955, Sex dimorphism and size trends in the cave bear, *Ursus spelaeus, Acta. Zool. Fennica* 90, uses Simpsons standard range, and V.

J. G. Hilliard and J. W. Cahn, 1959, *An evaluation of procedures in quantitative metalography I, Volume-fraction analysis*, General Electric Research Laboratory, Report No. 59-RL-2294M, Schenectady, New York. V is used as an aid in determining the most efficient means of performing volume fraction analysis of polished specimen.

INTERVAL ESTIMATION

Means of a Normal Distribution

Discussion of estimation problems in Chapter 4 centered on what has been termed "point estimation," that is, for example, estimations of a specific parameter, of specific distributions. In many instances, a range or interval of estimation is to be preferred. When this interval has a probability statement attached to it, the technique immediately falls in the realm of statistics. The previous discussions on point estimation permit a natural development of the concept of interval estimation.

Confidence Intervals for μ of a Normal Distribution

σ^2 Is Known

Since $\bar{x}$ is $N(\mu, \sigma^2/n)$, then

$$P\left\{-c \leq \frac{\bar{x} - \mu}{\sigma/\sqrt{n}} \leq c\right\} = 1 - \alpha$$

where

$$\Phi(c) = 1 - \frac{\alpha}{2}$$

Thus for a $(1 - \alpha)\%$ *confidence interval* about μ we obtain

$$P\left\{\bar{x} + \frac{\sigma}{\sqrt{n}} c \geq \mu \geq \bar{x} - \frac{\sigma}{\sqrt{n}} c\right\} = (1 - \alpha)\%$$

A symmetrical 95% confidence interval is obtained from

$$P\left\{-1.96 \leq \frac{\bar{x} - \mu}{\sigma/\sqrt{n}} \leq 1.96\right\} = 0.95$$

where

$$P\left\{\frac{\bar{x} - \mu}{\sigma/\sqrt{n}} \leq 1.96 = c\right\} = 1 - \frac{\alpha}{2}$$

and

$$\Phi[c = 1.96] \cdot 1 - \frac{\alpha}{2} = 0.975$$

In general, then, 95% confidence limits about μ are

$$\left[\bar{x} + \frac{\sigma}{\sqrt{n}} 1.96 \geq \mu \geq \bar{x} - 1.96 \frac{\sigma}{\sqrt{n}}\right]$$

σ^2 Is Unknown

Under these circumstances, σ^2 is estimated by s^2, then by $(6.3a)$

$$P\left\{-t_{n-1(1-\alpha/2)} \leq \frac{\bar{x} - \mu}{s/\sqrt{n}} \leq t_{n-1(1-\alpha/2)}\right\} = 1 - \alpha$$

Thus a $(1 - \alpha)\%$ confidence interval about μ is

$$\left[\bar{x} + t_{n-1,1-\alpha/2} \frac{s}{\sqrt{n}} \geq \mu \geq \bar{x} - t_{n-1,(1-\alpha/2)} \frac{s}{\sqrt{n}}\right]$$

EXAMPLE

Melton[1] (1960) tested and accepted the hypothesis of no significant difference in valley-side slope angles, between south-facing slopes and north-facing slopes in southern Arizona. Measuring opposite pairs of valley-side slope angles and taking their differences, he found an average difference of $\bar{\theta} = -0.0255$ degrees,

[1] M. A. Melton, 1960, Intravalley variation in slope angles related to microclimate and erosional environment, *Bull. Geol. Soc. Amer.* 71: 133–144.

with a standard deviation of the differences at 1.97 degrees for a sample of size 47. What is the interval within which the true mean difference lies?

Here $\quad \theta = \bar{x} = -0.0255$ degrees

$$s = 1.97 \text{ degrees}$$

$$\sqrt{n} = \sqrt{47} = 6.85$$

$$t = 2.01$$

Thus $P\left(-2.01 \leq \dfrac{-0.0255 - \mu}{1.97/6.85} \leq 2.01\right) = 0.95$ and the confidence interval is -0.60 degrees $\leq \mu \leq +0.55$ degrees. Thus on average, with random sampling, we would expect the true difference between north-facing valley-side slopes and south-facing valley-side slopes to be between -0.61 degrees and $+0.55$ degrees 95% of the time.

Variances of a Normal Distribution

We have shown that

$$P\left(\chi^2_{n-1,1-\alpha/2} \geq \frac{s^2(n-1)}{\sigma^2} \geq \chi^2_{n-1,\alpha/2}\right) = (1-\alpha)\%$$

Thus $\qquad P\left(\dfrac{\chi^2_{n-1,1-\alpha/2}}{s^2(n-1)} \geq \dfrac{1}{\sigma^2} \geq \dfrac{\chi^2_{n-1,\alpha/2}}{s^2(n-1)}\right) = (1-\alpha)\%$

and $\qquad P\left(\dfrac{s^2(n-1)}{\chi^2_{n-1,\alpha/2}} \geq \sigma^2 \geq \dfrac{s^2(n-1)}{\chi^2_{n-1,1-\alpha/2}}\right) = (1-\alpha)\%$

A $(1-\alpha)\%$ confidence interval about σ^2 is thus

$$\frac{s^2(n-1)}{\chi^2_{n-1,\alpha/2}} \geq \sigma^2 \geq \frac{s^2(n-1)}{\chi^2_{n-1,1-\alpha/2}}$$

TOLERANCE LIMITS

Confidence limits for the parameters of a distribution will give a limit (or limits) within which the sample values of the parameter will fall *with a stated confidence*. Thus a confidence limit for the mean of the population may be in the form of an upper and lower limit around the sample mean $\bar{X} \pm s_{\bar{x}}$, such that a certain percentage of times, the population mean μ may be expected to fall within the range $\bar{X} \pm s_{\bar{x}}$.

Tolerance limits, on the other hand, do not deal with the parameters. The tolerance limit we shall discuss here will give a range centered about the sample mean $\bar{X}$ which will include at least a proportion P of the individuals in the population distribution with a stated confidence. It is thus possible to state with a given confidence an upper and a lower limit centered around the sample mean, such that a certain percentage of all future observations will lie within these limits.

The form of the tolerance limit is

$$\bar{X} \pm Ks$$

where $\bar{X}$ is the sample mean, s the sample standard deviation, and K is a coefficient. It is necessary to enter the tables with the desired proportion P, the confidence level γ, and sample size n. Tables and a discussion are to be found in *Techniques of statistical analysis*, Eisenhart, Hastay, and Wallis, 1947, pp. 97–109. The tables are on pp. 102–107. See also Dixon and Massey, 1952, Table 16. The assumption for the tables is that the population is normal. Tolerance limits for non-normal populations and non-parametric tolerance limits have been discussed by Wald (1946) and by Wilks (1942). However, at the time of this particular publication, no general answer is available as to which type of tolerance limit to use in applied problems. If one is not willing to make any assumptions about the distribution form of the population, tables for nonparametric tolerance limits are given in R. B. Murphy, 1948, Nonparametric tolerance limits, *Annals of Math. Stats.* 19: 581–589. In such a case fairly large samples are required to give a useful set of limits. For example, if it is desired to include 95% of the population with a risk of error of 0.10 a minimum sample of 79 is required.[1] Unfortunately, collections of data in various areas of interest in the earth sciences are rarely that large, e.g., geochemistry, paleontology.

As an example in paleontology, consider the situation where a new fossil specimen is found and is somewhat larger than those in the initial collection. It is possible (within the limits of the required assumptions of normality) not only to decide whether the new specimen "belongs" but to set up a "taxonomic range" about the mean of the initial collection such that all future specimens may either be assigned to the species or considered to belong to a different species. Suppose the arithmetic mean of the original 5 is 10.00 and the standard deviation is 2.916. Referring to the tables it is found that 99% (P) of the population lies within the range $\bar{X} \pm 6.6345 \, s$, and so this becomes 10.00 ± 19.345 with a risk of 0.01; 90% of the population lies within the range $\bar{X} \pm 3.494$ with a risk of 0.10, which is 10.00 ± 10.189. There is no reason to reject the new specimen from sample B.

For samples this small the range is so large as to be impractical for comparison of most closely related species, which is where this kind of approach may be useful. However, for samples of 50, for example, the multiplicative coefficient drops to $\bar{X} + 1.916 \, s$ (for $P = 90\%$, $\gamma = 0.90$).

In construction of a "statistical" ecotype one may (in addition to

<hr>

[1] Dixon and Massey, 1951, *Introduction to Statistical Analysis*, McGraw-Hill Book Co., New York, p. 259.

estimating the population parameters) wish to set upper or lower limits or both, within which say 99 % of all future individuals should lie. If, for example, measurements are taken on adult mammal teeth, both upper and lower tolerance limits for linear proportions of the teeth would be of taxonomic importance.

In the example given above, the Mann-Whitney test may be more appropriate, although the question of independence of samples may arise. The Mann-Whitney test is for comparison of two independent samples. In the present case, one of the samples would be of size $n_1 = 1$, the other the initial collection. A general discussion of the Mann-Whitney test is given on p. 131, and an application in which one of the samples is of size one, is given on p. 131.

Several other applications of tolerance limits have been published in the context of this book. H. Ramberg and G. DeVore, 1951, The distribution of Fe^{++} and Mg^{++} in coexisting olivines and pyroxenes, *Jour. Geol.* 59: 193–210, use tolerance limits in graphing the relationship between atomic percentage of Al in orthopyroxenes plotted against $(Mg/Mg) + Fe$. A. B. Vistelius, 1951, On the probability of the eolian field of L. B. Rushin, on the field diagram of sand types, *Acad. of Sci. U.S.S.R. Bull.*, uses tolerance limits to show the stability of the eolian sand field on Rushin's diagram.

TWO PAPERS DESCRIBING STATISTICAL TECHNIQUES

These papers are relatively simple to apply and are often most useful for quick preliminary answers.

W. Allen Wallis, 1951, *Rough and ready statistical tests.* Paper presented at the Fifth Annual Convention of the American Society for Quality Control. Author's address, University of Chicago.

W. Kruskal, *Usable but not widely known statistical techniques.* Work sponsored by Joint Services Advisory Comm. for Res. Groups in Applied Math. and Statistics Contract no. N6ori-02035. Author's address, Department of Statistics, Univ. of Chicago.

EXTREME VALUES

A Nonparametric Test of Extreme Values, or "Gross Errors," for Small Samples

Suppose a series of measurements are made in an experiment, with the following results arranged in order of size: 2, 7, 8, 10, 12, 13. The first value is considerably further from the next largest than the adjacent pairs are from each other. We ask if the value two may be considered as a "gross error," or may be considered to have been drawn from the same population as the other five. Dixon and Massey (1957, *ibid.*, p. 277) discuss a possible test and give a table of critical values on p. 412 (Table A-8c).

A convention is established that the smallest value is X_1 and the largest X_K for an ordered sequence of K different values, when the smallest is under consideration. When the largest in the sequence is considered, the ordering is reversed so that the largest is X_1 and the smallest X_K for K numbers. In the present example we have:

$$
\begin{array}{cc}
2 & X_1 \\
7 & X_2 \\
8 & X_3 \\
10 & X_4 \\
12 & X_5 \\
13 & X_K
\end{array}
$$

The null hypothesis is that the number 2 is from the same population as the other five. We compute a ratio given in the tables, the form of which is dependent on sample size. If the computed value of the ratio exceeds the critical value for $\alpha = 0.05$ or $\alpha = 0.01$, the null hypothesis is rejected, depending on the investigator's choice of α. In the present case for $K = 6$ we compute the ratio $\dfrac{X_2 - X_1}{X_K - X_1} = \dfrac{7 - 2}{13 - 2} = \dfrac{5}{11} = 0.455$. The critical value at the 95th percentile ($\alpha = 0.05$) for $K = 6$ is 0.560, and the null hypothesis is accepted.

A somewhat different application was made in a comparison of the packing density of a single specimen of St. Peter sandstone from Pacific, Missouri, with a series of 22 samples of the same formation from Wedron, Illinois. The largest value of packing density at Wedron is 85.1%, and the packing density for the Pacific, Missouri sample is 89.6%. All 23 values are arranged in order, including the Pacific specimen, with the *largest* first as X_1 and the smallest last as X_K. For $K = 23$ the ratio computed is $\dfrac{X_3 - X_1}{X_{K-2} - X_1} = \dfrac{82.7 - 89.6}{60.1 - 89.6} = 0.234$. This does not exceed the critical value, which at the 95th percentile ($\alpha = 0.05$) = 0.421, and the null hypothesis is accepted.

We are, however, not sure of the legitimacy of this second application in that the extreme value or "outlier" was not collected at the same place as the other data and actually represents an independent sample. The Mann-Whitney U-test for two independent samples seems more appropriate, with $N_1 = 1$ and $N_2 = 21$. (See p. 132 for discussion of the method.) In the present case, U is computed according to one of two methods described in Siegal (1956, *ibid.*, pp. 120–121) since N_2 is large. We give the first method since either one may be used.

$$
U = N_1 N_2 + \frac{N_1(N_1 + 1)}{2} - R_1 \qquad (6.20)
$$

where R_1 is the sum of ranks assigned to the group whose size is R_1. The ranks are found as follows: first, rank all entries from both sample N_1 and sample N_2; second, assign the integer 1 to the lowest entry, 2 to the next, and so on. Then R_1 is the sum of the ranks for the entries from the smallest sample (of size N_1).

Turning to the data, we have arranged in order of size the packing density values from Wedron and the single value from Pacific, Missouri, which is 89.6, and is underlined below. 58.0, 59.2, 60.1, 63.4, 64.7, 65.1, 65.6, 66.3, 66.3, 66.5, 66.6, 67.2, 69.6, 70.6, 72.7, 73.2, 75.4, 77.8, 77.9, 81.5, 82.7, 85.1, $\overline{89.6}$. In this case $N_1 = 1$ the Pacific, Missouri value. Its rank is 23, and so $R_1 = 23$.

Then from (6.20) $U = 1(22) + [1(1 + 1)]/2 - 23 = 0$; as N_1, N_2, increase in size the sampling distribution of U approaches the normal distribution. For $N_2 > 20$ the normal tables are appropriate. Here, the mean of U is approximately $N_1 N_2/2 = 22/2 = 11.0$ and the standard deviation is approximately

$$\sqrt{\frac{(N_1)(N_2)(N_1 + N_2 + 1)}{12}} = \sqrt{\frac{(1)(22)(1 + 22 + 1)}{12}} = 6.63$$

We now compute $Z = \dfrac{U - \text{mean}(U)}{\text{st. dev.}(U)} = \dfrac{0 - 11.0}{6.63} = -1.66$, which is approximately normally distributed with zero mean and unit variance $N(0, 1)$. The probability that $Z \leq -1.66 = 0.0485$. In this example the null hypothesis H_1 is that the two samples are drawn from the same population with the alternative hypothesis H_2 that the Pacific, Missouri sample is drawn from a larger valued population than the Wedron, Illinois sample.

The rejection region is one-tailed, and if we choose $\alpha = 0.05$, H_1 is rejected since the probability of a Z as small or smaller than $-1.66 = 0.0485$ under the null hypothesis. Thus, we accept the alternative hypothesis H_2 that the packing density in the Pacific, Missouri sample is significantly larger than that of the Wedron, Illinois specimens. This reverses the conclusion achieved by a questionable application of the test for extreme values.

General Discussion of Extreme Value Analysis.
Applications and Relevant Literature

The method described in the preceding section is restricted to small samples, e.g., the tables go up to $n = 30$. The subject of extreme values has been of interest in both theoretical and applied areas of statistical analysis. W. C. Krumbein and J. Lieblein, 1956, Geological application of extreme-value methods to interpretation of cobbles and boulders in gravel deposits, *Trans. Am. Geophys. Union* 37: 313–319, discuss and apply a method for extreme value analysis according to the context of the title. The method is described in an appendix. It should not be considered suitable for very small samples, since the method is asymptotic, improving in accuracy as sample size increases. The paper also includes a description of "extreme value probability paper" and a discussion of its uses.

RELEVANT PAPERS ON THE TOPIC OF EXTREME VALUES
Statistical
W. J. Dixon, 1950, Analysis of extreme values, *Annal. Math. Stats.* 21: 488–506.

R. A. Fisher and L. C. H. Tippett, 1928, Limiting forms of the frequency distribution of the largest or smallest member of a sample, *Proc. Camb. Phil. Soc.* 24: 180–190.

E. J. Gumbel, 1954, Statistical theory of extreme values and some practical applications, *Nat. Bur. Standards, Applied Math. Ser.* No. 33.

E. J. Gumbel and J. Lieblein, 1954, Some applications of extreme-value methods, *Am. Statistician* 8: 14–17.

U.S. National Bureau of Standards, 1953, Probability tables for the analysis of extreme-value data, *Nat. Bur. Standards, Applied Math. Ser.* No. 22.

Statistical Applications in Earth Sciences
E. J. Gumbel, 1941, Probability interpretation of the observed return periods of floods, *Trans. Am. Geophys. Union*, Pt. 3, 836–850.

A. Court, 1952, Some new statistical techniques in geophysics, *Advances in Geophysics*, 1: 75–85.

J. S. Longuet-Higgens, 1952, On the statistical distribution of the heights of sea waves, *J. Marine Research* 11: 245–266.

chapter 7

Statistical Inference: Estimation of Parameters and the Testing of Hypotheses

ONE-WAY ANALYSIS OF VARIANCE

Models I and II: Statement of Problem

As a means of introducing the technique of analysis of variance which goes hand in hand with the subject of experimental design, consider the two following problems, each representing two fundamentally different experimental models, yet both similar in many respects as far as mathematical manipulations are concerned.[1]

Model I

A manufacturer of plastic rods produces the rods on fourteen machines. Recent complaints from purchasers indicate that there has been a decrease in the strength of the rods. After some study the manufacturer realizes that this can be due only to the failure of some machines. But which one(s) of the fourteen? He decides to take an equal number of samples from each of the machines and submit them to strength-of-materials tests.

Model II

On the other hand, consider the collection of fourteen hand specimens from a certain granite body in New York State. From each sample a single thin section is prepared. Assuming that fourteen samples are truly representative and amply cover the area in question, we may ask whether the granite is uniform in composition. We shall state at present that the possible answers to this question are yes or no. The question may be

---

[1] The approach taken in this chapter follows closely that taken by C. Eisenhart, 1947, The assumptions underlying the analysis of variance, *Biometric.* 3: 1–21.

answered by examining a number of traverses in each slide and then comparing the estimates of the mineral composition from slide to slide. For example, we may let the compositional constituents under consideration be quartz, untwinned feldspar, twinned feldspar, and biotite. We therefore wish to ascertain if the fourteen slides differ from each other on the basis of mineral composition.

Differences between Models

Here are two analogous problems in design. However, their fundamental differences will serve as a means of distinguishing between two fundamental types of analysis of variance. Consider first the example of the granite body. The fourteen samples from which the mineral composition estimates will be made must be considered as only one group of an infinite group of fourteen samples which could have been chosen from the granite body. The thin section which was cut from the hand specimen sample was but one of the infinite which could have been cut. In this manner the slides from which mineral composition estimates will be made are *random samples* of slides which could have been made. The traverses within slides are also to be considered random traverses from an infinite number of traverses which could have been selected.

As for the plastic rods, the machines which manufacture them are certainly not random. There are but fourteen of them, each producing an equal number of rods. Our sample of rods is such that an equal number is taken from each of the fourteen. The machines are thus conceived to be *fixed* or *systematic* or *nonrandom*, since from this finite population of machines all were used. The rods which will be submitted to a strength-of-materials test may be considered a random selection of plastic rods from an extremely large number of plastic rods manufactured by these fourteen machines over a restricted period of time.

ONE-WAY OR NESTED OR HIERARCHIAL ANALYSIS OF VARIANCE

Model I

The results of the tests of the strength of the plastic rods may be recorded as in Table 7.1. Here x_{ij} represents the test result of the jth rod examined from the ith machine. Thus these entered numbers are thought to be variables distributed about a true fixed mean or expected value, constant for a particular machine. That is,

$$E(x_{ij}) = \mu_i \tag{7.1}$$

Hence, if repeated measurements of the strength of the rods manufactured

TABLE 7.1
Summary of Results

Measurements			Sums	Means
Machines	1 $x_{11}, x_{12}, \cdots, x_{1j} \cdots, x_{1c}$		$x_{1.}$	$\bar{x}_{1.}$
	2 $x_{21}, x_{22}, \cdots, x_{2j} \cdots, x_{2c}$		$x_{2.}$	$\bar{x}_{2.}$
	. . .	.	.	.
	. . .	.	.	.
	. . .	.	.	.
	i $x_{i1}, x_{i2}, \cdots, x_{ij} \cdots, x_{ic}$		$x_{i.}$	$\bar{x}_{i.}$
	. . .	.	.	.
	. . .	.	.	.
	. . .	.	.	.
	r $x_{r1}, x_{r2}, \cdots, x_{rj} \cdots, x_{rc}$		$x_{r.}$	$\bar{x}_{r.}$

by the ith machine were made, it would be found that the values obtained would be distributed about a mean value equal to μ_i.

For a fixed i

$$E(x_{ij}) = \mu_i$$
$$\text{Var } x_{ij} = \sigma^2$$

The following terms are here defined:

$$\sum_{j=1}^{c} x_{ij} = x_{i.} \tag{7.1a}$$

$$\sum_{j=1}^{c} \frac{x_{ij}}{c} = \bar{x}_{i.} \tag{7.1b}$$

$$\sum_{i=1}^{r} \sum_{j=1}^{c} x_{ij} = x_{..} \tag{7.1c}$$

$$\sum_{i=1}^{r} \sum_{j=1}^{c} \frac{x_{ij}}{rc} = \bar{\bar{x}}_{..} = \bar{x} \tag{7.1d}$$

$$\sum_{i=1}^{r} \mu_i = \mu_{.} \tag{7.1e}$$

$$\sum_{i=1}^{r} \frac{\mu_i}{r} = \bar{\mu}_{.} = \mu \tag{7.1f}$$

Any μ_i, i.e., the true average tensile strength of the ith machine, can be thought of as consisting of the over-all mean value μ plus a deviation of the average tensile strength for the ith machine from the over-all means, namely,

$$\mu_i = \mu + (\mu_i - \mu) \tag{7.2}$$

That is, the true tensile strength of the jth plastic rod manufactured by the ith machine is equal to the over-all true *fixed* mean plus a *fixed* deviation of the average strength of plastic rods produced by the machine. Equation (7.2) is known as the *assumption of additivity*. We never observe or measure μ_i. We observe, or measure, a variable, x_{ij}, which like μ_i, consists of an over-all true mean, plus the deviation of the average strength, produced by the ith machine from the over-all mean, plus unassigned or unknown or ignored or random variation. This may be explicitly stated as

$$x_{ij} = \mu + (\mu_i - \mu) + \epsilon_{ij} \tag{7.3}$$

where the random variable ϵ_{ij}, whose expectation is zero, represents the unassigned, unknown, or ignored variation plus random variation among plastic rods produced by the same machine. The variance of ϵ_{ij}, σ^2 thus represents the nonuniform tensile strength of plastic rods manufactured by the same machine.

As yet we have not answered the question we began at first to consider, namely, which machines are producing the defective plastic rods. Indeed, as yet we cannot answer that question. The present development merely permits us to summarize our experimental results, as was done in Table 7.1. What we can do, however, is to define some other algebraic relations of the data which are independent of any type of variable being considered. Namely, we can consider the problem of first defining and then decomposing the total sum of squares of the experiment.

Decomposition of Sums of Squares
   The total sum of squares of this experiment is defined as

$$\sum_i \sum_j (x_{ij} - \bar{x})^2$$

This may be rewritten as

$$\sum_i \sum_j [(x_{ij} - \bar{x}_{i.}) + (\bar{x}_{i.} - \bar{x})]^2 \tag{7.4}$$

This expression becomes, upon squaring,

$$\sum_i \sum_j (x_{ij} - \bar{x}_{i.})^2 + \sum_i \sum_j (\bar{x}_{i.} - \bar{x})^2 + 2\sum_i \sum_j (x_{ij} - \bar{x}_{i.})(\bar{x}_{i.} - \bar{x})$$

Now

$$2\sum_i \sum_j (x_{ij} - \bar{x}_{i.})(\bar{x}_{i.} - \bar{x})$$

becomes upon summing on j

$$2c\sum_i (\bar{x}_{i.} - \bar{x}_{i.})(\bar{x}_{i.} - \bar{x}) = 0$$

Thus (7.4) reduces to

$$\sum_i \sum_j (x_{ij} - \bar{x}_{i.})^2 + \sum_i \sum_j (\bar{x}_{i.} - \bar{x})^2$$

This first sum of squares is a measure of the departure of the jth observation on the ith machine from the average estimated value of the strength of the ith machine; whereas the second sum of squares measures the departure of the average estimated strength of the rods produced by any machine from the estimated strength of rods produced by all machines.

For convenience, the following table may be constructed which summarizes the sources of variation of the experiment as well as the sums of squares and mean squares or sample variances.

TABLE 7.2
Decomposition of Sum of Squares—Summary Table
Model I

Source of Variation	Sum of Squares	Mean Square
Among machines	$\sum_i \sum_j (\bar{x}_{i.} - \bar{x})^2 = S_m^2$	$S_m^2/(r - 1)$
Among rods produced by the same machines	$\sum_i \sum_j (x_{ij} - \bar{x}_{i.})^2 = S_r^2$	$S_r^2/m(r - 1)$
Total	$\sum_i \sum_j (x_{ij} - \bar{x})^2 = S_T^2$	$S_T^2/(mr - 1)$

Having established that

$$x_{ij} = \mu + (\mu_i - \mu) + \epsilon_{ij}$$

where ϵ_{ij} is a random variable whose expectation is zero and whose variance is σ^2, we conclude at least that x_{ij} must itself be a *random variable*, whose expectation is μ_i. If we further assume that all x_{ij} have the *same variance* and any covariance between them is 0,[1] then

$$\text{Var } x_{ij} = E(x_{ij} - \mu_i)^2 = \sigma^2 \tag{7.5}$$

Thus

$$\bar{x}_{i.} = \mu + (\mu_i - \mu) + \sum_{j=1}^{c} \frac{\epsilon_{ij}}{c}$$

where

$$E\bar{x}_{i.} = \mu_i$$

and

$$\text{Var } \bar{x}_{i.} = E(\bar{x}_{i.} - \mu_i)^2 = \frac{\sigma^2}{c} \tag{7.6}$$

[1] This is known as the assumption of homogeneous variances, or, we may say, the variables x_{ij} are homoscedastic and mutually uncorrelated.

Finally,

$$\bar{\bar{x}}_{..} = \bar{x} = \mu + \frac{\sum_i \sum_j x_{ij}}{rc}$$

where

$$E(\bar{x}) = \mu$$

and

$$\text{Var } \bar{x} = E(\bar{x} - \mu)^2 = \frac{\sigma^2}{rc} \tag{7.7}$$

Thus unbiased estimates of the population mean μ_i, in this case the true tensile strength of plastic rods, produced by the ith machine, as well as the true mean of all machines, may be obtained from the sample means for the ith machine, $\bar{x}_{i.}$, and from the over-all sample mean for all machines, $\bar{x}$.

The discussion has so far explicitly permitted us to summarize our data in an analysis of variance tables, as well as to obtain estimates of population means and really of any linear combination of these population means; for example, an estimate of $(\mu_i - \mu_{i+1})$ is $(\bar{x}_i - \bar{x}_{i+1})$. Having established estimates of μ_i's we are as yet unable to decide which μ_i's are significantly different. This will be discussed in a later section. At the present, let us focus our attention on obtaining estimates of the experimental error, σ^2, which is the variance of any x_{ij}. One of the more reasonable places to look for such an estimate would be the sums of squares described above.

Expectations of Sums of Squares

Consider

$$E \sum_i \sum_j (x_{ij} - \bar{x}_{i.})^2 \tag{7.8}$$

Rewrite this as

$$E \sum_i \sum_j (x_{ij} - \mu_i - \bar{x}_{i.} + \mu_i)^2 = E \sum_i \sum_j [(x_{ij} - \mu_i) - (\bar{x}_{i.} - \mu_i)]^2$$

Square and obtain

$$E \sum_i \sum_j [(x_{ij} - \mu_i)^2 + (\bar{x}_{i.} - \mu_i)^2 - 2(x_{ij} - \mu_i)(\bar{x}_{i.} - \mu_i)]$$

$$= \sum_i \sum_j E(x_{ij} - \mu_i)^2 + \sum_i \sum_j E(\bar{x}_{i.} - \mu_i)^2$$

$$- 2E \sum_i \sum_j (x_{ij}\bar{x}_{i.} - x_{ij}\mu_i - \mu_i\bar{x}_{i.} + \mu_i^2)$$

Taking expectations, summing, and utilizing the results of (7.5) and (7.6) we obtain

$$rc \text{ var } x_{ij} + rc \text{ var } \bar{x}_{i.} - 2 \sum_i E(c\bar{x}_{i.}^2 - c\bar{x}_{i.}\mu_i - c\bar{x}_{i.}\mu_i + c\mu_i^2)$$

$$= rc\sigma^2 + rc\frac{\sigma^2}{c} - 2c \sum_i E(\bar{x}_{i.} - \mu_i)^2$$

$$= rc\sigma^2 + r\sigma^2 - 2r\sigma^2$$

$$= r(c - 1)\sigma^2 \tag{7.9}$$

Hence

$$E \sum_i \sum_j (x_{ij} - \bar{x}_{i.})^2 = r(c - 1)\sigma^2$$

Therefore

$$\frac{E \sum_i \sum_j (x_{ij} - \bar{x}_{i.})^2}{r(c - 1)} = \sigma^2$$

Thus the sum of squares of the deviations among rods produced by the same machine, divided by its *degrees of freedom*, is an unbiased estimate of the variance of a single observation σ^2. Thus the experimental error or dissimilarity or dishomogeneity of rods extruded by the same machine is reflected by σ^2 and its estimate.

Let us next consider

$$E \sum_i \sum_j (\bar{x}_{i.} - \bar{x})^2$$

Rewrite this as follows:

$$E \sum_i \sum_j [(\bar{x}_{i.} - \mu_i) - (\bar{x} - \mu) + (\mu_i - \mu)]^2 \tag{7.10}$$

$$= E \sum_i \sum_j [(\bar{x}_{i.} - \mu_i)^2 + (\bar{x} - \mu)^2 + (\mu_i - \mu)^2$$

$$\overset{A}{\overbrace{- 2(\bar{x}_{i.} - \mu_i)(\bar{x} - \mu)}} + \overset{B}{\overbrace{2(\bar{x}_{i.} - \mu_i)(\mu_i - \mu)}} - \overset{C}{\overbrace{2(\bar{x} - \mu)(u_i - \mu)}}]$$

Let us consider the expectations and sums of the three cross products (A), (B), and (C), neglecting signs and the constant 2.

(A) $$\qquad E \sum_i \sum_j (\bar{x}_{i.} - \mu_i)(\bar{x} - \mu)$$

Sum over i to obtain

$$rE \sum_j (\bar{x} - \mu)^2$$

Taking expectations this reduces to rc var $\bar{x}$. Hence

$$E \sum_i \sum_j (\bar{x}_{i.} - \mu_i)(\bar{x} - \mu) = \sigma^2$$

(B) $$\quad E \sum_i \sum_j (\bar{x}_{i.} - \mu_i)(\mu_i - \mu) = \sum_i \sum_j E(\bar{x}_{i.} - \mu_i)(\mu_i - \mu)$$

$$= \sum_i \sum_j (\mu_i - \mu) E(\bar{x}_{i.} - \mu_i)$$

and since

$$E\bar{x}_{i.} = \mu_i, \; E(\bar{x}_{i.} - \mu_i) = 0$$

Hence

$$E \sum_i \sum_j (\bar{x}_{i.} - \mu_i)(\mu_i - \mu) = 0$$

(C)
$$E \sum_i \sum_j (\bar{x} - \mu)(\mu_i - \mu)$$

Rewriting this as

$$\sum_i \sum_j (\mu_i - \mu) E(\bar{x} - \mu)$$

we obtain

$$\sum_i \sum_j (\mu_i - \mu) \cdot 0 = 0$$

The first three squares of (7.10) have the following expectations:

$$E(\bar{x}_{i.} - \mu_i)^2 = \text{var } \bar{x}_{i.} = \frac{\sigma^2}{c}$$

$$E(\bar{x} - \mu)^2 = \text{var } \bar{x} = \frac{\sigma^2}{rc}$$

$$E(\mu_i - \mu)^2 = (\mu_i - \mu)^2$$

Thus

$$E \sum_i^r \sum_j^c (\bar{x}_{i.} - \mu_i)^2 = r\sigma^2$$

$$E \sum_i^r \sum_j^c (\bar{x} - \mu)^2 = \sigma^2$$

and

$$E \sum_i^r \sum_j^c (\mu_i - \mu)^2 = c \sum_i^r (\mu_i - \mu)^2$$

With the results above, (7.10) may now be rewritten as

$$r\sigma^2 + \sigma^2 + c \sum_{i=1}^r (\mu_i - \mu)^2 - 2\sigma^2 = (r - 1)\sigma^2 + c \sum_{i=1}^r (\mu_i - \mu)^2$$

TABLE 7.3
Analysis of Variance Table—Model I

Source of Variation	Degrees of Freedom	Sums of Squares	Mean Squares	E(Mean Square)
Among machines	$(r - 1)$	$\sum_i \sum_j (\bar{x}_{i.} - \bar{x})^2 = S_m^2$	$S_m^2/(r - 1)$	$\sigma^2 + \dfrac{c}{r-1}\sum_{i=1}^r \xi_i^2$
Among rods manufactured on the same machine	$r(c - 1)$	$\sum_i \sum_j (x_{ij} - \bar{x}_{i.})^2 = S_r^2$	$S_r^2/r(c - 1)$	σ^2
Total	$(rc - 1)$	$\sum_i \sum_j (x_{ij} - \bar{x})^2 = S_T^2$	$S_T^2/(rc - 1)$	

EXERCISE. Show that $S_T^2/(rc - 1)$ is not an unbiased estimate of σ^2.

Hence

$$E\left[\frac{\sum_{i}^{r}\sum_{j}^{c}(\bar{x}_{i.} - \bar{x})^2}{r - 1}\right] = \sigma^2 + \frac{c}{r - 1}\sum_{i=1}^{r}(\mu_i - \mu)^2 = \sigma^2 + \frac{c}{r - 1}\sum_{i=1}^{r}\xi_i^2$$

where

$$\xi_i = \mu_i - \mu$$

Thus the summary in Table 7.2 may be rewritten as an analysis of variance Table 7.3, which now includes the degrees of freedom of the mean squares or sample variances as well as their expectations.

Model II Anov

Returning to the example of the homogeneous granite, we may establish a table of the raw data such as Table (7.1).

Here the slides are to be thought of as a random sample of r slides from a population of infinite slides which could have been selected.

Any observation x_{ij} is to be thought of as

$$x_{ij} = \mu + (\bar{y}_{i.} - \mu) + \epsilon_{ij}$$

where $(\bar{y}_{i.} - \mu)$ is the random variable representing random deviation of the average composition of the ith slide, from the over-all expected or grand average of composition for all possible slides from the entire rock.

TABLE 7.4
Decomposition of Sums of Squares—Summary Table
Model II

Source of Variation	Sum of Squares	Mean Squares
Among slides	$\sum_{i}\sum_{j}(\bar{x}_{i.} - \bar{x})^2 = S_s^2$	$S_s^2/(r - 1)$
Among traverses within slides	$\sum_{i}\sum_{j}(x_{ij} - \bar{x}_{i.})^2 = S_t^2$	$S_t^2/r(c - 1)$
Total	$\sum_{i}\sum_{j}(x_{ij} - \bar{x})^2 = S_T^2$	$S_T^2/(cr - 1)$

$E(\bar{y}_{i.} - \mu)$ is 0. Var $(\bar{y}_{i.} - \mu) = \sigma_s^2$ and represents compositional dishomogeneity among slides. ϵ_{ij} represents experimental error, i.e., unknown or unassigned variability plus random compositional variations from traverse to traverse within the same slide. $E(\epsilon_{ij}) = 0$, var $\epsilon_{ij} = \sigma^2$ and represents the dishomogeneous compositional aspect of traverses within the same slide.

x_{ij}, consisting structurally of random variables, is indeed a random variable, such that

$$Ex_{ij} = \mu + 0 + 0 = \mu$$

and

$$\text{var } x_{ij} = \text{var } \mu + \text{var } (\bar{y}_{i.} - \mu) + \text{var } \epsilon_{ij} = \sigma_s^2 + \sigma^2$$

Thus

$$\bar{x}_{i.} = \mu + (\bar{y}_{i.} - \mu) + \bar{\epsilon}_{i.}$$

and

$$\text{var } \bar{x}_{i.} = \sigma_s^2 + \frac{\sigma^2}{c}$$

also

$$\bar{\bar{x}}_{..} = \bar{x} = \mu + \frac{\sum_i (\bar{y}_{i.} - \mu)}{r} + \bar{\bar{\epsilon}}_{..}$$

and

$$\text{var } \bar{x} = \frac{\sigma_s^2}{r} + \frac{\sigma^2}{rc}$$

Decomposition of the Total Sum of Squares

As was the case with Model I, the total sum of squares of the experiment may be defined as

$$\sum_i^r \sum_j^c (x_{ij} - \bar{x})^2 = \sum_i \sum_j (x_{ij} - \bar{x}_{i.})^2 + \sum_i \sum_j (\bar{x}_{i.} - \bar{x})^2$$

Again for convenience we can construct a table of sources of variation and their sample measures of deviation. (See Table 7.4.)

Let us now examine the expected values of the above sums of squares and mean squares.

$E\sum_i \sum_j (x_{ij} - \bar{x}_{i.})$ is as before (7.9) $r(c - 1)\sigma^2$, since

$$E \sum_i \sum_j (x_{ij} - \bar{x}_i)^2 = E \sum_i \sum_j [x_{ij} - \mu) - (\bar{x}_{i.} - \mu)]^2$$

$$= rc \text{ var } x_{ij} + rc \text{ var } \bar{x}_{i.} - 2E \sum_i \sum_j (x_{ij}\bar{x}_{i.} - \mu\bar{x}_{i.} + \mu^2 - x_{ij}\mu)$$

$$= rc \text{ var } x_{ij} + rc \text{ var } \bar{x}_{i.} - 2rc \text{ var } \bar{x}_{i.}$$

$$= rc \text{ var } x_{ij} - rc \text{ var } \bar{x}_{i.}$$

$$= rc\left(\sigma_s^2 + \sigma^2 - \sigma_s^2 - \frac{\sigma^2}{c}\right)$$

Thus

$$E \sum_i \sum_j (x_{ij} - \bar{x}_i)^2 / r(c - 1) = \sigma^2$$

Now

$$\sum_i \sum_j (\bar{x}_{i.} - \bar{x})^2 = E \sum_i \sum_j [(\bar{x}_{i.} - \mu) - (\bar{x} - \mu)]^2$$

$$= rc \, \text{var} \, \bar{x}_{i.} + rc \, \text{var} \, \bar{x} - 2rc \, \text{var} \, \bar{x}$$

$$= rc \, \text{var} \, \bar{x}_{i.} - rc \, \text{var} \, \bar{x} = rc[\text{var} \, \bar{x}_{i.} - \text{var} \, \bar{x}]$$

$$= rc\left(\sigma_s^2 + \frac{\sigma^2}{c} - \frac{\sigma_s^2}{r} - \frac{\sigma^2}{rc}\right)$$

$$= rc\sigma_s^2\left(\frac{r-1}{r}\right) + rc\frac{\sigma^2}{c}\left(\frac{r-1}{r}\right)$$

$$= c\sigma_s^2(r-1) + (r-1)\sigma^2$$

$$= \sigma^2(r-1) + c(r-1)\sigma_s^2$$

Hence

$$E \sum_i \sum_j (\bar{x}_{i.} - \bar{x})^2/(r-1) = \sigma^2 + c\sigma_s^2$$

Thus an analysis of variance table may be constructed for the Model II or random component model of the analysis of variance. (See Table 7.5.)

TABLE 7.5
Analysis of Variance Table
Model II

Source of Variation	D.F.	Sum of Squares	(M.S.)	E(M.S.)
Among slides	$(r-1)$	$\sum_i \sum_j (\bar{x}_{i.} - \bar{x})^2 = S_s^2$	$S_s^2/(r-1)$	$\sigma^2 + c\sigma_s^2$
Among traverses within slides	$r(c-1)$	$\sum_i \sum_j (x_{ij} - \bar{x}_{i.})^2 = S_t^2$	$S_t^2/r(c-1)$	σ^2
Total	$(rc-1)$	$\sum_i \sum_j (x_{ij} - \bar{x})^2 = S_T^2$	$S_T^2/(rc-1)$	

TWO-WAY ANALYSIS OF VARIANCE

The two-way experimental design which easily leads to an analysis of variance of the data is a natural consequence of data or observations which are classified according to two attributes. The analysis of variance resulting from this design may also be called, under certain conditions, a completely randomized block design. As an example of such a design, consider the array (Chapter 1) developed from a consideration of sedimentary rocks being classified according to two attributes: composition and grain size. Any observation on a sedimentary rock, for example, color of the specimen in wavelength, bulk density, permeability, etc., may be classified in that square to which its grain size and composition attribute it.

Another example of a two-way design would result if a series of samples of different reefs were sent to several laboratories for chemical analysis. The analysis could then be classified according to the laboratory which did the analysis as well as the reef from which it came.

Data such as the preceding give rise to an array of numbers or matrix such as is depicted in Table 7.6. Let there be r rows, c columns, and but one observation or entry per cell.

The following is here defined:

$$\sum_{i=1}^{r} x_{ij} = x_{.j} \tag{7.11a}$$

$$\frac{\sum_{i=1}^{r} x_{ij}}{r} = \frac{x_{.j}}{r} = \bar{x}_{.j} \tag{7.11b}$$

$$\sum_{j=1}^{c} \bar{x}_{.j} = c\bar{x} \tag{7.11c}$$

$$\sum_{i=1}^{r} \bar{x}_{i.} = r\bar{x} \tag{7.11d}$$

$$\sum_{i,j} \frac{x_{ij}}{rc} = \bar{\bar{x}}_{..} = \bar{x} \tag{7.11e}$$

$$\sum_{j=1}^{r} \mu_{ij} = \mu_{i.} \tag{7.11f}$$

$$\sum_{j=1}^{r} \frac{\mu_{ij}}{r} = \bar{u}_{i.} \tag{7.11g}$$

$$\sum_{i,j} \frac{\mu_{ij}}{rc} = \mu \tag{7.11h}$$

$$\sum_{i,j} \frac{\mu_{ij}}{c} = r\mu \tag{7.11i}$$

$$\sum_{i,j} \frac{\mu_{ij}}{r} = c\mu \tag{7.11j}$$

Model I Statistical Inference Concerning Systematic Components

This design, as were the designs discussed in the preceding sections, may be represented by one of three models: Model I—a model consisting of systematic or fixed effects; Model II—a model consisting of random components; or Model III—a model represented by both fixed and random effects. Much of the mechanics involved in establishing an analysis of variance table for any one of the three models is common to all three models. Each model permits the following: a summary of data in an analysis of variance table; estimation of certain parameters and linear

TABLE 7.6

rc **Matrix of Observations**

		Column (*c*) Attribute						Row Sum (Over All Columns)	Row Means (Averaged Over Columns)
		1	2	3 $\cdots$	*j*	$\cdots$	*c*		
	1	x_{11}	x_{12}	x_{13} $\cdots$	x_{1j}	$\cdots$	x_{1c}	$x_{1.}$	$\bar{x}_{1.}$
	2	x_{21}	x_{22}	x_{23} $\cdots$	x_{2j}	$\cdots$	x_{2c}	$x_{2.}$	$\bar{x}_{2.}$
	3	x_{31}	x_{32}	x_{33} $\cdots$	x_{3j}	$\cdots$	x_{3c}	$x_{3.}$	$\bar{x}_{3.}$
Row (*r*) attribute		.	.	.	.	.	.	.	.
		.	.	.	.	.	.	.	.
		.	.	.	.	.	.	.	.
	i	x_{i1}	x_{i2}	x_{i3} $\cdots$	x_{ij}	$\cdots$	x_{ic}	$x_{i.}$	$\bar{x}_{i.}$
		.	.	.	.	.	.	.	.
		.	.	.	.	.	.	.	.
		.	.	.	.	.	.	.	.
	r	x_{r1}	x_{r2}	x_{r3} $\cdots$	x_{rj}	$\cdots$	x_{rc}	$x_{r.}$	$\bar{x}_{r.}$
Columns summed over rows		$x_{.1}$	$x_{.2}$	$x_{.3}$ $\cdots$	$x_{.j}$	$\cdots$	$x_{.c}$	$x_{..}$	
Column means averaged over rows		$\bar{x}_{.1}$	$\bar{x}_{.2}$	$\bar{x}_{.3}$ $\cdots$	$\bar{x}_{.j}$	$\cdots$	$\bar{x}_{.c}$		$\bar{\bar{x}}_{..}$

combinations of these parameters; methods for testing hypotheses concerned with inferring inherent variability. Each does some of these identically, others in a different manner. This design will serve as a means of elucidating the above similarities and differences as well as indicating explicitly why certain assumptions will be made in developing the following analysis of variance, as were made in the previous discussion.

Consider one of the problems alluded to in the introduction of this section, namely, the measurement of the permeability of a series of core samples. Let us assume for convenience that each core sample may be classified according to the attribute's grain size and rock type (composition) and further assume that a measure of permeability is obtained for every cell in the matrix of Table 7.6. Since we assume but a finite number of size classes and since we will obtain representatives from all rock types and all size classes, then we may rightly conclude that the two attributes essential to our classification of permeabilities are fixed or systematic effects, one representing the column attribute, the other the row attribute. Thus the variable x_{ij} is to be thought of as distributed about a mean value, which depends on the cell location of the observation. Thus, if we repeated the experiment many times, the variable x_{ij} would be found to generate a frequency distribution whose mean would be μ_{ij}. Furthermore, we assume that this mean value is an additive function of the over-all population mean, μ, defined as

$$\mu = \frac{\sum_i \sum_j \mu_{ij}}{rc}$$

plus the deviation of the row mean from the over-all mean, the row effect, plus the deviation of the column mean from the over-all mean, the column effect.

Thus

$$\mu_{ij} = \mu + \xi_i + \eta_j \tag{7.12}$$

where

$$\bar{\mu}_{i.} - \mu = \xi_i$$
$$\bar{\mu}_{.j} - \mu = \eta_j$$

Equation (7.12) is known as the *assumption of additivity*, without which certain linear combinations of unbiased estimates, as will be shown in a later section, could not be made. Furthermore, estimates of the variance of x_{ij} could not be made.

Thus we can construct a table similar to Table 7.6, but containing the expectations of the values in Table 7.17. The structure of any porosity determination x_{ij}, may be thought of, therefore, as being due to a contribution from the over-all population mean defined as μ, plus a contribution from the row in which it is located; or in terms of this particular example, from the rock type from which it was selected, plus a contribution from column effects, in this case an effect due to grain size.

Finally, to x_{ij} (as yet not a random variable) must be added a random factor ϵ_{ij} the experimental error or unassigned or unknown variation, where, by definition

$$E\epsilon_{ij} = 0$$

and

$$\text{var } \epsilon_{ij} = \sigma^2$$

Thus, x_{ij} consisting of fixed components and also a random component is now itself a *random variable, bringing our experimental data into the realm* of statistics. Without this assumption, no statistical inference could be made. Here

$$x_{ij} = \mu + \xi_i + \eta_j + \epsilon_{ij}$$

where

$$E(x_{ij}) = \mu + \xi_i + \eta_j = \mu_{ij} \tag{7.13}$$

and

$$\text{var } (x_{ij}) = E(x_{ij} - \mu_{ij})^2 = \sigma^2 \tag{7.14}$$

TABLE 7.7
Expectations of Observations

	c_1	c_2	...	c_j	...	c_c	Sums	Means
r_1	μ_{11}	μ_{12}	...	μ_{1j}	...	μ_{1c}	$\mu_{1.}$	$\bar{\mu}_{1.}$
r_2	μ_{21}	μ_{22}	...	μ_{2j}	...	μ_{2c}	$\mu_{2.}$	$\bar{\mu}_{2.}$
.	.	.	...	.	...	.	.	.
.	.	.	...	.	...	.	.	.
.	.	.	...	.	...	.	.	.
r_i	μ_{i1}	μ_{i2}	...	μ_{ij}	...	μ_{ic}	$\mu_{i.}$	$\bar{\mu}_{i.}$
.	.	.	...	.	...	.	.	.
.	.	.	...	.	...	.	.	.
.	.	.	...	.	...	.	.	.
r_r	μ_{r1}	μ_{r2}	...	μ_{rj}	...	μ_{rc}	$\mu_{r.}$	$\bar{\mu}_{r.}$
Sums	$\mu_{.1}$	$\mu_{.2}$	...	$\mu_{.j}$	...	$\mu_{.c}$	$\mu_{..}$	
Means	$\bar{\mu}_{.1}$	$\bar{\mu}_{.2}$	...	$\bar{\mu}_{.j}$	...	$\bar{\mu}_{.c}$		$\bar{\bar{\mu}} = \mu$

Thus (7.14) assumes a *common variance* for x_{ij} and not one depending on i or j. This is commonly called the *assumption of homogeneous variance* or *equal variances* or the assumption of homoscedasticity. Furthermore, in order to obtain unbiased estimates of σ^2, we must further assume that any correlation between the x_{ij}'s is zero, i.e.,

$$E[(x_{ij} - \mu_{ij})(x_{kl} - \mu_{kl})] = 0$$

for all $i \neq k$ and $j \neq l$.

Since

$$x_{ij} = \mu + \xi_i + \eta_j + \epsilon_{ij}$$

then

$$\bar{x}_{i.} = \mu + \xi_i + 0 + \bar{\epsilon}_i$$

where

$$\sum_{j=1}^{c} \frac{\bar{u}_{.j} - \mu}{c} = 0 = \sum_{j=1}^{c} \frac{\eta_j}{c}$$

and

$$\bar{\epsilon}_{i.} = \frac{\sum_{j=1}^{c} \epsilon_{ij}}{c}$$

Thus

$$E(\bar{x}_{i.}) = \mu + \xi_i = \bar{\mu}_{i.} \qquad (7.15)$$

and

$$\text{var} (\bar{x}_{i.}) = E(\bar{x}_{i.} - \mu_{i.})^2 = \text{var} \frac{\sum\limits_{j=1}^{c} x_{ij}}{c} = \frac{\sigma^2}{c} \qquad (7.16)$$

Similarly

$$E(\bar{x}_{.j}) = \mu + \eta_j = \bar{\mu}_{.j} \qquad (7.17)$$

and

$$\text{var} (\bar{x}_{.j}) = E(\bar{x}_{.j} - \bar{u}_{.j})^2 = \frac{\sigma^2}{r} \qquad (7.18)$$

Finally

$$E(\bar{x}) = \mu \qquad (7.19)$$

and

$$\text{var} (\bar{x}) = E(\bar{x} - \mu)^2 = \frac{\sigma^2}{rc} \qquad (7.20)$$

By means of (7.1a), (7.11b), and (7.11e) the following are identities:

$$\sum_{j=1}^{c} (x_{ij} - \bar{x}_{i.}) = 0 \qquad (7.21)$$

$$\sum_{i=1}^{r} (x_{ij} - \bar{x}_{.j}) = 0 \qquad (7.22)$$

$$\sum_i \sum_j (x_{ij} - \bar{x}) = 0 \qquad (7.23)$$

Decomposition of Sums of Squares

Regardless of the variables under consideration, the entries in Table 7.6 obey the following algebraic identity:

$$x_{ij} - \bar{x} = (\bar{x}_{i.} - \bar{x}) + (\bar{x}_{.j} - \bar{x}) + (x_{ij} - \bar{x}_{i.} - \bar{x}_{.j} + \bar{x})$$

Square both sides of the equation to obtain

$$(x_{ij} - \bar{x})^2 = (\bar{x}_{i.} - \bar{x})^2 + (\bar{x}_{.j} - \bar{x})^2 + (x_{ij} - \bar{x}_{i.} - \bar{x}_{.j} + \bar{x})^2$$
$$+ 2(\bar{x}_{i.} - \bar{x})(\bar{x}_{.j} - \bar{x}) + 2(\bar{x}_{i.} - \bar{x})(x_{ij} - \bar{x}_{i.} - \bar{x}_{.j} + \bar{x})$$
$$+ 2(\bar{x}_{.j} - \bar{x})(x_{ij} - \bar{x}_{.j} - \bar{x}_{i.} + \bar{x})$$

The following sums of squares are obtained if both sides of the equation are summed over i and j and (7.21) and (7.22) are utilized.

$$\sum_i^r \sum_j^c (x_{ij} - \bar{x})^2 = \sum_{i,j} (\bar{x}_{i.} - \bar{x})^2 + \sum_{i,j} (\bar{x}_{.j} - \bar{x})^2 + \sum_{i,j} (\bar{x}_{ij} - \bar{x}_{i.} - \bar{x}_{.j} + \bar{x})^2$$

The expression
$$\sum_{i,j} (x_{ij} - \bar{x})^2$$

is, as was defined before, the total sum of square deviations. It is the sum of the squares of the deviation of every entry from the over-all sample mean. Hence, we have decomposed the total number of sums of squares into the following three parts:

$$\sum_{i,j} (\bar{x}_{i.} - \bar{x})^2 \tag{7.24}$$

$$\sum_{i,j} (\bar{x}_{.j} - \bar{x})^2 \tag{7.25}$$

$$\sum_{i,j} (x_{ij} - \bar{x}_{i.} - \bar{x}_{.j} + \bar{x})^2 \tag{7.26}$$

Expression (7.24) represents the sum of square deviations of the sample row means from the over-all sample mean. In this example it is a measure of the deviation of the average or mean permeability value for different rock types from the average permeability measure for all cores, regardless of rock type or grain size. Expression (7.25) represents an analogous sum of squared deviations of the sample column means from the over-all sample mean, which in this problem is a measure of the departure of the permeability measures for the different grain sizes from the over-all average permeability measure, regardless of rock type or grain size. Expression (7.26) is at times difficult to interpret physically. It is frequently called the interaction sum of squares. It is perhaps easier to examine this sum of squares not as presented in (7.26) but rather in terms of what on average this expression is purporting to estimate, i.e., in terms of its expectation.

We can arrange the sums of squares which we have just arrived at, with the aid of algebraic manipulation, into Table 7.8. Here the sources of the deviation and hence variation are stated with their respective sums of squares, as well as their respective degrees of freedom and mean squares.

Estimation of Population Parameters

Our development to this point has permitted a summarization of the data, (Table 7.6) and a decomposition of the total sum of squares into component parts, (Table 7.8). What statistical inference can be made at this point? Certainly, we can estimate population parameters by examining the statistics x_{ij}, $\bar{x}_{i.}$, $\bar{x}_{.j}$, and $\bar{x}$.

These, by (7.13), (7.15), (7.17), and (7.19) respectively are unbiased estimates of μ_{ij}, $\mu_{i.}$, $\mu_{.j}$ and μ. Furthermore, we can estimate linear combinations of these parameters, e.g., an estimate of $\mu_{.j} - \mu_{.j+1}$ is $(\bar{x}_{.j} - \bar{x}_{.j+1})$.

We are once again faced with the problem of estimating the experimental error σ^2. A suitable place to look for such an estimate would be Table 7.8, in particular, the expectations of the sums of squares.

TABLE 7.8

Decomposition of Total Sum of Squares into Respective Sources of Deviation

Source of Deviation (Variation)	Sum of Squares	Degrees of Freedom	Sample Variance of Mean Square
Among row means	$\sum_{i,j} (\bar{x}_{i.} - \bar{x})^2 = S_r^2$	$(r - 1)$	$S_r^2/(r - 1)$
Among column means	$\sum_{i,j} (\bar{x}_{.j} - \bar{x}) = S_c^2$	$(c - 1)$	$S_c^2/(c - 1)$
Residual; interaction; remainder	$\sum_{i,j} (x_{ij} - \bar{x}_{i.} - \bar{x}_{.j} + \bar{x})^2 = S_{rc}^2$	$(r - 1)(c - 1)$	$S_{rc}^2/(r - 1)(c - 1)$
Total	$\sum_{i,j} (x_{ij} - \bar{x})^2 = S_T^2$	$(rc - 1)$	$S_t^2/(rc - 1)$

Expectations of Sums of Squares and Mean Squares for Two-Way Anov without Replication

Consider first the expectation of the sum of squares for rows. Here

$$E \sum_{i,j} (\bar{x}_{i.} - \bar{x})^2 = E\sum_{i,j}[(\bar{x}_{i.} - \bar{\mu}_{i.}) - (\bar{x} - \mu) + (\bar{\mu}_{i.} - \mu)]^2 \quad (7.27)$$

Now square the terms within the bracket and obtain

$$\sum_{i,j} E(\bar{x}_{i.} - \bar{\mu}_{i.})^2 + \sum_{i,j} E(\bar{x} - \mu)^2 + \sum_{i,j} E(\bar{\mu}_{i.} - \mu)^2 - 2\sum_{i,j} E(\bar{x}_{i.} - \bar{\mu}_{i.})(\bar{x} - \mu)$$
$$+ 2\sum_{i,j} E(\bar{x}_{i.} - \bar{\mu}_{i.})(\bar{\mu}_{i.} - \mu) - 2E\sum_{i,j} (\bar{x} - \mu)(\bar{\mu}_{i.} - \mu)$$

Consider the first three expectations. The first is clearly the variance of $\bar{x}_{i.}$, namely, var $\bar{x}_i = \sigma^2/c$ by (7.16). The second is var $\bar{x} = \sigma^2/rc$ by (7.20), whereas the third term, consisting entirely of constants, is itself a constant, namely, $\sum_{i,j} \xi_i^2$. The first three terms thus become, after taking expectations and summing over i and j,

$$rc \frac{\sigma^2}{c} + rc \frac{\sigma^2}{rc} + \sum_i \sum_j \xi_i^2$$

Consider next the last two cross product terms, which are 0 by virtue of the following: since

$$E(\bar{x}_{i.} - \bar{\mu}_{i.})(\bar{\mu}_{i.} - \mu) = (\bar{\mu}_{i.} - \bar{\mu}_{i.})(\bar{\mu}_{i.} - \mu)$$

Thus

$$\sum_{i,j} (\bar{\mu}_{i.} - \bar{\mu}_{i.})(\bar{\mu}_{i.} - \mu) = 0$$

and

$$\sum_{i,j} E(\bar{x} - \mu)(\bar{\mu}_{i.} - \mu) = \sum_{i,j} (\mu - \mu)(\bar{\mu}_{i.} - \mu) = 0$$

Now consider $E\sum_{i,j}(\bar{x}_{i.} - \bar{\mu}_{i.})(\bar{x} - \mu)$. Multiply through and sum as follows:

$$E[\sum_{i,j}(\bar{x}_{i.}\bar{x} - \bar{x}_{i.}\mu - \bar{\mu}_{i.}\bar{x} + \bar{\mu}_{i.}\mu)]$$

$$= E\left(\bar{x}\sum_{i,j}\bar{x}_{i.} - \mu\sum_{i,j}\bar{x}_{i.} - \bar{x}\sum_{i,j}\bar{\mu}_{i.} + \mu\sum_{i,j}\bar{\mu}_{i.}\right)$$

$$= rcE(\bar{x}^2 - 2\mu\bar{x} + \mu^2) = rcE[\bar{x} - \mu]^2 = rc \text{ var } \bar{x}$$

$$= \sigma^2$$

Hence (7.27) becomes

$$r\sigma^2 + \sigma^2 - 2\sigma^2 + \sum_{i,j}\xi_i^2 = (r - 1)\sigma^2 + \sum_{i,j}\xi_i^2$$

and

$$E\left[\sum_{i,j}(\bar{x}_i - \bar{x})^2\right] = (r - 1)\sigma^2 + \sum_{i,j}\xi_i^2$$

In an exactly analogous manner

$$E\left[\sum_{i,j}(\bar{x}_{.j} - \bar{x})^2\right] = (c - 1)\sigma^2 + \sum_{i,j}\eta_j^2 \qquad (7.28)$$

Consider the expectation of the interaction of the residual sum of squares

$$E\sum_{i,j}(x_{ij} - \bar{x}_{i.} - \bar{x}_{.j} + \bar{x})^2$$

$$= E\sum_{i,j}[(x_{ij} - \mu_{ij}) - (\bar{x}_{i.} - \bar{\mu}_{i.}) - (\bar{x}_{.j} - \bar{\mu}_{.j})$$

$$+ (\bar{x} - \mu) + (\mu_{ij} - \bar{\mu}_{i.} - \bar{\mu}_{.j} + \mu)]^2 \qquad (7.29)$$

This is obtained by adding and subtracting μ_{ij}, $\bar{\mu}_{i.}$, $\bar{\mu}_{.j}$ and μ. But by our assumption of additivity, namely, $\mu_{ij} = \mu + (\bar{\mu}_{i.} - \mu) + (\bar{\mu}_{.j} - \mu)$, the last bracketed term is necessarily 0. Hence (7.29) becomes

$$\sum_{i,j}E(x_{ij} - \mu_{ij})^2 + \sum_{i,j}E(\bar{x}_{i.} - \bar{\mu}_{i.})^2 + \sum_{i,j}E(\bar{x}_{.j} - \bar{\mu}_{.j})^2 + \sum E(\bar{x} - \mu)^2$$

plus a series of cross products which will be considered below. The first four squares and their expectations are with the aid of (7.14), (7.16), (7.18), and (7.20), respectively

$$rc\sigma^2 + rc\frac{\sigma^2}{c} + rc\frac{\sigma^2}{r} + rc\frac{\sigma^2}{rc} = (rc + r + c + 1)\sigma^2 = (r + 1)(c + 1)\sigma^2$$

Let us consider the six cross products one by one.

(1) $$E\sum_{i,j}(x_{ij} - \mu_{ij})(\bar{x}_{i.} - \bar{\mu}_{i.})$$

Sum over j and obtain

$$c \sum_i E(\bar{x}_{i.} - \bar{\mu}_{i.})(\bar{x}_{i.} - \bar{\mu}_{i.}) = c \sum_i E(\bar{x}_{i.} - \bar{\mu}_{i.})^2 = cr \text{ var } \bar{x}_{i.}$$

$$= cr \frac{\sigma^2}{c} = r\sigma^2$$

(2) $$E \sum_{i,j} (x_{ij} - \mu_{ij})(\bar{x}_{.j} - \mu_{.j}) = r \sum_j E(\bar{x}_{.j} - \bar{\mu}_{.j})^2 = cr \text{ var } \bar{x}_{.j} = c\sigma^2$$

(3) $$E \sum_{i,j} (x_{ij} - \mu_{ij})(\bar{x} - \mu)$$

Sum over i and then j to obtain

$$E(\bar{x} - \mu)^2 = \text{var } \bar{x} = \sigma^2$$

(4) $$E \sum_{i,j} (\bar{x}_{i.} - \bar{\mu}_{i.})(\bar{x}_{.j} - \bar{\mu}_{.j})$$

Sum over i then j to obtain

$$Erc(\bar{x} - \mu)^2 = \sigma^2$$

(5) $$E \sum_{i,j} (\bar{x}_{i.} - \bar{\mu}_{i.})(\bar{x} - \mu) = rc \text{ var } \bar{x} = \sigma^2$$

(6) $$E \sum_{i,j} (\bar{x}_{.j} - \bar{\mu}_{.j})(\bar{x} - \mu) = rc \text{ var } \bar{x} = \sigma^2$$

Therefore,

$$E \sum_{i,j} (x_{ij} - \bar{x}_{i.} - \bar{x}_{.j} + \bar{x})^2$$

$$= \sigma^2(rc + r + c + 1 - 2r - 2c + 2 + 2 - 2 - 2)$$

$$= \sigma^2(r - 1)(c - 1)$$

Thus the expectations of the mean squares in Table 7.3 are as follows, when additivity prevails:[1]

$$\frac{E \sum_{i,j} (\bar{x}_{i.} - \bar{x})^2}{r - 1} = \sigma^2 + \frac{\sum_{i,j} (\bar{\mu}_{i.} - \mu)^2}{r - 1}$$

$$\frac{E \sum_{i,j} (\bar{x}_{.j} - \bar{x})^2}{c - 1} = \sigma^2 + \frac{\sum_{i,j} (\bar{\mu}_{.j} - \mu)^2}{c - 1}$$

$$\frac{E \sum (x_{ij} - \bar{x}_{i.} - \bar{x}_{.j} + \bar{x})^2}{(r - 1)(c - 1)} = \sigma^2$$

We thus can complete Table 7.8 by adding to it the expectations of the mean squares. (See Table 7.9.)

[1] If nonadditivity prevails

$$E \sum_{i,j} (x_{ij} - \bar{x}_{i.} - \bar{x}_{.j} + \bar{x})^2 = \sigma^2(r - 1)(c - 1) + \sum_{i,j} (\mu_{ij} - \bar{\mu}_{i.} - \bar{\mu}_{.j} + \mu)^2$$

TABLE 7.9

Two-Way Anov Table (without Replication), Additivity Model

Source of Variation	Sum of Squares	D.F.	M.S.	Expected M.S.
Rows	$c\Sigma_i(\bar{x}_{i.} - \bar{x})^2 = S_r^2$	$(r-1)$	$S_r^2/(r-1)$	$\sigma^2 + \dfrac{\sum_{i,j}(\bar{\mu}_{i.} - \mu)^2}{r-1}$
Columns	$r\Sigma_j(\bar{x}_{.j} - \bar{x})^2 = S_c^2$	$(c-1)$	$S_c^2/(c-1)$	$\sigma^2 + \dfrac{\sum_{i,j}(\bar{\mu}_{.j} - \mu)^2}{c-1}$
Residual	$\Sigma_i\Sigma_j(x_{ij} - \bar{x}_{i.} - \bar{x}_{.j} + \bar{x})^2 = S_{rc}^2$	$(r-1)(c-1)$	$S_{rc}^2/(r-1)(c-1)$	σ^2
Total	$\Sigma_i\Sigma_j(x_{ij} - \bar{x})^2$	$(rc-1)$	—	—

MODEL II STATISTICAL INFERENCE CONCERNING COMPONENTS OF VARIANCE

The development of a Model I—two-way analysis of variance as described previously is similar in many respects to development of a Model II—two-way analysis which will be described below. Here any observation x_{ij} is structurally composed of a sum of random variables, namely,

$$x_{ij} = \mu + y_i + z_j + \epsilon_{ij} \tag{7.30}$$

where μ is some constant about which x_{ij} is distributed.

As an example of such an experimental approach, consider the measurement of the loudness of sound waves traveling through water and detected by means of instruments located at the bottom of the ocean floor. Let us assume that the sound waves and hence their detection are subjected to random changes in both wind speed and current velocity. Here y_i might represent the random contribution of wind speed variations to the intensity of the detected sound, whereas z_j, on the other hand, would represent the contribution of random current fluctuations or variations to the intensity of the sound detected by the instruments. y_i and z_j thus are assumed to be random variables, the latter being structurally $(\bar{y}_i - \mu)$, the deviation of the average intensity of sound for the ith wave velocity from the true average intensity of sound μ averaged over all wind speeds. The former is structurally the deviation of the average sound intensity for the jth wind speed from the true average intensity of sound i.e., $(z_{.j} - \mu)$. By definition, the expectation of y_i and z_j are both assumed 0, whereas their variances are defined to be $Ey_i^2 = \sigma_r^2$, and $Ez_j^2 = \sigma_c^2$. ϵ_{ij} once again represents unassigned, ignored, or unknown variation. The variance of ϵ_{ij}, σ^2, represents the dishomogeneity of columns from row to row. Expression (7.30) is the now familiar *assumption of additivity*.

Thus x_{ij}, structurally constructed of random variables, is also a *random variable*, whose expectation is

$$Ex_{ij} = \mu$$

and whose variance is

$$\text{var } x_{ij} = \text{var } y_i + \text{var } z_j + \text{var } \epsilon_{ij} = \sigma_r^2 + \sigma_c^2 + \sigma^2 \qquad (7.31)$$

With the aid of (7.30) and (7.31) the following identities hold:

(1) $\qquad \bar{x}_{i.} = \dfrac{\sum\limits_{j=1}^{c} x_{ij}}{c} = \mu + (\bar{y}_{i.} - \mu) + \dfrac{\sum\limits_{j=1}^{c}(\bar{z}_{.j} - \mu)}{c} + \dfrac{\sum\limits_{j=1}^{c}\epsilon_{ij}}{c}$

Thus

$$E\bar{x}_{i.} = \mu$$

and

$$\text{var } \bar{x}_{i.} = \sigma_r^2 + \frac{\sigma_c^2}{c} + \frac{\sigma^2}{c} \qquad (7.32)$$

(2) $\qquad \bar{x}_{.j} = \dfrac{\sum\limits_{i=1}^{r} x_{ij}}{r} + \dfrac{\sum\limits_{i=1}^{r}(\bar{y}_{i.} - \mu)}{r} + (\bar{z}_{.j} - \mu) + \dfrac{\sum\limits_{i=1}^{r}\epsilon_{ij}}{r}$

Thus

$$E(\bar{x}_{.j}) = \mu$$

and

(3) $\qquad \text{var } \bar{x}_{.j} = \dfrac{\sigma_r^2}{r} + \sigma_c^2 + \sigma_r^2 \qquad (7.33)$

Finally

$$\bar{x}_{..} = \bar{x} = \frac{\sum\limits_{i,j} x_{ij}}{rc}$$

$$= \mu + \frac{\sum\limits_{i,j}(\bar{y}_{i.} - \mu)}{rc} + \frac{\sum\limits_{i,j}(\bar{z}_{.j} - \mu)}{rc} + \frac{\sum\limits_{i,j}\epsilon_{ij}}{rc}$$

Thus

$$E(\bar{x}) = \mu$$

and

$$\text{var } \bar{x} = \frac{\sigma_r^2}{r} + \frac{\sigma_c^2}{c} + \frac{\sigma^2}{rc} \qquad (7.34)$$

Decomposition of Total Sum of Squares

The total sum of squares is once again defined as

$$\sum_i \sum_j (x_{ij} - \bar{x})^2$$

This sum of squares is decomposed as before into the following three parts:

$$\sum_i \sum_j (\bar{x}_{i.} - \bar{x})^2$$

$$\sum_i \sum_j (\bar{x}_{.j} - \bar{x})^2$$

$$\sum_i \sum_j (x_{ij} - \bar{x}_{i.} - \bar{x}_{.j} + \bar{x})^2$$

Expectations of Sums of Squares for Two-Way Model II Analysis of Variance without Replication

$$E \sum_{i,j} (\bar{x}_{i.} - \bar{x})^2$$

$$= E \sum_{i,j} [(\bar{x}_{i.} - \mu) - (\bar{x} - \mu)]^2$$

$$= E \sum_{i,j} (\bar{x}_{i.} - \mu)^2 + E \sum_{i,j} (\bar{x} - \mu)^2 - 2E \sum_{i,j} (\bar{x}_{i.} - \mu)(\bar{x} - \mu)$$

$$= rc \text{ var } \bar{x}_{i.} + rc \text{ var } \bar{x} - 2E \sum_{i,j} (\bar{x}_{i.}\bar{x} - \bar{x}_{i.}\mu - \mu\bar{x} + \mu^2)$$

$$= rc \text{ var } \bar{x}_{i.} + rc \text{ var } \bar{x} - 2E(\bar{x} - \mu)^2$$

$$= rc[\text{var } \bar{x}_{i.} - \text{var } \bar{x}]$$

$$= rc\left(\sigma_r^2 + \frac{\sigma_c^2}{c} + \frac{\sigma^2}{c} - \frac{\sigma_r^2}{r} - \frac{\sigma_c^2}{c} - \frac{\sigma^2}{rc}\right)$$

$$= (r - 1)(\sigma^2 + c\sigma_r^2) \tag{7.35}$$

Similarly,

$$E \sum_{i,j} (\bar{x}_{.j} - \mu)^2 = (c - 1)(\sigma^2 + r\sigma_c^2) \tag{7.36}$$

Finally, let us consider

$$E \sum_{i,j} (x_{ij} - \bar{x}_{i.} - \bar{x}_{.j} + \bar{x})^2$$

which upon the addition and subtraction of 2μ is equivalent to

$$E \sum_{i,j} [(x_{ij} - \mu) - (\bar{x}_{i.} - \mu) - (\bar{x}_{.j} - \mu) + (\bar{x} - \mu)]^2$$

Squaring this expression leads us to the following:

$rc \text{ var } x_{ij} + rc \text{ var } \bar{x}_{i.} + rc \text{ var } \bar{x}_{.j} + rc \text{ var } \bar{x} + 6$ pairs of cross products.

Expectation of Cross Products

1. $$E \sum_i \sum_j (x_{ij} - \mu)(\bar{x}_{i.} - \mu) = E \sum_i \sum_j (x_{ij}\bar{x}_{i.} - x_{ij}\mu - \bar{x}_{i.}\mu + \mu^2)$$

$$= c \sum_i E(\bar{x}_{i.}^2 - 2\bar{x}_{i.}\mu + \mu^2)$$

$$= cr \text{ var } \bar{x}_{i.} \tag{7.37}$$

2.
$$E \sum_i \sum_j (x_{ij} - \mu)(\bar{x}_{.j} - \mu) = E \sum_i \sum_j (x_{ij}\bar{x}_{.j} - x_{ij}\mu - \mu\bar{x}_{.j} + \mu^2)$$

$$= r \sum_j E(\bar{x}_{.j}^2 - 2\bar{x}_{.j}\mu + \mu^2)$$

$$= cr \text{ var } \bar{x}_{.j} \qquad (7.38)$$

3.
$$E \sum_i \sum_j (x_{ij} - \mu)(\bar{x} - \mu) = E \sum_{i,j} (x_{ij}\bar{x} - x_{ij}\mu - \mu\bar{x} + \mu^2)$$

$$= rcE(\bar{x}^2 - 2\bar{x}\mu + \mu^2)$$

$$= rc \text{ var } \bar{x} \qquad (7.39)$$

4.
$$E \sum_i \sum_j (\bar{x}_{i.} - \mu)(\bar{x}_{.j} - \mu) = E \sum_{i,j} (\bar{x}_{i.}\bar{x}_{.j} - \bar{x}_{i.}\mu - \mu\bar{x}_{.j} + \mu^2)$$

$$= rcE(\bar{x}^2 - 2\mu\bar{x} + \mu^2)$$

$$= rc \text{ var } \bar{x} \qquad (7.40)$$

5.
$$E \sum_i \sum_j (\bar{x}_{i.} - \mu)(\bar{x} - \mu) = E \sum_{i,j} (\bar{x}_{i.}\bar{x} - \bar{x}_{i.}\mu - \mu\bar{x} + \mu^2)$$

$$= rcE(\bar{x}^2 - 2\bar{x}\mu + \mu^2)$$

$$= rc \text{ var } \bar{x} \qquad (7.41)$$

6.
$$E \sum_i \sum_j (\bar{x}_{.j} - \mu)(\bar{x} - \mu) = E \sum_i \sum_j (\bar{x}_{.j}\bar{x} - \bar{x}_{.j}\mu - \mu\bar{x} + \mu^2)$$

$$= rcE(\bar{x}^2 - 2\bar{x}\mu + \mu^2)$$

$$= rc \text{ var } \bar{x} \qquad (7.42)$$

Thus the expectations of the cross products become

$$E \sum_{i,j} (x_{ij} - \bar{x}_{i.} - \bar{x}_{.j} + \bar{x})^2$$

$$= rc(\text{var } x_{ij} + \text{var } \bar{x}_{i.} + \text{var } \bar{x}_{.j} + \text{var } \bar{x}$$

$$- 2 \text{ var } \bar{x}_{i.} - 2 \text{ var } \bar{x}_{.j} + 2 \text{ var } \bar{x} + 2 \text{ var } \bar{x} - 2 \text{ var } \bar{x} - 2 \text{ var } \bar{x})$$

$$= rc(\text{var } x_{ij} - \text{var } \bar{x}_{i.} - \text{var } \bar{x}_{.j} + \text{var } \bar{x})$$

which with the aid of (7.31), (7.32), (7.33), and (7.34) reduces to

$$rc\sigma^2 \left(1 - \frac{1}{c} - \frac{1}{r} - \frac{1}{rc}\right) = (r - 1)(c - 1)\sigma^2$$

The decomposed total sum of squares as well as their expectations are summarized in Table 7.10.

TABLE 7.10

Analysis of Variance Table. Model II, Two Way, without Replication

Source of Variation	Sum of Squares	D.F.	M.S.	Expectation of M.S.
Rows	$\sum_{i,j}(\bar{x}_{x.} - \bar{x})^2 = S_r^2$	$(r - 1)$	$S_r^2/(r - 1)$	$\sigma^2 + c\sigma_r^2$
Columns	$\sum_{i,j}(\bar{x}_. - \bar{x})^2 = S_c^2$	$(c - 1)$	$S_c^2/(c - 1)$	$\sigma^2 + r\sigma_c^2$
Interaction	$\sum_{i,j}(x_{ij} - \bar{x}_{i.} - \bar{x}_{.j} + \bar{x})^2 = S_{rc}^2$	$(r - 1)(c - 1)$	$S_{rc}^2/(r - 1)(c - 1)$	σ^2
Total	$\sum_{i,j}(x_{ij} - \bar{x})^2$	$(rc - 1)$	—	—

Statistical Inferences to Present Development

At this stage we can easily find estimates of μ, σ_r^2, σ_c^2, and σ^2, namely,

$$\bar{x}, \quad \frac{S_r}{c(r - 1)} - \frac{S_{rc}}{c(r - 1)(c - 1)}, \quad \frac{S_c}{r(c - 1)} - \frac{S_{rc}}{r(r - 1)(c - 1)}$$

$$\frac{S_{rc}}{(r - 1)(c - 1)}$$

MODEL III MIXED COMPONENT MODEL

In many real problems we are faced with the need to consider *both random and fixed components in our experiment.*

As an example, consider the collection of samples from different reefs. We might very well be interested in the insoluble residue of these samples. The samples are sent to the c and only c laboratories which conduct such studies. Here the percentage of insoluble residue, x_{ij}, is constructed as:

$$x_{ij} = \mu + (\bar{y}_{i.} - \mu) + (\bar{\mu}_{.j} - \mu) + \epsilon_{ij}$$
$$= \mu + a_i + \xi_j + \epsilon_{ij} \tag{7.43}$$

where μ = a constant. $(\bar{\mu}_{.j} - \mu) = \xi_j$ = a constant representing the systematic deviation between the true average insoluble residue for all samples as determined by the jth laboratory, from the true over-all percentage insoluble residue for all samples and all laboratories. $(\bar{y}_{i.} - \mu) = a_i$ is a random variable representing the random variation or deviation of the average insoluble residue for the ith sample, as determined by all laboratories, from the over-all true insoluble residue of all samples and all laboratories. Here $Ea_i = 0$ and var $a_i = \sigma_r^2$. As usual $E\epsilon_{ij} = 0$ and var $\epsilon_{ij} = \sigma^2$.

Thus $Ex_{ij} = \bar{\mu}_{.j}$ and

$$\text{var } (x_{ij}) = \sigma_r^2 + \sigma^2 \tag{7.44}$$

Decomposition of Sum of Squares

Since $\bar{x}_{i.} = \mu + a_i + \epsilon_{i.}$, then

$$E\bar{x}_{i.} = \mu$$

and

$$\text{var } \bar{x}_{i.} = \sigma_r^2 + \frac{\sigma^2}{c} \tag{7.45}$$

and since

$$\bar{x}_{.j} = \mu + \frac{\sum\limits_{i=1}^{r} a_i}{r} + \xi_j + \bar{\epsilon}_{.j}$$

then

$$E\bar{x}_{.j} = \mu + \xi_j = \bar{\mu}_{.j}$$

and

$$\text{var } \bar{x}_{.j} = \frac{\sigma_r^2}{r} + \frac{\sigma^2}{r} \tag{7.46}$$

Finally, since

$$\bar{x} = \bar{\bar{x}}_{..} = \mu + \frac{\sum\limits_{i=1}^{r} a_i}{r} + \bar{\bar{\epsilon}}_{..}$$

then

$$E\bar{x} = \mu$$

and

$$\text{var } \bar{x} = \frac{\sigma_r^2}{r} + \frac{\sigma^2}{rc} \tag{7.47}$$

The total sum of square is defined as

$$\sum_{i=1}^{r} \sum_{j=1}^{c} (x_{ij} - \bar{x})^2$$

and is, as before, equivalent to

$$\sum_i \sum_j (\bar{x}_{.j} - \bar{x})^2 + \sum_i \sum_j (\bar{x}_{i.} - \bar{x})^2 + \sum_i \sum_j (x_{ij} - \bar{x}_{i.} - \bar{x}_{.j} + \bar{x})^2$$

The first sum of squares represents, in this example, that portion of total variability contributed by different laboratory determinations of the insoluble residue of all samples. The second sum of squares represents the variability contributed by the differences among the insoluble residues of the different samples. The last sum of squares once again represents the interaction or residual or unknown or unassigned variation due to the inconsistency of insoluble residue determinations from laboratory to laboratory.

Expectations of Sums of Squares .

A.
$$E \sum_{i=1}^{r} \sum_{j=1}^{c} (\bar{x}_{i.} - \bar{x})^2 = E \sum_i \sum_j [(\bar{x}_{i.} - \mu) - (\bar{x} - \mu)]^2$$

With the aid of (7.45) and (7.47) this reduces to

$$rc \operatorname{var} \bar{x}_{i.} + rc \operatorname{var} \bar{x} - 2 \sum_i \sum_j E(\bar{x}_{i.}\bar{x} - \mu\bar{x}_{i.} - \mu\bar{x} + \mu^2)$$

$$= rc(\operatorname{var} \bar{x}_{i.} - \operatorname{var} \bar{x}) = rc\left(\sigma_r^2 + \frac{\sigma^2}{c} - \frac{\sigma_r^2}{r} - \frac{\sigma^2}{rc}\right)$$

$$= rc \frac{(r-1)}{r}\left(\sigma_r^2 + \frac{\sigma^2}{c}\right)$$

$$= (r-1)(\sigma^2 + c\sigma_r^2) \tag{7.48}$$

B. $E \sum_i \sum_j (\bar{x}_{.j} - \bar{x})^2 = E \sum_i \sum_j [(\bar{x}_{.j} - \bar{\mu}_{.j}) - (\bar{x} - \mu) + (\bar{\mu}_{.j} - \mu)]^2$

With the aid of (7.46) and (7.47) this partially reduces to

$rc \operatorname{var} \bar{x}_{.j} + rc \operatorname{var} \bar{x} + \sum_i \sum_j (\bar{\mu}_{.j} - \mu)^2 + E \sum_i \sum_j$ (three pairs of cross products).

Let us next consider the three different cross products, ignoring the signs.

1.
$$E \sum_i \sum_j (\bar{x}_{.j}\bar{x} - \mu\bar{x}_{.j} - \bar{\mu}_{.j}\bar{x} + u\bar{u}_{.j})$$

Summing first on j, then taking expectations, and finally summing over i, this reduces to

$$rc \operatorname{var} \bar{x}$$

2.
$$E \sum_i \sum_j (\bar{x}_{.j} - \bar{\mu}_{.j})(\bar{\mu}_{.j} - \mu)$$

Rewriting this as

$$\sum_i \sum_j (\bar{\mu}_{.j} - \mu)E(\bar{x}_{.j} - \bar{\mu}_{.j})$$

and taking the expectation we obtain 0.

3. Finally,

$$E \sum_i \sum_j (\bar{x} - \mu)(\bar{\mu}_{.j} - \mu) = \sum_i \sum_j (\bar{\mu}_{.j} - \mu)E(\bar{x} - \mu) = 0$$

Thus

$$E \sum_i \sum_j (\bar{x}_{.j} - \bar{x})^2 = rc \operatorname{var} \bar{x}_{.j} + rc \operatorname{var} \bar{x} + \sum_i \sum_j (\bar{\mu}_{.j} - \mu)^2 - 2rc \operatorname{var} \bar{x}$$

Substituting from (7.46) and (7.47) this reduces to

$$rc\left(\frac{\sigma_r^2}{r} + \frac{\sigma^2}{r} - \frac{\sigma_r^2}{r} - \frac{\sigma^2}{rc}\right) + \sum_i \sum_j (\bar{\mu}_{.j} - \mu)^2$$

$$= (c-1)\sigma^2 + \sum_i \sum_j (\bar{\mu}_{.j} - \mu)^2 \quad (7.49)$$

C. $E \sum_i \sum_j (x_{ij} - \bar{x}_{i.} - \bar{x}_{.j} + \bar{x})^2$

$$= E \sum_i \sum_j [(x_{ij} - \bar{\mu}_{.j}) - (\bar{x}_{i.} - \mu) - (\bar{x}_{.j} - \bar{\mu}_{.j}) + (\bar{x} - \mu)]^2$$

$$= rc[\text{var } x_{ij} + \text{var } \bar{x}_{i.} + \text{var } \bar{x}_{.j} + \text{var } \bar{x}]$$

$+ E \sum_i \sum_j$ (three pairs of cross products)

1. $$E \sum_i \sum_j (x_{ij} - \bar{\mu}_{.j})(\bar{x}_{i.} - \mu)$$

which if summed on j, then expectations taken, then summed over i becomes

$$rc \text{ var } \bar{x}_{i.}$$

2. $$E \sum_i \sum_j (x_{ij} - \bar{\mu}_{.j})(\bar{x}_{.j} - \bar{\mu}_{.j})$$

which if summed on i, then expectations taken, and finally summed over j becomes

$$rc \text{ var } \bar{x}_{.j}$$

3. $$E \sum_i \sum_j (x_{ij} - \bar{\mu}_{.j})(\bar{x} - \mu) = rc \text{ var } \bar{x}$$

This is obtained if one sums first over i and j and then takes expectations.

4. $$E \sum_i \sum_j (\bar{x}_{i.} - \mu)(\bar{x}_{.j} - \bar{\mu}_{.j}) = rc \text{ var } \bar{x}$$

5. $$E \sum_i \sum_j (\bar{x}_{i.} - \mu)(\bar{x} - \mu) = rc \text{ var } \bar{x}$$

6. $$E \sum_i \sum_j (\bar{x}_{.j} - \bar{\mu}_{.j})(\bar{x} - \mu) = rc \text{ var } \bar{x}$$

Thus (7.49) becomes

$rc(\text{var } x_{ij} + \text{var } \bar{x}_{i.} + \text{var } \bar{x}_{.j} + \text{var } \bar{x} - 2 \text{ var } \bar{x}_{i.} - 2 \text{ var } \bar{x}_{.j}$

$\qquad + 2 \text{ var } \bar{x} + 2 \text{ var } \bar{x} - 2 \text{ var } \bar{x} - 2 \text{ var } \bar{x})$

$$= rc\left(\sigma_r^2 + \sigma^2 - \sigma_r^2 - \frac{\sigma^2}{c} - \frac{\sigma_r^2}{r} - \frac{\sigma^2}{r} + \frac{\sigma_r^2}{r} + \frac{\sigma^2}{rc}\right)$$

$$= rc\sigma^2\left(1 - \frac{1}{c} - \frac{1}{r} - \frac{1}{rc}\right)$$

$$= (r-1)(c-1)\sigma^2 \quad (7.50)$$

The sum of squares, the sources of variation, the mean squares and their expectations are summarized as in Table 7.11.

TABLE 7.11

Source of Variation	Degrees of Freedom	Sum of Squares	Mean Squares	Expectation of Mean Squares
Rows	$(r - 1)$	$\sum_{i,j} (\bar{x}_{i.} - \bar{x})^2 = S_r^2$	$S_r^2/(r - 1)$	$\sigma^2 + c\sigma_r^2$
Columns	$(c - 1)$	$\sum_{i,j} (\bar{x}_{.j} - \bar{x})^2 = S_c^2$	$S_c^2/(c - 1)$	$\sigma^2 + \dfrac{\sum_i \sum_j (\bar{\mu}_{.j} - \mu)^2}{c - 1}$
Residual	$(r - 1)(c - 1)$	$\sum_{i,j} (x_{ij} - \bar{x}_{i.} - \bar{x}_{.j} + \bar{x})^2 = S_\epsilon^2$	$S_\epsilon^2/(r - 1)(c - 1)$	σ^2
Total	$(rc - 1)$	$\sum_{i,j} (x_{ij} - \bar{x})^2 = S_T$	$S_T^2/(rc - 1)$	

TESTING HYPOTHESES WITH THE AID OF THE ANALYSIS OF VARIANCE

The estimation of parameters and the summarization of data are a small portion of the effectiveness and utility of the analysis of variance technique. Statistical inference concerned with the testing of hypotheses, a rather important phase of statistical analysis, can be performed with the aid of the assumed mathematical models and can be developed from those preceding sections in which the estimation and summary phases of the analysis of variance techniques were discussed. Examination of the mathematical models will suggest those hypotheses which can be readily examined and tested.

Consider the systematic or nonrandom factors associated with the experimental designs described earlier. These factors, ignoring the population constant μ, were, for example, $(\mu_i - \mu)$, ξ_i, and η_j.

When considering a model containing such factors, we do so with the goal of determining their effectiveness in contributing to the inherent variability of the variable under consideration. Thus the variable was structurally decomposed in each of the mathematical models (perhaps more nearly structurally exposed). Do these systematic or nonrandom factors have an effect on the variable one observes? An appropriate hypothesis would be concerned with the values of these effects, for example, are they zero, or, are they identical? Thus when systematic factors are involved, a null hypothesis of the following form bears consideration, namely, H_1: $\mu_1 = \mu_2 = \cdots = \mu_r$ with the alternative H_2: some $\mu_i > \mu_j$. Hypotheses of the standard parametric type were discussed in Chapters 5 and 6. There it was apparent that in order to test any hypothesis certain facts had to be known and certain properties had to be determined or assumed. For example, after a level of significance or α-error was selected a suitable statistic to test our hypothesis was essential. After this was chosen, an examination of all possible outcomes of the experiment had to be performed in order to select some criterion or criteria for accepting or rejecting the hypothesis, or for deferring a decision. This is tantamount to knowing the probability density function or frequency distribution or simply, the distribution of the test statistic, assuming the null hypothesis were true. However, the determination of the distribution of a test statistic involves some knowledge of the distribution of the random variable observed or measured in the experiment and which contributes to the value of the test statistic. Once the distribution of the variable under consideration is known, the distribution of the test statistic can at times be determined, and the rejection-acceptance regions can be defined and then, and only then, can the hypothesis be tested.

Thus in the problem of testing the hypothesis: $\mu_1 = \mu_2 = \cdots = \mu_r$ one must proceed in the manner outlined above and decide upon those facts which are known and those assumptions which must be made. Here it is apparent that one must assume or determine in some manner the distribution of the random variable x in order to determine the distribution of the test statistic, whatever it might be. Thus the need for the fourth and final assumption essential to complete analysis of variance procedure has been heuristically developed. It is worth noting once again that the assumption of the form of the distribution of x is not essential to that phase of the analysis of variance procedure concerned with merely summarization and estimation. The development of the analysis of variance technique up to now has been performed without any knowledge of the distribution of x, a factor frequently overlooked in statistical analysis. The assumptions made up to this point have been randomness, additivity, and homogeneous variance. The specific form of the distribution of x is developed in the following sections.

Tests of Hypotheses

Fixed Components

As an example, consider the one-way analysis of variance, Model I, developed on page 134. In this example a hypothesis of interest would be H_1: $\mu_1 = \mu_2 = \cdots = \mu_r$. Considering this hypothesis, what shall the test statistic be? Examination of Table 7.3 will aid in answering this question. If the null hypothesis were true, that is, if the fourteen different machines were producing rods with essentially identical strengths, then $\sum_{i=1}^{14} (\mu_i - \mu)^2 = \sum_{i=1}^{r} \xi_i^2$ would be identically 0, and the expected mean square of machines would be identical to the expected mean square of rods manufactured by the same machine, namely, σ^2. That is, if H_1 were true

$$E\left(\frac{S_m^{\,2}}{r-1}\right) = E\left[\frac{S_r^{\,2}}{r(c-1)}\right] = \sigma^2$$

Furthermore, the ratio of

$$\frac{S_m^2/(r-1)}{S_r^2/r(c-1)}$$

would be, on average, one. Thus, a test statistic of this form appears satisfactory and would be so, provided one knew its distribution assuming H_1 to be true.

To elicit the distribution of this ratio we add to our previous assumptions of additivity, randomness, and homogeneous variance, the assumption for this specific model that ϵ_{ij} is normally distributed with mean $E(\epsilon_{ij}) = 0$ and var $(\epsilon_{ij}) = \sigma^2$. This therefore makes x_{ij} a normal deviate with mean μ and variance σ^2.

With this assumption, the reader will recall that the mean squares in the numerator and denominator of the test statistic are distributed in the form of $\sigma^2\chi^2/n$ with n degrees of freedom (Chapter 4), and the ratio of two such distributed variates is itself distributed as F with n_1 and n_2 degrees of freedom. With the knowledge of the distribution of this variance ratio one can now establish a rejection-acceptance region and hence test the hypothesis in question.

Random Components

In considering a model with random components such as the one-way analysis of variance design, Model II, it is not the means of the components that interests us, but rather their variances. The variance of the random component(s) is a factor contributing to the variability of the random variable x which is observed. The question of significance here is, do these components of variance exist? Thus, for example, to answer the question of the homogeneity of the slides obtained from the granite, Table 7.5, the hypothesis of concern is H_1: $\sigma_s^2 = 0$. An examination of Table 7.5 is of aid in selecting a statistic appropriate to the testing of this hypothesis. *If the null hypothesis were true*, then the expectation of the mean square for slides is identical with the expectation of the mean square for differences among slides. On average, the ratio of

$$\frac{S_s^2/(r-1)}{S_t^2/r(c-1)} \tag{7.51}$$

would be 1. If one assumes that ϵ_{ij} and $(y_i - \mu)$ are normal variates with means 0 and variances σ^2 and σ_s^2 respectively, then x_{ij} is a normal deviate with mean μ and variance $\sigma_s^2 + \sigma^2$. Thus the distribution of (7.51) is F with $(r-1)$ and $r(c-1)$ degrees of freedom. Acceptance-rejection criteria can now be established and the hypothesis can be tested.

This procedure may be continued for the other mathematical models discussed in this work as well as for those not considered in any detail.

In each of the cases the test statistic for the hypotheses in question may be obtained from the mathematical models pertinent to the example and design; furthermore, the assumption of the form of the distribution of the random components permits the distribution of the observed random variable to be known; this in turn permits a determination of the distribution of the test statistic to be made. Whether the factors are random or systematic, the test statistic in either case is an F distributed variable. This generalization is summarized in a series of analysis of variance tables (Tables 7.12 to 7.16), each appropriate to the particular design and model discussed in this chapter.

LOCATING THE SIGNIFICANT DIFFERENCES

If the hypothesis of equal means is rejected, when more than two means have been compared, we are faced with the problem of deciding which of the means differ from which other means. The analysis of variance procedure merely indicates that differences exist, it does not indicate the exact location of these differences. It may be generally stated that no one procedure for determining these significantly different values has been agreed upon. Two methods are described below which appear quite satisfactory and which can be utilized quite easily. They are the Tukey or T-method of multiple comparisons and the Scheffé or S-method of finding all contrasts.

Tukey's Method of Multiple Comparisons or T-method of Multiple Comparisons[1]

The method described below is based on the upper percentage points $q_{f,n}$, of the Studentized range or q distribution. Here, confidence statements concerning an array of comparisons can be made. Thus if s^2 represents the estimate of experimental error, based on f degrees of freedom, and if one of the true differences of the $[n(n-1)]/2$ possible differences is $\mu_i - \mu_j$, where $i \neq j$, $i, j = 1, \cdots, n$, then

$$P\{a_{ij} - q_{f,n}ks \leq \mu_i - \mu_j \leq a_{ij} + q_{f,n}ks\} = 1 - \alpha,$$

where $q_{f,n}$ is the upper α percent of the q distribution.[2]
Here

$$Ea_{ij} = \mu_i - \mu_j.$$

[1] Tukey's method of multiple comparisons was first brought to Kahn's attention by Professor George Snedecor in a graduate course in *Experimental Design* at the Iowa State University in Fall 1954. Professor H. Scheffé in his *The Analysis of Variance*, John Wiley, New York, 1959, refers to Tukey's method of multiple comparisons as the "T" method. With but slight modification we have adopted Scheffé's notations in developing this method. (Scheffé, *op. cit.* pp. 73–75).

[2] See Scheffé, *op. cit.* pp. 444–445 or E. S. Pearson, and H. D. Hartley, *Biometrika Tables for Statisticians*, Cambridge University Press, Cambridge, 1954.

TABLE 7.12

Complete Analysis of Variance Table. Model I, One-Way Anov

Source of Variation	Degrees of Freedom	Sum of Squares	Mean Squares	Expectation of Mean Squares	To Test Hypothesis:	Statistic
Among machines	$(r-1)$	$\sum_i \sum_j (\bar{x}_{i.} - \bar{x})^2 = S_m^2$	$S_m^2/(r-1)$	$\sigma^2 + \dfrac{c}{r-1}\sum_{i=1}^r \xi_i^2$	$\mu_i = \mu_2 = \cdots = \mu_r$	$\dfrac{S_m^2/(r-1)}{S_r^2/r(c-1)}$
Among rods manufactured by the same machine	$r(c-1)$	$\sum_i \sum_j (x_{ij} - \bar{x}_{i.})^2 = S_r^2$	$S_r^2/r(c-1)$	σ^2	$\left(\sum_{i=1}^r \xi_i^2 = 0\right)$ —	—
Total	$(rc-1)$	$\sum_i \sum_j (x_{ij} - \bar{x})^2 = S_T^2$	$S_T^2/(rc-1)$	—	—	—

Model: $X = x_{ij} = \mu + (u_i - \mu) + \epsilon_{ij}$
Distribution assumptions: ϵ_{ij} is $N[0, \sigma^2]$
Distribution of X: $N[\mu, \sigma^2]$

TABLE 7.13
Complete Analysis of Variance Table. Model II, One-Way Anov

Source of Variation	Degrees of Freedom	Sum of Squares	Mean Squares	Expectation of Mean Squares	To Test Hypothesis:	Statistic
Among slides	$(r-1)$	$\sum_i \sum_j (\bar{x}_{i.} - \bar{\bar{x}})^2 = S_s^2$	$S_s^2/(r-1)$	$\sigma^2 + c\sigma_s^2$	$\sigma_s^2 = 0$	$\dfrac{S_s^2/(r-1)}{S_t^2/r(c-1)}$
Among traverses within slides	$r(c-1)$	$\sum_i \sum_j (x_{ij} - \bar{x}_{i.})^2 = S_t^2$	$S_t^2/r(c-1)$	σ^2	—	—
Total	$(rc-1)$	$\sum_i \sum_j (x_{ij} - \bar{\bar{x}})^2 = S_T^2$	$S_T^2/(rc-1)$			

Model: $X = x_{ij} = \mu + (\bar{y}_{i.} - \mu) + \epsilon_{ij}$
Distribution assumptions: ϵ_{ij} is $N(0, \sigma^2)$
$(\bar{y}_{i.} - \mu)$ is $N[0, \sigma_s^2]$
Distribution of X: $N[\mu, \sigma_s^2 + \sigma^2]$.

TABLE 7.14

Complete Analysis of Variance Table. Model I, Two-Way Anov

Source of Variation	Degrees of Freedom	Sum of Squares	Mean Squares	Expectation of Mean Squares	To Test Hypothesis:	Statistic
Rows	$(r-1)$	$c\sum_i(\bar{x}_{i.} - \bar{x})^2 = S_r^2$	$S_r^2/(r-1)$	$\sigma^2 + \dfrac{\sum_{i,j}(\bar{\mu}_{i.} - \mu)^2}{r-1}$	$\bar{\mu}_{1.} = \bar{\mu}_{2.} = \cdots = \bar{\mu}_{r.},$ $\left(\sum_{i,j}\xi_i^2 = 0\right)$	$\dfrac{S_r^2/(r-1)}{S_{rc}^2/(r-1)(c-1)}$
Columns	$(c-1)$	$r\sum_j(\bar{x}_{.j} - \bar{x})^2 = S_c^2$	$S_c^2/(c-1)$	$\sigma^2 + \dfrac{\sum_{i,j}(\bar{\mu}_{.j} - \mu)^2}{c-1}$	$\bar{\mu}_{.1} = \bar{\mu}_{.2} = \cdots = \bar{\mu}_{.c}$ $\left(\sum_{i,j}\eta_j^2 = 0\right)$	$\dfrac{S_c^2/(c-1)}{S_{rc}^2/(r-1)(c-1)}$
Residual	$(r-1)(c-1)$	$\sum_i\sum_j(x_{ij} - \bar{x}_{i.} - \bar{x}_{.j} + \bar{x})^2 = S_{rc}^2$	$S_{rc}^2/(r-1)(c-1)$	σ^2	—	—
Total	$(rc-1)$	$\sum_i\sum_j(x_{ij} - \bar{x})^2 = S_T^2$	$S_T^2/(rc-1)$	—	—	—

Model: $X = x_{ij} = \mu + \xi_i + \eta_j + \epsilon_{ij}$
Distribution assumptions: ϵ_{ij} is $N[0, \sigma^2]$
Distribution of X: $N[\mu + \xi_i + \eta_j, \sigma^2]$

TABLE 7.15
Complete Analysis of Variance Table. Model II, Two-Way Anov

Source of Variation	Degrees of Freedom	Sum of Squares	Mean Squares	Expectation of Mean Squares	To Test Hypothesis:	Statistic
Rows	$(r-1)$	$\sum_{i,j}(\bar{x}_{i.}-\bar{\bar{x}})^2 = S_r^2$	$S_r^2/(r-1)$	$\sigma^2 + c\sigma_r^2$	$\sigma_r^2 = 0$	$\dfrac{S_r^2/(r-1)}{S_{rc}^2/(r-1)(c-1)}$
Columns	$(c-1)$	$\sum_{i,j}(\bar{x}_{.j}-\bar{\bar{x}})^2 = S_c^2$	$S_c^2/(c-1)$	$\sigma^2 + r\sigma_c^2$	$\sigma_c^2 = 0$	$\dfrac{S_c^2/(c-1)}{S_{rc}^2/(c-1)(r-1)}$
Interaction	$(r-1)(c-1)$	$\sum_{i,j}(x_{ij}-\bar{x}_{i.}-\bar{x}_{.j}+\bar{\bar{x}})^2 = S_{rc}^2$	$S_{rc}^2/(r-1)(c-1)$	σ^2	—	
Total	$(rc-1)$	$\sum_{i,j}(x_{ij}-\bar{\bar{x}})^2 = S_T^2$	$S_T^2/rc-1$			

Model: $X = x_{ij} = \mu + y_i + z_j + \epsilon_{ij}$

Distribution assumptions:
ϵ_{ij} is $N[0, \sigma^2]$
y_i is $N[0, \sigma_r^2]$
z_j is $N[0, \sigma_c^2]$

Distribution of X: $N[\mu, \sigma_r^2 + \sigma_c^2 + \sigma^2]$

TABLE 7.16

Complete Analysis of Variance Table. Model III, Two-Way Anov

Source of Variation	Degrees of Freedom	Sum of Squares	Mean Squares	Expectation of Mean Squares	To Test Hypothesis:	Statistic
Rows	$(r-1)$	$\sum_i \sum_j (\bar{x}_{i.} - \bar{x})^2 = S_r^2$	$S_r^2/(r-1)$	$\sigma^2 + c\sigma_r^2$	$\sigma_r^2 = 0$	$\dfrac{S_r^2/(r-1)}{S_{rc}^2/(r-1)(c-1)}$
Columns	$(c-1)$	$\sum_i \sum_j (\bar{x}_{.j} - \bar{x})^2 = S_c^2$	$S_c^2/(c-1)$	$\sigma^2 + \dfrac{\sum_{i,j}(\bar{\mu}_{.j} - \mu)^2}{c-1}$	$\bar{\mu}_{.1} = \bar{\mu}_{.2}^2 = \cdots = \bar{\mu}_{.c}$ $\left(\sum_{i,j}(\bar{\mu}_{.j} - \mu)^2 = 0\right)$	$\dfrac{S_c^2/(c-1)}{S_{rc}^2/(r-1)(c-1)}$
Residual	$(r-1)(c-1)$	$\sum_i \sum_j (x_{ij} - \bar{x}_{i.} - \bar{x}_{.j} + \bar{x})^2 = S_{rc}^2$	$S_{rc}^2/(r-1)(c-1)$	σ^2	—	
Total	$(rc-1)$	$\sum_i \sum_j (x_{ij} - \bar{x})^2 = S_T^2$	$S_T^2/(rc-1)$			

Model: $X = x_{ij} = \mu + a_i + \xi_j + \epsilon_{ij}$
Distribution assumptions: ϵ_{ij} is $N[0, \sigma^2]$
a_i is $N[0, \sigma_r^2]$
Distribution of X: $N[\mu + \xi_j, \sigma_r^2 + \sigma^2]$.

TABLE 7.17

Complete Analysis of Variance Table. Two-Way Anov with Replications

Source of Variation	Degrees of Freedom	Sum of Squares	Mean Squares	Expectation of Mean Squares	To Test Hypothesis:	Statistic
Rows	$(r-1)$	$cp\sum_i(\bar{\bar{x}}_{i..} - \bar{x})^2 = S_r^2$	$S_r^2/(r-1)$	$\sigma^2 + p\sigma_{rc}^2 + cp\sigma_r^2$	$\sigma_r^2 = 0$	$\dfrac{S_r^2/(r-1)}{S_{rc}^2/(r-1)(c-1)}$ [1]
Columns	$(c-1)$	$rp\sum_j(\bar{\bar{x}}_{.j.} - \bar{x})^2 = S_c^2$	$S_c^2/(c-1)$	$\sigma^2 + p\sigma_{rc}^2 + rp\sigma_c^2$	$\sigma_c^2 = 0$	$\dfrac{S_c^2/(c-1)}{S_{rc}^2/(r-1)(c-1)}$ [1]
Rows × columns (interaction)	$(r-1)(c-1)$	$p\sum_{i,j}(\bar{x}_{ij.} - \bar{\bar{x}}_{.j.} - \bar{\bar{x}}_{i..} + \bar{x})^2 = S_{rc}^2$	$S_{rc}^2/(r-1)(c-1)$	$\sigma^2 + p\sigma_{rc}^2$	$\sigma_{rc}^2 = 0$	$\dfrac{S_{rc}^2/(r-1)(c-1)}{S_\epsilon^2/rc(p-1)}$
Replications	$rc(p-1)$	$\sum_{i,j,k}(x_{ijk} - \bar{x}_{ij.})^2 = S_\epsilon^2$	$S_\epsilon^2/rc(p-1)$	σ^2		
Total	$(rcp-1)$	$\sum_{ijk}(x_{ijk} - \bar{x})^2$	$S_T^2/(rcp-1)$			

Model: $X = x_{ijk} = \mu + y_i + z_j + w_{ij} + \epsilon_{ijk}$

Distribution assumptions: y_i, z_j, w_{ij} and ϵ_{ijk} are $N[0, \sigma_r^2], N[0, \sigma_c^2], N[0, \sigma_{rc}^2]$ and $N[0, \sigma^2]$, respectively.

Distribution of X: $N[\mu, \sigma_r^2 + \sigma_c^2 + \sigma_{rc}^2 + \sigma^2]$

[1] If H_1: $\sigma_{rc}^2 = 0$ is accepted, then $S_{rc}^2/(r-1)(c-1)$ or $S_\epsilon^2/rc(p-1)$ may be used as the denominator to test σ_r^2, $\sigma_c^2 = 0$. Furthermore, if $\sigma_{rc}^2 = 0$ is accepted, then $S_{rc}^2/(r-1)(c-1)$ and $S_\epsilon^2/rc(p-1)$ both estimate σ^2; hence one may pool these two estimates and obtain a new estimate with increased degrees of freedom. Thus $S_{rc}^2 + S_\epsilon^2/(r-1)(c-1) + rc(p-1)$ is the pooled error estimate of σ^2, the experimental error.

Modifying Scheffé's notation (Scheffé, 1960, pp. 73–75), *all possible comparisons* may be expressed as

$$\Psi = \sum_{i=1}^{n} c_i \mu_i$$

where $\sum_{i=1}^{n} c_i = 0$. In this case

$$P\left\{ b_{ij} - q_{f,n,\alpha} \, ks\left(\frac{1}{2} \sum_{i=1}^{n} |c_i| \right) \leq \Psi \leq b_{ij} + q_{f,n,\alpha} \, ks\left(\frac{1}{2} \sum_{i=1}^{n} |c_i| \right) \right\} = 1 - \alpha$$

where $E[b_{ij}] = \Psi$.

The assumptions for this test are:

1. The estimates of the parameters to be compared are statistically independent.
2. The estimates are $N[\mu_i, a^2\sigma^2]$ where $i = 1, \cdots, n$, and a is a known positive constant.
3. s^2 is distributed as $\sigma^2\chi^2/f$, and is independent of the set of estimates of the parameters being compared.

TABLE 7.18

Average Values for Packing Density Averaged over All Traverses (in per cent)

Plane		XY	XZ	YZ
Direction	0°	61.86	59.24	62.40
	30°	61.86	64.52	57.92
	60°	60.01	65.66	63.87
	90°	62.42	58.42	54.34
	120°	62.76	59.17	64.40
	150°	57.85	49.99	55.66
Slide averages		61.13	59.50	59.77

EXAMPLES

If, in an analysis of variance, the hypothesis $H_1\colon \mu_1 = \mu_2 = \cdots = \mu_n$ is rejected, where $\{\mu_i\}$ are estimated by $\bar{x}_i$, then a comparison of any pair of the $\frac{1}{2}n(n-1)$ differences between different μ's would give rise to the following interval:

$$P\left\{ (\bar{x}_i - \bar{x}_j) - q_{f,n,\alpha} \frac{s}{\sqrt{n}} \leq \mu_i - \mu_j \leq (\bar{x}_i - \bar{x}_j) + q_{f,n,\alpha} \frac{s}{\sqrt{n}} \right\} = 1 - \alpha$$

Here
$$k = \frac{1}{\sqrt{n}}$$

$$a_{ij} = \bar{x}_i - \bar{x}_j$$

The *allowance* between any pair of means is $q_{f,n,\alpha}\, s/\sqrt{n}$. If the difference between the pair of means is greater than the allowance, then the parameters are significantly different. If the difference between the estimates is less than the allowance, the parameters are not significantly different from one another.

In a study of the three-dimensional nature of packing, it was shown (Kahn, 1959)[1] that, for different directions within three mutually perpendicular faces of an oriented cube of Pottsville Sandstone, there were significantly different estimates of the packing parameters. The average packing values averaged over all traverses (five for each direction) are summarized in Table 7.18. The problem here is which directions within which of the faces are significantly different. Applying the T-method, we proceed as follows:

$$s^2 = 22.3866 \qquad \frac{s}{\sqrt{n}} = \frac{4.73}{4.23} = 1.12$$

$$f = 72$$

$$n = 18$$

$$q_{f,n,\alpha} = q_{72,18,0.05} = 5.1$$

$$5.1 \times 1.12 = 5.71 = \text{Allowance}$$

Thus in the XZ plane the $150°$ direction differs significantly from any direction whose average packing value is greater than 55.75%, i.e., all others. This is a direction of minimum packing, whereas the $60°$ direction is a direction of maximum packing, since it is greater than all others.

In the YZ plane, using the Tukey method, nothing can be said about locating unique maximum and minimum.

Scheffé or S-method of Finding all Contrasts

If the hypothesis H_1: $\mu_1 = \mu_2 = \cdots = \mu_k$, where μ_i represents a set of means from a normal population is rejected, what further statistical inference can be made except that the μ_i are not identical? One means of attacking this problem was proposed by Scheffé (1953, 1959).[2,3] His method permits the comparison of any pair, or, as a matter of fact, permits the totality of comparisons between and among estimates of all of the parameters of μ_i.

Scheffé has shown that if a comparison or contrast is defined as

$$\theta = \sum_{i=1}^{k} c_i \mu_i$$

where

$$\sum_{i=1}^{k} c_i = 0$$

[1] J. S. Kahn, 1959, Anisotropic sedimentary parameters, *Trans. N.Y. Acad. Sci.* Ser. II, 21: 373–386.

[2] H. Scheffé, 1953, A method for judging all contrasts in the analysis of variance, *Biometrika* 40: 87–104.

[3] H. Scheffé, 1959, *The Analysis of Variance*, John Wiley, New York. pp. 66–72.

and where $\bar{x}_1, \bar{x}_2, \cdots, \bar{x}_k$ and s^2 are estimates of $\mu_1, \mu_2, \cdots, \mu_k$ and σ^2 from samples of size $n_1, n_2, \cdots, n_k$, such that $\bar{x}_1, \bar{x}_2, \cdots, \bar{x}_k$ are jointly normally distributed and independent of s^2 and where

$$E\bar{x}_i = \mu_i$$

and further, that the covariance of any two means cov $(\bar{x}_i, \bar{x}_j)$ is constant, then

$$P\{\hat{\theta} - S\hat{\sigma}_{\hat{\theta}} \leq \theta \leq \hat{\theta} + S\hat{\sigma}_{\hat{\theta}}\} = 1 - \alpha$$

Here

$$\hat{\theta} = \sum_{i=1}^{k} c_i \bar{x}_i$$

$$\hat{\sigma}_{\hat{\theta}}^2 = \text{var } \hat{\theta} = \text{var} \sum_{i=1}^{k} c_i \bar{x}_i$$

and

$$S = \left\{(k-1)F_\alpha\left[\frac{k-1}{n_k - 1}\right]\right\}^{\frac{1}{2}}$$

Thus if

1. $\{-S\hat{\sigma}_{\hat{\theta}} < \hat{\theta} < S\hat{\sigma}_{\hat{\theta}}\}$, this implies θ is not significantly different from 0.

2. $\{\hat{\theta} \geq S\hat{\sigma}_{\hat{\theta}}\}$, this implies θ is significantly different from 0 and is greater than 0.

3. $\{\hat{\theta} \leq -S\hat{\sigma}_{\hat{\theta}}\}$, this implies that θ is significantly different from 0 and is less than 0.

SUGGESTED READING

L. Horberg and P. E. Potter, 1955, *Stratigraphic and sedimentologic aspects of Lemont Drift of Northeastern Illinois*, Illinois State Geol. Survey Rept. of Investigations 185. Includes an application of the Scheffé method.

ESTIMATES OF COMPONENTS OF VARIANCES

Models II and Models III of the analysis of variance are concerned totally or in part with variance components and the hypothesis that they are zero. If this hypothesis is rejected, then some means of estimating the component(s) of variance is in order.

In the one-way analysis of variance Model II (Table 7.13) the sum of squares between groups is an estimate of $c\sigma_s^2 + \sigma^2$. Also the sum of squares within groups is an estimate of the experimental error σ^2. Thus estimates of σ^2 and σ_s^2 are $S^2_t/r(c-1)$ and $\dfrac{S_s^2/(r-1) - S_t^2/r(c-1)}{c}$, respectively.

In the completely randomized block design, with p replication, the estimates of σ^2, $\sigma_r{}^2$, and $\sigma_{rc}{}^2$ are $\widehat{\sigma^2}$, $\widehat{\sigma_r{}^2}$, $\widehat{\sigma_c{}^2}$, and $\widehat{\sigma_{rc}{}^2}$ respectively, where

$$\widehat{\sigma^2} = \frac{S_\epsilon{}^2}{rc(p-1)} \; ;$$

$$\widehat{\sigma_{rc}^2} = \frac{S_{rc}^2/(r-1)(c-1) - \widehat{\sigma^2}}{p}$$

$$\widehat{\sigma_c{}^2} = \frac{S_c{}^2/(c-1) - \widehat{\sigma^2} - p\widehat{\sigma_{rc}^2}}{rp}$$

and

$$\widehat{\sigma_r{}^2} = \frac{S_r{}^2/(r-1) - \widehat{\sigma^2} - p\widehat{\sigma_{rc}^2}}{cp}$$

If $p = 1$, then the analysis in Table 7.17 reduces to that in Table 7.15. Here estimates of σ^2, $\sigma_r{}^2$, and $\sigma_c{}^2$ are

$$\widehat{\sigma^2} = \frac{S_{rc}^2}{(r-1)(c-1)}$$

$$\widehat{\sigma_c{}^2} = \frac{S_c{}^2/(c-1) - \widehat{\sigma^2}}{r}$$

and

$$\widehat{\sigma_r{}^2} = \frac{S_r{}^2/(r-1) - \widehat{\sigma^2}}{c}$$

In the mixed model, described in Table 7.16 σ^2 is estimated as before, $\sigma_r{}^2$ is estimated as

$$\frac{S_r{}^2/(r-1) - \widehat{\sigma^2}}{c}$$

Components of variance for other models are found in a similar manner.

Variance Stabilization and Transformation of Variables

The problem of meeting the basic assumptions underlying the analysis of the variance technique as a device for testing hypothesis is not insurmountable. The most treacherous departures from the theoretical assumptions are extreme skewness, marked departure from additivity, changes in error variance, and the presence of gross errors (Cochran, 1947).[1] Anomolous observations are best removed by omission. From a pragmatic point of view, skewness and dishomogeneous variance are most harmful; their effects, however, can usually be removed by a suitable transformation of the original variate. Frequently, dishomogeneous variance is associated with a functional relationship between the variance and the mean level of

[1] W. G. Cochran, 1947, Some consequences when the assumptions for the analysis of variance are not satisfied, *Biometrics* 3: 22–38.

the measurements. If this relationship can be determined either *a priori* or empirically, then a proper transformation can be chosen to uncorrelate these statistics. Bartlett[1] (1947) has discussed this problem and has summarized those transformations appropriate to particular relationships

TABLE 7.19

Summary of Transformations

Variance in Terms of Mean m	Transformation	Approximate Variance on New Scale	Relevant Distribution
m	$\sqrt{x}$, (or $\sqrt{(x + \frac{1}{2})}$	0.25	Poisson
$\lambda^2 m$	for small integers)	$0.25\lambda^2$	Empirical
$2m^2/(n - 1)$	$\ln x$	$2/(n - 1)$	Sample variances
$\lambda^2 m^2$	$\ln x$, $\ln (x + 1)$	λ^2	Empirical
	$\log_{10} x$, $\log_{10} (x + 1)$	$0.189\lambda^2$	
$m(1 - m)/n$	$\mathrm{Sin}^{-1} \sqrt{x}$, (radians)	$0.25/n$	Bionomial
	$\mathrm{Sin}^{-1} \sqrt{x}$, (degrees)	$821/n$	
$m(1 - m)/n$	Probit	Not constant	
$m(1 - m)/n$	$\ln [x/(1 - x)]$	$1/[mn(1 - m)]$	
$\lambda^2 m^2 (1 - m)^2$	$\ln [x/(1 - x)]$	λ^2	Empirical
$(1 - m^2)^2/(n - 1)$	$\frac{1}{2} \ln [(1 + x)/(1 - x)]$	$1/(n - 3)$	Sample correlations
$m + \lambda^2 m^2$	$\lambda^{-1} \sinh^{-1} [\lambda \sqrt{x}]$, or	0.25	Negative binomial
	$\lambda^{-1} \sinh^{-1} [\lambda \sqrt{(x + \frac{1}{2})}]$		
$\mu^2(m + \lambda^2 m^2)$	for small integers	$0.25\mu^2$	Empirical
—	To expected normal scores	1 for large n	Ranked data

Taken from M. S. Bartlett, 1947, The use of transformations, *Biometrics* 3: 39–52.

between the mean and variance of a set of samples, as well as to the type of data collected. These transformations are summarized in Table 7.19.

Thus, for example, if the variances of a set of samples are proportional to the means of the samples, i.e., for example, large variances occur with large mean values, then the proper transformation is a square root transformation of the original variate.

It is possible that the particular functional relationship between the means and variances of a set of independent samples, taken from a population, is not one of the many relationships explicitly listed in Table 7.19. Under these circumstances, a line or curve of best fit to the data should be determined. The relationship is easily observed on a graph where the

[1] M. S. Bartlett, 1947, The use of transformations, *Biometrics* 3: 39–52.

variance is plotted as the dependent variate and the mean as the independent variate. If the function is of the form $\sigma^2 = f(m)$, then the required transformation is obtained by integrating the function

$$g(m) = \int \frac{c\, dm}{f(m)} \tag{7.51}$$

As an example of the use of transformations in the stabilization of variance as well as transforming a set of data to a normal distribution, consider the work performed at the Pennsylvania State University in 1953, by Rosenfeld and Griffiths.[1] Their concern, initially, was an evaluation of visual comparison techniques for the estimation of the sphericity and roundness of quartz grains in sedimentary deposits. The writers compared empirical distributions and concluded, among other things, that the data were not normally distributed. With sphericity data, a plot of the means and variances of each of 21 independent samples yielded no functional relationship between the mean and variance. Since the range of values for any sphericity observation is between 0 and 1, i.e., of the percentage or proportion form, it was decided to transform the data by means of an arc sine transformation.

With roundness data, which too is of proportion or percentage form, a functional relationship existed between the means and variances of a series of independent samples. A transformation to the arc sine failed to improve either the normalcy of the distribution curve or the functional relationship between the mean and variance. Use was then made of Bartlett's suggestions stated previously (7.51).

A line of best fit (Chapter 8) between the variates—variance and mean—yielded an expression of the form

$$s^2 = 0.01107 - 0.01208\bar{x} = f(m)$$

Following the recommendation above, this function was integrated as

$$c\int \frac{dm}{f(m)} = c\int \frac{d\bar{x}}{0.01107 - 0.0120821}$$

and a transformation of the form

$$P_A = (0.01107 - 0.0121\, P)^{\frac{1}{2}}$$

where $P =$ measured roundness value and $P_A =$ adjusted roundness value were determined.

Thus, by these relatively simple procedures, some of the difficulties associated with the testing of hypotheses were avoided.

---

[1] M. A. Rosenfeld and J. C. Griffiths, 1953, A visual comparison technique in estimating two dimensional sphericity and roundness of quartz grains, *Am. Jour. Sci.* 251: 553–585.

Two-Way Analysis of Variance Design with Replications

The two-way design discussed in this chapter had but one observation per cell. To decrease the error of row or column comparisons, it is best to repeat (*to replicate*) the observations a number of times for each cell. If each cell has p replications, or repeated measurements, then any observation may be written as x_{ijk}, where $i = 1, \cdots, r$; $j = 1, \cdots, c$ and $k = 1, \cdots, p$, and $x_{ijk} = \mu + a_i + b_j + w_{ij} + e_{ijk}$, where $E(x_{ijk}) = \mu$ and var $x_{ijk} = \sigma_a^2 + \sigma_b^2 + \sigma_{ab}^2 + \sigma^2$.

The analysis of variance table for the random model, as well as the hypotheses which can be tested with this design, is summarized in Table 7.17.

Computational Formulae and the Analysis of Variance Technique

The sums of squares listed in Tables 7.2 to 7.5 and 7.8 to 7.17 are suitable to work with in real problems, provided the number of observations is relatively small and too that the magnitude of the numbers is not too cumbersome. For most work, except that programmed for the high-speed computer, one uses what is generally called the computational formulae for the analysis of variance technique. The formulae permit the data to be handled in their original form and not in the form of measures from the average values for the different sources of variability. The computational formulae for the analysis of variance procedures described in this chapter are summarized in Tables 7.20 to 7.22.

GENERAL APPLICATIONS

The analysis of variance in one form or another is probably the most widespread method of statistical analysis in present use in the earth sciences. In recent years just about every branch of investigation in this area has had publications including some application of the analysis of variance.

In addition to these papers, many papers not repeated here are given in the section on analysis of variance in mapping, Chapter 17.

W. C. Krumbein and R. L. Miller, 1953, Design of experiments for statistical analysis of geological data, *Jour. Geol.* 61: 510–532; J. S. Olson and P. W. Potter, 1954, Variance components of crossbedding direction in some basal Pennsylvanian sandstones of the eastern interior basin: statistical methods, *Jour. Geol.* 62: 26–49; W. C. Krumbein, 1955, Experimental design in the earth sciences, *Trans. A.G.U.* 36: 1–11. The first two are referred to in detail elsewhere in this chapter.

Examples of the diversity of fields in which application has been are: Felix Chayes, 1946, Linear analysis of a medium grained granite, *Am. Min.* 31: 261–275; an investigation of precision (repeatability) in the linear traverse method in petrography.

R. L. Miller, 1949, An application of the analysis of variance to paleontology, *Jour. Paleon.* 23: 635–640; in which the analysis of variance is applied to differentiation of six subspecies of *Spirifer Whitneyi* on the basis of 11 measurable characteristics.

A. B. Vistelius, 1951, On the Paleozoic pebbles of the productive beds of the Apsheronian peninsula, *Dokl. Akad Nayk. Trans.* 79, No. 3. Paleozooic pebbles are found in

TABLE 7.20

Generalized Computational Formulas for the Sums of Squares for the One-Way Analysis of Variance—All Models

Sources of Variation	Sum of Squares
Among machines, slides, for (example)	$\sum_{i=1}^{m}\left[\sum_{j=1}^{r} x_{ij}\right]^2 \Big/ r - \left(\sum_{i,j} x_{ij}\right)^2 \Big/ mr$
Within machines, slides or equivalently among rods, traverses	Difference between below and above
Total	$\sum_{i,j} x_{ij}^2 - \left(\sum_{i,j} x_{ij}\right)^2 \Big/ mr$

TABLE 7.21

Generalized Computational Formulas for the Sums of Squares in the Two-Way—No Replications—Analysis of Variance—All Models

Sources of Variation	Sum of Squares
Rows	$\sum_{i=1}^{r}\left[\sum_{j=1}^{c} x_{ij}\right]^2 \Big/ c - \left(\sum_{i,j} x_{ij}\right)^2 \Big/ rc = S_r^2$
Columns	$\sum_{j=1}^{c}\left[\sum_{i=1}^{r} x_{ij}\right]^2 \Big/ r - \left(\sum_{i,j} x_{ij}\right)^2 \Big/ rc = S_c^2$
Residual	Difference: $S_T^2 - S_r^2 - S_c^2$
Total	$\sum_{i,j}^{rc} x_{ij}^2 - \left(\sum_{i\,j} x_{ij}\right)^2 \Big/ rc = S_T^2$

TABLE 7.22

Generalized Computational Formulas for the Sums of Squares in the Two-Way—p Replications per Cell—Analysis of Variance—All Models

Sources of Variation	Sum of Squares
Rows	$\sum_{i=1}^{r}\left[\sum_{jk}^{cp} x_{ijk}\right]^2 \Big/ cp - \left(\sum_{ijk} x_{ijk}\right)^2 \Big/ rcp = S_r^2$
Columns	$\sum_{j=1}^{c}\left[\sum_{ik}^{pr} x_{ijk}\right]^2 \Big/ pr - \left(\sum_{ijk} x_{ijk}\right)^2 \Big/ rcp = S_c^2$
Residual	$\sum_{i,j}^{cr}\left[\sum_{k}^{p} x_{ijk}\right]^2 \Big/ p - S_r^2 - S_c^2 - \left(\sum_{ijk} x_{ijk}\right)^2 \Big/ rcp = S_{rc}^2$
Within cells (sampling error)	$S_T^2 - S_r^2 - S_c^2 - S_{rc}^2$
Total	$\sum_{ijk} x_{ijk}^2 - \left(\sum_{ijk} x_{ijk}\right)^2 \Big/ rcp = S_T^2$

tertiary productive beds of Baku. Analysis of variance is applied to the distribution of pebble size from different localities.

Felix Chayes, 1952, The finer grained calkalkaline granites of New England, *Jour. Geol.* 60: 207–254, includes a single factor analysis used in comparison of granites.

J. C. Griffiths, 1953, Estimation of error in grain size analysis, *Jour. Sed. Petrol.* 23: 75–84. The estimation of error in grain size analysis and its comparison with the variation in size and size-sorting are reduced to a test of significance by means of analysis of variance.

E. C. Olson and R. L. Miller, 1951, Relative growth in Paleontological studies, *Jour. Paleon.* 25: 212–223. Apply analysis of variance to compare sample regression lines in terms of significance of difference of slopes and intercepts.

W. C. Krumbein, 1953, Statistical designs for sampling beach sand, *Trans. Am. Geophys. Union*, 34. Includes a general discussion.

D. M. Shaw and W. D. Harrison, 1955, Determination of the mode of a metamorphic rock, *Am. Mineral.* 40: 614–623. Applies analysis of variance to modal composition in sillimanite gneiss along three axes.

D. Carroll, 1957, A statistical study of heavy minerals in sands of the South river, Augusta County, Virginia. *Jour. Sed. Petrol.* 27: 387–404.

F. Chayes, 1956, *Petrographic Modal Analysis*, John Wiley, New York, Chapters 1, 10. Includes a discussion of sampling design, e.g., simple random, stratified random and systematic sampling.

Examples in which several variables are considered in the analysis are:

A. Swineford and F. Swineford, 1946, A comparison of three sieve shakers, *Jour. Sed. Petrol.* 16: 3–13, who use a three factor form.

J. J. Hutta and J. C. Griffiths, 1955, Directional permeability of sandstones; a test of technique, *Producers Monthly*, V 19: 11; 26–34 and 12; 24–31. A randomized block design is used for the study of flow rates.

J. R. Curray and J. C. Griffiths, 1955, Sphericity and roundness of quartz grains in sediments, *Bull. G.S.A.* 66: 1076–1096. A randomized block design was considered inappropriate because of wide variation inherent in several of the higher categories, thus implying heterogeneous variance. Therefore, a completely randomized design was used. Subsequent analysis of variance indicated that sphericity did not vary significantly between graywackes and quartzites. No clearcut conclusion was reached on the variation in roundness between the three sedimentary rock categories studied.

P. E. Potter and R. Siever, 1956, Sources of basal Penn. sediments in the eastern interior basin I. Cross bedding, *Jour. Geol.* 64: 225–244, utilize analysis of variance hiearchal sampling, components of variance and estimates of optimum sample size.

J. S. Kahn, 1959, Anisotropic sedimentary parameters, *Trans. New York Acad. Sci.* Ser. II, 21: 5; 373–386. Consideration is given to particle size and orientation and packing density in sedimentary rocks. An experimental design is used as well as a sampling plan leading to one-way analysis of variance design referred to as completely randomized. He finds that the three parameters considered are anisotropic, and suggests that this anisotropicity is a function of many variables, including measurement techniques sampling procedure, and more importantly, geological effects such as diagenesis, tectonics, and sedimentary processes.

Derek Flinn, 1959, An application of statistical analysis to petrochemical data, *Geochim. et Cosmochim. Acta.* 17: 161–175, applies *t*-test, one-way, two-way and three-way partially nested analysis of variance to published rock analyses. Appropriate schemes for the various tests are also discussed.

Components of variance are given particular consideration in F. Chayes, 1950, Composition of the granites of Westerly and Bradford, Rhode Island, *Am. Jour. Sci.* 248: 378–407. A point counter analysis of three thin sections cut from each of several specimens of the Bradford and Westerly granites are recorded, and a variance analysis is used. Interest is focused on samples from large populations (the granite quarries) in which components of variablility contribute at each level of sampling from point count of individual thin section, to the quarry itself. (See also F. Chayes, 1956, *Petrographic Modal Analysis*, John Wiley and Sons, New York, Chapter 10.)

P. E. Potter and R. Siever, 1956, Sources of basal Pennsylvanian sediments, etc., I: cross bedding, *Jour. Geol.* 64.

J. S. Olson and P. W. Potter, 1954, Variance components of cross bedding direction in some basal Pennsylvanian sandstone of the eastern interior basin: statistical methods, *Jour. Geol.* 62: 26–49. General discussion of analysis of variance including statistical tests of equality of variances, test of equality of several means, analysis of variance for several sampling levels (including unequal sample sizes), and confidence limits for mean and for variance components.

"Operator variation" used to investigate the reliability of laboratory techniques and measurement techniques in general in earth science problems has been applied by several investigators.

C. J. C. Ewing, 1931, A comparison of the methods of heavy mineral separation, *Geol. Mag.* 68: 136–140, gives an early qualitative discussion of the effect of operator variation on laboratory technique.

F. Chayes and H. W. Fairbairn, 1951, A test of the precision of thin section analysis by point counter, *Am. Mineral.* 36: 704–712. Application of operator variation for the purpose indicated in the title.

M. A. Rosenfeld and J. C. Griffiths, 1953, An experimental test of visual comparison technique in estimating two dimensional sphericity and roundness of quartz grains, *Am. Jour. Sci.* 251: 553–585. An experiment is conducted to evaluate the visual comparison technique for the estimation of sphericity and roundness of quartz grains in sediments. The experiment was designed to enable the data to be analyzed by analysis of variance for the analysis of "operator variation." Results indicated that valid estimates of sphericity and roundness may be obtained by visual comparison with standards, but unless the variation due to differences between operators is suitably evaluated, visual estimation cannot be attributed solely to differences between grains, but are affected to an unknown degree by operator variation. They conclude that the apparent correlation between these two properties of quartz grains may be due to psychological bias on the part of the operators.

J. C. Griffiths and M. A. Rosenfeld, 1954, Operator variation in experimental research, *Jour. Geol.* 62: 274–91. A general discussion of the philosophy and background of operator variation, extended in applications in the earth sciences.

W. C. Krumbein and R. L. Miller, 1953, *Ibid.*, Some general discussion, and application to replicate analysis of magnetite in two samples of diabase.

F. Chayes, 1956, *Petrographic modal analysis*, John Wiley, New York. Gives a detailed analysis.

W. C. Krumbein, 1953, Latin square experiments in sedimentary petrology, *Jour. Sed. Petrol.* 23: 280–283.

D. D. McIntyre, 1959, The hydraulic equivalence and size distributions of some mineral grains from a beach, *Jour. Geol.* 67: 278–301.

NONPARAMETRIC ANALYSIS OF VARIANCE: THE KRUSKAL-WALLIS ONE-WAY ANALYSIS OF VARIANCE USING RANKS

The Kruskal-Wallis statistic, Kruskal (1952)[1] and Kruskal and Wallis (1952),[2] is used to test the null hypothesis that the sample averages for K independent samples for a given variable do not differ significantly. It is assumed that the variable has a continuous distribution, but nothing is said about the form of the population distribution or distributions from which the samples were drawn. This is in contrast to the underlying assumptions in the main body of this chapter, i.e., parametric analysis.

The statistic is

$$H = \frac{12}{N(N+1)} \sum_{i=1}^{K} \frac{R_i^2}{n_i} - 3(N+1) \tag{7.52}$$

where K is the number of samples with sizes $n_1, \cdots n_k$ and N is the grand total of all observations over all the samples. R_i is the sum of the ranks in the ith sample. The ranking is done by ordering all observations with respect to size regardless of which sample the observation came from, such that the smallest has the rank 1, the next smallest the rank 2, etc., up to the rank N for the largest. Special treatment is needed for ties, and this is described by Kruskal and Wallis, (1952, *ibid*.)[2] and Siegal, 1956.[3] If there are more than five observations in each sample ($n_i > 5$), the statistic is distributed as χ^2 with $K - 1$ degrees of freedom. When the number of observations in any sample is 5 or less, and the number of samples is 3, exact probabilities are given by M. Friedman, 1937, and a discussion of procedure plus reproduction of Friedman's table is given in Siegal, 1956, pp. 185–186. The probability of the statistic H can also be approximated by a standard normal variable so that normal tables can be used. See Wallis and Roberts, 1956, pp. 599–601.[4]

Table 7.23 is based on data collected by J. Weiser, 1952.[5] Specimens of the fresh water gastropod, *Limnea*, were grown in four separate tanks, each kept at different constant temperatures. At the end of a suitable growing period, the shells were examined to determine the amount of

---

[1] W. H. Kruskal, 1952, A nonparametric test for the several sample problem, *Annals. Math. Stats.* 23: 525–540.

[2] W. H. Kruskal and W. A. Wallis, 1952, Use of ranks in one criterion variance analysis, *J. Amer. Stat. Assoc.* 47: 583–621.

[3] S. Siegel, 1956, *Nonparametric statistics for the behavorial sciences*, McGraw-Hill Book Co., New York.

[4] W. Allen Wallis and H. V. Roberts, 1956, *Statistics, a new approach*, The Free Press, Glencoe, Illinois.

[5] J. Weiser, 1952, University of Chicago, personal communication.

certain trace elements taken up from the environment. The results for barium in parts per million are in Table 7.23 (adjusted to avoid ties and assuming that the accuracy of analysis is sufficient to establish reliably the reality of differences of the magnitudes given).

TABLE 7.23

Tank I		Tank II		Tank III		Tank IV	
Barium	Rank	Barium	Rank	Barium	Rank	Barium	Rank
20	2	21	3	18	1	27	6
30	8	25	5	24	4	28	7
44	13	33	9	35	10	37	11
51	14	39	12	62	17	55	15
65	19	60	16	75	23	64	18
72	21	80	24	85	25	68	20
100	26	$R_2 = 69$		$R_3 = 80$		73	22
$R_1 = 103$						$R_4 = 99$	

$$N = 26, \quad n_1 = 7, \quad n_2 = 6, \quad n_3 = 6, \quad n_4 = 7, \quad K = 4$$

$$H = \frac{12}{26(26+1)}\left[\frac{(103)^2}{7} + \frac{(69)^2}{6} + \frac{(80)^2}{6} + \frac{(99)^2}{7}\right] - 3(26+1) = 0.19$$

The null hypothesis is that there is no difference between the means for the four tanks. We set a significance level of $\alpha = 0.05$. The region of rejection then includes all values of H so large that the probability of an H that large occurring under the null hypothesis is less than or equal to 5 in 100. For degrees of freedom, $K - 1 = 4 - 1 = 3$, the χ^2 value at 0.05 is 7.82. Since $H = 0.19$ is considerably smaller than 7.82, we accept the null hypothesis of equal means. Had the value of H exceeded the critical value of 7.82 we would have rejected the hypothesis of equal means.

The preceding method is available when the investigator does not feel that the assumptions basic to formal analysis of variance are justified under the particular situation at hand (e.g., assumption of normality and assumption of homogeneity of variances).

chapter 8

Linear Regression Analysis

Chapters 8, 9, 10, and 11 deal with regression and correlation analysis. A general discussion of the philosophical relationship between correlation and causality is given by Sewell, Wright, 1921, Correlation and causation, *Jour. Ag. Res.* 20: 557–585, and a review of the methods of correlation and regression analysis is found in D. M. Shaw and J. D. Bankier, 1954, Statistical methods applied to geochemistry, *Geochim. et Cosmochim. Acta* 5: 111–123. A. B. Vistelius, 1951, Further comments on the correlation question of C. B. Konstantenov, *Min. Soc. of U.S.S.R. Bull.* 80: No. 1, gives a general discussion of the sense and methods of calculating correlation coefficients.

A very useful paper warning of possibilities of misuse of the correlation coefficient and by implication of misapplication of regression methods is the one by C. Eisenhart, 1935, A test for significance of lithological variation, *Jour. Sed. Petrol.* 5: 137–145. In this paper it is pointed out that the notion of homogeneity is dependent on the classification used. Sampling fluctuations are such that two or more samples are rarely identical for any classification; therefore some criterion is needed to indicate the plausibility of homogeneity. The chi-square test is an appropriate criterion, and examples are given. Eisenhart discusses the pitfalls encountered in incorrectly applying correlation analysis for example as in L. Dryden, 1935, A statistical method for the comparison of heavy mineral suites, *Am. Jour. Sci.* 29: No. 173; 393–408. The pitfalls are:

1. Use of percentages prevents taking into account sample size and thus invalidates comparison between sample correlation coefficients.
2. The correlation coefficient is not applicable to qualitative characteristics with an arbitrary ordering, but can instead be applied only to quantitative characteristics with a real ordering.

The problem of extrapolation of data by least squares beyond the data points is given in a paper by Collins, Russel, and Farquehar, 1953,

Maximum age of elements and age of the earth's crust, *Canadian Jour. Physics* 31: 402–418. Further references are included in this paper.

Ratio correlations are often found useful in petrology and geochemistry. This topic is not discussed elsewhere in the book and so a short discussion will be presented here, based on G. Herdan, 1953, *Small particle statistics*, Elsevier Press, New York, pp. 296ff. The general formula for correct computation between two ratios involving four different variables follows.

Let the first ratio be $Y = x_1/x_2$ and the second $Z = x_3/x_4$. Then the correlation between Y and Z is

$$r_{YZ} = \frac{r_{13}C_1C_3 - r_{14}C_1C_4 - r_{23}C_2C_3 + r_{24}C_2C_4}{(C_1^2 + C_2^2 - 2r_{12}C_1C_2)^{1/2}(C_3^2 + C_4^2 - 2r_{34}C_3C_4)^{1/2}} \quad (8.1)$$

where r_{ij} is the correlation coefficient of x_i and x_j and C_i is the coefficient of variation of x_i. An example follows. Suppose that it is desired to calculate the correlation coefficient between K_2O/Na_2O and Na_2O. We then have according to the general equation $Y = x_1/x_2 = K_2O/Na_2O$ and $Z = x_3/x_4 = Na_2O/1$. By referring to Eq. (8.1), $x_2 = x_3$ and $x_4 = 1$. Therefore $r_{23} = 1$, $r_{12} = r_{13}$, $r_{14} = r_{24} = r_{34} = 0$, $C_2 = C_3$, $C_4 = 0$. Substituting

$$r_{YZ} = \frac{r_{13}C_1C_3 - r_{23}C_2C_3}{(C_1^2 + C_2^2 - 2r_{12}C_1C_2)^{1/2}(C_3^2)^{1/2}}$$

$$= \frac{r_{12}C_1 - C_2}{(C_1^2 + C_2^2 - 2r_{12}C_1C_2)^{1/2}} \quad (8.2)$$

or

$$r_{\frac{K_2O}{Na_2O}, Na_2O} = \frac{r_{K_2O,Na_2O}C_{K_2O}C_{Na_2O}}{(C_{K_2O}^2 + C_{Na_2O}^2 - 2r_{K_2O,Na_2O}C_{K_2O}C_{Na_2O})^{1/2}} \quad (8.3)$$

If the correlation between K_2O and Na_2O is not zero, then correlation will exist between the ratios and is expressed in the form above. But if there is no correlation between K_2O and Na_2O, Eq. (8.3) reduces to

$$r_{\frac{K_2O}{Na_2O}} = \frac{-C_{Na_2O}^2}{(C_{K_2O}^2 + C_{Na_2O}^2)^{1/2}}$$

which gives a negative number, but is actually a measure of spurious correlation. Herdan refers to a study of Tasmanian dolerites and another of stony meteorites where such pitfalls were encountered. He advises against the use of ratio correlations and suggests that partial correlation techniques are more satisfactory for problems of this kind.

In general, ratios are difficult to interpret and should be avoided if statistical analysis is contemplated. The numerical result of correlation of ratios, for example, does not allow pinpointing of the contributions of the components of the ratios to the resulting numerical measure. Two papers discussing the topic are

F. Chayes, 1949, Ratio correlations in petrography, *Jour. Geol.* 57: 239ff and F. Chayes, 1950, On a distinction between late magmatic and postmagmatic replacement reactions, *Am. Jour. Sci.* 248: 22–36. See also Shaw, 1956, annotated in Chapter 9.

EXAMPLES OF THE DIVERSITY IN THE EARTH SCIENCES OF APPLICATION OF REGRESSION ANALYSIS AND CURVE FITTING

F. J. Pettijohn and A. C. Lundahl, 1943, Shape and roundness of Lake Erie beach sands, *Jour. Sed. Petrol.* 13: 69–78, A. B. Vistelius, 1950, *Dokl. Akad. Nayk Trans.* 6: No. 1 in which the copper content of oil waters of Baku are correlated with the mineralization of the water and the regression of Cu on water mineralization is computed.

K. E. Chave, 1954, Aspects of the biogeochemistry of magnesium 1. Calcareous marine organisms, *Jour. Geol.* 62: 266–283, fits regression lines to water temperature vs. chemical elements for various forms of marine organisms, and J. F. Rominger, 1954, Relationships of plasticity and grain size of Lake Agassiz sediments, *Jour. Geol.* 62: 537–572, uses regression analysis as a basis for geological interpretation. Usually bivariate regression analysis involves assignment of an independent vs. a dependent variable. If the assignment is reversed a different line of "best fit" will result. In many situations in the earth sciences it is not possible to decide which variable is independent and which dependent.

E. J. Conway, 1945, Mean losses of Na, Ca, etc., in one weathering cycle and potassium removal from the ocean, *Am. Jour. Sci.* 243: 583–605 uses lines of best fit through logarithm of values of CaO, MgO, etc., against logs of corresponding NaO content in a single shale sample. However, he measures deviations in least square analysis as perpendicular distance of points from the line of "best fit." The result is a single line which he refers to as the "co-equal" line of best fit. In this way he avoids the iniquity of artificially assigning independence to one of a pair of variables. Comparison of Conway's method should be made with that described in Chapter 8, called the "unique regression line."

Correlation coefficients have also been widely used. Examples are:

N. A. Riley, 1941, Projection sphericity, *Jour. Geol.* 11: 94–97, Percival Allen, 1947. Correlation between allogenic grade size and allogenic frequency in sediments, *Jour. Sed. Petrol.* 17: 3–7. Percival Allen, 1949, Wealdon petrology: the top Ashdown pebble bed and the top Ashdown sandstone, *Quart. Jour. Geol. Soc. London*, 54: 257–323. J. C. Griffiths, 1951, Size vs. sorting in some Caribbean sediments, *Jour. Geol.* 59: 211–233 and A. N. Strahler, 1954, Statistical analysis in geomorphic research, *Jour. Geol.* 62: 1–25.

Partial correlation has not been widely used outside of paleontology. However, there are several examples available. Among them are A. B. Vistelius, 1948, On the distribution of magnesite in the eastern Paleozoic of the Russian Platform. Symposium No. 2, All Union Institute of Oil Geol. (U.S.S.R.) and A. B. Vistelius, 1952, The natural paragenesis of some components of the oil of Azerbaiijan, *Dokl. Akad. Nauk. Azerbaiijana* VIII, No. 1: 17–23, in which the paragenesis of the minor elements of ash and components of oil are studied with the aid of both partial and multiple correlation, and the radius of ions of the minor elements are correlated against elements of the oil components. J. C. Griffiths, 1959, Size and shape of rock fragments in the Tuscaraora Scree, *Jour. Sed. Petrol.* 29: 391–401, utilizes partial correlation coefficients in analysis of the three linear axes of rock fragments, and A. B. Vistelius, 1954, Sands of the middle and lower Volga. Short papers of Lab. Aeromethods Leningrad, *Akad. Sci. U.S.S.R.* Analyses of paragenesis in mineral grains in the heavy fractions with the aid of partial correlation.

An application of the test for the homogeneity of a suite of correlation coefficients is made by M. A. Rosenfeld, L. Jacobsen, and J. C. Ferm, 1953, A comparison of sieve and thin section technique for size analysis, *Jour. Geol.* 61: 114–132. An unusual application of correlation coefficients is given by A. B. Vistelius, 1947, On the correlation bond between apatite and nepheline in the Kukicutchor-Yukcporian sphere deposit of the Kola peninsula, *Dokl. Acad. Nayk.* Trans. 55, No. 4. Here, apatite and nepheline are shown to be correlated in the alkaline rocks of the central Kola peninsula. Vistelius then constructs an isopleth map of the correlation coefficients, as an aid in the regional summary.

J. Imbrie, 1955, Quantitative lithofacies and biofacies study of Florena shale (Permian) of Kansas, *Bull. A.A.P.G.* 39: 649–670. Discusses correlation vs. causation in quantitative studies of lithofacies vs. biofacies. Concludes analysis of correlation by statistical methods is only the first step in an investigation.

C. S. Piggot, 1938, Radium in rocks: V The radium content of the four groups of PreCambrian granites of Finland, *Am. Jour. Sci.* 350: 226–245. Uses a visual analysis of scatter diagrams to assess degree of association and position of straight line visual fits. Concludes that the evidence favors correlation of radium with mineralogy rather than with the chemistry of a granite.

MOTIVATION IN LINEAR REGRESSION ANALYSIS

Frequently an investigator does more than examine one variable or characteristic; he may examine coincidentally two or three or even more. For example, Strahler (1958),[1] Melton (1957),[2] and Griffiths (1960).[3] Thus the observation of pairs of variables (x, y) or (y, z) or groups of variables (x, y, z), (p, q, r, s, t) is not uncommon.

When two variables are considered, i.e., bivariate analysis, the question may arise as to the relationship between the two variables. Is there any? What form is it? Knowing the value of one variable, can the other be predicted? One method of attacking this problem is to first assume the form of the relationship between the variates. Thus we might assume that y, the dependent variable, is a function of x, the independent variable, and further, that the average or expected value

[1] A Strahler, 1958, Dimensional analyses applied to fluvially eroded landforms, *Bull. Geol. Soc. Amer.* 69: 270–300.

[2] M. Melton, 1957, *An analysis of the relations among elements of climate, surface properties, and geomorphology*, Tech. Rept. No. 11, Dept. of Geology, Columbia Univ., New York.

[3] J. C. Griffiths, 1960, *Modal analysis of sediments*, Revue de Geographie physique et de Geologie Dynamique (2), Vol. III, F. 1, pp. 29–48, Paris, 1960.

of y for a given value of x is a constant. For example, if we let $y = f(x)$, then $f(x)$ might be

$$k_1 x + k_2 \tag{8.4}$$

or $f(x)$ might be of the form

$$k_3 x^{k_4} + k_5 x^3 + \log 2x \tag{8.5}$$

or

$$f(x) = \log x \tag{8.6}$$

or

$$f(x) = \log (1 + x)$$

where k_1, k_2, k_3, k_4, and k_5 are fixed constants or parameters.

Once the form of the relationship is assumed, the next step would be to look for estimates of the unknown fixed parameters. For example, k_1 and k_2 define (8.4); similarly k_3, k_4, and k_5 define (8.5). Once estimates of the parameters are obtained and their distributions determined then tests of hypotheses concerning them can be made.

LINEAR REGRESSION WITHIN A GROUP OF SAMPLE SIZE n WITH ONE OBSERVATION FOR EACH VALUE OF THE INDEPENDENT VARIABLE

Let us assume that $f(x)$ is of the form

$$f(x) = \text{constant} + (\text{constant})(x) \tag{8.7}$$

where the constants are linearly arranged within $f(x)$, e.g., they are not in the form of exponents such as in (8.5). The *relationship we therefore assume is linear with respect only to the unknown parameters*, i.e., the constants. Expression (8.7) may be written in the form of

$$f(x) = \alpha + \beta x$$

or as

$$f(x) = \alpha + \beta(x - \bar{x}) \tag{8.8}$$

We shall assume the form of (8.8).

From our introductory remarks

$$E[y \mid x] \text{ is of the form } \alpha + \beta(x - \bar{x}) = \mu \tag{8.9}$$

and

$$\text{var } (y \mid x) \text{ is of the form } \sigma^2$$

Specifically,

$$E[y_i \mid x_i] = \mu_i$$

and

$$\text{var } [y_i \mid x_i] = \sigma_i^2 = \sigma^2$$

**Estimates of the Parameters α, β, and σ^2, and the Assumption
of the Form of the Distribution of y**

We must assume some distribution function for our random variable y,
for if our estimating functions are themselves functions of y we must know
their distribution in order that tests of hypotheses concerning the unknown
parameters can be made. Thus *we assume that for each value of x, y is
normally distributed about $\alpha + \beta(x - \bar{x}) = \mu$ with variance σ^2.*

With the aid of the maximum likelihood function, L (see Chapter 9),
we may now proceed to obtain estimates of the parameters α, β, and σ^2.
The likelihood function is

$$\frac{1}{(2\pi\sigma)^{n/2}} \exp \left\{ - \frac{1}{2\sigma^2} \sum_{i=1}^{n} [y_i - \alpha - \beta(x_i - \bar{x})]^2 \right\}$$

and

$$\ln L = - \frac{n}{2} \ln 2\pi - \frac{n}{2} \ln \sigma^2 - \frac{1}{2\sigma^2} \sum_{i=1}^{n} [y_i - \alpha - \beta(x_i - \bar{x})]$$

Thus

$$\frac{\partial \ln L}{\partial \alpha} = \frac{1}{\sigma^2} \sum_{i=1}^{n} [y_i - \alpha - \beta(x_i - \bar{x})] \tag{8.10}$$

$$\frac{\partial \ln L}{\partial \beta} = \frac{1}{\sigma^2} \sum_{i=1}^{n} [y_i - \alpha - \beta(x_i - \bar{x})](x_i - \bar{x}) \tag{8.11}$$

and

$$\frac{\partial \ln L}{\partial \sigma^2} = - \frac{n}{2\sigma^2} + \frac{1}{2\sigma^4} \sum_{i=1}^{n} [y_i - \alpha - \beta(x_i - \bar{x})]^2 \tag{8.12}$$

Letting a, b, and $\widehat{\sigma^2}$ represent the estimates of α, β, and σ^2 respectively,
and solving the above equations simultaneously, we obtain the following
estimates:

$$a = \bar{y} \tag{8.13}$$

$$b = \frac{\sum_{i=1}^{n} y_i(x_i - \bar{x})}{\sum_{i=1}^{n} (x_i - \bar{x})^2} \tag{8.14}$$

$$\widehat{\sigma^2} = \frac{\sum_{i=1}^{n} [y_i - a - b(x_i - \bar{x})]^2}{n} \tag{8.15}$$

It becomes apparent from (8.14) why it is imperative to have at least two
different values of x in the analysis. If but one value of x were used,

(8.14) would be indeterminate and estimates of β and σ^2 would be meaningless.

Properties of the Estimators a and b

$$E(a) = E(\bar{y}) = \frac{E\sum_{i=1}^{n}[\alpha + \beta(x_i - \bar{x})]}{n} = \alpha \qquad (8.16)$$

$$\text{var}(a) = \text{var}\,\bar{y} = \frac{\sigma^2}{n} \qquad (8.17)$$

$$E(b) = E\frac{\sum_i y_i(x_i - \bar{x})}{\sum_i (x_i - \bar{x})^2} = \frac{E\sum_i (x_i - \bar{x})[\alpha + \beta(x_i - \bar{x})]}{\sum_{i=1}^{n}(x_i - \bar{x})^2}$$

$$= \beta\frac{\sum_{i=1}^{n}(x_i - \bar{x})^2}{\sum_{i=1}^{n}(x_i - \bar{x})^2} = \beta \qquad (8.18)$$

$$\text{var}(b) = \text{var}\frac{\sum_{i=1}^{n}y_i(x_i - \bar{x})}{\sum_{i=1}^{n}(x_i - \bar{x})^2} = \frac{\sum_{i=1}^{n}(x_i - \bar{x})^2\,\text{var}\,y_i}{[\sum_{i=1}^{n}(x_i - \bar{x})^2]^2}$$

$$= \frac{\sigma^2}{\sum_{i=1}^{n}(x_i - \bar{x})^2} \qquad (8.19)$$

DECOMPOSITION OF SOURCES OF VARIATION

The deviation of any observation from its expected value is

$$[y_i - \alpha - \beta(x_i - \bar{x})] = y_i - \mu_i$$

and is illustrated in Fig. 8.1. This deviation may furthermore be separated into two parts:

$$[y_i - a - b(x_i - \bar{x})] \quad \text{and} \quad [a + b(x_i - \bar{x}) - \alpha - \beta(x_i - \bar{x})]$$

which represent, respectively, the deviation of any observation from the estimated regression and the deviation of the estimated regression from the true regression. Thus

$$y_i - \mu_i = [y_i - a - b(x_i - \bar{x}) + (a - \alpha) + (b - \beta)(x_i - \bar{x})]$$

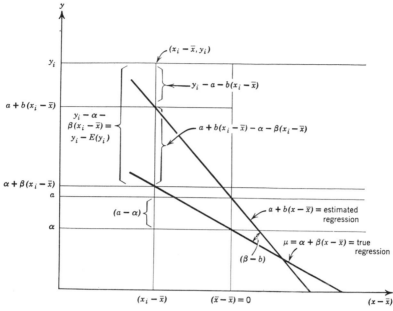

$[y_i - a - b(x_i - \bar{x})]$ = deviation of any observation from the estimated regression

$[y_i - \alpha - \beta(x_i - \bar{x})] = y_i - \mu_i$ = deviation of any observation from the theoretical or true regression

$[a + b(x_i - \bar{x}) - \alpha - \beta(x_i - \bar{x})]$ = deviation of theoretical regression from the estimated regression

FIG. 8.1. Graphical representation of the sources of variation in linear regression with one independent variable within a group and n observations within the group.

The sum of squares representing the deviation of the observations from the true regression line is thus decomposed as follows:

$$\sum_{i=1}^{n}(y_i - \mu_i)^2 = \sum_{i=1}^{n}[y_i - a - b(x_i - \bar{x})]^2$$
$$+ n(a - \alpha)^2 + (b - \beta)^2 \sum_{i=1}^{n}(x_i - \bar{x})^2$$

plus a series of cross products.

The cross product terms disappear as follows:

$$n(a - \alpha) \sum_{i=1}^{n}[y_i - a - b(x_i - \bar{x})]$$
$$= n(a - \alpha)[n\bar{y} - n\bar{y} - b(n\bar{x} - n\bar{x})] = 0$$
$$(b - \beta) \sum_{i=1}^{n}[y_i - a - b(x_i - \bar{x})](x_i - \bar{x})$$
$$= (b - \beta)\left[\sum_{i=1}^{n}y_i(x_i - \bar{x}) - b\sum_{i=1}^{n}(x_i - \bar{x})^2\right]$$

which by (8.14) reduces to 0. Finally

$$n(a - \alpha)(b - \beta) \sum_{i=1}^{n} (x_i - \bar{x}) = 0$$

Thus the total sum of squares representing the departure of the random variable y from its expected value has been decomposed into three parts:

$$\sum_{i=1}^{n} (y_i - \mu_i)^2 = \sum_{i=1}^{n} [y_i - a - b(x_i - \bar{x})]^2$$
$$+ n(a - \alpha)^2 + (b - \beta)^2 \sum_{i=1}^{n} (x_i - \bar{x})^2 \quad (8.20)$$

representing respectively the departure of the estimated regression line from the observations, the difference between the estimate of α and α, and the difference between the estimate of β and β.

Distribution of a and b

Since $\sum_{i=1}^{n} (y_i - \mu_i)^2$ is distributed as $\sigma^2 \chi^2$ (see Chapter 4) with n degrees of freedom and has been decomposed into three sums of squares whose linear restraints are $(n - 2)$, 1, and 1, it follows from the partition theorem for the χ^2 distribution that $\sum_i [y_i - a - b(x_i - \bar{x})]^2$, $n(a - \alpha)^2$, and $(b - \beta)^2 \times \sum_{i=1}^{n} (x_i - \bar{x})^2$ are stochastically independent and distributed as $\sigma^2 \chi^2$ with $(n - 2)$, 1, and 1 degrees of freedom respectively. Thus a, b, and $\hat{\sigma^2}$ are independent.

Furthermore, since $n(a - \alpha)^2 = \sigma^2 \chi^2$, therefore

$$\frac{(a - \alpha)^2}{\sigma^2/n} = \chi^2$$

Then by (8.16) and (8.17)

$$\frac{[a - E(a)]^2}{\text{var } a} = \chi^2$$

and thus a is $N(\alpha, \sigma^2/n)$. Similarly, b is $N\left(\beta, \dfrac{\sigma^2}{\sum_{i=1}^{n} (x_i - \bar{x})^2}\right)$ since

$$\sum_{i=1}^{n} (x_i - \bar{x})^2 (b - \beta)^2 = \sigma^2 \chi^2$$

Therefore

$$\frac{(b - \beta)^2}{\sigma^2/\sum_{i=1}^{n} (x_i - \bar{x})^2} = \chi^2$$

But this is identical to $[b - E(b)]^2/\text{var } b$.

Tests of the Hypothesis $\alpha = 0$; $\beta = 0$

Since a and b are normal variates, tests concerning their expectations, namely, α and β, may be made in a manner identical with that outlined in Chapter 6, where we examined hypotheses concerned with estimates of μ from any population of normal deviates. In the case where the variance σ^2 was unknown, we computed an estimate. Thus in an analogous manner the statistics

$$\frac{a}{\sqrt{\sum_{i=1}^{n}[y_i - a - b(x_i - \bar{x})]^2/n(n-2)}}$$

and

$$\frac{b\sqrt{\sum_{i=1}^{n}(x_i - \bar{x})^2}}{\sqrt{\sum_{i=1}^{n}[y_i - a - b(x_i - \bar{x})]^2/(n-2)}}$$

are both distributed as a t variate with $(n-2)$ degrees of freedom, if the hypotheses $\alpha = 0$, $\beta = 0$ are true.

Relationship between the Analysis of Variance and Regression within a Group; and the Reason Why We Have Selected a Linear Regression of the Form $Y = a + b(x - \bar{x})$ and Not of the Form $Y = a + b\bar{x}$

The sources of variation associated with regression within a group of sample size n are summarized in Table 8.1. A comparison of the sums of squares in Table 8.1 and the tests of the hypothesis $\alpha = 0$, $\beta = 0$ suggest some relationship between the two. Indeed, this is the case. For example, the test criterion of $\alpha = 0$ is

$$t_{(n-2)} = \sqrt{s_a^2/s^2}$$

and the test criterion of $\beta = 0$ is

$$t_{(n-2)} = \sqrt{s_b^2/s^2}$$

Furthermore, the ratio s_a^2/s^2 is distributed as $F\left[\begin{smallmatrix}1\\n-2\end{smallmatrix}\right]$ since s_a^2 is distributed as $\sigma^2\chi^2$ with one degree of freedom, and s^2 is distributed as $\sigma^2\chi^2$ with $(n-2)$ degrees of freedom. Similarly, the ratio s_b^2/s^2 is an F distributed variable with $(1, n-2)$ degrees of freedom since s_b^2 is distributed as $\sigma^2\chi^2$ with one degree of freedom. This is true regardless of the values of α and β, for when the regression is of the form $y = a + b(x - \bar{x})$, and the total sum of square deviations from the theoretical regression line is decomposed into three parts, (8.20), α and β are independent; α and β are not independent if the regression is of the form $a + bx$.

That the relationship between the sums of squares and the tests of the hypotheses concerning α and β is as described above should not be surprising, for we will show the relationship between a "t" distributed variable and an "F" distributed variable (see p. 197).

TABLE 8.1
Summary of Sources of Variation Associated within a Group of Sample Size n

Source of Variation	D.F.	Sum of Squares	Mean Squares
Deviation from estimated regression	$(n-2)$	$\sum_{i}^{n} [y_i - a - b(x_i - \bar{x})]^2 = S^2$	$S^2/(n-2) = s^2$
a from α	1	$n(a - \alpha)^2 = S_a^2$	$S_a^2/1 = s_a^2$
b from β	1	$(b - \beta) \sum_{i=1}(x_i - \bar{x})^2 = S_b^2$	$S_b^2/1 = s_b^2$
Total	n	$\sum_{i=1}^{n} (y_i - \mu_i)^2$	

EXTENSION OF LINEAR REGRESSION WITH ONE INDEPENDENT VARIABLE, FROM n OBSERVATIONS TO n_i OBSERVATIONS FOR EACH INDEPENDENT VARIABLE x_i

For each x_i we shall assume n_i observations of y where $i = 1, \cdots, c$. Thus, as before $E[y \mid x]$ is of the form $\alpha + \beta(x - \bar{x})$ and in particular $E[y_{ij} \mid x_i] = \mu_i = \alpha + \beta(x_i - \bar{x})$, where

$$i = 1, \cdots, c$$
$$j = 1, \cdots, n_i$$

and

$$\text{var }[y_{ij} \mid x_i] = \sigma_i^2 = \sigma^2, \quad \text{for all } i, j$$

Estimates of Parameters

The likelihood equation is

$$\frac{1}{(2\pi\sigma^2)^{n/2}} \exp\left\{ -\frac{1}{2\sigma^2} \sum_{i=1}^{c} \sum_{j=1}^{n_i} [y_{ij} - \alpha - \beta(x_i - \bar{x})]^2 \right\}$$

where $n = \sum_{i}^{c} n_i$

Thus the equations for solution of estimates of α, β, and σ^2 are

$$\frac{1}{\sigma^2} \sum_{i}^{c} \sum_{j}^{n_i} [y_{ij} - \alpha - \beta(x_i - \bar{x})]$$

$$\frac{1}{\sigma^2} \sum_{i}^{c} \sum_{j}^{n_i} [y_{ij} - \alpha - \beta(x_i - \bar{x})](x_i - \bar{x})$$

and

$$-\frac{n}{2\sigma^2} + \frac{1}{2\sigma^4} \sum_{i=1}^{c} \sum_{j=1}^{n_i} [y_{ij} - \alpha - \beta(x_i - \bar{x})]^2$$

Thus

$$a = \frac{\sum\limits_{i}^{c}\sum\limits_{j}^{n_i} y_{ij}}{n} = \frac{\sum\limits_{i=1}^{c} n_i \bar{y}_{i.}}{n} = \bar{y},$$

$$b = \frac{\sum\limits_{i=1}^{c}\sum\limits_{j=1}^{n_i} y_{ij}(x_i - \bar{x})}{\sum\limits_{i=1}^{c} n_i(x_i - \bar{x})^2}$$

which may be rewritten as

$$\frac{\sum\limits_{i=1}^{c} y_{i.}(x_i - \bar{x})}{\sum\limits_{i=1}^{c} n_i(x_i - \bar{x})^2} = \frac{\sum\limits_{i=1}^{c} n_i \bar{y}_{i.}(x_i - \bar{x})}{\sum\limits_{i=1}^{c} n_i(x_i - \bar{x})^2}$$

and

$$\widehat{\sigma^2} = \frac{\sum\limits_{i=1}^{c}\sum\limits_{j=1}^{n_i} [y_{ij} - a - b(x_i - \bar{x})]^2}{n}$$

Properties of a, b

$$E(a) = \alpha$$
$$E(b) = \beta$$
$$\text{var } a = \frac{\sigma^2}{n}$$
$$\text{var } b = \frac{\sigma^2}{\sum\limits_{i=1}^{c} n_i(x_i - \bar{x})^2}$$

Decomposition of Sum of Squares

The sum of squares representing the departure of the y observations from their expected values is

$$\sum\limits_{i=1}^{c}\sum\limits_{j=1}^{n_i} [y_{ij} - \alpha - \beta(x_i - \bar{x})]^2 = \sum\limits_{i}\sum\limits_{j} (y_{ij} - \mu_i)^2$$

and this is distributed as $\sigma^2 \chi^2$ with n degrees of freedom and may be decomposed into the following sums of squares, each independently distributed as $\sigma^2 \chi^2$ with $\sum\limits_{i=1}^{c} n_i - c$, $c - 2$, 1, and 1 degrees of freedom, namely,

$$\sum\limits_{i}\sum\limits_{j} (y_{ij} - \bar{y}_{i.})^2$$

$$\sum\limits_{i}\sum\limits_{j} [(\bar{y}_{i.} - a - b(x_i - \bar{x})] = \sum\limits_{j} n_i[\bar{y}_{i.} - a - b(x_i - \bar{x})]^2$$

$$\sum\limits_{i} n_i(a - \alpha)^2 \quad \text{and} \quad (b - \beta)^2 \sum\limits_{i=1}^{c} n_i(x_i - \bar{x})^2$$

This is illustrated in Fig. 8.2 and summarized in Table 8.2.

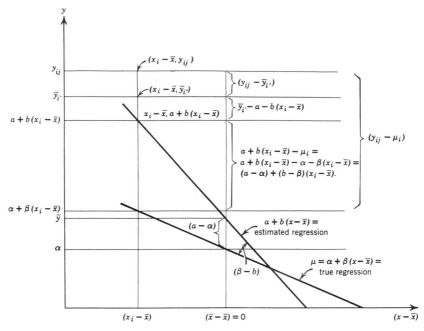

$(y_{ij} - \mu_i) = [y_{ij} - \alpha - \beta(x_i - \bar{x})] =$ deviation of any observation from its mean or expected value

$y_{ij} - \bar{y}_{i.}$ $=$ deviation of any observation from its group mean

$[\bar{y}_{i.} - a - b(x_i - \bar{x})]$ $=$ deviation of group mean from estimated regression

$(a - \alpha) + (b - \beta)(x_i - \bar{x})$ $=$ deviation of estimated regression from true regression

$\bar{y}_{i.} - \mu$ $=$ deviation of group mean from true regression

FIG. 8.2. Graphical representation of sources of variation in linear regression with one independent variable and n observations of $x_i - x$.

Each of the sums of squares in Table 8.2 is distributed as $\sigma^2 \chi^2$ with its respective degrees of freedom to the left. Thus

$$\frac{(a - \alpha)^2 \sum_{i=1}^{c} n_i}{\sigma^2} = \chi^2$$

and a is thus $N[\alpha, \sigma^2/n]$. Similarly b is

$$N\left[\beta, \frac{\sigma^2}{\sum_{i=1}^{c} n_i(x_i - \bar{x})^2}\right]$$

TABLE 8.2

Summary Table of Source of Variation

Source of Variation	D.F.	Sum of Squares	Mean Square
Within groups	$\sum\limits_{i=1}^{c} (n_i - 1)$	$\sum\limits_{i=1}^{c} \sum\limits_{j=1}^{n_i} (y_{ij} - \bar{y}_{i.})^2 = S_g^2$	$S_g^2 / \sum\limits_{i=1}^{c} (n_i - 1) = s_g^2$
Average deviations from estimated regression	$(c - 2)$	$\sum\limits_{i}^{c} n_i[\bar{y}_{i.} - a - b(x_i - \bar{x})]^2 = S^2$	$S^2/(c - 2) = s^2$
a from α	1	$(a - \alpha)^2 \sum\limits_{i=1}^{c} n_i = n(a - \alpha)^2 = S_a^2$	$S_a^2/1 = s_a^2$
b from β	1	$(b - \beta)^2 \sum\limits_{i=1}^{c} n_i(x_i - \bar{x})^2 = S_b^2$	$S_b^2/1 = s_b^2$
Total	n	$\sum\limits_{i,j} (y_{ij} - \mu_i)^2$	

Hence a test criterion for the hypotheses $\alpha = 0$, $\beta = 0$ is a t-test since

$$\frac{a}{\sum\limits_{i=1}^{c} n_i[\bar{y}_{i.} - a - b(x_i - \bar{x})]^2/n(n - 2)} = \sqrt{\frac{s_a^2}{s^2}} \qquad (8.21)$$

and

$$\frac{b \sum\limits_{i}^{c} n_i(x_i - \bar{x})^2}{\sum\limits_{i=1}^{n} n_i[y_i - a - b(x_i - \bar{x})]^2/(n - 2)} = \sqrt{\frac{s_b^2}{s^2}} \qquad (8.22)$$

are both "t" variates with $(n - 2)$ degrees of freedom respectively.

The identities in (8.21) and (8.22) point to the relationship between the tests of the hypotheses $\alpha = 0$, $\beta = 0$ and the analysis of variance. The ratios, s_a^2/s^2 and s_b^2/s^2 are F distributed variates with $(1, c - 2)$ degrees of freedom, and thus tests of these hypotheses may be made as indicated in (8.21) and (8.22) or by means of variance ratios as indicated previously.

Tests of the Assumptions of Linear Regression

The development of any linear regression analysis depends upon the ease with which the assumptions necessary to its theoretical development may be tested or rationalized. The foregoing discussion on linear regression analysis with one independent variable has assumed:

1. y_{ij} to be a normal deviate distributed about a mean
2. μ_i of the form $\alpha + \beta(x_i - \bar{x})$ with variance
3. σ_i^2, and all variances are equal.

It is advisable to examine these assumptions before undertaking a tedious analysis only to find at some later date that statistical inference is invalid due to an inability to satisfy the assumptions necessary for the analysis.

Normality

For each x, say x_i, we observe n_i values of y. Thus, for every x_i we generate a frequency distribution of y values regardless of the size of n_i. If n_i is large enough, then $f(y \mid x_i)$ can be compared with a theoretical normal distribution and a test of goodness-of-fit (see Chapter 6) may be made. However, if n_i is small and thus a test of normality cannot be met, then there is no test of the normality assumption.

Equal Variances

Since for each x a frequency distribution of y is generated, we can always obtain an estimate of the variance σ_i^2, provided $n_i > 1$. If we let $s_i^2 = \sum_{j=1}^{n_i}(y_{ij} - \bar{y}_{i.})^2/(n_i - 1)$ be our estimate of σ_i^2, then the ratio of any pair of sample variances, assuming normality which we have either tested for and accepted, or not tested but assumed, is an F distributed variate. If we have more than two values of x, then the hypothesis in question is $H_0: \sigma_1^2 = \sigma_2^2 = \cdots \sigma_c^2 = \sigma^2$ and this is tested by means of Bartlett's test (see Chapter 6).

Linearity

Suppose $\mu_i \neq \alpha + \beta(x_i - \bar{x})$. Consider $\bar{y}_{i.} - E\bar{y}_{i.} = \bar{y}_{i.} - \mu_i$. Rewrite this as

$$\bar{y}_{i.} - a - b(x_i - \bar{x}) - \mu_i + \alpha + \beta(x_i - \bar{x}) + a + b(x_i - \bar{x}) - \alpha$$
$$- \beta(x_i - \bar{x}) = \{[\bar{y}_{i.} - a - b(x_i - \bar{x})] - [\mu_i - \alpha - \beta(x_i - \bar{x})]\}$$
$$+ [(a - \alpha) + (b - \beta)(x_i - \bar{x})] \quad (8.23)$$

Now $\sum_{i=1}^{c} n_i(\bar{y}_{i.} - \mu_i)^2$ is distributed as $\sigma^2\chi^2$ with c degrees of freedom and therefore $E\sum_{i=1}^{n} n_i(\bar{y}_{i.} - \mu_i)^2 = \sigma^2 c$. Thus if we square (8.23), and multiply through by n_i and sum over i, we obtain

$$\sum_{i=1}^{c} n_i[\bar{y}_{i.} - a - b(x_i - \bar{x}) - \mu_i - \alpha - \beta(x_i - \bar{x})]^2$$
$$+ (a - \alpha)^2 \sum_{i=1}^{c} n_i + (b - \beta)^2 \sum_{i=1}^{n} n_i(x_i - \bar{x})^2 = \sum_{i=1}^{n} n_i(\bar{y}_{i.} - \mu_i)^2$$

All of which are distributed as $\sigma^2\chi^2$, with $(c - 2)$, 1, and 1 degrees of freedom.

Thus

$$E \sum_i n_i[\bar{y}_{i.} - a - b(x_i - \bar{x}) - \mu_i + \alpha + \beta(x_i - \bar{x})]^2 = \sigma^2(c - 2)$$

$$E \sum_i n_i[\bar{y}_{i.} - a - b(x_i - \bar{x})]^2 + E \sum_i n_i[\mu_i - \alpha - \beta(x_i - \bar{x})]^2$$

$$- 2 \sum_i n_i[\mu_i - \alpha - \beta(x_i - \bar{x})]E[\bar{y}_{i.} - a - b(x_i - \bar{x})] = \sigma^2(c - 2)$$

Now $E[\bar{y}_{i.} - a - b(x_i - \bar{x})] = \mu_i - \alpha - \beta(x_i - \bar{x})$. Therefore

$$\sigma^2(c - 2) = E \sum_i n_i[\bar{y}_{i.} - a - b(x_i - \bar{x})]^2 - \sum_i n_i[\mu_i - \alpha - \beta(x_i - \bar{x})]^2$$

and

$$\frac{E \sum_{i=1}^c n_i[\bar{y}_{i.} - a - b(x_i - \bar{x})]^2}{c - 2} = \sigma^2 + \frac{\sum_{i=1}^c n_i[\mu_i - \alpha - \beta(x_i - \bar{x})]^2}{c - 2}$$

Thus if $\mu_i \neq \alpha + \beta(x_i - \bar{x})$, the expectations of the mean square for deviations from the estimated regression $E[s^2]$ is not σ^2, but rather σ^2 plus the deviation of μ_i from the line $\alpha + \beta(x_i - \bar{x})$. If on the other hand H_1: $\mu_i = \alpha + \beta(x_i - \bar{x})$, then

$$Es^2 = \sigma^2 + \frac{\sum n_i(\mu_i - \mu_i)}{c - 2} = \sigma^2$$

Hence to test the hypothesis $\mu_i = \alpha + \beta(x_i - \bar{x})$ and hence the assumption of *linearity of the parameters*, we can look at the ratio s_g^2/s^2, Table 8.2, which, if H_1 is true, is distributed as

$$F\left[\frac{\sum_{i=1}^c (n_i - 1)}{c - 2}\right]$$

SEVERAL ADDITIONAL REFERENCES

P. A. Chenoweth, 1952, Statistical methods applied to Trentonian stratigraphy in New York, *Bull. G.S.A.* 63: 521–560. Regression analysis is used in studying facies change, including standard error of estimate and tests of the regression coefficients.

Marie Morisawa, 1958, Measurement of drainage basin outline form, *Jour. Geol.* 66: 587–591. Applies regression analysis and significance tests of β in a comparison of several different methods for expressing drainage basin form.

F. J. Flanagan, R. C. Kellagher, and U. L. Smith, 1959, The slotted cone splitter, *Jour. Sed. Petrol.* 29: 108–115. Uses regression analysis with confidence limits to test operating characteristics of a device to subdivide sediment samples.

Felix Chayes, 1956, *Petrographic Modal Analysis*, John Wiley, New York, Chapters 8, 9. Uses regression analysis (curve fitting) to show the variation of log of average analytical error for major constituents as a function of log of square root of measurement area, and also on log of estimated average major mineral analytical error as a function of log of coarseness (*IC* number) for different measurement areas.

S. A. Schumm, 1956, Evolution of drainage systems and slopes in badlands at Perth Amboy N.J., *Bull. G.S.A.* 67: 97–646. Uses regression analysis for depth of erosion as a function of percent distance from top of the straight slope segment of slope profiles. It turns out that the slope of the regression lines are not significantly greater than zero. Schumm then draws conclusions on the basis of this evidence.

A. N. Strahler, 1950, Equilibrium theory of erosional slopes approached by frequency distribution analysis, *I. Am. Jour. Sci.* 248: 673–696. Regression analysis was done for variables channel slope (S_c) and ground slope (S_g). A series of points plotted on double-log paper yielded a fairly linear trend. A straight line fit gave the relationship $\ln S_g = 0.60 + 0.80 \log S_c$. Each point represents the mean of a large number of measurements. Unfortunately, distribution of the individual measurements is not given, so that it is not possible to judge whether (1) the straight line fit on double log paper is better than, say, a curved line, and (2) what the degree of association or correlation is. However, Strahler presents a detailed discussion of the assumptions and limitation inherent in this analysis. He obtains good fit of several distribution of slope to the normal curve, suggesting that for mature drainage basins, valley slopes are normally distributed.

A. N. Strahler, 1952, Quantitative geomorphology of erosional landscapes, *Comptes Rendus*, 19th Internat. Geol. Congress, 1952, sec. 13, pt. 3, pp. 341–354, 1954. A general discussion of the quantitative geomorphology of erosional landscapes was given in which a plea is made for quantitative methods, e.g., dynamic analytical and statistical methods. Specific examples are given including fitted regression analysis.

chapter **9**

Regression Analysis with Emphasis on Paleobiometrics

Since the publication of *Problems of Relative Growth* by Julian Huxley (1932), a number of articles on various aspects of this subject have appeared. A few of these have been devoted to studies of fossils, e.g., Hersch (1934), Robb (1942), Phleger and Putnam (1942), and Gray (1946). The earlier papers have suggested in various ways that relative growth of two or more parts of the skeleton might be used as a character of a species or larger taxonomic unit. However, more rigorous treatment of the data was not discussed until the work of Reeve (1940, 1941), appeared. Formal treatment was also discussed in Tessier (1948), Kermack and Haldane (1950), and Olson and Miller (1951). Since that time further approaches were explored and discussed, notably by Kermack (1954), Pastiels (1953), and Imbrie (1956).

Much of the work on relative growth of skeletal parts of animals has been based on the proposition that the relative change of two parts is well expressed by the general equation $y = bx^k$. If k equals 1 the parts grow at the same rate, and the equation takes the linear form $y = a + bx$.[1] This

---

[1] The following more formal discussion of allometric growth is based on excerpts from Huxley (1932) and Kermack (1954). Consider two morphological dimensions x and y. Then the growth rate of x is the derivative of x with respect to time (age) expressed as dx/dt. Similarly for y the derivative is dy/dt. The relative growth rates may be expressed as $(1/X)(dx/dt)$ and $(1/y)(dy/dt)$. According to Huxley the ratio of the two relative growth rates should be equal to a constant which we shall call K. Then

$$\frac{\dfrac{1}{y}\left(\dfrac{dy}{dt}\right)}{\dfrac{1}{X}\left(\dfrac{dx}{dt}\right)} = K \quad \text{or} \quad \frac{1}{y}\frac{dy}{dt} = K\left(\frac{1}{x}\frac{dx}{dt}\right)$$

is called *isogonic* growth. If one of the parts grows at a different rate from that of the second, the coefficient k differs from 1 and the equation takes the form $y = a + bx^k$. This is called *heterogonic* growth.

The meaning of this equation was fully investigated by Huxley (1932) who originally intended it to apply to the growth of an organ (e.g., limb) relative to a measurement of the body as a whole, such as body weight or body length. It has, however, been applied in later works to the relative growth of any two parts. Other papers of interest on this subject include Richards (1936), Reeve (1940), Feller (1940), and Lumer (1942). Studies of fossil reptiles and amphibians by Olson and Miller (1951) have indicated that the linear equation $y = a + bx$ is satisfactory in many cases. Even where k is as high as 1.25 or as low as 0.75, the heterogonic equation does not appear to offer a better fit. Thus a formal test for linearity of the line of best fit to pairs of measurements is of value. We shall discuss tests for linearity of a regression line as well as methods for comparing the coefficients of several regression lines.

In general, studies of relative growth among pairs of parts in fossil animals may be assigned to two categories:

A. Taxonomic studies, in which growth patterns are considered as group characters.

B. Interpretation of relative growth patterns in terms of function and development.

(*a*) Two or more morphological dimensions may be recorded for samples of individuals of the same species, but collected from various ecological niches, such as mud versus sandy bottom, versus rocky

---

Rearranging, the following differential equation is formed:

$$\frac{1}{y}\frac{dy}{dt} = K\frac{1}{x}\frac{dx}{dt}$$

But

$$\frac{\dfrac{dy}{dt}}{\dfrac{dx}{dt}} = \frac{dy}{dx}$$

so that we have $(x/y)(dy/dx) = K_1$. Solving

$$\int \frac{dy}{y} = K \int \frac{dx}{x}$$

$$\ln y = K \ln x + \ln c \quad \text{or} \quad y = bx^K$$

denoting c by the symbol b which is the allometric growth equation.

bottom for certain invertebrates. See, e.g., Kermack (1954), Eager (1952b), and Miller and Olson (1955).

(b) The interest of the paleontologist may be focused on spatial relationship involving the effect of spatial distribution on morphological form, e.g., on solitary individuals or on colonial animals. It is possible that relative growth analysis may prove of value in problems of this type. For example, the relative growth of several morphological dimensions may alter in response to close physical contact with other individuals, as in Ostrea. Although such relative growth responses are not due to inheritable causes, they are preserved in individuals. It is possible that postnatal change in form due to environment as suggested in (a) and (b) may be misinterpreted as evidence of an inheritable and hence an evolutionary trend.

(c) Investigation of relative growth in which primary interest is focused on function and development. The following describes the reasoning in just one of the many possible approaches to this type of problem:

Given minor changes in gene complex,
1. The initial state of the organism is different from that of its parents.
2. During early growth, results of genetic changes become incorporated in the differentiating parts of the organism, and the influence of these changes spreads as the complexity of the organism increases during growth.
3. The adult form is a product of relative growth patterns. The relative importance of initial ontogenetic change may be indirectly measured by noting the resulting change in adult morphology.[1]

With the preceding as motivation, we now examine and discuss several types of regression lines, and various statistical tests which may be applied in the analysis and interpretation of these regression lines.

REGRESSION METHODS

A detailed discussion of analysis of relative growth in paleontological problems by conventional regression methods is given in Olson and Miller (1951a). Included are tests for linearity (isometric versus allometric), as well as significance tests for slopes, intercepts, and the comparison of two regression lines. We shall not present the tests here because we feel that the reduced major axis growth line discussed next is usually preferred.

[1] E. C. Olson and R. L. Miller, 1951, A mathematical model applied to a study of the evolution of species, *Evolution* 5: 256–338.

THE UNIQUE LINE OF ORGANIC CORRELATION (REDUCED MAJOR AXIS)

Since the assumption of dependent and independent variates in the case of morphological dimensions is often without real foundation according to Kermack (1950), the use of the conventional regression-line suffers from a serious drawback. There is usually no clear justification for saying, e.g., that increase in skull length is dependent upon increase of body length; it is more realistic to consider changes in skull length and body length as due to a set of common factors.

When conventional regression methods are used, the slope of the regression line is directly dependent upon which one of the two morphological dimensions is chosen as the independent variable. Considerations of rates of growth, e.g., would depend on the choice of dependent variable. This difficulty is magnified in cases where the correlation is low, thus resulting in a large angle of intersection between the two possible regression lines. Pearson (K. Pearson, 1901, On lines and planes of closest fit to systems of points in space, *Phil. Mag.* 6: 2; 559ff.) utilizes in the place of regression lines the single line which forms the major axis of the correlation surface. In accord with this proposal, a single line called the *reduced major axis* has been suggested [Jones (1937) and Tessier (1948)] whose properties are better suited for analysis of paired morphological dimensions than Pearson's major axis.

The properties of the reduced major axis (also referred to as the unique line of organic correlation) have been worked out and discussed by Kermack and Haldane (1950) and Kruskal (1953). A detailed discussion with examples of both regression methods and reduced major axis methods is

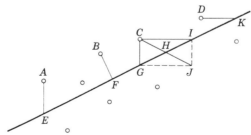

FIG. 9.1. Diagram to show various methods of fitting a line to a scatter of points. A regression *y* on *x* minimizes the sum of the squares of the deviations measured as *AE*. A regression line *x* on *y* minimizes the corresponding sum of deviations measured as *DK*. A major axis minimizes the sum of the squares of the deviations measured as *BF*. A reduced major axis minimizes the sum of the areas of triangles *GCI*. (Taken from Imbrie, 1956, The place of biometrics in taxonomy, *Bull. Amer. Mus. Nat. Hist.* 108: 2; 211–252.)

given by Imbrie (1956a). Figure 9.1, reproduced from Imbrie (1956a), shows the relationships between the several methods of fitting a line to a scatter of points.

If inspection of the scatter diagram indicates that a straight line of the form $y = b + Kx$ will not satisfactorily fit the points, it is suggested that the new scatter diagram be plotted on double log paper. If a straight line appears to give a satisfactory fit to the points in this second case, then the straight line may be expressed in the form $\log y = \log b + k \log x$, which is equivalent to the allometric equation, $y = b + x^K$. The following statistics may be used equally well where now all x and all y in the equations are replaced by their log values. For the reduced major axis in the form of a straight line $y = b + Kx$ (the isogonic growth equation) the statistics which follow are available.

The Statistics
The slope

$$K = \frac{s_y}{s_x}$$

where s_y is the standard deviation of y and s_x the standard deviation of x.

This may be put in convenient computing form as

$$K = \sqrt{\frac{\sum y^2 - \bar{y}\sum y}{\sum x^2 - \bar{x}\sum x}}$$

The standard error of the slope s_K is expressed as

$$s_K = \frac{s_y}{s_x}\sqrt{\frac{1 - r^2}{n}}$$

where r^2 is the square of the correlation coefficient and n the size of the sample.

The intercept

$$b = \bar{y} - \bar{x}K$$

The standard error of the intercept s_b is expressed as

$$s_b = s_y\sqrt{\frac{1 - r^2}{n}\left(1 + \frac{\bar{x}^2}{s_x^2}\right)}$$

Dispersion around the reduced major axis, S_d

$$S_d = \sqrt{2(1 - r)(S_x^2 + S_y^2)}$$

Comparison of the slopes of two separate reduced major axes. The hypothesis is that the difference between K_1 and K_2 is no greater than that expected by chance.

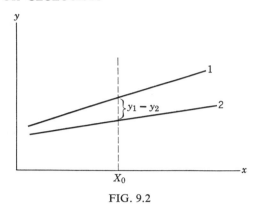

FIG. 9.2

1. Compute the statistic Z where Z is defined as

$$Z = \frac{K_1 - K_2}{\sqrt{s_{K_1}^2 + s_{K_2}^2}}$$

2. Refer to the tables of Z which gives areas of the normal curve.

Test of the hypothesis that two reduced major axes represent samples from a single population; that is, that the differences between the two observed growth lines represent sampling variation rather than a real difference. Several methods are described, but we shall here present the one given by Imbrie (1956) as being relatively simple in operation and interpretation. Essentially, the test consists of selecting a biologically meaningful point on the X-axis[1] and comparing at that value the vertical difference between the two lines by forming the ratio,

$$\left(\frac{\text{Vertical difference between the lines at } X = X_0}{\text{Standard error of the vertical difference}} \right)$$

Specifically, to test the hypothesis that at X_0 (see Fig 9.2) the true growth lines coincide,[2] the following statistic is computed,

$$Z = \frac{x_0(K_1 - K_2) + (b_1 - b_2)}{\sqrt{S_{K_1}^2(x_0 - \bar{x}_1)^2 + S_{K_2}^2(x_0 - \bar{x}_2)^2}}$$

[1] The choice of the value of X depends on the nature of the problem. For example, an investigator seeking to show that a significant difference exists between the two lines may choose the X intercept of the minimum vertical difference between the two lines as X_0. See Imbrie, 1956, pp. 237, 238 for discussion. Because of the subjective nature of the choice of X_0, and since the statistic is based on the assumption that X_0 is chosen in advance, there is a danger of circularity in this method.

[2] As far as we know the case where the lines coincide but dispersions differ ($\rho_1 \neq \rho_2$) is not considered. Clearly, it should be.

Refer to the normal tables of significance levels corresponding to various values of Z.

The following example illustrates the application of the reduced major axis and tests of significance. Two random samples of 40 each were taken from a collection of several thousand *Spirifer pennatus*, a brachiopod, all taken from a single locality. The two variables considered were maximum width and number of costae on the dorsal side.

Let X = maximum width

Y = number of costae

Table 9.1 gives the necessary information.

From the data in Table 9.1 we compute the properties of the reduced major axis in each sample, and for sample A, the two standard regression lines y on x and x on y. (See Table 9.2.)

TABLE 9.1

	Sample A	Sample B
$\sum_{i=1}^{n} x_i$	1,240.00	1,257.00
$\sum_{i=1}^{n} y_i$	496.00	497.00
$\sum x_i^2$	39,011.00	39,861.00
$\sum y_i^2$	6,246.00	6,273.00
$\sum xy$	15,461.00	15,677.00
$\bar{x}$	31.00	31.42
$\bar{y}$	12.40	12.425
n	40.00	40.00
S_x	1.566	1.582
S_y	3.828	3.063

TABLE 9.2

	Sample A	Sample B
r_{xy}	0.364	0.312
K	0.4091	0.5165
S_k	0.0603	0.0776
b	0.2821	−3.8034
S_b	4.9047	6.4862
Slope y on x	0.1489	
Intercept y on x	7.80	
Slope x on y	0.8891	
Intercept x on y	19.98	

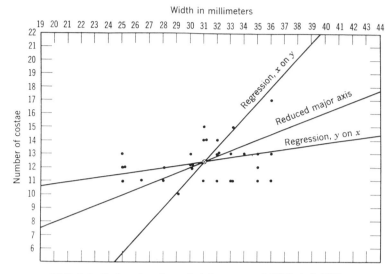

FIG. 9.3. Reduced major axis (*A*). $y = -0.2821 + 0.4091x$.

Figure 9.3 shows the reduced major axis for sample *A*. The two conventional regression lines y on x and x on y are also plotted. Note the considerable difference in slope between the regression of y on x and x on y. This illustrates the major difficulty in applications of conventional regression analysis when there is no strong reason for considering either x or y as the dependent variable.

Figure 9.4 shows the reduced major axis for both samples *A* and *B*. We shall proceed to compare the slopes and then the total lines.

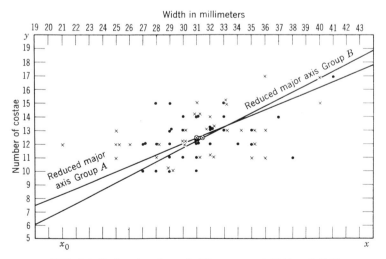

FIG. 9.4. Reduced major axis (*B*). $y = -3.8034 + 0.5165x$.

**Comparison of the Slopes (Growth Ratios) between
Sample *A* and Sample *B***

$$Z = \frac{K_A - K_B}{\sqrt{S_{K_A}^2 + S_{K_B}^2}} = \frac{0.4091 - 0.5165}{\sqrt{0.0603^2 + 0.0776^2}} = -1.0926$$

The absolute value of Z, $|1.0926|$, indicates that we expect a difference between K_A and K_B to be larger than that observed when drawing pairs of samples from a homogeneous population, about 28 % of the time. There is no reason, therefore, to reject the hypothesis that K_A and K_B are homogeneous (of course, we would not ordinarily expect a significant difference to appear, since the two samples were drawn from a larger collection of individuals of a single species taken from a single locality).

**Comparison of the Two Reduced Major Axes
for Samples *A* and *B***

Following Imbrie's suggestion we shall choose the widest vertical difference between the two lines in order to fix the value X_0. This difference will be chosen within the range of the measurements. Extrapolation of the lines to the intercept is, in the opinion of the writers, unjustified in the case we are now considering. That is, only the late ontogenetic stages are represented and we *do not know from these data* the distribution of X and Y in the earlier stages. The suggested method appears to be really a comparison of slopes, which can be done more directly.

Referring to Fig. 9.4, we select X_0 at the value 21 which represents the smallest individual for the combined samples. At $X_0 = 21$, $Y_A - Y_B = 1.2$ (see Fig. 9.2)

$$Z = \frac{21(0.4091 - 0.5165) + [(-0.2821) - (-3.8034)]}{\sqrt{(0.0603)^2(21 - 31)^2 + (0.0776)^2(21 - 31.42)^2}}$$

$$Z = 1.2558$$

Referring to Z tables we find that a difference larger than the one noted between Y_A and Y_B could be expected about 21 % of the time in a homogeneous population. There is no reason to reject the hypothesis that the two lines for samples *A* and *B* were drawn from a homogeneous population. Imbrie applies the methods described above to Triassic amphibians in conjunction with range.[1]

SUMMARY: REGRESSION ANALYSIS IN PALEOBIOMETRICS

Analysis of scatter diagrams where each point is represented by a pair of morphological dimensions measured on an individual animal may be made

[1] E. H. Colbert and J. Imbrie, 1956, Triassic Metoposaurid amphibians, *Bull. Am. Mus. Nat. Hist.* 110; art. 6: 403–452.

on a subjective basis or by one of several formal methods. The relative growth hypothesis is a unifying concept which motivates the fitting of lines of "best fit" to the points as an objective step toward meaningful interpretation. This line may then be expressed as a linear function $y = b + Kx$, or a function of the form $y = bx^k$. The parameters in either case have biological implications, e.g., b is the initial growth index, and k is the growth ratio [Huxley (1932), Kermack (1954)].

A model is developed in E. C. Olson and R. L. Miller, 1958, *Morphological integration*, University of Chicago Press, Chapter IV, which illustrates the steps which lie between the growth rates of single morphological dimensions and the scattergram. It is apparent from consideration of this model that the validity of scatter-diagram analysis may be questioned in dealing with fossils, particularly when samples are small as is commonly the case, and when variation in individual growth rates is large. This difficulty is due in large part to the fact that the paleontologist usually does not know (other than within very broad limits) the age of the animal at death, although other causes are also discussed.

Formal scattergram analysis whether by conventional regression methods or by the preferable reduced major axis is a widespread and important technique in paleontology.

As pointed out in the following chapter, regression and correlation are closely related to the "analysis of variance."

REFERENCES ON REGRESSION ANALYSIS IN PALEOBIOMETRICS

J. S. Huxley, 1932, *Problems of relative growth*, Methuen and Co., London.

R. C. Robb, 1929, On the nature of hereditary size-limitations. II. The growth of parts in relationship to the whole, *Brit. J. Exper. Biol.* 6: 311–24.

G. Tessier, 1948, La relation d'allometrie, sa signification statistique et biologique, *Biometrics* 4: 14–52.

K. A. Kermack and J. B. S. Haldane, 1950, Organic correlation and allometry, *Biometrika* 37: 30–41.

E. C. Olson and R. L. Miller, 1951, Relative growth in paleontological studies, *Jour. Paleontol.* 25: 212–23.

W. Kruskal, 1953, On the uniqueness of the line of organic correlation, *Biometrics* 9: 47–58.

E. C. Olson and R. L. Miller, 1951, A mathematical model applied to a study of the evolution of species, *Evolution* 5: 256–338.

E. C. R. Reeve, 1940, Relative growth in the snout of the anteaters, *Proc. Roy. Zool. Soc. London, S.A.* 3: 279–302.

A. H. Heroh, 1934, Evolutionary relative growth in titanotheres, *Am. Naturalist* 68: 537–561.

S. W. Gray, 1946, Relative growth in a phylogenetic series, *Am. Jour. Sci.* 244: 297–807.

E. C. R. Reeve, 1941, A statistical analysis of taxonomic differences within the genus Tamandua, *Royal Zool. Soc. London Proc., Ser. A*, 111: 279–302.

O. W. Richards, 1936, *Analysis of the constant differential growth ratio*, Carnegie Inst., *Washington Pub.* 29: 171–183.

W. Feller, 1940, On the logistic law of growth and its empirical verification, *Acta Biotheoretica* 5:2; 51–66.

H. Lumer et al., 1942, On the significance of the constant b in the law of allometry y equals b times x to the sigma, *Am. Naturalist*, 76: 364–375.

K. A. Kermack and J. B. S. Haldane, 1950, Organic correlation and allometry, *Biometrika* 37: 30–41.

K. A. Kermack, 1954, A biometrical study of Micraster corangrinum and M. Isomicraster senonenis, *Phil. Trans. Roy. Soc. London*, Ser. B, 237: 375–428.

Andre Pastiels, 1953, Etude biometrique des Anthracosiidae du Westphalien, *A de la Belgique*, Assoc. Etude Paleont., Stratigraphie Houilleres Publ., No. 16, 55 pp.

John Imbrie, 1956, The place of biometrics in taxonomy, *Bull. American Museum of Natural History*, 108, art. 2: 211–52.

R. L. Miller and E. C. Olson, 1955, The statistical stability of quantitative properties as a fundamental criterion for the study of environments, *Jour. Geol.* 4: 376–87.

Further papers in the context of this chapter:

D. M. Raup, 1958, The relation between water temperature and morphology in Dendraster, *Jour. Geol.* 66: 668–677. Regression analysis is used to establish an empirical correlation between water temperature and test weight in shallow water forms of the contemporary echinoid *Dendraster exceutricus*. The correlation implied by the fitted regression lines is interpreted as the result of phenotypic (noninheritable) adaptations to water temperature.

D. Parkinson, 1954, Quantitative studies of brachiopods from the lower Carboniferous reef limestones of England 1. Schizophoria resupinata (Martin), *Jour. Paleon.* 28: 367–381. A statistical investigation including regression analysis of *S. resupinata* from the reef facies in various localities reveals significant differences in shell shape in several zones. Relative growth between several dimensions is shown to be allometric. The regression method is that of Kermack and Haldane, 1950, *ibid*. Two further papers along the same scheme form numbers 2 and 3 of the series by Parkinson, and are published also in the *Jour. Paleon.*, 1954, 28: 563–567 and 668–676.

H. Chronic, 1952, Molluscan fauna from the Permian Kaibab formation, Walnut canyon, Arizona, *Bull. G.S.A.* 63: 95–166.

F. Phleger and W. S. Putnam, 1942, Analysis of Merycoidodon skulls, *Amer. Jour. Sci.* 240: 547–566. The coefficients α and β are computed by least squares methods for the relative growth equation $y = \beta x^{\alpha}$, and the validity of relative growth analysis is checked by using correlation coefficients. Twelve quantitative characteristics are used in the study.

R. C. Bright, 1959, A paleoecologic and biometric study of the middle Cambrian Trilobite Elrathia kingi (Meek), *Jour. Paleon.* 33: 83–98.

E. L. Lundelius, 1955, *Skeletal adaptations in two species of Sceloporus as determined by regression lines*. Ph.D. Thesis, Univ. of Chicago library. Regression analysis is applied to growth series of skeletons of two species of *Sceloporus* in order to determine the extent and magnitude of species differences, and the adaptive significance of these differences. Tests for significant differences between the regression lines are used as a check on qualitative interpretation based on other sources of information.

Bjorn Kurten, 1954, Observation on allometry in mammalian dentitions: its interpretation and evolutionary significance, *Acta Zool. Fennica*, 85. A general discussion of allometry and its meaning. Recognizes the difficulty in least squares regression, in choosing independent versus the dependent variable and describes the steps leading to a single regression line intermediate between the lines y on x and x on y. Suggests caution in its use, and points out certain difficulties inherent in the method.

Bjorn Kurten, 1957, On the bears of the Holsteinian interglacial, *Stockholm Contrib. in Geol.* II; 5; 73–102. This paper includes considerations of allometry, curve fitting between humerus and third metacarpal in brown and cave bears.

ADDITIONAL REFERENCES ON THE GENERAL SUBJECT OF PALEOBIOMETRICS

Kurt Schmid, 1934, Biometrische Untersuchungen an Foraminiferen aus dem Pliacaen von Ceram, *Ecologae Geological Helvetiae* 27; 1: 46–128. A very early and detailed discussion of statistical analysis in paleontology. Treats regression and correlation with tests of significance, and discusses application of the normal bivariate surface through elliptical contours of equal probability. *Also includes an extensive bibliography of paleobiometrics from the period 1890 to 1934 in both Europe and North America.*

A. B. Shaw, 1956, Quantitative trilobite studies 1. The statistical description of trilobites, *Jour. Paleon.* 30: 209–224.

——— 1957, Measurement of the dorsal shell of non Agnostidean Trilobites, *Jour. Paleon.* 31: 193–207. These two papers contain a general discussion of statistical methods which are applicable in particular to the study of trilobites. Discusses with examples linear regression, ratios, t test, correlation coefficients, and tests of significance of correlation and regression parameters.

Benjamin H. Burma, 1948, Studies in quantitative paleontology: 1. Some aspects of the theory and practice of quantitative invertebrate paleontology, *Jour. Paleon.* 22: 725–761. A general discussion with examples, including treatment of correlation and regression.

D. Marsal, 1949, *Zur Methodik der Paleontologie: Die statistische Sicherung Mittelwerten und Korrelationsziffern*, Neuen Jahrbuch F. Minerologie, etc., Abt. B. Heft 8: 248–256. Discussion of mean variance and correlation coefficients in paleontological applications. Examples are given in detail including several from R. Brinkmann, 1929, *Statistisch-Biostratigraphische Untersuchungen an mittejurassischen Ammoniten, etc.,* Berlin. (Werdmann'sche Buchandlung) *Abh. Ges. Wiss. Gottingen Math-phys.* K1.N.F. 13 Heft 3: 1–249.

R. E. Sloan, 1955, Paleoecology of the Pennsylvanian marine shales of Palo Pinto Co., Texas, *Jour. Geol.* 63: 412–427. Application of correlation and partial correlation to ecological factors such as percent organic material in sediment, sediment size parameters, ratios of echinoids to pelecypods. Also discusses a Poisson model for death frequency distribution of size in a species at a single locality.

D. Nichol, 1944, New West American species of the foraminiferal genus Elphidium, *Jour. Paleon.* 18: 172–185. A very detailed paper on application of statistical analysis to determining a new species. Discusses and applies correlation, regression, slope coefficient.

D. J. Carter, 1953, A statistical study of Operculina, *Jour. Paleon.* 27: 238–250. Correlation and regression are both implied in a graphic analysis of scattergrams. The weakness of the method lies in that no provision is made for inference from sample to population. Extension from actual data to general case is subjective, but is a convenient way to present data.

T. Kotaka, 1953, Variation of Japanese *Anadara granosa*, *Trans. Proc. Paleon. Soc. Japan*, 10: 31–36. Uses bivariate normal probability ellipse as a graphic method for comparing groups of specimens. See also P. G. Hoel, *Introduction to mathematical statistics*, John Wiley, New York, p. 103, pp. 106–108 for discussion and derivation of "bivariate normal probability ellipse" in a plane.

G. G. Simpson, A. Roe, and R. C. Lewontin, 1960, *Quantitative Zoology*, rev. ed., Harcourt Brace, New York. Unfortunately, the revised edition of the very widely used *Quantitative Zoology* by Simpson and Roe became available just after completion of this manuscript. For this reason reference to the many discussions which would otherwise have been referred to in our book were not made. However, the revised edition of *Quantitative Zoology* contains a very wide range of statistical applications to problems which are in the field of paleontology.

chapter 10

Analysis of Variance and Regression

ANALYSIS OF COVARIANCE

Statement of the Problem

Experiments in the earth sciences are frequently involved with observing and measuring more than one variable for a particular sample element. Thus an observation may have k variates associated with it and each of these variates may be observed n times. See discussion in Chapter 5.

In work performed by Melton (1957)[1] at Columbia University, as many as six variables were included simultaneously in elucidating the relationships among and between elements of climate, surface properties, and geomorphology.

In a study of ambient sound in Narragansett Bay, Rhode Island (Dietz, Kahn, and Birch, 1960),[2] simultaneous readings were made for 19 different sound frequencies, wind direction, wind speed, wave height, phase of tide, and amount of rainfall: a total of 24 variates.

In any of the above experiments, one of the k variates might truly be a dependent variable in a mathematical sense and the other independent. The designation of dependence and independence would be made on the basis of knowledge of the variables; a decision best reserved for the investigator.

Each of the individual variables could be analyzed separately and in perhaps different ways. For example, with a continuous variate satisfying the necessary assumptions, the analysis of variance (see Chapter 7) is a

[1] M. A. Melton, 1957, An analysis of the relations among elements of climate, surface properties, and geomorphology. *Tech. Rept.* No. 11, Dept. of Geology, Columbia Univ., New York.

[2] F. T. Dietz, J. S. Kahn, and W. B. Birch, 1960, *Effects of wind on shallow water ambient noise.* Abstract of paper presented at A.S.A. meeting at Brown Univ., June 9, 1960.

possible method. However, it is feasible that there are associations between and among the k variates mentioned above, the association or relationship being such that they contribute to the variability of the related variables. The relationships between pairs of variables, for example, may have been expressed by means of a linear regression function (see Chapter 8), and the degree of association between any two pairs of variables may have been estimated by correlation analysis. (See Chapter 6.) The contribution of one variate to the value observed in another may cause significant differences to occur in that variate when indeed they are attributable not to true differences in the variate observed, but rather to differences associated with a concommitantly correlated variate. It is desirable therefore to eliminate any initial differences in a variate due to associations with other variates prior to analyzing the variate. It would then be desirable to reanalyze the corrected variate to see just what effect the removal of the associated variate had on the significant differences at various levels of assigned variation.

A combination of regression analysis and analysis of variance is a method by which the preceding goals may be reached. This procedure is known as the analysis of covariance.

Models

Since the analysis of covariance *is* a combination of linear regression analysis and analysis of variance, the mathematical model associated with analysis of covariance is a combination of the mathematical models associated with the two analyses.

In particular, to any of the models discussed in the analysis of variance sections of this book we simply add a factor of the form $\beta(x - \bar{x})$, where β is the regression coefficient of the variable y on x, and $\bar{x}$ is the grand average of all x's.

Utilizing the form adopted in the section on analysis of variance and experimental design, the following are some of the Model I and Model II mathematical models for the analysis of covariance.

Model I Mathematical Models. All Factors Fixed

1. Complete randomized design (generalized)—one-way design

$$y_{ijkl...} = \mu + \beta(x_{ijkl...} - \bar{x}) + \alpha_i + \gamma_{ij} + \delta_{ijk} + \cdots + \epsilon_{ijkl...}$$

2. Randomized complete block—two-way design

$$y_{ij} = \mu + \beta(x_{ij} - \bar{x}) + \alpha_i + \gamma_j + \epsilon_{ij}$$

3. Latin Square

$$y_{ijk} = \mu + \beta(x_{ijk} - \bar{x}) + \alpha_i + \gamma_j + \delta_k + \epsilon_{ijk}$$

The other designs naturally follow.

Model II Mathematical Models. All Random Components
1. Completely randomized

$$y_{ijkl...} = \mu + \beta(x_{ijkl...} - \bar{x}) + a_i + b_{ij} + c_{ijk} + \cdots + \epsilon_{ijkl...}$$

2. Randomized complete block

$$y_{ij} = \mu + \beta(x_{ij} - \bar{x}) + a_i + c_j + \epsilon_{ij}$$

3. Latin Square

$$y_{ijk} = \mu + \beta(x_{ijk} - \bar{x}) + a_i + c_j + d_k + \epsilon_{ijk}$$

Model III Mathematical Model

The mathematical models associated with models vary from problem to problem; hence to write down all possibilities would indeed be impossible. The particular experiment will dictate which factors are random and which are fixed; however, to whichever factors are fixed or random will be added the regression expression of the form $\beta(x - \bar{x})$.

Illustrative Example

Model

For illustrative purposes, let us consider the following mixed model, combining aspects of both regression analysis and the analysis of variance, namely,

$$Y = y_{ijkl} = \mu + \rho_i + f_{ij} + s_{ijk} + t_{ijkl} + \beta(x_{ijkl} - \bar{x})$$

where

$$E[Y \mid X] = \mu + \rho_i + \beta(x_{ijkl} - \bar{x}),$$

where $X = x_{ijkl}$, and

$$\text{var}\,[Y \mid X] = \sigma_f^2 + \sigma_s^2 + \sigma^2$$

ρ_i = a constant representing the departure of the ith group mean from the average for groups.

f_{ij} = random variable representing the deviation of the jth subgroup mean from the mean for the ith group.

s_{ijk} = random variable representative, the random deviation of the kth sub-subgroup from the mean of the jth subgroup.

t_{ijkl} = random or unassigned variation.

β = regression coefficient of Y on X.

x_{ijkl} = fixed value for which Y is observed.

Analysis of Variance and Covariance

Each variable, x and y, could just as well be analyzed separately. The total sum of squares associated with each may be divided into various sources of variation in the manner described in Chapter 7. Furthermore, regression estimates as well as estimates of correlation may be obtained for each source of variation with the aid of the sums of cross products of x and y. This may be summarized conveniently in Table 10.1. containing the

TABLE 10.1
Analysis of Covariance. Summary Table

Source of Variation	Degrees of Freedom	Sum of Squares	Sum of Cross Products	Correlation Coefficient	Regression Coefficient
Between groups (r)	$(r-1)$	$\sum_{ijkl}(\bar{\bar{y}}_{i...} - \bar{y})^2 = S^2_{r(y)}$	$\sum_{ijkl}(\bar{\bar{y}}_{i...} - \bar{y})(\bar{\bar{x}}_{i...} - \bar{x}) = S_{r(xy)}$	$r_r = \dfrac{S_{r(xy)}}{\sqrt{S^2_{r(y)}S^2_{r(x)}}}$	$b_r = \dfrac{S_{r(xy)}}{S^2_{r(x)}}$
Between subgroups within groups (f)	$r(f-1)$	$\sum_{ijkl}(\bar{\bar{y}}_{ij..} - \bar{\bar{y}}_{i...})^2 = S^2_{f(y)}$	$\sum_{ijkl}(\bar{\bar{y}}_{ij..} - \bar{\bar{y}}_{i...})(\bar{\bar{x}}_{ij..} - \bar{\bar{x}}_{i...}) = S_{f(xy)}$	$r_f = \dfrac{S_{f(xy)}}{\sqrt{S^2_{f(y)}S^2_{f(x)}}}$	$b_f = \dfrac{S_{f(xy)}}{S^2_{f(x)}}$
Between sub-sub-groups within subgroups and groups (s)	$rf(s-1)$	$\sum_{ijkl}(\bar{y}_{ijk.} - \bar{\bar{y}}_{ij..})^2 = S^2_{s(y)}$	$\sum_{ijkl}(\bar{y}_{ijk.} - \bar{\bar{y}}_{ij..})(\bar{x}_{ijk.} - \bar{\bar{x}}_{ij..}) = S_{s(xy)}$	$r_s = \dfrac{S_{s(xy)}}{\sqrt{S^2_{s(y)}S^2_{s(x)}}}$	$b_s = \dfrac{S_{s(xy)}}{S^2_{s(x)}}$
Error	$rfs(t-1)$	$\sum_{ijkl}(y_{ijkl} - \bar{y}_{ijk.})^2 = S^2_{t(y)}$	$\sum_{ijkl}(y_{ijkl} - \bar{y}_{ijk.})(x_{ijkl} - \bar{x}_{ijk.}) = S_{t(xy)}$	$r_t = \dfrac{S_{t(xy)}}{\sqrt{S^2_{t(x)}S^2_{t(y)}}}$	$b_t = \dfrac{S_{t(xy)}}{S^2_{t(x)}}$
Total	$(rfst-1)$	$\sum_{ijkl}(y_{ijkl} - \bar{y})^2 = S^2_{T(y)}$	$\sum_{ijkl}(y_{ijkl} - \bar{y})(x_{ijkl} - \bar{x}) = S_{T(xy)}$	$r_T = \dfrac{S_{T(xy)}}{\sqrt{S^2_{T(x)}S^2_{T(y)}}}$	$b_T = \dfrac{S_{T(xy)}}{S^2_{T(x)}}$

sums of squares for x and y, the sums of cross products, the estimates of the regression coefficients associated with each level of variation, as well as the simple correlation coefficients associated with each level.

Assuming y and x are related by a regression function at the various levels of sources of variation, the problem of analyzing y depends upon our ability to remove from y any effects due to regression at the various levels of the sources of variation and in this way reduce our error in testing for differences. Table 10.1 lists the variation in y associated with different levels of contributing variation. Furthermore, for the sources of variation at the subgroup levels we have estimates of the regression coefficients of y or x. The analysis of covariance permits us to remove from y any effects of x due to regression at these levels of sources of variation.

The sum of squares for the total variation in y, not corrected for regression, is $\sum\limits_{ijkl} (y_{ijkl} - \bar{y})^2$; whereas $\left[\sum\limits_{ijkl} y_{ijkl} - \bar{y} - b_T(x_{ijkl} - \bar{x})\right]^2$, where b_T is defined as $\dfrac{\text{Total sum of cross products}}{\text{Total sums of squares of } x}$, is the corrected total sums of squares of y after the regression effect has been removed.

Error Sums of Squares Corrected for Regression Effects; Tests of Significant Reduction in Error

A table can be prepared for the partitioned variation in y where the error sums of squares have been corrected for regression. (See Table 10.2.) Note that a degree of freedom is lost for each corrected error sum of

TABLE 10.2

Error Sums of Squares Corrected for Regression

Error Source	Degrees of Freedom	Corrected Error Sums of Squares
Between subgroups within groups	$rf - r - 1$	$\sum\limits_{ijkl} [\bar{\bar{y}}_{ij..} - \bar{y}_{i..} - b_f(\bar{\bar{x}}_{ij..} - \bar{x}_{i..})]^2$
Between sub-subgroups within subgroups	$rfs - rf - 1$	$\sum\limits_{ijkl} [\bar{y}_{ijk.} - \bar{\bar{y}}_{ij..} - b_s(\bar{x}_{ijk.} - \bar{\bar{x}}_{ij..})]^2$
Experimental error	$rfst - rfs - 1$	$\sum\limits_{ijkl} [y_{ijkl} - \bar{y}_{ijk.} - b_t(x_{ijkl} - \bar{x}_{ijk.})]^2$

squares by virtue of our use of $\bar{x}$ in estimating the corrected sums of squares.

Any one of the corrected error sums of squares for a particular source of variation (level of variation) may now be compared with the uncorrected sums of squares for that particular source of variation. This is illustrated schematically in Table 10.3. Here the uncorrected error sums of squares has been broken into two parts, namely, a portion of error attributable to regression and a corrected sum of squares for testing adjusted y. A reduction in the uncorrected error term would suggest an increase in experimental precision. Furthermore, since the ratio of the mean square

TABLE 10.3

Test of Significant Reduction in Error Sum of Squares

Source of Variations	Degrees of Freedom	Sum of Squares	Mean Squares
Uncorrected error (between subgroups)	$r(f-1)$	$S^2_{f(y)}$	$S^2_{f(y)}/r(f-1)$
Regression	1	$b_f S_{xy(f)}$	$b_f S_{xy(f)}$
Adjusted error for testing subgroups	$r(f-1)-1$	$S^2_{f(y)} - b_f S_{xy(f)}$	$\dfrac{S^2_{f(y)} - b_f S_{xy(f)}}{r(f-1)-1}$
Uncorrected error	$1 + r(f-1) - 1$	$S^2_{f(y)}$	$S^2_{f(y)}/r(f-1)$

Test for significant reduction due to regression. (Test of hypothesis that regression coefficient $= 0$.)

$$F\left[\frac{1}{r(f-1)-1}\right] = \frac{b_f S_{xy(f)}}{(S^2_{f(y)} - b_f S_{xy(f)})/r(f-1)}$$

attributable to regression to the error mean square, corrected for regression, is an F distributed variate, we can test the significance of the reduction due in part to the linear relationship of y on x, i.e., the reduction due to regression.

Procedure for Correcting y Values

Assuming the reduction due to regression is significant, i.e., the regression at a particular level of variation is significantly different from 0, we can proceed to correct the y values for fluctuations in x. Corrections may be made at any level in the analysis by means of the regression coefficient within the level of interest, i.e., using the regression coefficients for the error term. The procedure is simply to correct y for x by considering the rate of change of y for a unit change in x (the regression coefficient of y on x for a particular level of variation). For example, if the average x value is $\bar{x}$, then $(x - \bar{x})$ is the number of units x is above or below $\bar{x}$, and if b is the regression coefficient of y on x, then $b(x - \bar{x})$ is the correction for y. Thus

$$y - b(x - \bar{x})$$

is the corrected or adjusted value of y. Of course, if b is not significantly different from 0, this adjustment procedure is not applicable.

Sums of Squares for Adjusted Means

Assuming that the reduction in error due to regression has been significant (Table 10.3) and the y values have been corrected to a common value of x, one can test the following hypotheses. (1) The parameters estimated by the adjusted means are not significantly different for the various levels of variation. (2) The components of variance are zero, assuming the model

TABLE 10.4

Computation of Adjusted Sum of Squares for Testing y Adjusted to a Common Value of x

Source of Variation	D.F.	Sums of Squares and Cross Products		
		S_y^2	S_{xy}	S_x^2
A particular level of variation, e.g., groups	$(r-1)$	$S_{r(y)}^2$	$S_{r(xy)}$	$S_{r(x)}^2$
Error for groups (subgroups)	$r(f-1)$	$S_{f(y)}^2$	$S_{f(xy)}$	$S_{f(x)}^2$
Groups + error for groups	$(r-1)+r(f-1)=(rf-1)$	$S_{r(y)}^2 + S_{f(y)}^2$		
Regression: (for groups + error for groups)	1	$\dfrac{[S_{r(xy)}+S_{f(xy)}]^2}{S_{r(x)}^2+S_{f(x)}^2}$		
Groups + error for groups corrected for regression	$(rf-1)-(1)=rf-2$	$S_{r(y)}^2 + S_{f(y)}^2 - \dfrac{[S_{r(xy)}+S_{f(xy)}]^2}{S_{r(x)}^2+S_{f(x)}^2}$		
Corrected error sum of squares	$r(f-1)-1=rf-r-1$	$S_{f(y)}^2 - \dfrac{[S_{f(xy)}]^2}{S_{f(x)}^2} = S_{f(y_c)}^2$		
Adjusted group sum of squares (corrected for y adjusted to a common x)	$(r-1)$	$S_{r(y)}^2 - \dfrac{[S_{r(xy)}+S_{f(xy)}]^2}{S_{r(x)}^2+S_{f(x)}^2} + \dfrac{S_{f(xy)}}{S_{f(x)}^2} = S_{r(y_c)}^2$		

contains such. To test these hypotheses one must first compute the sums of squares of y, at the various levels of variation, adjusted to a common x. A satisfactory method for doing this is with the aid of the corrected error sums of squares for the specific source of variation. Since the sums of squares of the source of variation and its error are additive, one may sum them, correct this sum of squares for adjusted y by subtracting the effect due to regression, and then remove from this sum of squares the corrected error sum of squares, leaving a residual sum of squares, the sum of squares of y adjusted for a common x. This is outlined in Table 10.4.

Tests of the Hypothesis of the Form: $\mu_1 = \mu_2 = \cdots = \mu_k$, *and* $\sigma_j^2 = 0$

The test of these hypotheses are identical. It consists of dividing the adjusted mean square for testing adjusted means by the corrected error mean square. This ratio is an F distributed statistic with the same number of degrees of freedom that this ratio would have had prior to the commencement of the analysis of covariance. (See Table 10.4.)

MULTIPLE REGRESSION AND MULTIPLE CORRELATION ANALYSIS

Multiple Regression

The functional relationship among different variables is familiar to us. The equation

$$pV = nRT$$

expressing the relationship between pressure (p), volume (V), and the temperature (T) of an ideal gas is such an example. The object of much experimentation is prediction based on empirical data. The simple linear relationship between two variables has been discussed. This relationship can easily be extended from two variables to any number. A general expression may thus be put in the form

$$E(y) = \mu = \alpha + \beta(x_1 - \bar{x}_2) + \beta(x_2 - \bar{x}_2) + \cdots + \beta_k(x_k - \bar{x}_k)$$

In particular,

$$E[y_{ij} \mid x_{i1}, x_{i2}, \cdots, x_{ik} = X_i] = \mu_i$$
$$= \alpha + \beta_1(x_{i1} - \bar{x}_{.1}) + \cdots + \beta_k(x_{ik} - \bar{x}_{.k})$$

where

$$i = 1, \cdots, c$$
$$j = 1, \cdots, k$$

and

$$\text{var } [y_{ij} \mid x_i] = \sigma^2 \qquad \text{for all } i, j$$

Furthermore, y is assumed normally distributed, for each X, with mean μ_j and variance σ^2.

β_j are known as the partial regression coefficients. Their estimates are written $b_{yx_j} \cdot x_1, x_2, \cdots, x_{j-1}, x_{j+1}, \ldots, x_k$, i.e., the regression of y on variable x_j *independent* of $x_1, x_2, \cdots, x_{j-1}, x_{j+1} \cdots, x_k$. The estimating equation is written as

$$y = a + b_1(x_1 - \bar{x}_1) + b_2(x_2 - \bar{x}_2) + \cdots (x_k - \bar{x}_k)$$

where $a, b_1, b_2, \cdots, b_k$ are estimates of $\alpha, \beta_1, \beta_2, \cdots, \beta_k$, respectively.

The next step is to obtain estimates of the unknown parameters. Utilization of the method of maximum likelihood gives rise to $k + 1$ equations to be solved for k estimates of the regression coefficients and one estimate of

α. $(k + 1)$ equations with $(k + 1)$ unknowns can be solved simultaneously, provided the determinant of the form

$$\Delta = \begin{vmatrix} S_{x_1}^2 & S_{x_1 x_2} & \cdots & S_{x_1 x_k} \\ S_{x_1 x_2} & S_{x_2}^2 & & \cdot \\ \cdot & \cdot & \cdot & \cdot \\ \cdot & \cdot & \cdot & \cdot \\ \cdot & \cdot & \cdot \cdot & \cdot \\ S_{x_1 x_k} & \cdot & \cdots & S_{x_k}^2 \end{vmatrix} \neq 0$$

There are different methods for solving for these regression coefficients. It would indeed be possible to select one, if not two, methods and proceed step by step to the solution. However, this will not be done. For the reader who wishes such an analysis, we recommend the material in Hald,[1] Snedecor,[2] Ezekiel,[3] and Ostle[4] to mention a few.

The authors feel that with the advent of the automatic computer, it has become outmoded and time consuming to spend days, even weeks, performing, checking, and rechecking multiple regression analyses. The model, as presented, is a *standard program*. The researcher brings his data to the now commonplace computing center, prepares his tape or cards, and has the data run through the computer either by himself, after a brief introduction to the operation of the machine, or with the aid of personnel from the computing center.

Once the estimates of the parameters and their variances are obtained, the testing of hypotheses concerning the unknown parameters proceeds as before. For example, if $s_{b_j}^2$ is the variance of any b_j, the test of the hypothesis

$$H_1: \beta_j = \beta_j$$

with the alternative

$$H_2: \beta_j \neq \beta_j$$

is a two-tailed test, with the variable

$$t = \frac{b_j - \beta_j}{s_{b_j}}$$

as the test criterion.

[1] A. Hald, 1952, *Statistical theory with engineering applications*, John Wiley, New York.

[2] G. W. Snedecor, 1953, *Statistical Methods*, 4th ed., Iowa State College Press, Ames, Iowa.

[3] M. Ezekiel, 1930, *Methods of correlation analysis*, 2nd ed., John Wiley, New York.

[4] B. Ostle, 1954, *Statistics in research*, Iowa State College Press, Ames, Iowa.

Similarly, since a is a normal deviate with mean μ and variance σ^2/ck, the test of the hypotheses

$$H_1: \alpha = 0$$
$$H_2: \alpha \geqq 0$$

is a one-tailed test of the form

$$t = \frac{a}{\hat{\sigma}\sqrt{ck}}$$

where $\hat{\sigma}$ is an estimate of σ, namely, the square root of the sum of the squares of the deviation of the observed values of y from the estimated regression or predicted values, divided by the square root of the number of observations of y, (ck), less the number of linear restrictions on y, which in this case is $k + 1$.

$\hat{\sigma}$ is also known as the standard error of estimate and may be used as a sort of error band about the plane of best fit.

SUGGESTED REFERENCE

W. C. Krumbein, 1959, The sorting out of geological variables illustrated by regression analysis of factors controlling beach firmness, *Jour. Sed. Petrol.* 29: 575–587. Uses multiple regression and multiple correlation analysis in a method devised to "sort out" degrees of independence among a collection of variables relative to a single dependent variable. An appendix gives the method in detail, including the relevant information for I.B.M. high speed computer programming.

Correlation Analysis among Three or More Variates

Having obtained an expression for the relationship between y and k variates, it is often desirable to obtain the correlation or linear association between y and any x_j. This procedure has been described in Chapter 6. When y has been shown to be functionally dependent on more than one variable, it is possible to obtain a false impression of the association between y and any x_j if consideration has not been given to the relationships among y, x_j, and other x's. Thus, we wish to look not at the simple linear correlation coefficient r_{yx} but rather at a measure which correlates the associations of y on x_j, conditional on some value for the remaining independent variates. That is, we wish to look at a measure of the form

$$r_{[yx_j \mid x_1, x_2, \ldots, x_{j-1}, x_{j+1}, \ldots x_k]}$$

Such a measure is the parameter, the partial correlation coefficient, or conditional correlation coefficient,[1] ρ_{yx_j}.

[1] T. W. Anderson, 1958, *An introduction to multivariate statistical analysis*, John Wiley, New York, Chapter 4, Section 3, gives a detailed discussion of partial correlation.

HOMOGENEITY OF CORRELATION COEFFICIENTS

Interpretation and Significance Tests of Fluctuations in the Correlation Coefficient in Paleontological Context

Meaningful utilization of the correlation coefficient in comparisons between populations is dependent upon two assumptions.[1]

I. *Correlations of pairs of dimensions are stable within a natural population, where that population is the smallest homogeneous taxonomic unit.*

II. *Large differences in r values in comparison of several populations for a pair of measurements, are not due to sampling fluctuations but represent real biologically interpretable differences in degree of association.*

TABLE 10.5

Interpretation of Correlation Coefficient

Sample	Sample Size n_i	Correlation Coefficient	Tanh$^{-1} r = Z_i$	$(n_i - 3)$	$(n_i - 3)Z_i$	$(n_i - 3)Z_i^2$
1	50	0.364	0.38	47	17.86	6.7868
2	50	0.312	0.32	47	15.04	4.8128
3	30	0.405	0.43	27	11.61	4.9923
4	25	0.327	0.34	22	7.48	2.5432
				$n = 143$	$T_1 = 51.99$	$T_2 = 19.1351$

A test of the homogeneity of sample correlation coefficients is described in Rao (1952), pp. 233–235. This test is suitable for comparing two or more r values with varying sample sizes. The following statistic is computed:

$$\chi^2 = T_2 - \frac{T_1^2}{N}$$

$$T_1 = \sum_{i=1}^{k}(n_i - 3)Z_i$$

for k correlation coefficients. n_i is the sample size corresponding to the ith correlation coefficient and Z_i is the transformation of r_i, where tanh$^{-1} r_i = Z_i$

$$T_2 = \sum_{i=1}^{k}(n_i - 3)Z_i^2 \qquad N = \sum_{i=1}^{k}(n_i - 3)$$

$T_2 - (T_1^2/N)$ may then be used as χ^2 with $(k - 1)$ degrees of freedom. The following example illustrates the test. Two samples of 50 were drawn at

[1] See also Rosenfeld, Jacobsen, and Ferm, 1953, *ibid.* for application in another context.

random from a collection of *Spirifer pennatus* and the correlation coefficients computed. Drawing two additional samples of sizes 30 and 25
gives us a total of four correlation coefficients:

$$+0.364 \quad +0.312 \quad +0.405 \quad +0.327$$

Are these correlation coefficients homogeneous, or are the differences
larger than can be attributed to sampling fluctuations within a single
population?

$$\chi^2 = T_2 - \frac{T_1^2}{N} = 19.1351 - \frac{2702.96}{143} = 0.2333$$

$$\text{Degrees of freedom} = (k = 1) - (4 - 1) = 3$$

$\chi^2_{3,\,0.95}$ is 7.81. We therefore conclude that the r values are homogeneous.
Olson and Miller, 1958, *Morphological integration, ibid.*, pp. 78–83,
tested the assumptions just given as follows:

1. *Homogeneity of r values within a breeding population.* Five samples of
size 20 each were drawn from a breeding population of pigeons. The
correlations between all possible pairs of 10 morphological measurements
were computed for a total of 45 tests of homogeneity. The correlation
coefficients proved to be homogeneous for 44 of the 45 tests at an α risk
of 0.05 in each test.

2. *Nonhomogeneity of r values from one population to the next in an
evolutionary sequence.* Nine morphological measurements were taken on
samples at various time levels in two evolutionary lines of *Pentremites*.
Assumption II implies that r values for any pair of measurements should
vary significantly between samples drawn from different time levels in an
evolutionary line. In case 1, the "godoniform" evolutionary line, four
separate time levels were studied. Twenty-nine of the 36 tests indicated
nonhomogeneity of correlation coefficients. In case 2, the "pyriform"
evolutionary line, three separate time levels were studied. All 36 of the
tests indicated nonhomogeneous r values. One should not expect that *all*
the correlation coefficients should vary from one time level to the next.
It is, in fact, meaningful to consider those correlation coefficients which do
not vary as stable in an evolutionary sense, and consider those which do
vary as reflecting underlying changes in the evolving population.

3. *Homogeneity of r values over the ontogenetic series.* An inbred stock
of the albino rat was studied. Ten morphological measurements were
taken on each of 20 individuals at 5 separate ontogenetic stages (1 day,
10 day, 20 day, 40 day, and adult (250) days). The tests for homogeneity of
r values were made over the 5 ontogenetic stages. The results were about
equally divided between homogeneous and nonhomogeneous r values.

However, when the 1 day and 10 day stages were removed, 43 of the 45 tests showed homogeneity at $\alpha = 0.05$ level. This suggests that when significantly large fluctuations of correlation coefficients are found within a single inbred population, they are contributed primarily by the very earliest ontogenetic stages (rarely preserved in fossils).

DISCUSSION OF RELEVANT LITERATURE

An analysis was made by Morisawa (1958)[1] of the correlation between several form ratios and runoff. The five form ratios are of hydrologic and geomorphic interest. The data came from twenty-five watersheds of the Appalachian plateau. Of the five tested only circularity (C), Miller (1953)[2] and elongation (E), Schumm (1954),[3] showed significant correlation. A form ratio proposed by Chorley, Malm, and Pogorzelski (1957a)[5] based on the properties of the lemniscate curve, as well as two due to Horton, were found to show no significant correlation with runoff.

The use of correlation to prove or disprove relations between several variables is a risky procedure, particularly when the variables are members of a larger complex suite. The presence of correlation, especially if high as in an example given by Melton (1958a)[4] between channel frequency (F) and drainage density (D) with correlation of $r = +0.97$, is usually indicative of a relationship of some sort, but the causality is only rarely glimpsed without further searching analysis. On the other hand, lack of correlation is even more difficult to interpret. A discussion of interpretation of correlation in geomorphic context is given by Chorley (1957b), pp. 637 to 638.[6]

SUGGESTED REFERENCES IN THE CONTEXT
OF THIS CHAPTER

G. M. Friedman, 1958, Determination of sieve-size distribution from the thin-section data for sedimentary petrological studies, *Jour. Geol.* 66: 394–416. A new graph paper is developed to facilitate conversion of thin section size data to a cumulative frequency curve with size parameters equivalent to those expected from sieve analysis of the same rock. Analysis of covariance is used as well as other statistical methods.

Percival Allen, 1945, Sedimentary variation: some new facts and theories, *Jour. Sed. Petrol.* 15: 75ff. Efficient statistics for the estimation of mineralogical variation and covariation are indicated. Among the topics discussed and methods employed are "efficiency", covariance, and sample size.

[1] M. Morisawa, 1958, Measurement of drainage-basin outline form, *Jour. Geol.* 66: 5; 587–591.

[2] V. C. Miller, 1953, *ibid.*

[3] S. Schumm, 1954, *ibid.*

[4] M. Melton, 1958a, *ibid.*

[5] R. J. Chorley, D. E. G. Malm, and H. A. Pogorzelski, 1957a, A new standard for estimating drainage basin shapes, *Am. Jour. Sci.* 255: 138–141.

[6] R. J. Chorley 1957b, Climate and morphometry, *Jour. Geol.* 65: 6; 628–638.

D. Leitch, 1940, A statistical investigation of the *Anthracomyas* of the basal Simulis Pulchra zone of Scotland, *Quart. Jour. Geol.* 96: 1–38. An attempt is made to give numerical values to the general variation character of a community by means of regression equations. These are based on multiple correlation assuming linear regression (isometric growth) among all characters.

A. B. Vistelius, 1958, Paragenesis of sodium, potassium and uranium in volcanic rocks of Lassen Volcanic National Park, California, *Geochim. et Cosmochim. Acta.* 14: 29–34. Previously published data are reanalyzed by Vistelius using computed regression and correlation coefficients, partial correlation, and taking sample size and statistical significance into account.

E. S. Deevey, 1940, Limnological studies in Connecticut, V, a contribution of regional limnology, *Am. Jour. Sci.* 238: 717–741. Utilizes multiple correlation coefficients in a study of plankton production.

Paul Horst, 1932, A short method for solving for a coefficient of multiple correlation, *Annals. of Math. Stats.* 3: 40ff. An aid in the laborious computations involved in computing multiple correlation coefficients.

R K. Guthrie and M. H. Greenberger, 1955, The use of multiple correlation analysis for interpreting petroleum engineering data. Preprint. Division of production, A.P.I. Dallas, Texas. A general discussion of multiple correlation with numerous illustrations and references.

C. R. Pelto, 1952, The mechanical analysis of sediments from thin section data: a discussion, *Jour. Geol.* 60: 402–406. Discusses and applies covariance analysis, and also some probability theory and statistical efficiency.

chapter 11

Synthesis of Statistical Inference

Statistical inference, the estimation of parameters and the testing of hypotheses involving parameters and their estimates, was presented as a general study of some of the techniques and methods available to a researcher in the earth sciences. As a means of illustrating this material and demonstrating the nonisolation of different techniques and various methods, use will be made of a study made by Kahn (1956*a*, *b*).[1,2] The study is of a petrographic nature, but the procedures are by no means restricted to this specialization. The example will merely be used to demonstrate the many tools at the disposal of the researcher and the utility of these tools.

MOTIVATION

The petrographic study was concerned with the textural parameter-packing. The investigation was suggested by J. C. Griffiths and was prompted by the general lack of information on the nature of the variable. Measurement techniques for measuring the parameter were decided upon. Two aspects of packing were considered; the first, a measure of the amount of space taken up by grains, was measured by packing density, P_d, the other, a measure of the closeness of the grains, was measured by packing proximity, P_p.

---

[1] J. S. Kahn, 1956*a*, The analysis and distribution of the properties of packing in sandstones, *Jour. Geology*, 64: 4; 385–395.

[2] J. S. Kahn, 1956*b*, The analysis and distribution of the properties of packing in sand-size sediments. II. The distribution of packing measurements and an example of packing analysis, *Jour. Geology*, 64: 6; 578–606.

Rock Types	Formations	Slides	Traverses
Quartzite	Tuscarora	LM742-B P-72	
	Oriskany	O7A-3A O7A-3B	
	Cuche	GR 1200^6-96471 AGH 3676	
Low-rank graywacke	Pocono	6225 6285	Five traverses in each slide
	Oswego	6307 6301	
	Bradford	5820-3 P(4)-(6)	
Arkose	Portland	Mid5-2 Mid8-8B	
	Roslyn	ab-3a ef-2a	
	Stockton	1 2	
	Totals	3 Rock types 9 Formations 18 Slides 90 Traverses	

FIG. 11.1. Schematic outline of sampling plan for study of packing in sediments

SAMPLING

It was decided that the three sedimentary rock types as defined by Krynine (1947)[3] would be sampled in the following manner:

Each rock type would be sampled for three formations; each formation would be sampled for two different thin sections; and each thin section would be sampled for five traverses.

The sampling for this work is presented schematically in Fig. 11.1. The formations within rock types are considered a random sample of formations from many possible formations which could have been selected. Similarly, slides (thin sections) were randomly selected from a series of slides

[3] P. D. Krynine, 1947, *The Megascopic Study and field classification of sedimentary rocks. Mineral Industries*, Experimental Station Tech. Paper 130, College of Mineral Industries, The Pennsylvania State University, State College, Penn.

which could have been selected. Finally, the traverses were randomly sampled from the infinite number of traverses that could have been examined.

The questions of immediate interest were:

1. What is the probability distribution functions of the random variables P_d? P_p?
2. What are the population parameters which identify these probability distribution functions?
3. What are the estimates of P_d and P_p for the different rock types; formations, slides, and traverses?
4. Are there significant differences among the packing parameters for the three rock types?
5. What are the estimates of the various components of variance?
6. Is there a linear relationship between P_d and P_p?
7. Is any of the variation associated with P_p attributable to a relationship between P_p and P_d? Between P_p and other variates?

Experimental Design

The questions posed demanded an experimental design, capable of coping with the problems, which motivated the work. The design selected was a one-way mixed model analysis of variance, where any observation y is constructed as

$$\mu + \rho_i + f_{ij} + s_{ijk} + t_{ijkl}$$

Here, $\rho_i = $ a constant, representing the deviation of a rock type from the over-all mean μ; f_{ij} is a random variable representing the random departure of a formation mean from its rock-type mean and is assumed to be $N(0, \sigma_f^2)$; s_{ijk} is the random departure of a slide mean from its formation mean and is $N(0, \sigma_s^2)$; t_{ijkl} is random or unexplained variation or experimental error and is $N(0, \sigma^2)$. The analysis of variance table, with computational formulas, is illustrated in Table 11.1.

Distribution of the Variables

It was pointed out in Chapter 6 that if the form of the probability density function that governs a variable is known, then the number of parameters associated with the type of curve, and which determine a specific curve, is known. Furthermore, if values of these parameters can be determined, or if estimates of them can be obtained, then one is in the enviable position of knowing all there is to know about a specific variable. For example, if a variable y is distributed as a normal variable, we know its probability density function and the parameters in question, namely, μ and σ. To determine which specific normal distribution would depend upon the exact values of μ and σ.

TABLE 11.1
Mathematical Model for Nested Analysis of Variance

Source of Variation	D.F.	Sum of Squares	Mean Square	Components of Variance
Rock types (r)	$(r-1)$	$\sum_i^r \left(\sum_{j,k,l}^{fst} X\right)^2 \Big/ fst - T = S_r^2$	$S_r^2/(r-1)$	$\sigma_t^2 + t\sigma_s^2 + st\sigma_f^2 + \dfrac{fst}{r-1}\sum_i^r \rho_i^2$
Formations (f) (within r)	$r(f-1)$	$\sum_{i,j}^{rf}\left(\sum_{k,l}^{st} X\right)^2 \Big/ st - T - S_r^2 = S_f^2$	$S_f^2/r(f-1)$	$\sigma_t^2 + t\sigma_s^2 + st\sigma_f^2$
Slides (s) (within f and r)	$rf(s-1)$	$\sum_{i,j,k}^{rfs}\left(\sum_l^t X\right)^2 \Big/ t - T - S_r^2 - S_f = S_s^2$	$S_s^2/rf(s-1)$	$\sigma_t^2 + t\sigma_s^2$
Traverses (t) (within s, f, and r)	$rfs(t-1)$	$S_{\text{total}}^2 - \text{all others} = S_t^2$	$S_t^2/rfs(t-1)$	σ_t^2
Total	$(rfst-1)$	$\sum_{i,j,k,l}^{rfst} X^2 - T = S_{\text{total}}^2$		

$$T = \left(\sum_{i,j,k,l}^{rfst} X\right)^2 \Big/ rfst$$

$$X = x_{ijkl} = \mu + \rho_i + f_{ij} + s_{ijk} + t_{ijkl},$$

$$i = 1, \cdots, r,$$
$$j = 1, \cdots, f,$$
$$k = 1, \cdots, s,$$
$$l = 1, \cdots, t.$$

where ρ_i = a constant, i.e., deviation of a rock-type mean from the over-all mean; f_{ij} is a random variable, $N(0, \sigma_f^2)$; s_{ijk} is a random variable, $N(0, \sigma_s^2)$; and t_{ijkl} is a random variable, $N(0, \sigma_t^2)$.

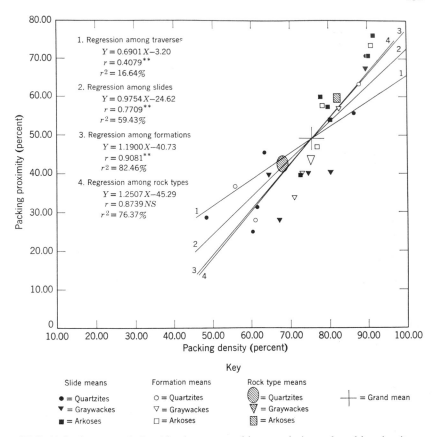

1. Regression among traverses
   $Y = 0.6901\,X - 3.20$
   $r = 0.4079^{**}$
   $r^2 = 16.64\%$

2. Regression among slides
   $Y = 0.9754\,X - 24.62$
   $r = 0.7709^{**}$
   $r^2 = 59.43\%$

3. Regression among formations
   $Y = 1.1900\,X - 40.73$
   $r = 0.9081^{**}$
   $r^2 = 82.46\%$

4. Regression among rock types
   $Y = 1.2507\,X - 45.29$
   $r = 0.8739\,NS$
   $r^2 = 76.37\%$

Key

Slide means	Formation means	Rock type means	
● = Quartzites	○ = Quartzites	◐ = Quartzites	┼ = Grand mean
▼ = Graywackes	▽ = Graywackes	▽ = Graywackes	
■ = Arkoses	□ = Arkoses	▨ = Arkoses	

FIG. 11.2. Average relationships between packing proximity and packing density.

A priori the density functions of P_d and P_p are unknown. One procedure used to determine the closeness of an observed distribution to some theoretical distribution is a comparison of the frequencies of the actually observed distribution with those in the theoretical distribution. This procedure was described in detail in Chapter 6. The data available are those collected by the sampling procedure outlined previously. The raw data are summarized as a frequency table in Table 11.2. The P_d data were compared, class by class, with a normal distribution with the same mean and variance as estimated by the empirical distribution. This comparison was made in detail in Chapter 6. The statistic

$$\sum_{i=1}^{5} \frac{(f_i - np_i)^2}{np_i} = \chi^2_{(2)}$$

was computed and the hypothesis, which states there is no significant differences between the observed P_d empirical distribution and a normal distribution, was accepted.

TABLE 11.2

**Frequency Distributions of Packing Density (percent)
and Packing Proximity (percent) for Quartzites,
Graywackes, Arkoses, and All Combined**

Class	Quartzite (f)	Graywacke (f)	Arkose (f)	All (f)
		Packing Density		
90–100	4	1	6	11
80– 90	5	6	12	23
70– 80	1	13	9	23
60– 70	9	9	3	21
50– 60	8	1		9
40– 50	3	—	—	3
$N =$	30	30	30	90
$\bar{P}_d =$	68.00	74.00	82.00	74.67
$s =$	15.75	8.72	9.00	12.95
		Packing Proximity		
80– 90	—	—	3	3
70– 80	3	2	4	9
60– 70	4	1	9	14
50– 60	4	3	8	15
40– 50	4	11	2	17
30– 40	6	9	4	19
20– 30	6	4	—	10
10– 20	3	—	—	3
$N =$	30	30	30	90
$\bar{P}_p =$	43.00	43.00	60.33	48.78
$s =$	18.50	12.77	14.32	17.42

P_p, on the other hand, estimates the average number of grain-to-grain contacts in a traverse of n contacts and is defined as

$$\frac{\sum\limits_{i=1}^{n} c_i}{n}$$

where $\sum\limits_{i=1}^{n} c_i$ represents the total number of grain-to-grain contacts in a particular traverse. Here c_i represents the presence or absence of a contact made by the ith grain and its neighbor. If the ith grain is in contact with its neighbor, let $c_i = 1$. If it is not, let $c_i = 0$. If p represents the probability of obtaining a grain-to-grain contact in a single observation, then c_i is a random variable, distributed binomially (see Chapter 2), with values 1 and 0 and with parameter p. The probability distribution function of every c_i is as in Eq. 2.1. The expected value of c_i, $E(c_i)$ is p and its variance is $p(1 - p)$. Therefore, in a traverse of n contacts the variables c_1, c_2, $\cdots$, c_n are independent random variables, each with mean p and variance $p(1 - p)$. Applying the central limit theorem, (see Chapter 4), the arithmetic mean, $\sum_{i=1}^{n} c_i/n$, is normally distributed with mean $\mu = p$ and variance $\sigma^2 = [p(1 - p)]/n$. The reader will note that this arithmetic mean is P_p. Hence, on *a priori* grounds, one would expect P_p to be distributed normally with mean p and variance $[P(1 - p)]/n$. This is substantiated by comparing the observed P_p data with a theoretically normal curve. Here χ^2 is 2.82, and since the critical region is defined as $\chi^2_{(3),0.05} \geq 7.82$, the null hypothesis is accepted and P_p is thus assumed to be normally distributed.

TABLE 11.3
Formation and Rock-Type Means for Packing Proximity and Packing Density (percent)

Formation	P_d	P_p
Tuscarora	87.45	63.28
Oriskany	60.93	27.93
Cuche	55.73	36.85
Quartzite means	68.04	42.68
Pocono	72.59	39.85
Oswego	82.47	56.98
Bradford	70.77	33.61
Graywacke means	75.28	43.48
Portland	76.64	46.86
Roslyn	90.54	73.52
Stockton	78.52	58.54
Arkose means	81.90	59.64
Grand means	75.07	48.60

ESTIMATION OF PARAMETERS

The parameters of interest in the study of a normal variate are μ and σ. Thus, at the traverse, slide, formation, and rock-type level, estimates of these parameters can be made for both variates P_d and P_p. At the same time, by virtue of the characteristic of the normal distribution, estimates and measures of central tendency and spread, or variability about the measure of central tendency, are made simultaneously. The estimating functions are $\bar{x}$ and s respectively. These values are summarized in Tables 11.2 to 11.4.

TESTING OF HYPOTHESIS CONCERNED WITH μ AND σ

The experimental design described leads directly to a method of testing certain linear hypotheses containing the general parameters μ and σ. The reader will recall certain assumptions implicit in the analysis of variance procedure (see Chapter 7). The normality assumption has been examined and accepted. The assumption of random samples has also been made. The next important consideration is that of homogeneous variance. This, as has been pointed out before, is an important restriction on the validity of the analysis. A procedure for testing the hypothesis of homogeneous variance has already been presented (Chapter 6). The data in this study were processed through this test procedure and the hypothesis of homogeneous variance was accepted (Tables 11.5, 11.6).

The following hypotheses, with respect to both P_d and P_p, can now be examined, utilizing the analysis of variance technique.

1. H_1: $\rho_1 = \rho_2 = \rho_3$, i.e., there are no significant differences among rock types. Here, ρ_1 = arkose rock-type mean, ρ_2 = graywacke rocktype mean, ρ_3 = quartzite rock-type mean.
2. H_2: $\sigma_f^2 = 0$ with the alternative
   $\sigma_f^2 > 0$
3. H_3: $\sigma_s^2 = 0$ with the alternative
   $\sigma_s^2 > 0$

The analyses are summarized in Tables 11.7 and 11.9. The results are parallel for both variables, namely, one rejects H_1 and concludes that the rock types differ significantly with respect to the variables P_p and P_d. Also, one rejects H_2 and H_3, and infers that variability in both slides and formations contributes to the over-all variability of any packing observation. The estimates of the rock-type means are located in Table 11.3. Utilizing the Tukey method, we determine which means are significantly different (see Tables 11.8, 11.10). Thus, for example, for P_p the Roslyn formation differs significantly from the Cuche, Bradford, and Oriskany formations. The Tuscarora differs only from the Oriskany. There are no significant differences among the others. The estimates of σ_t^2, σ_s^2, and σ_f^2 are found in Table 11.11.

TABLE 11.4
Summary of Measurements for All Traverses in All Slides

Traverse	LM742-B	P-72	07-A-3A	07-A-3B	GR1200[6] 96471	AGH-3676[c]	6225	6285	6307	6301	5820-3	P(4)-1(6)	Mid5-2	Mid8-8B	ab-3a	ef-2a	No. 1	No. 2
										Slide								
						(a) Summary of Packing-Density Measurements (percent)												
1	91.01	89.25	66.92	62.03	49.11	63.47	78.93	73.68	88.21	75.13	68.88	68.09	80.97	65.44	85.35	91.72	82.32	85.91
2	78.33	86.06	56.31	58.68	46.92	64.77	79.30	63.85	89.55	76.60	68.63	78.63	84.73	77.77	93.59	90.83	82.30	77.30
3	88.86	90.54	58.51	58.24	40.34	65.59	79.28	57.83	88.51	77.91	64.43	76.77	81.31	79.25	90.01	92.75	79.86	73.26
4	87.25	90.00	65.76	64.57	50.25	63.39	85.05	63.93	87.12	71.97	68.91	72.97	76.27	68.22	89.00	95.33	75.48	76.99
5	82.60	90.59	60.16	58.14	54.67	58.74	81.79	62.30	92.96	76.70	64.52	75.85	80.53	71.88	88.34	88.50	65.60	86.20
$P_d =$	85.61	89.29	61.53	60.33	48.26	63.19	80.87	64.32	89.27	75.66	67.07	74.46	80.76	72.51	89.26	91.83	77.11	70.93
$s^2 =$	26.11	3.55	20.53	8.19	27.58	7.05	6.77	33.55	5.01	5.23	5.64	16.86	9.08	35.47	8.88	6.30	49.20	33.78
						(b) Summary of Packing-Proximity Measurements (percent)												
1	64.47	68.33	35.63	29.10	19.81	45.90	41.29	40.27	68.54	40.28	32.68	36.99	61.29	37.65	71.29	80.77	64.58	59.26
2	57.61	70.21	28.57	18.02	36.11	41.10	38.61	42.41	71.76	55.35	29.67	40.09	53.95	55.79	82.11	66.97	54.35	58.93
3	60.17	70.59	36.00	23.48	18.87	55.00	37.91	35.76	57.30	43.95	23.66	48.50	45.24	31.31	60.87	80.00	60.53	38.64
4	46.67	66.04	30.19	30.77	27.35	52.00	44.67	41.10	58.89	49.71	29.38	36.63	55.21	30.19	60.42	76.85	60.53	59.18
5	50.53	78.13	24.76	22.79	40.40	31.94	38.93	37.50	78.57	45.40	23.13	35.37	55.81	42.16	79.78	76.15	60.00	69.39
$P_p =$	55.89	70.66	31.03	24.83	28.51	45.19	40.28	39.41	67.01	46.94	27.70	39.52	54.30	39.42	70.89	76.15	60.00	57.08
$s^2 =$	52.16	20.70	22.99	26.47	92.28	83.85	7.63	7.39	79.69	33.52	17.18	28.23	33.54	107.40	103.78	30.23	13.37	126.04

TABLE 11.5

Tests of Homogeneity of Variance for Packing Proximity for All Rocks

Rock Type	D.F.	χ^2	Probability
Quartzite	5	4.37	$0.50 > p > 0.30$ NS*
Graywacke	5	8.34	$0.20 > p > 0.10$ NS
Arkose	5	6.96	$0.30 > p > 0.20$ NS
All combined	17	24.07	$0.20 > p > 0.10$ NS

* NS = no significant difference among variances.

TABLE 11.6

Tests of Homogeneity of Variances for Packing Density for All Rocks

Rock Type	D.F.	χ^2	Probability
Quartzite	5	6.14	$0.30 > p > 0.20$ NS*
Graywacke	5	7.01	$0.30 > p > 0.20$ NS
Arkose	5	7.19	$0.30 > p > 0.20$ NS
All combined	17	23.16	$0.20 > p > 0.10$ NS

* NS = no significant difference among variances.

TABLE 11.7

Analysis of Variance of Packing Proximity for the Three Sand-Size Sedimentary-Rock Types

Source of Variation	D.F.	Sum of Squares	Mean Square	F
Rock types	2	5,493.64	2,746.82	1.24
Formations (within rock types)	6	13,256.67	2,209.45	5.95*
Slides (within formations and rock types)	9	3,338.94	370.99	7.53†
Traverses (within slides, formations, and rock types)	72	3,545.69	49.25	—
Total ($n = 90$)	89	25,634.94		

* Significance at the 0.01 level.
† Significance at the 0.001 level.

TABLE 11.8
Packing-Proximity Differences among Formations

Formation	P_p	P_p — Allowance*
Roslyn	73.52	39.41
Tuscarora	63.28	29.17
Stockton	58.54	———
Cswego	56.98	24.43
Portland	46.86	
Pocono	39.85	
Cuche	36.85	
Bradford	33.61	
Oriskany	27.93	

* Allowance (0.05) = 34.11%.

TABLE 11.9
**Analysis of Variance of Packing Density for
the Three Sand-Size Sedimentary-Rock Types**

Source of Variation	D.F.	Sum of Squares	Mean Square	F
Rock types	2	2,885.46	1,442.73	1.12
Formations (within rock types)	6	7,718.99	1,286.50	5.55*
Slides (within formations and rock types)	9	2,085.83	231.76	13.47†
Traverses (within slides, formations, and rock types)	72	1,238.11	17.96	
Total ($n = 90$)	89	13,928.39		

* Significance at the 0.05 level.
† Significance at the 0.001 level.

TABLE 11.10
Packing-Density Differences among Formations

Formation	P_d	P_d—Allowance*
Roslyn	90.54	63.58
Tuscarora	87.45	60.49
Oswego	82.47	———
Stockton	78.52	55.51
Portland	76.64	
Pocono	72.59	
Bradford	70.77	
Oriskany	60.93	
Cuche	55.73	

* Allowance (0.05) = 26.96%.

TABLE 11.11

Components of Variance for Packing Density and Packing Proximity Measurements

Component of Variance	Estimate for	
	P_p	P_d
σ_t^2	49.25	17.96
σ_s^2	64.35	42.76
σ_f^2	183.85	105.47

Linear Relationships between P_d and P_p

Linear relationships between any two variables may be elicited in two ways. The first is by means of linear regressions analysis as described in Chapter 8. Here, one examines the possible linear functional relationship between an independent variable x and a dependent variable y, of the form

$$y = f(x) = \alpha + \beta(x - \bar{x}).$$

The second means by which linear relationships may be determined is with the aid of the linear correlation coefficient described in Chapter 6.

Linear Regression Analysis

The problem at hand is similar to that generalized in Chapter 8. The estimates of α and β for traverses, slides, formations, and rock types are summarized in Table 11.12 for the different levels of variation.

TABLE 11.12

Regression Equations, Correlation, and Regression Coefficients for Traverses, Slides, Formations, and Rock Types

	Regression Equations	b	r	$r_{0.05}$	$r_{0.01}$
Among traverses (within slides)	$y = 0.6901x - 3.20$ $n = 90$, d.f. $= 88$	0.6901	0.4079*	0.205	0.267
Among slides (within formations)	$y = 0.9754x - 24.62$ $n = 18$, d.f. $= 16$	0.9754	0.7709*	0.468	0.590
Among formations (within rock types)	$y = 1.1900x - 40.73$ $n = 9$, d.f. $= 7$	1.1900	0.9081*	0.666	0.798
Among rock types	$y = 1.2507 - 45.29$ $n = 3$, d.f. $= 1$	1.2507	0.8739 NS†	0.997	1.000

* Significance at the 0.01 level.
† NS = not significantly different from $\rho = 0$

On the basis of these tests of hypotheses we infer a significant linear relationship between the variates. This is summarized in Fig. 11.2, where the prediction curves for the different sources of variation are drawn.

Correlation Analysis

The correlation coefficients at the various levels of possible variability are listed in Table 11.12. The test of the hypothesis $\rho = 0$ is also indicated in Table 11.12 (see F-VI).

EXERCISE. Test the hypotheses that $\alpha = 0$ and $\beta = 0$ from the data in Table 11.12.

ANALYSIS OF COVARIANCE AND THE RELATIONSHIP BETWEEN PACKING PROXIMITY AND PACKING DENSITY

The analysis of covariance for the relationship between packing proximity and packing density, correcting the former to a constant value of the latter, is summarized in Table 11.13. The effects of the differences due to packing density $b_{yx}S_{xy}$ are removed from the sum of squares of packing proximity S_y for all sources of variation. The errors of estimate which result from this consist of uncontrolled variation in packing proximity, after due consideration has been made for packing density. These are the new error terms for testing differences.

In the simple analysis of variance for packing proximity, Table 11.7, we rejected the hypotheses that σ_f^2 and σ_s^2 were 0. There were no significant differences among rock types. How much of these results, attributed solely to packing proximity, are in reality variations in packing proximity associated with variations in packing density? The analysis of variance indicated those differences attributable to packing proximity; this analysis of covariance indicates those differences in packing proximity associated with packing density.

After the covariance analysis was performed as shown in Table 11.13, we still rejected the hypothesis that $\sigma_s^2 = 0$, and we still found significant differences among rock types. However, the hypothesis $\sigma_f^2 = 0$ is now accepted. The variability among formations, attributed to packing proximity, is, in fact, due to variations in packing density associated with packing proximity. Hence, packing proximity is dependent, in part at least, on packing density; i.e., the number of grain-to-grain contacts is dependent on the amount of space occupied to the grains.

Table 11.13 furnishes the information necessary for the comparison of the sums of squares of errors of estimate for testing differences and for indicating the advisability of employing this technique. The original sum of squares for formations was 13,256.67; upon correcting for packing density, this sum of squares reduced to 2,400.42. It is this reduction which is instrumental in changing the *F*-values, and altering our decision concerning the test of the hypothesis that $\sigma_f^2 = 0$.

The comparison of the error sum of squares, a reflection of the unassigned variation, and hence of precision, is made with the aid of Table

TABLE 11.13

Analysis of Covariance Correcting Packing Proximity for Packing Density

(x = Packing Density; y = Packing Proximity)

Source of Variation	D.F.	Sums of Squares and Products			r	b	Errors of Estimate		
		S_x^2	S_{xy}	S_y^2			Sum of Squares	D.F.	Mean Squares
Rock types (r)	2	2,885.46	3,478.92	5,493.64	0.8739	1.2057			
Formations (f) = E_r	6	7,718.99	9,185.97	13,256.67	0.9081	1.1900	2,325.36	5	465.07
Slides (s) = E_f	9	2,085.83	2,034.46	3,338.94	0.7709	0.9754	1,354.53	8	169.32
Traverses (t) = E_s	72	1,238.11	854.47	3,545.69	0.4079	0.6901	2,955.99	71	41.63
Total	89	13,928.39	15,553.89	25,634.94			8,265.99	88	
$r + E_r$	8	10,604.49	12,664.89	18,750.31			3,624.63	7	
$f + E_f$	15	9,804.82	11,220.44	16,595.61			3,754.95	14	
$s + E_s$	81	3,323.94	2,888.93	6,884.63			4,373.86	80	
Differences for testing adjusted rock-type means							1,299.27	2	649.63
Differences for testing adjusted formation means							2,400.42	6	400.07
Differences for testing adjusted slide means							1,417.86	9	157.54

11.14. If the original error terms are lowered in absolute value, then it indicates that some of the variation which had been classified as "experimental error" or "unassigned variation" has now been explained. That is, the variation in packing proximity associated with packing density has been evaluated and removed. This gives rise to a more precise basis for comparison.

The total sum of squares for each error term is analyzed in two parts. (See Table 11.14.) One, with one degree of freedom, measures the variation attributable to linear regression (i.e., that amount removed from the dependent variable to correct for the effect of the independent variable), and the other, with the remaining degrees of freedom, is assigned to error. The ratio of the former to the latter, an F-distributed variate, is a means of testing the significance of the reduction of error. The error term for testing formations was reduced significantly from 370.99 to 169.32, again attesting that packing density has a significant effect on packing proximity.

Analyses of covariance, identical in outline to the analysis employed above for the relationship between P_p and P_d, were performed for P_p and the size of the grains of the rock, and between P_d and size. These results indicated that the amount of space taken up by the grains, P_d, and the number of grain-to-grain contacts, P_p, are significantly affected by the size of the grains as measured by intercept size. Thus the interdependency among these three variables is established. Multiple regression is a means of expressing a functional relationship among P_p as the independent variable and P_d and intercept size as the dependent variables.

MULTIPLE REGRESSION

When the effect of packing density was removed from packing proximity, the variation in packing proximity associated with intercept size still remained. Similarly, when the intercept-size effect was removed from the packing proximity the effect of packing density remained. To express rigorously the mutual relationships among these variables, the changes in the dependent variable associated with one independent variable should be measured independent of any other variables. Hence, the change in packing proximity due to a unit change in packing density should be expressed independently of intercept size. Likewise, the change in packing proximity due to a unit change in intercept size should be expressed independently of packing density. In this manner, all the variation in packing proximity can be analyzed into two parts: first, the variation in packing proximity due to packing density, independent of intercept size; and second, the variation in packing proximity due to intercept size, independent of packing density. The term which measures the change

TABLE 11.14
Analysis of Error Mean Square

Analysis of Error Mean Square

Source of Variation	D.F.	S.S.	M.S.	F
E_r = uncorrected error	6	13,256.67	2,209.44 ⎫	
Reduction due to regression	1	10,931.31	10,931.31 ⎬	23.493 NS
Adjusted error	5	2,325.36	465.07 ⎭	
E_f = uncorrected error	9	3,338.94	370.99 ⎫	
Reduction due to regression	1	1,984.41	1,984.41 ⎬	11.720*
Adjusted error	8	1,354.53	169.32 ⎭	
E_s = uncorrected error	72	3,545.69	49.25 ⎫	
Reduction due to regression	1	589.69	589.69 ⎬	14.175†
Adjusted error	71	2,955.99	41.63 ⎭	

Adjusted F-values

For Testing	Adjusted F
Rock types	1.396 NS
Formations	2.360 NS
Slides	3.784 †

* Significant at 0.01 level.
† Significant at 0.001 level.
NS = No significant difference.

in a dependent variable for a unit change in the independent variable is
the multiple regression coefficient

$$\beta_{yx_j \cdot x_1, x_2, \cdots, x_{j-1}, x_{j+1}, \cdots, x_k}$$

The multiple regression coefficients for packing proximity versus packing
density independent of intercept size and for packing proximity versus
intercept size independent of packing density were, at the formation level,
1.5850 and -143.91, respectively.

This mutual relationship, at the formation level, can be expressed by a
multiple regression equation of the form

$$P_p = y = c + b_{yx_1.x_2}x_1 + b_{yx_2.x_1}x_2$$

where P_p = predicted packing proximity, x_1 = packing density, and
x_2 = intercept size. The expression, within certain limits, relates the
variables in a multiple regression equation, from which the packing
proximity of any formation can be predicted, with the knowledge of the
packing density and intercept size of that formation. The specific equation
is

$$y = 1.585x_1 - 143.9x_2 - 51.31.$$

The foregoing expression is valid only when formation means are substituted for x_1 and x_2. Frequently it is possible to deal with only one
formation, and then it may be necessary to obtain predicted packing-
proximity values for slides of that formation. For this purpose, a multiple
regression equation was derived at the slide level as follows:

$$Y = 0.8273x_1 - 101.79x_2 - 0.0081.$$

Here x_1 = packing-density slide mean and x_2 = intercept-size slide mean.

chapter 12

Multivariate Analysis

The general subject of multivariate analysis including some illustrative applications, is taken up in Chapters 12 and 13.

Literally, multivariate analysis is the analysis of problems involving two or more variables. There appears to be some disagreement beyond this point as to what should be included under the general topic of "multivariate analysis."

T. W. Anderson, 1958, *Introduction to multivariate statistical analysis*, John Wiley, New York, is the source for a portion of the present introductory discussion. He devides multivariate analysis into five main categories; scattered members of these categories are treated in the chapters that are included in this section.

CORRELATION

From the methods of measuring degree of dependence for two variables, extension is made to one dependent versus a number of independent variables by the multiple correlation coefficient, and to the measurement of dependence, when the effects of other correlated variables have been removed. Multiple regression is discussed and applied in the section on mapping and trends. Discussion of the principles, applications, and a review of applications in the earth sciences literature are included. See Chapters 8, 9, 10, and 17. Further discussion is given in Chapter 13 on factor analysis and related subjects.

ANALOGUES OF UNIVARIATE STATISTICAL METHODS

This category includes extensions from univariate tests into higher dimensions, for example, (1) *testing the hypothesis that the mean is zero →*
testing the hypothesis that several means are zero. (2) *The Student t test →*

generalized to the T^2 test. A large class of problems in applied statistical analysis concerns testing the mean of a distribution when the variance is unknown. If the population distribution is normally distributed with mean μ and variance σ^2, the statistic usually employed is the difference between sample mean $\bar{x}$ and population mean μ. Thus we have

$$t = \sqrt{n}\,\frac{\bar{x} - \mu}{s}$$

n = sample size, $s = \sqrt{\text{sample variance}}$ which has the t distribution with $(n - 1)$ degrees of freedom. (See Chapter 6.) Hypotheses can then be tested that the population mean is some specified value μ_0, or that an unknown μ lies on a certain interval with a certain confidence level.

In analogous terms, the multivariate form is T^2, the coefficient of racial likeness, which is treated in this chapter. (3) *Least squares → generalized to more than two variables,* and (4) *analysis of variance → generalized to several variables* completes the list. Testing the equality of means of several normal distributions with a common covariance matrix is included in this category. The analysis of dispersion is discussed in some detail with examples in this chapter.

PROBLEMS INVOLVING COORDINATE SYSTEMS

This category includes finding normalized linear combinations of variables with maximum or minimum variance (finding principal components). Essentially this involves finding a suitable rotation of axes that carries the covariance matrix to diagonal form. The rotation of axes to a new set with useful statistical properties leads to factor analysis which is listed in the next category. The following discussion of motivation for those interested in applications is quoted from Anderson (1958, *ibid.*).

In many exploratory studies the number of variables under consideration is too large to handle. Since it is the deviations in these studies which are of interest, a way of reducing the number of variables to be treated is to discard the linear combinations which have small variances and study only those with large variances. For example, a physical anthropologist may make dozens of measurements of lengths and breadths of each of a number of individuals, such measurements as ear length, ear breadth, facial length, facial breadth, and so forth. He may be interested in describing and analyzing how individuals differ in these kinds of physiological characteristics. Eventually he will want to "explain" these differences, but first he wants to know what measurements or combinations of measurements show considerable variation; that is, which should need further study. The principal components give a new set of linearly combined measurements. It may be that most of the variation from individual to individual resides in three linear combinations; then the anthropologist can direct his study to these three quantities; the other linear combinations vary so little from one person to the next that study of them will tell little of individual variation.

Extention of this motivation is readily made to many areas of interest in the earth sciences.

DETAILED PROBLEMS, IN WHICH THE VARIABLES ARE DIVIDED INTO SUBSETS, AND, FOR EXAMPLE, THE HYPOTHESIS OF INDEPENDENCE OF SUBSETS IS TESTED

Discussion of the D^2 generalized distance is given in this chapter. Factor analysis is discussed in Chapter 13.

DEPENDENT OBSERVATIONS

This fifth category of Anderson's includes serial correlations and stochastic difference equations. Serial correlation is discussed briefly in another section in Chapter 15 on time series, and the second topic is not treated in this book.

A major portion of multivariate analysis is based on normal theory. As Anderson (1958, *ibid.*) points out:

One of the reasons why the study of normal multivariate distributions is worthwhile is that the marginal and conditional distributions derived from multivariate normal distributions are also normal distributions. Moreover linear combinations of normal variates are again normally distributed. [See Chapter 4.]

The multinomial distribution extending the binomial distribution to several variables is mentioned here for completeness. It is, however, treated in Chapter 2.

Chapters 12 and 13 are intended as a sampling of multivariate analysis, not as a unified treatment. The interests and experience of the writers and of the earth science literature are reflected in the topics discussed and the examples used. We hope that substitution of subjects of interest to the individual reader may easily be made in the examples given. An occasional attempt is made to suggest which method may be best for any given situation. As elsewhere in this book, the reader is advised to turn to suitable statistics textbooks and the advice of professional statisticians whenever possible.

In this chapter a number of closely related topics are discussed. Tests of significance between means of a number of variables are given considerable attention. Rather than comparing for several samples the means of one variable at a time, a number of variables will be treated simultaneously so that not only the variances but also the covariances are considered. In this way interactions between variables are taken into account.

The first four topics are Hotellings T^2 test, the analysis of dispersion including the Λ criterion, the D^2 generalized distance, and the coefficient of racial likeness (C.R.L.). All four are intimately related. (The C.R.L. is now superseded by D^2 analysis in practice, but is included for its historical importance, and because it has been widely used and appears often in applications in the literature.)

For example T^2 differs from C.R.L. mainly in that sample estimates are used rather than population parameters. C.R.L. is equivalent to D^2 except that it is multiplied by a factor for the purpose of making a significance test. The relation between T^2 and Λ is referred to in the analysis of dispersion discussion. Parts of the structure of the last topic in the chapter, the linear discriminant function, are also related to T and Λ.

HOTELLING'S T^2 TEST

Hotelling's T^2 test (1931 and, for example, 1936) is a generalization of Student's t test for comparison of means of a single variable drawn from two samples. The T^2 statistic considers a number of variables simultaneously.[1]

The formula for T^2 is the same as that for the dependent coefficient of racial likeness (C.R.L.) discussed later, except that sample estimates of the variance and correlation are used instead of population variance and correlation. The distribution of T^2 is equivalent to the distribution of the dependent C.R.L. when the population variance and covariance are known or, in other words, the dependent C.R.L. is "Studentized."

Specifically the null hypothesis is that the two multivariate samples have the same means (H_0: $\mu_1 = \mu_2$) assuming population variances and covariances equal and from the same population ($\sigma_1 = \sigma_2 = \sigma$). It should be kept in mind that in many cases in actual practice, the assumptions themselves often represent precisely the questions of greatest importance, and that in these cases other tests should be sought regarding the variances or covariances (correlations). These are discussed in other parts of the book.

[1] H. Hotelling, 1931, The generalization of Student's ratio, *Ann. Math. Stat.* 2: 360–378. ———, 1936, Relations between two sets of variates, *Biometrika* 28: 321–377.

We shall proceed to present the T^2 statistic in detail. Let X_{aij} represent the value of the ith characteristic measured on the jth individual in sample a, where $a = 1, 2$ for samples 1 and 2, $i = 1, 2, \cdots p$ for p characters, and $j = 1, 2, \cdots N_a$ for a sample of size N_a.

We shall let $\bar{X}_{1i}$ and $\bar{X}_{2i}$ be the arithmetic means respectively of the ith characteristic for samples 1 and 2, and define

$$d_i = \frac{\bar{X}_{1i} - \bar{X}_{2i}}{\sqrt{1/n_1 + 1/n_2}} \qquad n = n_1 + n_2 - 2$$

and

$$ns_{ik} = \sum_{j=1}^{n_1}(X_{1ij} - \bar{X}_{1i})(X_{1kj} - \bar{X}_{1k}) + \sum_{j=1}^{n_2}(X_{2ij} - \bar{X}_{2j})(X_{2kj} - \bar{X}_{2k})$$

for characteristics i, k. The matrix A is then formed of the quantities s_{ik}

$$A = \begin{bmatrix} s_{11} & s_{12} & \cdots & s_{1p} \\ s_{21} & s_{22} & \cdots & s_{2p} \\ \cdots & & & \\ s_{p1} & \cdots & & s_{pp} \end{bmatrix}$$

The matrix[1] A is then inverted to form the matrix A^{-1} in which the elements are s^{ik}. This becomes very laborious for a large number p of characteristics or variables. The statistics may now be defined as

$$T^2 = \sum_{i=1}^{p} \sum_{k=1}^{p} s^{ik} d_i d_k \qquad (12.1)$$

$(n + 1 - p)/(n - p)T^2$ has an F distribution with p and $n + 1 - p$ degrees of freedom. The hypothesis that the two multivariate samples are drawn from the same population is rejected if T^2 is too large. The tables of percentage points of the F distribution are available for use in this test. In this chapter, Hotelling's T^2 test will not be applied to a real example. Instead we proceed to discussion and application of an alternative approach to essentially the same problem. An application to a paleontological problem is discussed later in this section.

ANALYSIS OF DISPERSION; DISCUSSION

Two closely related fossil species of mammals are found in White River time of the Oligocene. They resemble each other quite closely in

[1] Suggested references for treatment of matrices are D. C. Murdoch, 1957, *Linear algebra for undergraduates*, John Wiley, New York and S. Perlis, 1952, *Theory of matrices*, Addison-Wesley Press, Inc., Cambridge, Mass.

morphological appearance, and are thought to be different primarily in the length of face, width of skull, and the bullae.[1,2]

We shall test the hypothesis that the two species differ significantly by a simultaneous treatment of several variables. The example chosen seems

TABLE 12.1

Measurements of Four Characters on Each of 14 Individuals of *M. culbertsoni* and 12 Individuals of *P. meeki*

Merychoidodon culbertsoni (1)				Prodesmatochoerus meeki (2)			
X	Y	Z	$\mathcal{2}$	X	Y	Z	$\mathcal{2}$
45	91	16	7.5	37	88	17	3.9
46	93	17	6.5	43	79	14	4.0
48	92	19	5.0	43	84	19	4.2
46	91	19	6.0	42	80	17	5.2
45	86	15	6.5	39	83	12	4.5
51	93	19	7.5	39	87	15	4.5
47	92	16	5.0	40	86	18	4.5
48	89	18	6.5	34	77	16	4.8
47	91	17.5	6.0	35	82	15	4.6
50	91	17	7.2	45	88	17	4.9
48	91	19	7.6	33	80	15	3.9
49	93	17.5	7.0	42	85	13	4.0
49	87	17	6.5				
49	91	19	7.7				

where X = width of brain case at parietal squamosal suture
Y = maximum length of cheek-tooth row
Z = maximum length of bulla
$\mathcal{2}$ = maximum depth of bulla; measured from dorsal base at level with paroccipital process

to the writers to be well suited to this type of treatment because of the close similarity of the two groups and because the observed differences are based on qualitative observation rather than numerical analysis. A simultaneous treatment of the means of several variables will give a much more sensitive test than testing pairs of variables for significant difference.

This point is discussed in some detail with an illustrative figure in

[1] E. C. Olson, Univ. of Chicago, personal communication
[2] C. B. Schultz, and C. H. Falkenbach, 1954, Desmatochoerinae, a new subfamily of Oreodonts, *Bull. Am. Mus. Nat. Hist.* 105, art. 2.

Hald (1952),[1] who shows that even though the individual means are not significantly different, the simultaneous treatment may lead to rejection of the hypothesis of equal means since in the latter case the correlations are also taken into account.

We shall choose four measurements to quantify the qualitative statement of difference given above to use in a multivariate test of dispersion among

TABLE 12.2

Individual Arithmetic Means for the Two species Are Compared by t-Test for Pairs of Samples, Assuming Normal Distributions and $\sigma_{1i}^2 = \sigma_{2i}^2$ for the ith Character

	Means by Species		
Character	M. culbertsoni (1)	P. meeki (2)	Result of t-test
BC-W (X)	47.71	39.33	Means differ significantly
TR-L (Y)	90.79	83.25	Means differ significantly
Bu-L (Z)	17.57	15.67	Means do not differ significantly
BuHp ($\mathscr{P}$)	6.61	4.42	Means differ significantly

$$N_1 = 14 \qquad N_2 = 12 \qquad \text{Level of significance } \alpha = 0.05$$

means between *Merychoidodon culbertsoni* and *Prodesmatochoerus meeki*. The data and the measurements are given in Table 12.1, which were kindly supplied by E. C. Olson, *loc. cit.*; in Table 12.2 the results of application of the t-test to individual pairs of means are given.

It must be emphasized that the results of any study of this sort, based on four specific characters, would be greatly improved by utilizing *all* the characters available in numerical form. In this case the interest is focused on whether or not the simultaneous differences between the means of the four characters is sufficient to differentiate the two species. As shown in Table 12.2 three of the four characters differ significantly for means between the two species when taken one character at a time, and not taking into account the correlations between the characters. Thus this example is to be considered as a pilot study to illustrate the steps involved in the multivariate test.

To give the procedure real meaning it would seem we should ideally include as many anatomically meaningful measurements on the two species as could be taken, followed by programming for a high speed computor, to reduce the computing to practical size. However, difficulties arise if the number of characters exceed the number of individuals in the sample. For example, consider the assumption of equal variance-covariance

---

[1] A. Hald, 1952, *Statistical theory with engineering applications*, John Wiley, New York, pp. 616–621, Fig. 19.6.

matrices,[1] and the assumption of a multinormal p-dimensional distribution. It would appear that the inclusion of a great many variables would tend to weaken if not invalidate both these assumptions. As far as we know, the relevant research has not been done on this problem. Papers which apply to the general discussion include

> J. H. Chung and D. A. S. Fraser, 1958, Randomization tests for a multivariate two-sample problem, *Jour. Am. Stat. Assoc.* 53: 729–735.
> S. N. Roy and S. K. Mitra, 1956, An introduction to some non-parametric generalizations of analysis of variance and multivariate analysis, *Biometrika* 43: 361–376.

An approach of the type discussed in the chapter on factor analysis may be more appropriate, where number of variables exceed sample size. In any case, when possible a statistician should be consulted.

Multivariate testing is obviously laborious, and requires justification for its use in any case. The writers believe that a multivariate approach to differentiation is quite useful in just such a case as the present one where the basis for taxonomic discrimination is one of *degree* within characters rather than of *kind*. This would apply especially to comparisons of varieties, subspecies, and closely related species.

Even under such circumstances, the test serves only as the beginning of quantitative analysis. For example, if the two species are shown to differ significantly in the multivariate sense, the next steps should include a specific search for the characters which contribute to the differentiation, or for some sort of quantitative statement which will enable the worker to assign new specimens to one or the other species. A quantitative statement of this type may be found in the linear discriminant function, which will be applied in the next section after the present multivariate test of dispersion between the two present species.

Rao (1952) discusses and illustrates a number of further multivariate tests and analyses which are available for use in various ramifications of the class of problems discussed here. (See also M. G. Kendall, 1957, *Course in multivariate analysis*, Chas. Griffin and Co. Ltd., London.)

SUGGESTED REFERENCES

S. S. Wilks, 1932, Movements and distributions of estimates of population parameters from fragmentary samples, *Annals of Math. Stats.* 3: 163ff. Discusses the situation where the individuals samples form a multivariate population in which data on some of the variates are missing from various individuals as is commonly the case in paleontology or archeology. A general discussion in the present context is given in R. A. Fisher, 1936, Use of multiple measurements in taxonomic problems, *Annals of Eugenics*, 7: 179–188.

---

[1] For discussion of the concept of variance-covariance matrix see A. M. Mood, *Introduction to the theory of statistics*, 1950, 1st ed., McGraw-Hill Book Co., New York, p. 176.

If craniometric studies of fossil humans are excluded, the only application previous to the present text of multivariate comparisons of means of a number of characters in paleobiometrics was made in a study by B. Burma, 1949.[1]

In that paper two closely related forms of *Pentremites* (Mississippian blastoids) were compared on the basis of eight measurements on the calyx.

TABLE 12.3

Steps in the Computation

The data from this table are used to give the sums of squares, sums, and cross products.

		M. culbertsoni Sample I	*P. meeki* Sample II	Sums
Sums	ΣX	668	472	1,140
	ΣY	1,271	999	2,270
	ΣZ	246	188	434
	$\Sigma \mathcal{Q}$	92.5	53.0	145.5
	n	14	12	26
Sum of Squares	ΣX^2	31,916	18,732	50,648
	ΣY^2	115,447	83,317	198,764
	ΣZ^2	4,345.5	2,992.0	7,337.5
	$\Sigma \mathcal{Q}^2$	621.4	236.1	857.5
Cross Products	ΣXY	60,658	39,353	100,011
	ΣXZ	11,754	7,410	19,164
	$\Sigma X\mathcal{Q}$	4,420.1	2,087.7	6,507.8
	ΣYZ	22,349	15,670	38,019
	$\Sigma Y\mathcal{Q}$	8,398	4,410.0	12,808
	$\Sigma Z\mathcal{Q}$	1,627.6	832.6	2,460.2

where $N = n_{\mathrm{I}} + n_{\mathrm{II}}$

$\sum_{\mathrm{I,II}} X^2 = \sum X_{\mathrm{I}}^2 + \sum X_{\mathrm{II}}^2$ similarly for $\sum Y^2$ etc., for samples I, II,

Character X; $\sum_{\mathrm{I,II}} XY = \sum_{\mathrm{I}} XY + \sum_{\mathrm{II}} XY$ similarly for $\sum XZ$, etc.

Burma utilized the technique developed by Hotelling, which was discussed earlier in this section. The writers believe that the method applied in this section is less laborious and easier to interpret than Burma's. However, Burma's paper is recommended as an alternative approach to the paleontologist interested in paleobiometrics.

[1] B. Burma, 1949, Multivariate analysis—a new analytical tool for paleontology and geology *Jour. Paleon.* 23: 1; 95–103.

Analysis of Dispersion: Equations and Example

The "analysis of dispersion" which is essentially a multivariate analysis of variance is discussed in detail in Rao (1952).[1] The variances and co-variances are analyzed to test the differences in means of several variables.[2] The matrix which leads to unbiased estimates of the variances and co-variances is denoted by $|W|$, where the vertical bars indicate the determinant of the matrix. A second matrix leading to unbiased estimates of the variances and covariances only if the null hypothesis of equal means is true is denoted by $|Q|$.

The ratio of $|W|$ to $|W + Q|$ forms a test criterion called the Λ criterion, developed by Wilks (1932, *ibid*) and applied in illustrations by Rao (1952).[1] The writers have prepared a table of equations in computing form suitable for an electric table model computor. (See Fig. 12.1.) The procedure followed is that given in Rao (1952), pp. 262–264. The matrix W is actually the same as the matrix A in the previous discussion of Hotelling's T^2. Then, $\Lambda = 1/1 + (T^2/W)$, so that a close relationship appears between Λ and T^2.

The entries for the matrices $|W|$ and $|Q|$ are assembled in tabular form in Table 12.3. These entries are computed from the condensed data in the form of sums, cross products, etc., of Table 12.4 by following the convenient computing equations given in Fig. 12.1. The entries in row W_{ij} form the elements of the matrix

$$|W| = \begin{vmatrix} W_{11} & W_{12} & \cdots & W_{1p} \\ W_{21} & W_{22} & \cdots & \\ \cdot & & & \\ \cdot & & & \\ \cdot & & & \\ W_{p1} & \cdots & & \end{vmatrix}$$

where in our present example the first row would be $|W_{xx}\ W_{xy}\ W_{xz}\ W_{xq}|$ etc. The full matrix $|W|$ in the present example is

$$|W| = \begin{vmatrix} 21.0 & 72.2 & 31.6 & 9.5 \\ 72.2 & 208.0 & 34.8 & -2.0 \\ 31.6 & 34.8 & 70.0 & 4.5 \\ 9.5 & -2.0 & 4.5 & 13.0 \end{vmatrix} = 29{,}132{,}813.3$$

[1] C. R. Rao, 1952, *Advanced Statistical methods in biometrical research*, John Wiley.

[2] Although the present example is applied to two samples, the analysis of dispersion is readily applied to more than two. For two examples in actual practice the T^2 test is more appropriate.

S. P. matrix

	D.F.	X^2	Y^2	Z^2	XY	XZ	YZ
Between Q_{ij}	Number of samples minus one	$\left[\dfrac{(\sum X_I)^2}{n_I} + \dfrac{(\sum X_{II})^2}{n_{II}}\right] - \dfrac{(\sum X_I + \sum X_{II})^2}{n_I + n_{II}}$	Same for Y	Same	$\left(\dfrac{\sum X_I \sum Y_I}{n_I} + \dfrac{\sum X_{II}\sum Y_{II}}{n_{II}}\right)$ $- \left[\dfrac{(\sum X_I + \sum X_{II})(\sum Y_I + \sum Y_{II})}{n_I + n_{II}}\right]$	Same for XZ	Same for YZ
Within W_{ij}	Number of individual minus number of samples	$(\sum X_I^2 + \sum X_{II}^2)$ $- \left[\dfrac{(\sum X_I)^2}{n_I} + \dfrac{(\sum X_{II})^2}{n_{II}}\right]$			$\left(\sum_I XY + \sum_{II} XY\right)$ $- \left[\dfrac{\sum_I X \sum_I Y}{n_I} + \dfrac{\sum_{II} X \sum_{II} Y}{n_{II}}\right]$	Same for XZ	Same for YZ
Total S_{ij}		$(\sum X_I^2 + \sum X_{II}^2)$ $- \dfrac{(\sum X_I + \sum X_{II})^2}{n_I + n_{II}}$			$\left(\sum_I XY + \sum_{II} XY\right)$ $- \left[\dfrac{\left(\sum_I X \sum_{II} X\right)\left(\sum_I Y \sum_{II} Y\right)}{n_I + n_{II}}\right]$		

FIG. 12.1. Work arrangement for two samples denoted by I and II and three variables X, Y, Z. This form may be readily extended to any number of variables. $\mathscr{2}$ is omitted to simplify the presentation in this figure.

TABLE 12.4

Two samples, $n_I = 14$ $n_{II} = 12$ Four variables X, Y, Z, Q, $n_I + n_{II} = 26$
M. culbertsoni versus P. meeki

S. P. Matrix

	D.F.		X^2	Y^2	Z^2	Q^2	12 XY	13 XZ	14 XQ	23 YZ	24 YQ	34 ZQ
Between	1	Q_{ij}	(453)	(368)	(24)	(31)	408.0	103.2	118.7	92.7	106.7	27
Within	24	W_{ij}	(210)	(208)	(70)	(13)	72.2	31.6	9.5	34.8	−2.0	4.5
Total	25	S_{ij}	(663)	(576)	(94)	(44)	480.2	134.8	128.2	127.5	104.7	31.5

The entries in the matrix $|W + Q|$ are taken from the row entitled S_{ij} and represent the sum of the appropriate Q_{ij} and W_{ij} entries in Table 13.4. In the present example

$$|W + Q| = \begin{vmatrix} 663.0 & 480.2 & 134.8 & 128.2 \\ 480.2 & 576.0 & 127.5 & 104.7 \\ 134.8 & 127.5 & 94.0 & 31.5 \\ 128.2 & 104.7 & 31.5 & 44.0 \end{vmatrix} = 174{,}082{,}293.9$$

The test criterion Λ is now formed by taking the ratio of $|W|$ to $|W + Q|$. In this case

$$\Lambda = \frac{|W|}{|W + Q|} = \frac{28{,}132{,}813}{174{,}082{,}294} = 0.16735$$

The final test statistic $V = -m \ln \Lambda$ is distributed as χ^2 with pq degrees of freedom. The following notation is used:

Definitions	Present Example
$k =$ Number of samples	$k = 2$
$q = k - 1$	$q = 2 - 1 = 1$
$p =$ Number of variables	$p = 4$
$n = N_1 + N_2 - 1$	$n = 12 + 14 - 1 = 25$
$m = N - \dfrac{p + q + 1}{2}$	$m = 25 - \left(\dfrac{4 + 1 + 1}{2}\right) = 22$
$pq =$ Degrees of freedom	$pq = 4$

Thus $V = -m \ln \Lambda = 22(1.791) = 39.402$. $\chi^2_{4\text{d.f.}; 0.95\text{ level of signif.}} = 9.49$.

The null hypothesis of equal means is rejected if the critical level of χ^2 is exceeded. We therefore reject the null hypothesis of equal means for the two species *M. culbertsoni* and *P. meeki* for the four characters considered simultaneously.

APPLICATION OF ANALYSIS OF DISPERSION

R. L. Miller, 1954, A model for the analysis of environments of sedimentation, *Jour. Geol.* 42: 108–113, describes a model which defines a statistical universe for sampling sediments. The model is then applied to near shore sediments off La Jolla, California, and multivariate analysis of variance in the form of analysis of dispersion is applied and discussed.

R. Siever and P. E. Potter, 1956, Sources of basal Pennsylvanian sediments in the eastern interior basin, 2. Sedimentary petrology, *Jour. Geol.* 64: 317–335, apply analysis of dispersion to regional mineral associations.

THE GENERALIZED DISTANCE D^2

In 1927 Mahalanobis[1] presented a statistic referred to as the "caste distance" or "generalized distance." See also Mahalanobis (1930).[2] In its simplest form (provided $n_{1i} = n_{1j}$, $n_{2i} = n_{2j}$, i.e., the number of measurements in a given sample is equal for all characters) the generalized distance D^2 is the equivalent of Pearson's earlier coefficient of racial likeness (C.R.L.) with one important difference, the coefficient $n_1 n_2/(n_1 + n_2)$ is dropped. This has the effect of removing difficulties in use of the C.R.L. due to size of sample when a measure of divergence is desired. Since the C.R.L. has a definite tendency to increase as sample size increases, the D^2 statistic is free of this difficulty.

Let us now consider the following type of problem. We wish to compare a reasonably large collection of closely related species in such a way that a "taxonomic distance" of each species from all the other species is computed. The taxonomic distance should be some sort of numerical index in which a representative collection of characters taken on samples of each of the species forms the basis for the index. The characters should be treated simultaneously so that both covariance and variance are considered. If the generalized distance D^2 is used as our index and computed for the various possible pairs of species, one possible solution to the preceding problem is then available.

The basic equation for D^2 as given in Rao (1952) is

$$D^2 = \sum_i \sum_j \lambda^{ij} d_i d_j$$

in population parameters, where λ^{ij} is σ^{ij}, $d_i = \mu_{1i} - \mu_{2i}$. In sample terms we have

$$\hat{D}^2 = \sum_i \sum_j \hat{\lambda}^{ij} \hat{d}_i \hat{d}_j$$

and in expanded form is

$$D^2 = \frac{1}{|R|} \sum_{i=1}^{p} \sum_{j=1}^{p} R_{ij} \frac{\bar{x}_{1i} - \bar{x}_{2i}}{\sigma_i} \cdot \frac{\bar{x}_{1j} - \bar{x}_{2j}}{\sigma_j}$$

where R is the variance-covariance matrix in the form of correlation coefficients

$$R = \begin{vmatrix} 1 & r_{12} & \cdots & r_{1p} \\ r_{21} & 1 & \cdots & r_{2p} \\ \cdot & & \cdots & \cdot \\ r_{p1} & & \cdots & 1 \end{vmatrix}$$

[1] P. C. Mahalanobis, 1927, Analysis of race-mixture in Bengal, *J. As. Soc. Beng.* 23: 301–333.
[2] ——, 1930, On tests and measures of group divergence, *J. As. Soc. Beng.* 26: 541–588.

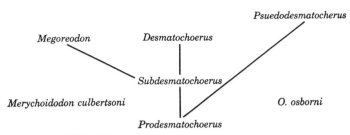

FIG. 12.2. Taxonomic affinities of Oreodonts.

and R_{ij} is the cofactor for the ith row and jth column. The characters are denoted by $1, 2, \cdots, i, j, \cdots p$, and x_{1i} is, for example, the arithmetic mean for sample 1 of the ith character; σ_i is the pooled variance of samples 1 and 2 for the ith character assuming $\sigma_{1i} = \sigma_{2i} = \sigma_i$.

For studies involving more than 3 or 4 characters and more than several species, the form of D^2 as given above is not practical for ordinary computational facilities since the labor rapidly becomes enormous. Rao (1952, p. 345ff)[1] gives a transformation which results in a new set of characters which are uncorrelated. In this way labor is greatly reduced since all correlations between the new set of variables are reduced to zero.

We shall proceed to illustrate the D^2 by applying it to a real example. Seven distinct species of Oreodonts were analyzed for mutual D^2 taxonomic distances. The relationships in a *stratigraphic* sense of the genera that include the seven species may be conveniently taken in part from Shultz and Falkenbach (1954); Figure 12.2 is in part based on Chart 1, p. 156 of the cited paper. The interconnecting lines give a measure of taxonomic affinity and are also taken from the same paper.

The same four measurements used in the section on multivariate comparison of means between *Merychoidodon culbertsoni* and *Prodesmatochoerus meeki* will be used in this study since they are representative of the qualitative differences which characterize the entire seven species. Table 12.5 gives the species names and the measurements. The four measurements are;

X = width of brain case at parietal-squamosal row

Y = maximum length of cheek-tooth row

Z = maximum length of bulla

$\mathcal{Q}$ = maximum depth of bulla; measured from dorsal base at level with paroccipital process

We shall now proceed to the operations required to complete the problem.

[1] C. R. Rao, 1952, *Advanced statistical methods in biometrical research*, John Wiley, New York.

TABLE 12.5

Subdesmatochoerus sp.

	X BC-W	Y TR-L	Z Bu-L	$\mathcal{Q}$ BuHP
Cm 907	47.0	99	26.0	15.0
49550	42.0	93	26.0	16.0
49640	40.0	90	22.0	13.0
45460	46.0	100	22.0	11.0
1310	46.0	96	24.0	16.0
45177	42.0	88	26.0	15.0
45320	43.0	89	23.0	14.0
45810	44.0	78	23.0	13.0
45181	44.0	90	25.0	11.0
P26138	47.0	99	27.0	15.0
P12725	47.0	92	27.0	13.0

$\sum(X) \quad 488 \qquad \sum(Y) \quad 1014 \qquad \sum(Z) \quad 271 \qquad \sum(\mathcal{Q}) \quad 152$

$\sum(X)^2 \ 21708 \qquad \sum(Y)^2 \ 93880 \qquad \sum(Z)^2 \ 6713 \qquad \sum(\mathcal{Q})^2 \ 2132$

$$\sum XY = 45067 \qquad n = 11 \qquad \bar{X} = 44.364$$
$$\sum XZ = 12041 \qquad\qquad\qquad \bar{Y} = 92.182$$
$$\sum X\mathcal{Q} = 6743 \qquad\qquad\qquad \bar{Z} = 24.636$$
$$\sum YZ = 25012 \qquad\qquad\qquad \bar{\mathcal{Q}} = 13.818$$
$$\sum Y\mathcal{Q} = 14030$$
$$\sum Z\mathcal{Q} = 3760$$

TABLE 12.5 (continued)

Megoreodon *gigas loomisi*

X BC-W	Y TR-L	Z Bu-L	$\mathcal{Q}$ Bu-HP
78.0	165.0	35.0	18.0
77.0	165.0	37.0	19.0
65.0	148.0	30.0	20.0
74.0	163.0	31.0	15.0
65.0	169.0	31.0	16.0
70.0	176.0	34.0	23.0
69.0	161.0	28.0	13.0
67.0	178.0	31.0	14.0
65.0	174.0	34.0	18.0
64.0	168.0	28.0	13.0
68.0	166.0	32.0	15.0

$\sum X$ 762 $\sum Y$ 1,833 $\sum Z$ 351 $\sum \mathcal{Q}$ 184

$\sum (X)^2$ 53,034 $\sum (Y)^2$ 306,121 $\sum (Z)^2$ 11,281 $\sum (\mathcal{Q})^2$ 3,178

$\bar{X}$ 69.273 $\bar{Y}$ 166.636 $\bar{Z}$ 31.909 $\bar{\mathcal{Q}}$ 16.727

$\sum XY = 126,947$ $n = 11$

$\sum XZ = 24,405$

$\sum X\mathcal{Q} = 12,784$

$\sum YZ = 58,554$

$\sum Y\mathcal{Q} = 30,653$

$\sum Z\mathcal{Q} = 5,930$

TABLE 12.5 (continued)

O. osborni

X BC-W	Y TR-L	Z Bu-L	$\mathcal{Q}$ Bu-HP
42.0	81.0	15.0	8.0
48.0	83.0	18.0	8.6
45.0	87.0	18.0	9.0
48.0	83.0	17.0	8.0
46.0	84.0	16.0	6.1
51.0	87.0	21.0	7.9
46.0	80.0	17.0	7.0
50.0	90.0	18.0	8.1
46.0	85.0	16.0	6.5
48.0	85.0	15.0	7.2
47.0	85.0	17.0	8.0
49.0	83.0	18.0	7.7
43.0	79.0	15.0	7.1
47.0	87.0	19.0	7.5
46.0	87.0	18.0	8.0

$N = 15$

$\sum (X)$ 702.00 $\quad \sum (Y)$ 1,266 $\quad \sum (Z)$ 258 $\quad \sum (\mathcal{Q})$ 114.7

$\sum (X)^2$ 32,934 $\quad \sum (Y)^2$ 106,976 $\quad \sum (Z)^2$ 4,476 $\quad \sum (\mathcal{Q})^2$ 885.23

$\bar{X}$ 46.800 $\quad \bar{Y}$ 84.400 $\quad \bar{Z}$ 17200 $\quad \bar{\mathcal{Q}}$ 7.647

$\sum XY = 59,306.00$

$\sum XZ = 12,112.00$

$\sum X\mathcal{Q} = 5,372.00$

$\sum YZ = 21,815.00$

$\sum Y\mathcal{Q} = 9,690.50$

$\sum Z\mathcal{Q} = 1,980.70$

TABLE   12.5 (continued)

Psuedodesmatochoerus

X BC-W	Y TR-L	Z Bu-L	$\mathcal{Q}$ Bu-HP
60.0	114.0	27.0	20.0
60.0	118.0	31.0	19.0
60.0	111.0	31.0	21.0
58.0	102.0	30.0	20.0
55.0	116.0	28.0	20.0
59.0	117.0	29.0	17.0
59.0	114.0	24.0	17.0
60.0	121.0	25.0	19.0
$N = 8$			

$\sum (X)$	471	$\sum (Y)$	913	$\sum (Z)$	225	$\sum (\mathcal{Q})$	153
$\sum (X)^2$	27,751	$\sum (Y)^2$	104,427	$\sum (Z)^2$	6,377	$\sum (\mathcal{Q})^2$	2,941
$\bar{X}$	58.875	$\bar{Y}$	114.125	$\bar{Z}$	28.125	$\bar{\mathcal{Q}}$	19.125

$\sum XY$	53,765
$\sum XZ$	13,247
$\sum X\mathcal{Q}$	9,006
$\sum YZ$	25,639
$\sum Y\mathcal{Q}$	17,439
$\sum Z\mathcal{Q}$	4,316

TABLE 12.5 (continued)

Desmatochoerus hatcheri

X BC-W	Y TR-L	Z Bu-L	2 Bu-HP
58.0	129.0	26.0	16.0
52.0	126.0	27.0	18.0
50.0	122.0	28.0	22.0
52.0	123.0	29.0	18.0
60.0	138.0	33.0	17.0
61.0	122.0	28.0	17.0
54.0	132.0	30.0	17.0
65.0	131.0	32.0	18.0
55.0	130.0	32.0	17.0
64.0	125.0	26.0	16.0
56.0	124.0	28.0	16.0
$N = 11$			

$\sum(X)$	627	$\sum(Y)$	1,402	$\sum(Z)$	319	$\sum(2)$	192
$\sum(X)^2$	35,991	$\sum(Y)^2$	178,944	$\sum(Z)^2$	9,311	$\sum(2)^2$	3,380
$\bar{X}$	57.000	$\bar{Y}$	127.455	$\bar{Z}$	29.000	$\bar{2}$	17.455

$\sum XY$ 79,989
$\sum XZ$ 18,200
$\sum X2$ 10,900
$\sum YZ$ 40,743
$\sum Y2$ 24,446
$\sum Z2$ 5,571

Table 12.5 (continued)

M. culbertsoni

X BC-W	Y TR-L	Z Bu-L	$\mathscr{Q}$ Bu-HP
45.0	91.0	16.0	7.5
46.0	93.0	17.0	6.5
48.0	92.0	19.0	5.0
46.0	91.0	19.0	6.0
45.0	86.0	15.0	6.5
51.0	93.0	19.0	7.5
47.0	92.0	16.0	5.0
48.0	89.0	18.0	6.5
47.0	91.0	17.5	6.0
50.0	91.0	17.0	7.2
48.0	91.0	19.0	7.6
49.0	93.0	17.5	7.0
49.0	87.0	17.0	6.5
49.0	91.0	19.0	7.7

$\sum (X)^2$ 31,916 $\sum (Y)^2$ 115,447 $\sum (Z)^2$ 4,345.5 $\sum (\mathscr{Q})^2$ 621.39

$\sum (X)$ 668 $\sum (Y)$ 1,271 $\sum (Z)$ 246.0 $\sum (\mathscr{Q})$ 92.5

$n = 14$

$\sum XY$ 60,658

$\sum XZ$ 11,754.0

$\sum X\mathscr{Q}$ 4,420.1

$\sum YZ$ 22,349.0

$\sum Y\mathscr{Q}$ 8,398.0

$\sum Z\mathscr{Q}$ 1,627.6

$\bar{X}$ 47.714

$\bar{Y}$ 90.786

$\bar{Z}$ 17.571

$\bar{\mathscr{Q}}$ 6.607

TABLE 12.5 (continued)

P. meeki

X BC-W	Y TR-L	Z Bu-L	$\mathcal{2}$ Bu-HP
37.0	88.0	17.0	3.9
43.0	79.0	14.0	4.0
43.0	84.0	19.0	4.2
42.0	80.0	17.0	5.2
39.0	83.0	12.0	4.5
39.0	87.0	15.0	4.5
40.0	86.0	18.0	4.5
34.0	77.0	16.0	4.8
35.0	82.0	15.0	4.6
45.0	88.0	17.0	4.9
33.0	80.0	15.0	3.9
42.0	85.0	13.0	4.0

$$\sum (X)^2 \quad 18{,}732 \qquad \sum (Y)^2 \quad 83{,}317 \qquad \sum (Z)^2 \quad 2{,}992 \qquad \sum (\mathcal{2})^2 \quad 236.06$$

$$\sum (X) \quad 472 \qquad \sum (Y) \quad 999 \qquad \sum (Z) \quad 188 \qquad \sum (\mathcal{2}) \quad 53.0$$

$$N = 12$$

$$\sum XY \quad 39{,}353$$
$$\sum XZ \quad 7{,}410$$
$$\sum X\mathcal{2} \quad 2{,}087.7$$
$$\sum YZ \quad 15{,}670$$
$$\sum Y\mathcal{2} \quad 4{,}410.0$$
$$\sum Z\mathcal{2} \quad 832.6$$

$$\bar{X} \quad 39.333$$
$$\bar{Y} \quad 83.250$$
$$\bar{Z} \quad 15.666$$
$$\bar{\mathcal{2}} \quad 4.417$$

TABLE 12.6

Mean Values by Groups and Characters

Group	X	Y	Z	$\mathcal{Q}$
(I) *M. culbertsoni*	47.714	90.786	17.571	6.607
(II) *Prodesmatochoerus*	39.333	83.250	15.666	4.417
(III) *Subdesmatochoerus*	44.364	92.182	24.636	13.818
(IV) *Psuedodesmatochoerus*	58.875	114.125	28.125	19.125
(V) *Desmatochoerus*	57.000	127.455	29.000	17.455
(VI) *O. osborni*	46.800	84.400	17.200	7.647
(VII) *Megoreodon*	69.273	166.636	31.909	16.727
$\sum$'s	363.359	758.834	164.107	85.796
Grand means by characters	51.908	108.405	23.444	12.257

In Table 12.6 we enter the mean values as shown. Next, it is necessary to compute the variance-covariance matrix, Table 12.7, and from this get the pooled estimates of correlations and standard deviations. We need, for example,

$$\lambda_{XX} = \frac{\left(\overset{M.\, culb.}{\sum X_i^2} + \overset{Prodesm.}{\sum X_i^2} + \cdots + \overset{Megoreodon}{\sum X_i^2} \right) - \left[\frac{(\sum X_i)^2}{n_I} + \frac{(\sum X_i)^2}{n_{II}} \right] + \cdots \frac{(\sum X_i)^2}{n_{VII}}}{n_I + n_{II} + \cdots + n_{VII} - 7}$$

where n_I = number of observations of X for *Merychoidodon culbertsoni* $\cdots$, n_{VII} = number of observations for *Megoreodon*.

Similarly, λ_{YY}, λ_{ZZ}, $\lambda_{\mathcal{Q}\mathcal{Q}}$ are computed. We also need λ_{XY}, $\lambda_{X\mathcal{Q}}$, λ_{XZ}, λ_{YZ}, $\lambda_{Y\mathcal{Q}}$, $\lambda_{Z\mathcal{Q}}$, for example,

$$\lambda_{XY} = \frac{\left(\sum_I XY + \sum_{II} XY + \cdots \sum_{VII} XY \right) - \left(\frac{\sum X_I \sum Y_I}{n_I} + \frac{\sum X_{II} \sum Y_{II}}{n_{II}} + \cdots + \frac{\sum X_{VII} \sum Y_{VII}}{n_{VII}} \right)}{n_I + n_{II} + \cdots + n_{VII} - 7}$$

To get the normalized variables x', y', z', q' use Table 12.6 as follows: for each mean given in the table, form the difference between this mean and the grand mean given at the bottom of the table, and divide this difference by the corresponding standard deviation. For example, to get the first entry in Table 12.9:

$$\frac{47.714 - 51.908}{3.406} = -\frac{4.194}{3.406} = -1.23140$$

The normalized variable may be expressed as $(\bar{x} - \bar{\bar{x}})/\sigma_{\bar{x}} = x'$. If the correlation coefficient ρ_{ij} is expressed in the form $\lambda_{ij}/\sqrt{\lambda_{ii}\lambda_{jj}}$ then the

TABLE 12.7

Variance-Covariance Matrix (Pooled Estimates)

	X	Y	Z	$\mathcal{Q}$
X	11.6	3.587	2.600	0.071
Y		25.360	2.880	−0.389
Z			4.467	1.363
$\mathcal{Q}$				2.610

normalized variables which have zero mean and unit variance become $\lambda_{ii} = 1$ and ρ_{ij} reduces to λ_{ij}. Thus Table 12.8 is not only the pooled estimates of correlations and standard deviations for X, Y, Z, $\mathcal{Q}$ but also the variance-covariance matrix for the normalized variables x', y', z', q'.

TABLE 12.8

Pooled Estimates of Correlations and Standard Deviations

	X	Y	Z	$\mathcal{Q}$
X	1	0.209	0.361	0.013
Y		1	0.271	−0.047
Z			1	0.767
$\mathcal{Q}$				1
Standard deviations	3.406	5.036	2.113	1.616

For example

$$\rho_{XY} = \frac{\lambda_{XY}}{\sqrt{\lambda_{XX}\lambda_{YY}}}$$

$$= \frac{3.587}{\sqrt{(11.6)(25.36)}}$$

$$= 0.209$$

For example,

$$\sqrt{11.6} = 3.406$$

We now want to transform the normalized variables x', y' z', q' so that they are uncorrelated, have zero means, and unit variance. Following Rao (1955) we have the transformation equations:

$$x = x'$$

$$y = y' - \rho_{XY}x$$

$$z = z' - a'_{32}y - a'_{31}x = z' - a'_{32}y - \rho_{XZ}x$$

$$q = q' - a'_{43}z - a'_{42}y - a'_{41}x = q' - a'_{43}z - a'_{42}y - \rho_{X\mathcal{Q}}$$

x, y, z, q, although uncorrelated, do not have unit variance. However, if x, y, z, q are divided by their respective standard deviations, they will have unit variance.

TABLE 12.9

Normalized Mean Values of Characters

Group	x'	y'	z'	$\mathcal{2}'$
M. culbertsoni	−1.231	−3.499	−2.779	−3.497
Prodesmatochoerus	−3.692	−4.995	−3.680	−4.853
Subdesmatochoerus	−2.215	−3.221	0.564	0.967
Psuedodematochoerus	2.046	1.136	2.215	4.251
Desmatochoerus	1.495	3.783	2.629	3.218
O. osborni	−1.500	−4.767	−2.954	−2.853
Megoreodon	5.098	11.563	4.006	2.167

We now need to compute a'_{32}, a'_{43}, a'_{42}; $V(y)$, $V(z)$ and $V(q)$. First,

$$a'_{21} = \rho_{XY} = 0.209$$

$$V(y) = 1 - \rho^2_{XY} = 1 - (0.209)^2 = 0.956; \quad \sqrt{V(y)} = 0.978$$

$$a'_{31} = \rho_{XZ} = 0.3612 \quad b'_{32} = \rho_{XZ} - \rho_{XY}\rho_{XZ}$$
$$= 0.271 - (0.209)(0.361) = 0.195$$

$$a'_{32} = \frac{b'_{32}}{V(y)} = \frac{0.195}{0.956} = 0.204$$

$$V(z) = 1 - \rho^2_{XZ} - b'_{32}a'_{32} = 1 - (0.361)^2 - \frac{(0.195)^2}{0.956} = 0.830;$$
$$\sqrt{V(z)} = 0.911$$

$$b'_{41} = \rho_{X\mathcal{2}} = 0.013 = a'_{41} \quad b'_{42} = \rho_{Y\mathcal{2}} - \rho_{XY}\rho_{X\mathcal{2}}$$
$$= -0.047 - (0.209)(0.013) = -0.050$$

$$a'_{42} = \frac{b'_{42}}{V(y)} = -\frac{0.050}{0.956} = -0.052$$

$$b'_{43} = \rho_{Z\mathcal{2}} - a'_{32}b'_{42} - \rho_{XZ}\rho_{X\mathcal{2}} = 0.768 + (0.204)(0.050)$$
$$- (0.361)(0.013) = 0.773$$

$$a'_{43} = \frac{b'_{43}}{V(z)} = \frac{0.773}{0.830} = 0.931$$

$$V(q) = 1 - \rho^2_{X\mathcal{2}} - b'_{42}a'_{42} - b'_{43}a'_{43} = 1 - (0.013)^2 - (0.050)(0.052)$$
$$- (0.773)(0.931) = 0.278; \quad \sqrt{V(q)} = 0.527$$

thus, as in Rao (1955), we have

$$x^* = x = x'$$
$$0.978y^* = y = y' - 0.209x$$
$$0.911z^* = z = z' - 0.204y - 0.361x$$
$$0.527q^* = q = q' - 0.931z + 0.052y - 0.013x$$

where the association between the notations is $y^* \sim$ Rao's y_2, $z^* \sim$ Rao's y_3, $q^* \sim$ Rao's y_4, $x \sim$ Rao's Y, $y \sim$ Rao's Y_2, $z \sim$ Rao's Y_3, and $q \sim$ Rao's Y_4. For each of the four defining equations, we run through the seven values for groups. First, the values of x, y, z, q of Table 12.10 are obtained by substitution of the values from Table 12.9; then by division of the entries in Table 12.10 by the corresponding standard deviations,

TABLE 12.10

	x	y	z	q
M. culbertsoni	−1.231	−3.241	−1.673	−2.092
Prodesmatochoerus	−3.692	−4.223	−1.485	−3.643
Subdesmatochoerus	−2.215	−2.758	1.927	−0.943
Psuedodesmatochoerus	2.046	0.708	1.331	3.022
Desmatochoerus	1.495	3.470	1.381	2.094
O. osborni	−1.500	−4.453	−1.504	−1.666
Megoreodon	5.098	10.497	0.023	3.227

x^*, y^*, z^*, q^* are derived. For example, the x^*'s are simply the entries in the first column of Table 12.11. For the y^*'s the following is given to illustrate:

For M. culbertsoni: $0.978y^* = -3.499 + (0.209)(1.23) = -3.241$
Therefore

$$y^* = -3.314$$

For Prodesmatochoerus:

$$0.978y^* = -4.995 + (0.209)(3.692) = -4.223$$

Therefore

$$y^* = -4.319$$

For Megoreodon: $0.978y^* = 11.563 - (0.209)(5.098) = 10.497$
Therefore

$$y^* = 10.735$$

The following z^*'s are given for illustration:
For M. culbertsoni:

$$0.911z^* = -2,779 + (0.204)(3.241) + (0.361)(1.231) = -1.673$$

Therefore

$$z^* = -1.837$$

For Megoreodon:

$$0.911z^* = 4.006 - (0.204)(10.497) - (0.361)(5.098) = 0.023$$

For the q^*'s for M. culbertsoni as illustration:

$$0.527q^* = -3.497 + (0.0931)1.673 - (0.052)(3.241)$$
$$+ (0.013)(1.234) = -2.092$$

Therefore

$$q^* = -3.969$$

To avoid clerical errors, it is convenient to compute the values of x, y, z, q and then divide these values by the right standard deviations to

TABLE 12.11

Mean Values of Transformed Characters

Group	x^*	y^*	z^*	q^*
M. culbertsoni	−1.231	−3.314	−1.837	−3.970
Prodesmatochoerus	3.692	−4.319	−1.630	−6.911
Subdesmatochoerus	−2.215	−2.820	2.115	−1.788
Psuedodesmatochoerus	2.046	0.724	1.462	5.733
Desmatochoerus	1.495	3.549	1.516	3.973
O. osborni	−1.500	−4.554	−1.651	−3.160
Megoreodon	5.098	10.735	0.025	6.123

get the starred values of Table 12.11. D^2 is computed from the relation $D^2_{A,B} = (X_A^* - X_B^*)^2 + (Y_A^* - Y_B) + \cdots$ for two species A, B, and any number of characters X, Y, $\cdots$. D^2 examples from Table 12.11 are $M.\ culbertsoni \leftrightarrow Prodesmatochoerus$:

$$D^2 = (-1.231 + 3.692)^2 + (3.314 + 4.319)^2 + (-1.837 + 1.630)^2$$
$$+ (-3.969 + 6.911)^2 = 15.761.$$

$Subdesmatochoerus \leftrightarrow Psuedodesmatochoerus$:

$$D^2 = (-2.215 - 2.046)^2 + \cdots + (-1.788 - 5.733)^2 = 87.723$$

READINGS IN MULTIVARIATE ANALYSIS

J. Bronowski and W. M. Long, 1952, Statistics of discrimination in anthropology, *Am. Jour. Phys. Anthrop.* 10: 385–394, gives a general discussion of the reasons for using multivariate analysis in discrimination, and a discussion of the differences between the discriminant function and the relative distance (D^2) function referred to as the "*S*-function." An appendix is included on the geometry and transformations of the "*S*-function." See also Bronowski and Long, 1953, discussed on p. 277 under the topic of linear discriminant functions.

Eugene Giles, 1960, Multivariate analysis of Pleistocene and recent coyotes. (Canis latrans) from California. *Univ. Calif. Publ. in Geol. Sci.* 36: 369–390, gives a general discussion of multivariate analysis. Application is made of D^2 analysis to the study of taxonomic affinities of both extant and fossil subspecies of coyotes. A detailed zoological interpretation is given. Also included is a comparison of the single available specimen of *Canis petroli* with coyote and wolf data, and the single specimen of *Canis andersoni* with several subspecies of coyotes, by using discriminant function analysis.

TABLE 12.12

	Mc	Pr	Su	Oo	Ps	De	Me
Oo	Oo 2.297	MC 15.761	Oo 19.586	MC 2.297	De 11.385	Ps 11.385	De 71.467
Pr	Pr 15.761	Oo 18.929	MC 21.585	Pr 18.929	Su 87.723	Me 71.467	Ps 111.746
Su	Su 21.585	Su 44.698	Pr 44.698	Su 19.586	Me 111.746	Su 87.882	Su 304.185
De	De 128.847	De 217.154	Ps 87.723	Ps 129.217	Oo 129.217	MC 128.847	MC 342.752
Ps	Ps 132.066	Ps 227.793	De 87.882	De 135.531	MC 132.066	Oo 135.531	Oo 366.258
Me	Me 342.752	Me 476.487	Me 304.185	Me 366.258	Pr 227.793	Pr 217.154	Pr 476.487

D^2 values for each of pairs of species. The D^2 value for each species is listed against the remaining six in order of magnitude of D^2. In this way degree of nearness can be quickly noted. For example, in the first column it is shown that for *M. culbertsoni*, *O. osborni* is nearest, whereas *Megoreodon* is the most distant, in terms of the morphology considered.

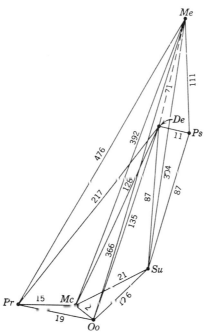

FIG. 12.3. A graphic representation of Table 12.12 showing the interrelationships of the seven species in terms of D^2 for all possible pairs of species. An extension into a formal method for detecting subgroups of closely related members (constellations) is described in Rao, 1952. For application of the D^2 analysis in the present context see D. W. Bailey, 1956, Reexamination of the diversity of Partula Taeniata, *Evolution* X:4; 360–366.

THE COEFFICIENT OF RACIAL LIKENESS

Early interest in the use of quantitative methods in the study of evolution led Karl Pearson to develop a statistical tool that was particularly useful for comparison of human crania, where small samples were the usual case. The test, referred to as the coefficient of racial likeness, was published by Pearson in a paper by M. Tildesley (1921) A first study of the Burmese skull, *Biometrika*, 13: 176–262. It was designed to take into account the smallness of the samples by considering a large number of measurements on each individual specimen.

The C.R.L. for two samples of sizes n_1 and n_2 and p characters is defined to be

$$\text{C.R.L.} = \frac{1}{p} \sum_{i=1}^{p} \frac{n_{1i} n_{2i}}{n_{1i} + n_{2i}} \left(\frac{\bar{x}_{1i} - \bar{x}_{2i}}{s_i} \right)^2 \tag{12.2}$$

where

$$s_i = \sqrt{\frac{n_{1i} s_{1i}^2 + n_{2i} s_{2i}^2}{n_{1i} + n_{2i} - 2}}$$

assuming common variance and covariance in the population and independent characters. Common variance is assumed since small samples are considered where n_{1i} is not necessarily equal to n_{2i}.

This C.R.L. depends on sample size, so that in comparing C.R.L. values for two pairs, we use

$$\text{C.R.L.} = \frac{\bar{n}_1 + \bar{n}_2}{\bar{n}_1 \bar{n}_2} \cdot \frac{1}{p} \left\{ \sum \frac{n_{1i} n_{2i}}{n_{1i} + n_{2i}} \left(\frac{\bar{x}_{1i} - \bar{x}_{2i}}{s_i} \right)^2 - 1 \right\} \qquad (12.3)$$

where $\bar{n}_1 = \sum_{i=1}^{p} n_{1i}/p$ and similarly for $\bar{n}_2$.

The reasoning is as follows:

1. If the two samples come from the same population, the expected value of $\bar{x}_{1i} - \bar{x}_{2i} = 0$ for the ith character.

2. The variance of $\bar{x}_{1i} - \bar{x}_{2i}$ in any case is estimated by $s_{1i}^2/n_1 + s_{2i}^2/n_2$.

3. Experience has shown that many biological measurements are at least approximately normally distributed; and arithmetic means tend to be normally distributed. We may then think of $\dfrac{\bar{x}_{1i} - \bar{x}_{2i}}{\sqrt{s_{1i}^2/n_1 + s_{2i}^2/n_2}}$ as a standard normal variate.[1]

If the reader turns back to the development of chi-square, Chapter 4, he should find no difficulty in the following reasoning: (1) if the above term is considered as a variable which is normally distributed with mean zero and unit variance, (2) and each such term represents a single character for p independent characters, then (3) the sum of squares of such terms is of the form $\sum_{i=1}^{p} x_i^2$ for p normally distributed independent variables, and is distributed as χ^2. Justification of the C.R.L. rests primarily upon the assumption of independence of the characters measured. Apparently Pearson felt this assumption was justified, at least for craniometric characters in *Homo sapiens*. Hodges, *loc. cit.*, quotes M. Tildesley (1921, *loc. cit.*) to the effect that, except for cranial characters which have portions in common or right and left measurements of homologous characters, correlation is never very high and indeed is often wholly negligible. This writer's experience has been confined to animals other than *Homo sapiens* but covering a very wide range over both vertebrate and invertebrate forms. In these studies[2] the correlations vary, but show on the whole that correlations are more often high than not. In addition the high correlations are not subject to the restrictions mentioned by Tildesley.

[1] In fact, this statement is strictly accurate only for large samples. See Chapter 6, Eq. (6.5).

[2] E. C. Olson and R. L. Miller, 1958, *Morphological integration*, Univ. of Chicago Press.

Pearson in 1926 pointed out that it would be easy in theory to allow for dependence of characters, but that the resulting computations would be impractical even for moderate numbers of characters. He suggests that characters which are little correlated should be selected for use in the C.R.L. Pearson[1] treats the independence assumption underlying the C.R.L. He suggests an alternative form suitable if the characters are *not* nearly independent and if there are only a few characters.

The assumption is made that the variance-covariance matrices are equal with the implication that $r_{1ik} = r_{2ik} = r_{ik}$ for characters i, k. However, at this point the writer again feels that for animals other than *Homo sapiens* this assumption is not justified and should be checked in each individual case. A large number of correlation coefficients collected over the same wide variety of animals referred to previously[2] have been found to vary significantly between species and even subspecies, and not only between contemporaneous groups but over evolutionary sequences.

However this may be, the alternative C.R.L. is developed as follows: let

$$y_i = \sqrt{n_1 n_2/(n_1 + n_2)} \cdot \frac{\bar{x}_{1i} - \bar{x}_{2i}}{\sigma_i}$$

for the *i*th character and let R be the correlation matrix

$$R = \begin{vmatrix} 1 & r_{12} & \cdots & r_{1p} \\ r_{21} & 1 & \cdots & r_{2p} \\ & & \cdots & \\ r_{p1} & r_{p2} & \cdots & 1 \end{vmatrix}$$

and let R_{ik} be the cofactor of R for the *i*th row and *k*th column. Then

$$\frac{1}{|R|} \sum_{i=1}^{p} \sum_{k=1}^{p} R_{ik} y_i y_k \tag{12.4}$$

will have a χ^2 distribution with p degrees of freedom, provided the matrix is exact and the samples are drawn from the same population.[3]

If the characters were all independent, then $r_{ik} = 0$, $i \neq k$, and the matrix R would be

$$\begin{vmatrix} 1 & 0 & \cdots & 0 \\ 0 & 1 & \cdots & \\ & & \cdots & 0 \\ 0 & 0 & \cdots & 1 \end{vmatrix} = 1$$

[1] K. Pearson, 1926, On the coefficient of racial likeness, *Biometrika* 18: 105–117.
[2] See Olson and Miller, 1958.
[3] The reasoning is as follows: if x is a variable with $N(0, 1)$, consider first x^2 and then the distribution of $\sum_{i=1}^{n} x_i^2$. This is the χ^2 distribution. See derivation of χ^2 in Chapter 4 pp. 60–62 and Appendices D, E, F pp. 458–463.

Any cofactor $R_{ik} = 1$ if $i = k$, $= 0$ otherwise, so that (12.4) reduces to $\sum_{i=1}^{p} \left(\sum_{i=1}^{p} y_i{}^2 \right)$. If the assumption is made that $\sigma_{1i} = \sigma_{2i} = \sigma_i$ so that $s_{1i}^2/n_1 + s_{2i}^2/n_2$ is equivalent to $n_1 n_2/(n_1 + n_2) \cdot 1/\sigma_i{}^2$, then (12.4) finally reduces to the form of the C.R.L. given in (12.1).

The resulting values of the C.R.L. between several species should not be used to establish relative taxonomic nearness or taxonomic distance. The test was designed to test the hypothesis that two samples were drawn from the source population. Either the C.R.L. exceeds some level of significance or it does not; further interpretation should not be made. For example, if the C.R.L. between species A and B is larger than between species A and C, although significant in both cases, there is no justification within this test to say A is taxonomically more distant from B than from C. We have dealt with the problem of taxonomic distance in the previous section.

THE LINEAR DISCRIMINANT FUNCTION

Applications

The linear discriminant function is intended to provide a numerical criterion or set of criteria for aid in assigning an individual to one of several populations. The method has been used in several areas of interest in the earth sciences.[1]

A matrix of correlation coefficients is formed for nine variables including bulk density, packing, and several mineral components. In preliminary considerations, the matrix of correlations is tested pair by pair to ascertain which pairs exhibit correlation not significantly greater than zero. The matrix is then reduced by pivotal condensation (see C. R. Rao, 1952, *Advanced statistical methods in biometrical research*, John Wiley, New York), finally resulting in a linear discriminant function. The discriminant index z is then used to compare barren versus ore bearing localities. But first, variables which do not contribute to the discrimination are eliminated. It appears that the variables which contribute most importantly to discrimination between barren and ore bearing sediments are: % quartz, % matrix, % silica, and % carbonates, whereas the variables which can be neglected are packing, grain size, size-sorting, and orientation.

The pivotal condensation data are given so that it is possible to follow all steps in the linear discriminant analysis, including the useful step of deleting those variables whose contributions are insignificant.

[1] J. C. Griffiths, 1957, *Petrographical investigation of the salt wash sediments: Final Report*, RME 3151, Office Tech. Services, Dept. Comm., Washington, D.C.

The same topic is taken in less detail using linear discriminant functions in an earlier paper, J. C. Griffiths, J. A. Cochran, J. J. Hutta, and R. Steinmetz, 1954, *Petrographical investigation of the salt wash sediments*, Annual Tech. Rept. RME 3122 (Pts. I, II), Office Tech. Services, Dept. Comm., Washington, D.C.

Another application is A. B. Vistelius, 1950, On the mineralogical composition of the heavy fraction of the sand on the lower productive strata of the Volga alluvium, *Dokl.-Akad. Nauk* 71: No. 2. In this paper three mineral associations are compared with the aid of discriminant functions.

Several papers in related fields follow, some of interest to paleontologists in particular, but they also contain generalized expositions and numerical examples.

PAPERS IN RELATED FIELDS

Pierre Jolicoeur, 1959, Multivariate geographical variation in the wolf Canis Lupus, L; *Evolution* 13: 283–299, contains a section discussing multivariate analysis from the viewpoint of the paleontologist-biometrician. Topics include linear discriminant analysis and the analysis of dispersion. Application is made to geographical variation in Canis Lupus, based on twelve skull dimensions.

Principal component analysis, referred to in the introduction to this section, is applied in a second paper by Jolicoeur, 1960, Size and shape variation in the painted turtle: a principal component analysis, *Growth* (in press).

J. Bronowski and W. M. Long, 1953, Australopithecine milk canines, *Nature* 172: 251ff uses linear discriminant functions on four dimensions of milk canines. This is followed by application of the generalized distance D^2 to the same four dimensions. The linear discriminant function was used to decide which of the two stated alternatives is to be preferred, in this case designation of ape versus human. The generalized distance then indicates the relative nearness of the specimens to each other. A second paper, Bronowski, 1951, Statistical methods in anthropology, *Nature* 168: 794ff, includes a general discussion of linear discriminant functions and multivariate analysis, with application to teeth in man versus chimpanzees.

Linear discriminant analysis is also applied by J. R. Emery, and J. C. Griffiths, 1954, Differentiation of oil-bearing from barren sediments by quantitative petrographic analysis, *Producers Monthly* 19: 33–37, to the Pocono and Berea sediments on the basis of five measured properties of these sediments.

Discussion

The linear discriminant function is due to R. A. Fisher,[1] and was first dealt with in the now famous study by Barnard (1935)[2] of a series of Egyptian skulls. Fisher (1936) discusses the linear discriminant function in detail. The problem arose in craniometric studies and essentially consists of the following: two populations, *known to be different on a priori*

[1] R. A. Fisher, 1936, The use of multiple measurements in taxonomic problems. *Annals of Eugenics*: 7: 179–188.

[2] M. M. Barnard, 1935, The secular variations of skull characters in four series of Egyptian skulls, *Annals of Eugenics* 6: 352–371.

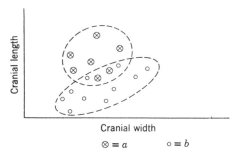

Cranial width

$\otimes = a$ $\circ = b$

FIG. 12.4. Scatter diagram of cranial length versus cranial width for illustration.

grounds, are sampled. For the sample from population A, a number of characters on each of N_A individuals is measured, and for B the same characters on each of N_B individuals are measured. There is now sought an "index" which will enable the worker to assign any new specimen to either population A or B.

Intuitively, a direct attack on this type of problem would be to compute the mean for some selected character for both sample a and sample b. The value of this character in the new individual could be compared with these two averages, to see which it approaches most closely. This as pointed out by Hodges (1950) is essentially the procedure used by Fisher. Suppose we consider a situation where two characters are measured for samples a and b and plotted on a scattergram, Fig. 12.4. A certain amount of overlap is present in this illustration. This overlap may be considered in terms of the degree of separation between the two clusters and the spread within each of the clusters. Fisher focuses attention on this by considering the ratio

$$\frac{\text{Separation between the sample means}}{\text{Standard error within the two samples}}$$

Hoel (1947, pp. 121–125) presents a geometric discussion which is recommended to the reader (Fig. 12.5). The following is based on this discussion. If the scattergram is considered as a plane and a third dimension R is introduced, it can be seen that projecting the points from the cranial l, cranial w plane, onto the plane shown in Fig. 12.5 may introduce a better separation of the two clusters. Optimum separation would be achieved by finding that plane which maximizes the separation between clusters and minimizes the spread within clusters. Let the plane be represented by the equation $R = \lambda_1 x_1 + \lambda_2 x_2$ where x_1, x_2 are the two characters measured. The problem then is to find the values of the coefficients $\lambda_1 \lambda_2$ which will achieve the desired separation. As Hoel points out, the two variable case

[1] P. G. Hoel, 1947, *Introduction to mathematical statistics*, John Wiley, New York.

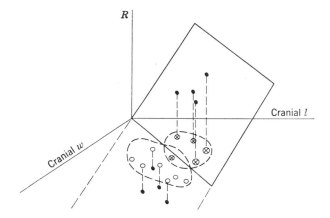

FIG. 12.5. Projection of scatter diagram points onto a separating plane.

treated here in three-dimensional geometry can be similarly treated for any number of variables.

We shall omit detailed development of the steps which lead from a formal statement of the foregoing to the final computing equations since these are to be found in a number of easily available textbooks. Especially recommended are the discussions referred to previously, e.g., Hoel (1947) and Hodges (1950).[1] See also the reference at the beginning of this topic.

The general solution for the λ's is conveniently put in the form:

$$S_{11}\lambda_1 + S_{12}\lambda_2 + \cdots + S_{1p}\lambda_p = d_1$$
$$S_{12}\lambda_1 + S_{22}\lambda_2 + \cdots + S_{2p}\lambda_p = d_2$$
$$\cdots$$
$$S_{p1}\lambda_1 + S_{p2}\lambda_2 + \cdots + S_{pp}\lambda_p = d_p$$

where S_{ij} is

$$\sum_{k=1}^{n_a}(x_{aki} - \bar{x}_{ai})(x_{akj} - \bar{x}_{aj}) + \sum_{k=1}^{n_b}(x_{bki} - \bar{x}_{ba})(x_{bkj} - \bar{x}_{bj})$$

for samples a, b, of sizes N_a and N_b and for variables (characters) $1, 2, \cdots i$, $j, \cdots, p$; $d_i = \bar{x}_{ai} - \bar{x}_{bi}$ for the ith variable. The form given represents a set of simultaneous linear equations for p unknowns, the λ's.

EXAMPLES

We now proceed to apply the linear discriminant function. Two closely related species *M. culbertsoni* and *P. meeki* will form the basis for a linear

[1] J. L. Hodges, 1950, *Discriminatory analysis*, USAF School of Aviation Medicine, Proj No. 21-49-004, Report No. 1.

discriminant function, using the same four measurements considered useful in the earlier multivariate means comparison, on the same two species. For convenience part of Table 12.13 is reproduced here.

It is important to note that in this case the two species have been shown to be distinct by using the multivariate means comparison discussed earlier. As pointed out, we must have *a priori* knowledge that the two populations are different, or the establishment of the linear discriminant function

TABLE 12.13

Means by Species

Character		*M. culbertsoni* (1)	*P. meeki* (2)
BC-W	(X)	47.71	39.33
TR-L	(Y)	90.79	83.25
Bu-L	(Z)	17.57	15.67
Bu Hp	($\mathcal{Q}$)	6.61	4.42

would be meaningless. In practical usage the multivariate T^2 test or its equivalent is usually applied as a preliminary to the linear discriminating function.

The determinant form for the linear discriminant function includes S_{ii} and S_{ij} from the covariance matrix. We may use the same computing form for the *within* (W_{ij}) sums of squares and products used in the multivariate dispersion test of means from Rao. The entries in the determinants are taken from Table 12.4.

The linear discriminant matrix for our case, comparing two samples for four variables, is composed of elements from:

$$S_{XX}\lambda_X + S_{XY}\lambda_Y + S_{XZ}\lambda_Z + S_{X\mathcal{Q}}\lambda_\mathcal{Q} = d_X$$
$$S_{YX}\lambda_X + S_{YY}\lambda_Y + S_{YZ}\lambda_Z + S_{Y\mathcal{Q}}\lambda_\mathcal{Q} = d_Y$$
$$S_{ZX}\lambda_X + S_{ZY}\lambda_Y + S_{ZZ}\lambda_Z + S_{Z\mathcal{Q}}\lambda_\mathcal{Q} = d_Z$$
$$S_{\mathcal{Q}X}\lambda_X + S_{\mathcal{Q}Y}\lambda_Y + S_{\mathcal{Q}Z}\lambda_Z + S_{\mathcal{Q}\mathcal{Q}}\lambda_\mathcal{Q} = d_\mathcal{Q}$$

$$d_X = \bar{X}_1 - \bar{X}_2 = \frac{668}{14} - \frac{472}{12} = 47.71 - 39.33 = 8.38$$

$$d_Y = \bar{Y}_1 - \bar{Y}_2 = \frac{1271}{14} - \frac{999}{12} = 90.78 - 83.25 = 7.53$$

$$d_Z = \bar{Z}_1 - \bar{Z}_2 = \frac{246}{14} - \frac{188}{12} = 17.57 - 15.67 = 1.90$$

$$d_\mathcal{Q} = \bar{\mathcal{Q}}_1 - \bar{\mathcal{Q}}_2 = \frac{82.5}{14} - \frac{53}{12} = 6.61 - 4.42 = 2.19$$

where the mean entries come from Table 12.13. Substituting from Table 12.4 we have after rounding for computation case,[1]

$$210.0\lambda_X + 72.2\lambda_Y + 31.6\lambda_Z + 9.5\lambda_{\mathscr{Q}} = 8.4$$
$$72.2\lambda_X + 208.0\lambda_Y + 34.8\lambda_Z - 2.0\lambda_{\mathscr{Q}} = 7.5$$
$$31.6\lambda_X + 34.8\lambda_Y + 70.0\lambda_Z + 4.5\lambda_{\mathscr{Q}} = 1.9$$
$$9.5\lambda_X - 2.0\lambda_Y + 4.5\lambda_Z + 13.0\lambda_{\mathscr{Q}} = 2.2$$

By solving by determinants,

$$\lambda_X = +0.02349$$
$$\lambda_Y = +0.03214$$
$$\lambda_Z = -0.01107$$
$$\lambda_{\mathscr{Q}} = +0.15991$$

Substituting these solutions in the linear discriminant function

$$R = \lambda_X X + \lambda_Y Y + \lambda_Z Z + \lambda_{\mathscr{Q}}\mathscr{Q}$$

we have finally

$$R = 0.02349X + 0.03214Y - 0.01107Z + 0.15991\mathscr{Q}$$

Applying this "optimum" linear combination to the original data of Tables 12.2, 12.4, we find a good separation has been achieved, as shown in Table 12.14.

TABLE 12.14

The Entries are Values for an Individual Specimen

M. culbertsoni	5.004	4.921	4.674	4.754	4.694	5.176	4.683
P. meeki	4.133	4.034	4.171	4.201	4.170	2.466	4.224
M. culbertsoni	4.828	4.795	5.062	5.057	5.066	4.798	5.097
P. meeki	3.864	4.027	4.481	3.804	4.214	—	—

There are no overlaps. The largest for *P. meeki* is the tenth entry, which is still considerably smaller than the smallest entry for *M. culbertsoni*.

A new specimen may now be assigned to either species by computing its value and placing it according to whether it fits with the lower or upper series of entries. Figure 12.6 shows the frequency distributions for the four characters over the two species. Note that overlap to varying degree

---

[1] More properly the same number of significant digits should be maintained throughout all computations.

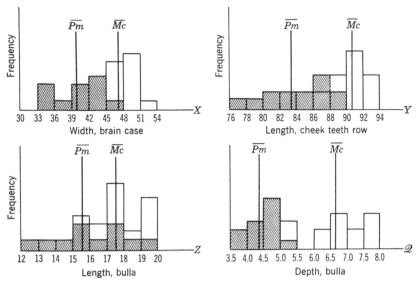

FIG. 12.6. Frequency distributions showing overlap by characters between *Merychoidodon culbertsoni* and *Prodesmatochoerus meeki*. $\overline{Pm}$ and $\overline{Mc}$ show position of arithmetic means.

is present for each character between the species. In a case such as this the linear discriminant function would appear to be of considerable value.[1]

A second application is made to two species of Mississippian blastoids which will be referred to as "Pyriform" and "Godoniform." They were collected from the Golconda of southern Illinois. The characters measured are length and width of the calyx.

	Sample Size	*Means*	
Pyriform	$N_p = 31$	$\overline{L}_p = 17.5882$	$\overline{W}_p = 11.3412$
Godoniform	$N_g = 32$	$\overline{L}_g = 9.3278$	$\overline{W}_g = 9.2500$

Pooled variances and covariance, over Pyriform and Godoniform together, are:

$$S_{LL} = 1074.444$$
$$S_{WL} = 443.528$$
$$S_{WW} = 252.904$$

[1] The significance of the result may be tested either by comparing the means of the two species in terms of standard error of means or by a one-way analysis of variance. For a discussion see M. A. Kendall, 1948, *The advanced theory of statistics*, vol. II, pp. 343ff, Mapleton House, Brooklyn, New York.

The d values are:

$$d_L = \bar{L}_p - \bar{L}_g = 8.2604$$
$$d_W = \bar{W}_p - \bar{W}_g = 2.0912$$

We now wish to seek solutions for the λ coefficients in

$$\lambda_1 S_{LL} + \lambda_2 S_{WL} = C d_L$$
$$\lambda_1 S_{WL} + \lambda_2 S_{WW} = C d_W$$

The C entries are inserted to facilitate the illustration of a suggestion by Hoel (1947, p. 126, 127). The computation of R values will be more convenient if C is chosen so that either λ_1 or λ_2 equals 1.

In using determinants to solve a set of linear equations, it is customary to arrange the determinants as follows $D_1/D = \lambda_1$, where in the above case D_1 is formed by substituting the values d_L and d_W in the first row of D. If we multiply D_1/D by D/D_1, then λ_1 becomes unity. Proceeding in this way,

$$1074.444\lambda_1 + 443.528\lambda_2 = 8.2604C$$
$$443.528\lambda_1 + 252.904\lambda_2 = 2.0912C$$

Let

$$C = \frac{\begin{vmatrix} 1074.44 & 443.528 \\ 443.528 & 252.904 \end{vmatrix}}{\begin{vmatrix} 8.2604 & 443.528 \\ 2.0912 & 252.904 \end{vmatrix}} = \frac{D}{D_1} = 64.58$$

then

$$\lambda_1 = 1, \text{ and } \lambda_2 = \frac{\begin{vmatrix} 1074.444 & 8.2604 \\ 443.528 & 2.0912 \end{vmatrix}(64.58)}{\begin{vmatrix} 1074.444 & 443.528 \\ 443.528 & 252.904 \end{vmatrix}} = -1.220$$

Thus for $R = \lambda_1 L + \lambda_2 W$ we have $R = L - 1.22W$

Applying this linear combination to the original data, once again a good separation is achieved as illustrated by computing R's for part of the specimens:

Godoniform	−0.86	−1.54	−1.68	−1.35	−1.56	−1.20	−0.24	−3.22	−2.56	+0.04	−3.18	etc.
Pyriform	+3.50	+8.15	+1.18	+0.61	+6.52	+3.76	+3.18	+4.25	+3.38	+5.25	+0.88	etc.

In applications of the linear function care should be taken that the populations A and B referred to in the beginning of this discussion are indeed different. It is recommended that, for example, a T^2 test be first applied to the samples from population A and population B to establish the reality of difference. Then, the linear discriminant function may be applied to establish a useful index for assignment of new data to either A or B.

chapter 13

Applications of Multivariate Analysis Including Factor Analysis

AN APPLICATION OF MULTIVARIATE ANALYSIS IN A PROBLEM IN THE GENERAL CONTEXT OF GEOMORPHOLOGY

Two papers are considered in some detail. These are sequential, and deal with a number of variables related to drainage basins.

The first of these deals with the geometric properties of mature drainage systems (Melton, 1958a).[1] Consideration is given to topographic texture as measured by two parameters: D (drainage density) and F (channel frequency). A regression analysis on F and D yields the relation $F = 0.694 D^2$ which is linear when plotted on double log paper. The fit is to 156 points (each representing a basin) and shows very little scatter. Computation of correlation coefficients indicates F/D^2 is "independent" of basin circularity.

The paper is built around a utilization of four-dimensional geometry to represent in a unified way (e.g., in a single coordinate system) the various morphometric properties of mature drainage systems. As the title of the paper indicates, this is done by choosing Euclidian four-space (hence E_4).

Melton focuses attention on four basin parameters: A (area), L (total channel length), R (basin relief), and P (basin perimeter, or circularity). The E_4 space is defined by four mutually perpendicular coordinates; $X_1 = \log \sqrt{A}$, $X_2 = \log L$, $X_3 = \log R$, and $X_4 = \log P$. (See Fig. 13.1.) Other basin parameters are functions of A, L, R, and P.

---

[1] M. A. Melton, 1958a, Geometric properties of mature drainage systems and their representation in E_4 phase space, *Jour. Geol.* 66:1; 35–54.

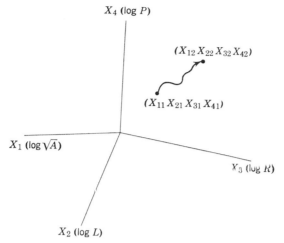

FIG. 13.1. A schematic representation of E_4 phase space.

A single drainage basin is now conveniently represented by an image point in the E_4 space. It may be thought of as a vector with components $X_{11}X_{21}X_{31}X_{41}$, where in Melton's notation X_{ij} is the ith coordinate and the jth image point. With time, the values of the total channel length, basin area, relief and circularity may change, so that the instantaneous position of the image point traces a path through E_4 space. Then at a later time it occupies position 2, with components X_{12}, X_{22}, X_{33}, X_{42}, as shown in the figure. Melton proposes that the E_4 space is adequate for representation of all other quantitative basin parameters.

Other parameters of interest in drainage basins are functions of one or more of the four coordinate forming parameters, for example,

$$\text{Drainage denity } (D) = f(A, L) = X_2 - 2X_1$$

and the collection of all possible values for D may be represented by a scalar field in the phase space.

The utility of the E_4 space is evidenced when growth models for drainage basins are considered. The path in E_4 (see Fig. 13.1) taken by a basin's image point is essentially a growth model. However, Melton states that the change of basin parameters are changes over space at a given time, whereas growth models involve change through time at a given space. Comparison is made with the ergodic problem of the kinetic theory of gases in order to justify the substitution of laws of change in space for laws of change in time.[1] Multiple regression analysis is also utilized; an example

---

[1] The applicability of the ergodic analogue appears to be widespread in geology. Another example where the ergodic problem seems analogous is discussed in R. L. Miller, 1954, *Symposium on Statistics in Geology*, Abstract G.S.A. meetings, Los Angeles.

is the estimation of θ (valley side slope) in terms of the four coordinate variables of the E_4 space. If $\log \theta$ is denoted by Y, the least squares surface is $\hat{Y} = 1.3831 - 0.9612X_1 + 0.2038X_2 + 0.5672X_3 + 0.2180X_4$. Analysis of the regression coefficient $b_{Y4.123}$ (read as slope of the regression line of Y on X_4 for fixed X_1, X_2, and X_3) showed that it was not significantly different from zero. The "independent variable" X_4 was eliminated and a new equation computed

$$\hat{Y} = 1.5253 - 0.7401X_1 + 0.2079X_2 + 0.5637X_3$$

$$\log \theta = 1.5253 - 0.7401 \log \sqrt{A} + 0.2079 \log L + 0.5637 \log R$$

or, taking antilogs,

$$\theta = 33.52 \frac{L^{0.2079}R^{0.5637}}{(\sqrt{A})^{0.7401}}$$

The details of the calculations are given in an appendix to Melton's paper. Rounding to nearest simple fractions and recalculating the coefficient gives the final form

$$\theta = 27.53 \frac{L^{0.25}R^{0.5}}{(\sqrt{A})^{0.75}}$$

Strahler's ruggedness number $HD = LR/A$ is a good estimator of θ (H is relief, D is drainage density). Thus it appears that the product of relief and drainage density is roughly equivalent to θ or valley side slope. (See Strahler, 1958, ibid., p. 289.)[1]

We now turn to the second of Melton's papers (1958b)[2] where multivariate analysis is applied to the morphometric properties of drainage systems. In this paper he investigates the correlation among fifteen variables (see Fig. 13.3) considered by him to be of primary importance in the quantitative analysis of drainage systems. Essentially the investigation consists of computing the correlations among all possible pairs of variables. The first step then is to construct a correlation matrix where all possible correlation coefficients are entered, and then subsequently to extract "clusters" and "basic pairs" after the methods proposed by Miller and Weller (1952)[3] and Olson and Miller (1948).[4] A detailed discussion of this

[1] A. N. Strahler, 1958, Dimensional analysis applied to fluvially eroded landforms, Geol. Soc. Am. Bull. 69: 279–300.

[2] M. A. Melton, 1958b, Correlation structure of morphometric properties of drainage systems and their controlling agents, Jour. Geol. 66:4; 442–460.

[3] R. L. Miller and J. M. Weller, 1952, Significant comparisons in Paleontology, Jour. Paleontol. 26:6; 993–996.

[4] Olson and Miller, 1958, Morphological integration, Chicago Univ. Press.

analytic methodology is given on pp. 295–299 and 304–307. Essentially the problem consists of the following elements:

1. A large number of variables of interest and importance in analysis of some natural phenomenon (in this case drainage basins).
2. The variables probably cannot change without involving changes in other variables.
3. The association between any pair of variables is often not linear. That is, a scatter plot of variable X against X_2 may take a form other than a straight line.
4. The population frequency distributions are for the most part unknown.
5. There exist varying degrees of *a priori* knowledge about the causal relations between the variables.

With these considerations in mind Melton proposes the concept of "variable systems."

A variable system V is an abstract set of variables such that (1) *each is, in reality, rather highly correlated with every other one;* (2) *the direction of causality (if any) between each pair of variables is stated, and* (3) *one or more variables in V may be correlated with variables not in V.*

We shall illustrate the preceding by discussing one of Melton's examples in detail. However, first some discussion of the structural elements of the variable system is required.

The Feedback System

Item 5 in the list of elements of the general problem given states that there exists varying degrees of *a priori* knowledge about the causal relations between the variables. In this instance, the *a priori* knowledge is coded in a diagram in which the causal relationships or lack of them are shown by using arrows, lines, and (+), (−) signs. If changes in variable A affect or "cause" changes in variable B, an arrow from A to B is used. (See Fig. 13.2.) If the change is such that an increase in A results in an increase in B, a (+)

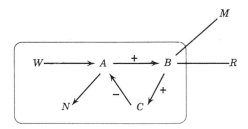

FIG. 13.2. Illustration of feedback system (from Melton, 1958, p. 444).

sign is used. If, on the other hand, an increase in A results in a decrease in B, a $(-)$ sign is used. If variable B and variable R are correlated but not in a causal sense (*within the system!*), then a line without a sense or arrow is used to connect the two. An illustrative example is the famous high correlation between human birth rate and stork population in Sweden. If the phenomenon of interest is that of population fluctuations, the stork population may or may not be included in the variable system of pertinent properties; but *a priori* knowledge would probably not allow the statement of a causal relation between the two.

Observation of the patterns formed by the variables and their connections show several important arrangements.

1. Variable M is outside the system and varies independently of elements in the system. However, changes in M "cause" changes in B, hence the arrow.

2. Similarly W is independent of changes within the system although it is also a member. But changes in W affect or "cause" changes in A.

3. N is dependent on A (arrow from A to N).

4. A feedback system is illustrated by the triad A, B, C. A change in A results in a positively correlated change in B. This is turn results in a positively correlated change in C. Finally there is a negatively correlated change in A. The causality following the arrows goes in a "loop" from A to B to C and back to A. This is *feedback*; in this case, negative feedback.

5. M and W are not both included in the variable system because $\rho_{MW} \approx 0$.

The Correlation Matrix

As mentioned earlier (item 3) few of the variables are linearly correlated. In addition (item 4) the population frequency distributions are with one exception unknown.[1] Melton therefore chooses to use a nonparametric measure of degree of correlation, Kendall tau (τ). The following illustrates the computational steps. We consider here the correlation between the variables L/P (ratio of total channel length to basin perimeter) and F/D^2 (relative channel density).[2]

First Step

The data for L/P are ordered with respect to size, so that the smallest value is first, the largest value last. For each of the 59 basins considered there is a value of F/D^2 corresponding to the value for L/P. Since the L/P

[1] A. Strahler, 1954, *Quantitative geomorphology of erosional landscapes*, Comptes Rendus, 19th Session, International Geological Congress Algiers, Sec. XIII p. 341–354.

[2] The data for the above example were kindly supplied by M. A. Melton, Univ. of Chicago.

values are now ordered with respect to size, we examine the resulting order in the corresponding F/D^2 values. It is apparent that if the F/D^2 values were also perfectly ordered with respect to size, the association would be complete.

Second Step

We consider the ordering of F/D^2. The results are as follows in values of F/D^2:

43, 13, 51, 38, 58, 49, 57, 31, 40, 46, 28, 39, 45, 48, 47, 56
12, 32, 59, 10, 16, 55, 30, 52, 2, 19, 50, 34, 33, 54, 37, 26
41, 6, 53, 9, 1, 7, 14, 35, 4, 29, 15, 44, 8, 18, 23, 42
22, 21, 24, 25, 5, 17, 36, 20, 11, 27, 3.

A tabulation is now made for each of the above entries in turn of the following $(N_H - N_I)$. N_H is the number of ranks higher than the entry and to its right, and N_I is the number of ranks smaller than the entry and to its right. Thus for the first entry with the value 43, there are 16 ranks to the right which are higher and 42 ranks to the right which are lower. Then $(N_H - N_L) = (16 - 42) = -26$. For the next to last entry with the value 27, the difference $(N_H - N_L) = (0 - 1) = -1$.

Third Step

We are now in a position to compute Kendall's rank correlation coefficient τ where

$$\tau = \frac{S}{\frac{1}{2}N(N-1)}$$

S is the sum of the values $(N_H - N_L)$ for each of the entries. In the present case it equals (-551). N is the number of entries or ranks, in this case, 59.

Therefore

$$\tau = \frac{-551}{\frac{1}{2}(59)(58)} = \frac{-551}{1711} = -0.322$$

Fourth Step

Test of significance. For N greater than 10, Kendall's τ is approximately normally distributed with mean $\mu_\tau = 0$ and standard deviation

$$\sigma_\tau = \sqrt{\frac{2(2N+5)}{9N(N-1)}}$$

We may therefore go to the normal tables by computing a z value where

$$Z = \frac{\tau - \mu_\tau}{\sigma_\tau}$$

In the present example,

$$\sigma_\tau = \sqrt{\frac{2(2)(59)+5}{9(59)(58)}} = 0.0894$$

X \ Y	θ	D	C	H	L/P	F/D^2	f	$P\text{-}E$	S_w	S_o	b	M	q	J	A_u
θ	1			+0.495		−0.294	+0.302						−0.236	0.391	
D		1					−0.273	−0.376			+0.649		+0.428	+0.285	−0.426
C			1	−0.160									+0.275		−0.216
H				1	+0.253	−0.560	+0.362	+0.133				+0.352	−0.308	+0.348	+0.178
L/P					1	−0.322									+0.506
F/D^2						1	−0.311	−0.225					+0.254	−0.197	−0.231
f							1	+0.341			−0.584		−0.737		+0.276
$P\text{-}E$								1		+0.496	−0.681	−0.307	−0.536		+0.366
S_w									1						
S_o										1					
b											1	+0.278	+0.488		−0.499
M												1			
q													1		−0.518
J														1	
A_u															1

FIG. 13.3. Matrix of τ values significantly different from zero. (From M. A. Melton, 1958, p. 450.)

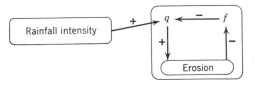

FIG. 13.4. A variable system (from Melton, 1958, p. 454).

substituting $Z = 0.322/0.0894 = 3.60$. From the normal tables the probability that the F/D^2 values are randomly ranked is approximately 0.00016. The conclusion is that the value $\tau = -0.322$ indicates a significant negative correlation.

For treatment of significance for $N \leq 10$ and a general discussion of Kendall's τ, see Siegal (1956, pp. 213–223).[1]

Figure 13.3 taken from Melton's paper gives the matrix of τ values which are significantly greater than zero. This matrix forms the basis on which the "correlation sets" and "cluster diagrams" are constructed. "Basic pairs" in which the reflexive property that each member of the pair is more highly correlated with the other than with any of the remaining variables are also listed. (See p. 306 for further discussion of "basic pairs.")

Once the intercorrelation matrix has been reduced to contain only those entries significantly greater than zero, Melton turns to the "variable system" for interpretation.

The variable system may thus be regarded as a hypothesis composed of elements which include not only those from the correlation matrix but others which are appropriate. To illustrate this we consider the variable system entitled: *infiltration capacity-runoff intensity positive feedback system.*

The system is constructed in the following way:

The variables q (runoff intensity) and f (infiltration capacity) show high negative correlation (see Fig. 13.4). The causal arrow (based on *a priori* grounds) goes from f to q. A hypothetical element, rate of erosion, is introduced and a variable system is thus formed. Suppose we start with f and follow the path indicated by the arrows. A decrease in infiltration capacity results in an increase in runoff intensity (negative correlation from Fig. 13.3). This in turn induces an increased erosion; thus a + sign going from q to erosion. Increase in erosion in turn induces lower infiltration capacity as the most permeable fractions of the soil are removed. Thus a feedback loop is established within the system. An additional element,

[1] S. Siegal, 1956, *Nonparametric statistics for the behavioral sciences*, McGraw-Hill Book Co., New York.

rainfall intensity, is introduced, which does not fall in the system and is independent of it. However, this element affects runoff intensity in a positive sense; increase in rainfall intensity results in increased runoff intensity. The feedback is positive in that changes in our arbitrary starting point f results in a series of changes in other variables which finally produces changes in turn in f in the same direction as the original changes.

One of the advantages of a method of this type is that conflicts in sign or direction of arrow will be brought sharply into focus, thus indicating reexamination of the *a priori* knowledge or of the correlation structure.

An interesting method for checking the reasonableness of an arrow between two variables is the application of partial correlation coefficients. For example, Melton considers whether an arrow should or should not be placed between H (ruggedness number) and θ (valley side slope). The partial correlation between H and θ for constant relief is the same as the correlation between D and θ since H is defined to be rD and r is total basin relief. Referring to Fig. 13.3 we find the correlation of D and θ is not significantly different from zero. The conclusion is that an arrow is not needed between H and θ.

It appears to the writers that an additional aspect to checking the internal consistency of the variable system hypothesis may lie in a more formal development of partial correlation in cases where normal theory can be applied, possibly taking the partial correlation between a pair of variables and holding several others constant, and permuting this computation for other possible pairs. A somewhat analogous approach to a general problem of the kind discussed by Melton, in which the conventional correlation coefficient r is utilized, is the method of path coefficients applied to genetics.[1]

FACTOR ANALYSIS

In its most restricted sense, we may consider factor analysis to be a consideration of the degree of association between pairs of variables. Usually a number of variables are involved, and the degree of association is taken between all possible pairs. The association is usually measured by the correlation coefficient r (ratio of covariance to geometric mean of variances).[2] However, nonparametric estimates of ρ or other measurements of correlation such as Spearman's rank correlation may be used, if

[1] Sewall Wright, 1934, The method of path coefficients, *Annal. Math. Stats.* 5: 161–215.

[2] R. L. Miller and J. M. Weller, 1952, Significant comparisons in paleontology, *Jour. Paleon.* 26: 993–996, discuss a multivariate technique which is very easy to apply. Use is made of Thurston's edge-marking method for quick estimates of intercorrelations. See L. L. Thurston, 1948, Edge marking method of analyzing data, *Jour. Amer. Stat. Assoc.* 43: 451–457.

Variable X Variable $Y \cdots$ Variable Z

Individual 1	x_1	y_1	$\cdots$	z_1	} Correlation gives Q
Individual 2	x_2	y_2	$\cdots$	z_2	} technique
.	.	.	.	.	
.	.	.	.	.	
.	.	.	.	.	
Individual N	x_N	y_N	$\cdots$	z_N	

Correlation gives
R technique

FIG, 13 5. Relation between R and Q techniques.

the situation requires it.[1] In fact, a recent study was completed using χ^2 between pairs.[2]

However the entries in the matrix (see Fig. 13.6) may have been arrived at, the second basic step in factor analysis consists of extraction of groups of variables from the matrix by one means or another Figure 13.5 describes the two most commonly used basic techniques used to assess the degree of association: The R technique and the Q technique. The R technique is based on the measurement of two variables at a time, where

	1	2	3	4	$\cdots$	N
1		r_{12}	r_{13}	r_{14}		r_{1N}
2			r_{23}	r_{24}		r_{2N}
3				r_{34}		r_{3N}
4						r_{4N}
.						
.						
.						
N						

FIG. 13.6. "r matrix."

[1] R. G. Johnson, 1960, Models and methods for analysis of the mode of formation of fossil assemblages, *Bull. G.S.A.* 71: 1075–1086, forms a correlation matrix in which the entries are Spearman's rank correlation coefficients.

[2] R. G. Johnson, *Interspecific associations in Pennsylvanian fossil assemblages* (in press), uses χ^2 test of independence as a measure of association between pairs of species to determine the existence and membership of fossil communities.

each pair of values, e.g., x, y, comes from a single individual; it requires a large number of individuals. The Q technique correlates two individuals on the basis of the variables; it also requires a large number of variables. In addition there are techniques referred to as the P and O techniques which apply factor analysis to single individuals.[1] We shall focus attention on R techniques as most immediately applicable to geological problems, and then discuss Q techniques.

Essentially the R technique of factor analysis starts out by computing the variate correlation of variables under consideration in all possible ways. Thus for N variables there will be $[N(N - 1)]/2$ correlation coefficients. (See Fig. 13.6.) This matrix of correlation coefficients forms the base from which "factors" are then extracted. We shall now discuss various ways by which the factors are extracted.

Multifactor Analysis

If the correlation between two variables is represented by, say, unit vectors, then the correlation coefficient is equal to the cosine of the angle between the two vectors. By a combination of the representation of variables as vectors, and the use of matrix manipulation, "factors" are extracted. Essentially, these factors represent the independent coordinates of the space required to enclose a set of correlations, when these correlations are represented in space as vectors.

Since the type of factor analysis just referred to is complex and laborious, and since it has not to the writer's knowledge been directly applied to the earth sciences as yet, we shall not attempt an exposition of the technique. The interested reader may refer to L. L. Thurstone, *Multiple factor analysis*, 1947, University of Chicago Press, K. J. Holzinger and H. H. Harman, *Factor analysis*, 1941, University of Chicago Press, or R. B. Cattell, 1952, *Factor analysis*, Harper Bros., New York, for a full exposition. There is a very large literature, particularly in psychometrics, on this subject, mostly in the last two decades.[2]

However, the above type of factor analysis is mentioned first because it is by far the most widely used if all fields of inquiry are considered.

---

[1] For details see R. B. Cattell, 1952, *Factor analysis*, Harper Bros., New York, and R. B. Cattell, 1954, Growing points in factor analysis, *Australian Jour. Psych.* 6: 105–140.

[2] C. P. Stroud, 1953, An application of factor analysis to the systematics of Kalotermes, *Systematic Zool.* 2: 76–92.

W. W. Howells, 1951, Factors of human physique, *Amer. Jour. Phys. Anthrop.* 9: 159–191.

An over-all discussion of factor analysis and summaries of over 200 references on the subject is given in Univ. of Calif. Report #2, U.S.A.F. School of Aviation Medicine Project 21-49-004, October 1950 by Evelyn Fix.

Interesting and suggestive studies which may be extended to paleontological and geological areas include a paper by C. P. Stroud (1953) on taxonomic problems, and one by W. W. Howells (1951) on morphological dimensions in man. See also M. G. Kendall, 1957, *A course in multivariate analysis*, Chas. Griffin and Co., London, under the topics "principal component analysis" and "factor analysis."

Cluster Analysis

Cattell (1944) and Tryon (1939)[1] and Sokal and Michener refer to the methods of extracting intercorrelated groups from the correlation matrix by "cluster analysis." The term factor is reserved for vector techniques referred to in the previous section. Cattell, in particular, feels that cluster analysis is superficial when compared to factor analysis. He does, however, point out that an outstanding advantage in cluster type analysis is the fact that comparisons can be made from one study to the next. In factor analysis on the other hand, due to the variation in mathematical systems and choice of technique within a system, synthesis of the results of several factor analyses are difficult if not practically impossible.

We shall define a cluster in what follows as a group of intercorrelated variables such that the correlation between all possible pairs of variables which are members of the group is greater than or equal to some arbitrarily selected level of correlation.[1]

The writers feel that for many problems in geology, some form of cluster analysis is to be preferred, because (1) the research worker is at all times in close touch with his original variables, and (2) the clusters are more easily and simply interpreted. We shall return to these points in later discussion of one of the methods for extracting clusters and subsequently interpreting them (the ρ-F technique).

METHODS FOR EXTRACTING CLUSTERS

The Ramifying Linkage Method[2]

We shall define a "link" between two variables as a correlation value satisfying some arbitrary level of correlation. Thus two variables are linked if their correlation is greater than or equal to the level of correlation set by the research worker for extracting clusters.

In some cases, the procedure may involve the requirement that the absolute value of the true correlation coefficient ρ be greater than or equal to some arbitrary value. In such an event, it is customary to refer, e.g.,

---

[1] R. C. Tryon, 1939, *Cluster analysis*, Edwards Bros., Ann Arbor, Michigan.

[2] R. B. Cattell, 1944, A note on correlation clusters and cluster search methods, *Psychometrika* 9:3; 169–184.

TABLE

Matrix of Approximate Correlation

Specimen Number	H. lysitensis				H. powellianis			
	14,618a	14,618b	12,716	4,718	15,622	15,612	14,617	4,147
14,618a		0.985	0.980	0.991	0.983	0.984	0.989	0.982
14,618b			0.985	0.974	0.993	0.991	0.985	0.992
12,716				0.990	0.986	0.986	0.985	0.987
4,718					0.996	0.998	0.996	0.991
15,622						0.989	0.989	0.987
15,612							0.991	0.991
14,617								0.985
4,147								
10,993								
11,387								
11,405								
11,913								

to David's tables[1] which will give, depending on sample size, that value that must be exceeded, so that the worker is sure with a given probability that the arbitrary level of ρ will be equaled or exceeded.

Step 1. Establish some definite ordering for the variables, e.g., from left to right across the top row of the matrix.

Step 2. In that order, write out on a card for each successive variable all the other variables with which it is linked.

Step 3. Start with the first card and select from the variables written on it the next one to the right. Examine this card next. Select from it the

[1] Reference to David's tables. F. N. David, 1948, *Tables of the ordinates and probability integral of the distribution of the correlation coefficient in small samples*, The Biometrika Office, London.

13.1

Coefficients (Accurate to Two Places)

H. paulus				Aotus trivarigatus		
10,993	11,387	11,405	11,913	66,430		
0.985	0.983	0.985	0.979	0.794	14,618a	⎫
0.990	0.988	0.982	0.989	0.836	14,618b	⎪
0.983	0.991	0.902	0.984	0.681	12,716	⎬ H. lysitensis
0.999	0.999	0.997	0.988	0.758	4,718	⎭
0.988	0.984	0.986	0.990	0.824	15,622	⎫
0.981	0.984	0.986	0.987	0.813	15,612	⎪
0.989	0.995	0.991	0.987	0.770	14,617	⎬ H. powellianus
0.986	0.988	0.980	0.988	0.826	4,147	⎭
	0.997	0.986	0.988	0.814	10,993	⎫
		0.980	0.991	0.801	11,387	⎪
			0.980	0.798	11,405	⎬ H. paulus
				0.848	11,913	⎭

first variable to its right *which is also on the first card.* Each new variable must be on preceding cards in that sequence. Proceed in this manner until all cards are exhausted. The cards which have been selected by this procedure form a cluster.

Step 4. Return to the first card and start a fresh sequence until all possibilities are exhausted.

Step 5. Turn over the first card, and start with the second card (variable). Proceed as before, recording as a cluster all cards again selected. This total procedure is repeated for all variables.

The result is a complete extraction of all maximum clusters. Recording of pairs is not necessary in this procedure since they can be obtained directly from the matrix.

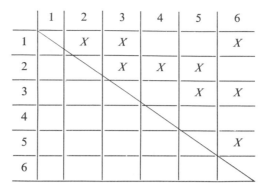

FIG. 13.7. A six-variable correlation matrix.

Figure 13.7 illustrates the procedure for a six-variable matrix. An X entry indicates that the pair of variables for that entry are linked, e.g., the correlation between that pair is greater than or equal to $|r \geq 0.9|$. Empty squares mean the correlation between that pair is not linked, e.g., $|r < 0.9|$.

(1)	(2)	(3)	(4)	(5)	(6)
(1), 2, 3, 6	1, (2), 3, 4, 5	1, 2, (3), 5, 6	2, (4)	2, 3, (5), 6	1, 3, 5, (6)

Card 1 links with 2, 3, 6. Going to *Card* 2, variable 3 is the first variable to the right of 2 which is also on *Card* 1. Proceeding to *Card* 3, the first variable to the right of 3 is 5. But 5 is not on *Card* 1. Stopping at this point, we record the cluster which consists of 1, 2, and 3. Now *Card* 1 is turned over and we start a new sequence of selection with *Card* 2. We find that a cluster of 2, 3, and 5 results. Proceeding similarly for *Card* 3 as the first in the selection sequence and proceeding always from left to right, we find cluster 3, 5, 6. For *Card* 4 a cluster pair is noted, 4, 2, but this can be obtained directly from the matrix. Similarly, for *Card* 5, the pair 5, 6 is recorded. The results are conveniently displayed for study in the following form:

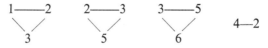

Returning to the first card as in Step 4, we start a fresh sequence. On the first card the first *untried* variable to the right is 3. Going to *Card* 3 we find a triplet exists, consisting of 1, 3, 6.

In the preceding display a line connecting a pair of variables indicates that the pair is linked. The maximum noncontained clusters are displayed.

By noncontained, we mean that a cluster is not completely contained through its members in a larger cluster, e.g., the pair, 1, 6. Our analysis also reveals the pair 5, 6 as a cluster. But this pair is contained in the larger cluster 3, 5, 6. Note that certain of the members are common to several clusters. This overlap or intersection is discussed and a way to reduce it is taken up in the section describing the "ρ-F" cluster analysis. It is sometimes suggestive to rearrange the clusters so that the overlaps are recognized. Thus in our example the total complex would look like this

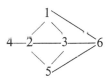

THE Q TECHNIQUE

As mentioned in the introduction to the section on factor analysis, the Q technique involves the correlation between a pair of individuals for a number of measurements. If the degree of association (measured, e.g., by the correlation coefficient r) is high, it may be inferred that the proportions of the various dimensions used in the test are similar. Over-all difference in size, independent of difference in proportion, will change the slope of a line through the points in this case but not the correlation. Thus if every dimension of specimen A, e.g., is almost exactly twice as large as every dimension of specimen B, the correlation will be very high. Similarly, if every dimension of specimen A is almost exactly the same as specimen B, the correlation will again be high, but the slope of a line through the points will have changed. Since the correlation is taken into account but not the slope, it can be said that the Q technique focuses attention on difference or similarity of proportions independent of over-all size differences.

We shall now consider an application to paleontology. We seek, on the basis of difference in correlation coefficients, to assign a collection of individuals to separate categories. These categories will be based on high correlation among members within a category and low correlation with all other individuals.

The Q technique is applied to three species of *Hyopsodus*, a fossil condylarth from the lower and middle Eocene. Four specimens each were taken from *H. lysitensis*, H. *powellianus*, and H. *paulus*. A total of 27 different measurements on the upper dental series was used. The correlations between all possible pairs of individual animals are entered in Table 13.1. The results seem to indicate that the differences in proportions of the teeth, independent of size, are not sufficient to allow for an assignment of the total of the 12 specimens to categories.

Before we can draw any conclusions further investigation is necessary. A single individual on which the same measurements were available was selected for comparison. A specimen of the monkey, *Aotus trivarigatus* was selected. The correlations between this individual and each of the 12 members of *Hyopsodus* are shown in Table 13.1. Since the teeth of the monkey is quite different in appearance from the fossil condylarths, we should expect clear distinction in the form of lower correlations. Examination of Table 13.1 shows that this is true.

A further analysis was made on selected individuals from a series of fossil Oreodonts of Oligocene age. In this case 44 cranial measurements were available for individuals of several distinct species. The correlation between two members of the same species (*Prodesmatochoerus meeki*) was found to be 0.994. The correlation between an individual of *Desmatochoerus* and an individual of a quite different species, *Megoreodon gigas loomisi*, is also quite high–0.983. Finally, the correlation between two similar species *Prodesmatochoerus meeki* and *Merychoidodon culbertsoni* was 0.993. As in the study of the Hyopsodi, no basis for assignment to categories is given by the consistently high correlation coefficients. It is of interest to note here that a multivariate comparison of means indicated that the two species, *Merychoidodon culbertsoni* and *Prodesmotochoerus meeki*, were clearly significantly different (see section on analysis of dispersion in Chapter 12.)

The tentative conclusion drawn is as follows: where linear dimensions are used exclusively, the *Q* technique appears to be sensitive only to rather gross differences, as between the widely separated fossil condylarths (Hyopsodus) and the monkey, *Aotos trivarigatus*. Where such an approach would have real value, i.e., in closely related series, the results are not usable, for e.g., the Hyopsodus series or the Oreodont series.

On the other hand, Sokal and Michener (1957)[1] in a study of taxonomy of bees published excellent preliminary results. It should be noted, however, that in their study a number of characters were based on counts and arbitrary assignment of integers to qualitative items such as color. When these are used in conjunction with continuous linear dimensions, a *relative* grossness is introduced with greater variation in the scatter of points and thus in the correlation coefficients.

A further consideration seems pertinent here. Organs or parts of closely related species tend to differ more in size than in proportion. Thus one would expect a higher correlation between a pair of animals when a number of measurements from the teeth alone (as in the Hyopsodi), or the cranium alone (as in the Oreodonts) are used than when the measurements are distributed over the whole animal.

[1] R. R. Sokal and C. D. Michener, 1957, *Evolution* (in press).

The writers conclude that where linear dimensions are used exclusively (as in most fossil studies), the Q test utilizing the correlation coefficient r is not sufficiently sensitive to give satisfactory results on closely related species. Further work along these lines, however, would appear to be very worthwhile. It is possible that some sort of weighting, or another way to measure the degree of association, can be found.

In general, the problem of assigning a collection of individuals to categories, on the basis of similarity or difference between the individuals and *where these categories are not established beforehand*, is a fundamental one in paleontology. The successful application of the Q technique to a modern family of bees as published by Sokal and Michener strongly suggests further investigation of this approach in paleontological context. See also Sokal and Michener (1956).[1]

THE METHOD OF CORRELATION PROFILES; INDEX OF INTEGRATION; AND ρ-F ANALYSIS

The method of correlation profiles due to Tryon (1939, *ibid.*) involves a quite different approach to the problem of extracting clusters from a correlation matrix. It has the advantage of avoiding overlap of clusters or, at least, reducing the overlap. There are essentially two ways to apply the correlation profile technique. A third method developed by the senior author is described in a later section. The first is called the method of trial graphs; the second is called the quantitative method and essentially utilizes a coefficient due to Holzinger (1937)[2] to form preliminary clusters. The coefficient called the B coefficient is the ratio of the mean intercorrelation of a member of a cluster to the mean remaining correlation. After the preliminary clusters are formed, the method of trial graphs is then used to form the final clusters. Although the second method has a smaller degree of subjectivity and is more practical for larger matrices, it is somewhat complicated. The interested reader is referred to Tryon's exposition. We shall confine our discussion to the first-mentioned method of trial graphs.

The procedure is quite direct. The correlation values for a given variable are plotted on a graph in which the ordinate represents r values from -1 to 1, and the abscissa gives the variables ordered for convenience in the way in which they occur in the matrix. The points on the graph are then connected to form a "correlation profile." (See Fig. 13.8.) By inspection,

[1] R. R. Sokal and C. D. Michener, 1956, *A statistical method for evaluating systematic relationships*, Contr. #945, Dept. of Entomology, Univ. of Kansas, Lawrence, Kansas.

[2] K. J. Holzinger, 1937, *Student manual of factor analysis*, Dept. of Education, Univ. of Chicago, Chapter III, section 1.

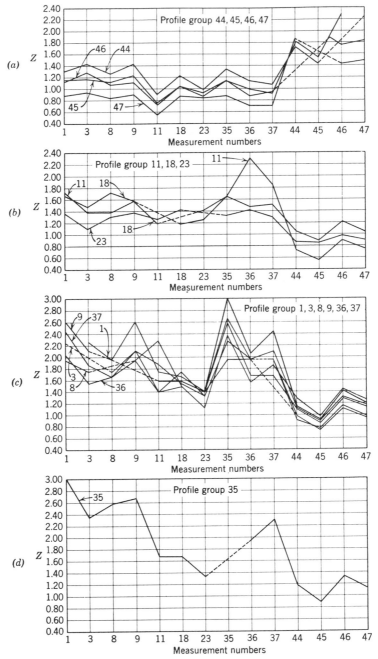

FIG. 13.8. Correlation profiles assigned to four groups by inspection.

correlation profiles are plotted for other variables which appear to be congruent with the first profile and with others in the group. In this way groups of congruent profiles represent clusters of variables. Referring to the r matrix in the example of the previous method (Fig. 13.6), we find by inspection those correlation profiles which appear congruent with each other. Tryon suggests that the variable with the highest Σr be plotted first. We have therefore added the column Σr (excluding the diagonal) to the right side of the correlation matrix. Once having plotted the correlation profile for the first selected variable, it is suggested that other trial variables may be selected by noting those variables most highly correlated with the first and then scanning the entire pair of rows for congruent ups and downs.

The degree of congruence required to accept a member of a cluster, or conversely the lack of congruence necessary to reject a variable from a cluster, is subjective. The arbitrary ordering of the variables will affect the apparent congruence. We will discuss interpretation through analysis of a real case.

Factor Analysis of Equus Hemionus Hemionus from Mongolia

A total of 14 measurements were made on each of 17 specimens of the wild Mongolian ass, *Equus hemionus hemionus*. Data were taken from H. Motohashi, 1930, Craniometrical studies on skulls of wild asses of West Mongolia, Memoirs Tottori Ag. College of Nippon, Vol. 1, No. 1, pp. 1–62. The data and the correlation coefficients were kindly supplied by Professor E. C. Olson, University of Chicago.

The measurements were all on the skull and lower jaws and selected from a much larger list to represent a wide variety of elements. The following list gives the code number for the measurement, followed by a description of that measurement.

Skull Length Measurements

1. *Basilar length* from median incisive border (base of central incisor) to anterior edge of foramen magnum.

3. *Nasal bone length* (median) from anterior end of nasal bone to posterior end of internasal suture.

8. *Horizontal diameter of orbit.* The basilar line is held horizontally.

9. *Palatal length* from median incisive border to posterior end of median palatine suture on horizontal part of palatine bone.

11. *Diastema length* from anterior end of alveolus or P^2 to posterior end of alveolus of I^3.

Skull Width Measurements

18. *Width of nasal bones* (anterior) in their anterior part at point of contact of maxilla and nasal bone.

23. *Width of occipital condyle* across two occipital condyles at their widest part.

Angles

35. *Facio-cranial angle* from optic foramen to middle incisive border as compared with basi-cranial line.

Mandible (Lower Jaw) Measurements

36. *Length of mandible* from median incisive point to middle of posterior edge of head of condyle.

37. *Diastema length* from anterior end of alveolus of P_2 to posterior end of alveolus of I_3.

44. *Height of coronoid process* at the middle point of the upper end of the coronoid process.

Upper Dental Series

45. *Rectangular diameter of incisor, I^1.* Largest diameter of wearing surface of each incisor was taken vertically to the tangential line of the center margin of the teeth.

46. *I^2,* as above.

47. *Height of incisor, I^1,* from middle edge of alveolus, outside, of each incisor to the middle of outer margin of wearing surface of incisor.

The correlation matrix is shown in Table 13.2. We shall now proceed to extract clusters by both the ramifying linkage method and the correlation profile method.

CLUSTER ANALYSIS BY THE RAMIFYING LINKAGE METHOD. APPLICATION OF THE ρ-F TECHNIQUE[1]

We define for illustration a pair of variables as "linked" if the population correlation coefficient ρ is greater than or equal to 0.95. Referring to David's tables we find that for sample size 17 and significance level 0.95, the sample correlation coefficient r must be greater than 0.86. By scanning the matrix of Table 13.1 the cards are constructed as previously described and the sorting begins. The resulting noncontained "ρ-groups" are:

    I. 1–3–8–9–11–35–36–37
    II. 1–3–8–9–18–23–35–36
    III. 3–46
    IV. 9–46
    V. 44–45–46–47

[1] E. C. Olson and R. L. Miller, 1958, *Morphological integration*, Univ. of Chicago Press, Chicago and E. C. Olson and R. L. Miller, 1951, A mathematical model applied to a study of evolution of species, *Evolution* 5: 325–338.

TABLE 13.2

Intercorrelation Matrix for Fourteen Variables. At level of $r \geq 0.90$, $r \geq 0.3887$ for Sample Size, $n = 17$.

| | Length Skull | | | | Width Skull | | Angle | Lower Jaw | | Upper Teeth | | | |
	3	8	9	11	18	23	35	36	37	44	45	46	47
1	0.978	0.96	0.989	0.94	0.93	0.88	0.999	0.967	0.985	0.80	0.70	0.85	0.81
3	/	0.94	0.97	0.88	0.90	0.80	0.982	0.91	0.95	0.85	0.74	0.89	0.82
8		/	0.96	0.88	0.94	0.86	0.968	0.93	0.93	0.79	0.68	0.85	0.80
9			/	0.92	0.92	0.88	0.990	0.96	0.97	0.81	0.71	0.89	0.84
11				/	0.83	0.85	0.93	0.980	0.95	0.51	0.50	0.72	0.65
18					/	0.89	0.93	0.90	0.91	0.78	0.71	0.84	0.78
23						/	0.87	0.89	0.86	0.70	0.69	0.75	0.72
35							/	0.96	0.98	0.81	0.70	0.87	0.81
36								/	0.96	0.71	0.61	0.81	0.75
37									/	0.74	0.60	0.79	0.73
44										/	0.954	0.94	0.950
45											/	0.89	0.91
46												/	0.98
47													/

Members of a group are correlated with all other members of that group such that $|\rho| \geq 0.95$ for any pair of measurements. It is apparent that a high degree of overlap of groups exists. Thus measurements 1, 3, 9, 35, and 36 are common to groups I and II. Further analysis and interpretation are obviously hampered by this situation. E. C. Olson, in Olson and Miller (1958), has proposed a technique for use in $\rho\text{-}F$ analysis which is designed to reduce overlap to a minimum.

The assumption is made that a pair of morphological measurements which have an exceptionally high degree of association (high correlation coefficient) will indicate an exceptionally high intensity of biological relationship, or more specifically, morphological integration. One would then expect that measurements which cluster around such a pair would also be highly integrated. In this sense, the pair is a nucleus of a group or cluster. The "basic pair" is thus defined to be that pair of measurements with the reflexive property that each is more highly correlated with the other than to any of the remaining measurements in the matrix. If we refer to Table 13.2, measurements 1 and 35 which form a basic pair are all encircled. The steps in reduction of overlaps are:

1. *List all basic pairs.* In this study these are: (1)–(35), length of skull and facis-cranial angle; (11)–(36), diastema length (skull) and mandible length; (44)–(45), height of coronoid process and diameter of incisor I^2; (46)–(47), diameter of incisor I^2 and height of incisor I^2.

2. *Reject all groups which do not contain one or more basic pair.* We reject groups III and IV on this basis.

3. (*a*) A member common to several groups is assigned that group which has the highest basic pair link with the common member.

(*b*) Reject any member of a group which has a higher link with an element of a basic pair in some other group.

On this basis we reject 36 from group II since it has a higher link with (11) in group I than with either (1) or (35) in group II. We also reject 18 and 23 from group II since they have a higher link with an element of (11)-(36) in group I than with an element in (1)-(35) in group II. This leaves in group II the following elements; (1), 3, 8, 9, (35). Since these are all contained in group I, group II is discarded. After basic pair analysis the remaining groups are:

I. (1), 3, 8, 9 (11), (35), (36), (37)
V. (44), (45), (46), (47)

Experience has shown that a factor of over-all size is usually present in osteometric studies. We shall therefore introduce the next step in the $\rho\text{-}F$ procedure before discussing the final results. The degree of association

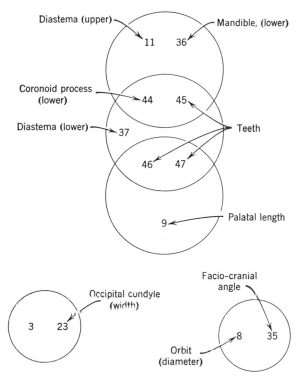

FIG. 13.9. Groups resulting after basic pair analysis with size effect removed.

between the pairs of measurements is recomputed as partial correlation coefficients by "holding constant" measurement 1 (basilar length), representing over-all skull length, and measurement 15 (frontal width), representing over-all skull width. The correlations of 15 with all other measurements, and the partial correlations $r_{xy:1,15}$, were kindly made available by E. C. Olson.

Table 13.3 gives the matrix of partial correlation coefficients. Basic pairs are encircled, and a blank entry means the partial correlation coefficient is not significantly greater than 0 at 0.10 level of significance.

The resulting groups after basic pair analysis in which the effect of size has been removed are shown in Fig. 13.9. Comparison of the matrix of Table 13.2 with that of Table 13.3 shows the drastic changes which occur when the effect of the over-all length and width measurements is removed. Although the choice of length measurements to "hold constant" in the partial correlation analysis is subjective, there is certainly an indication that an over-all size factor plays an important part in the intercorrelations of cranial measurements not only in the present animal but in many others

TABLE 13.3

Partial Correlation Matrix $r_{xy:1,15}$ Where No. 1 = Basilar Length, Essentially Skull Length, No. 15 = Frontal Width, Essentially Maximum Skull Width

	3	8	9	11	18	23	35	36	37	44	45	46	47
3				−0.64		−0.72		0.46	−0.39	0.49		0.44	
8					0.45								
9							0.52					0.40	0.45
11								0.82		−0.73	−0.64	−0.57	
18													
23													
35													
36										−0.55	−0.41	−0.61	−0.62
37										−0.48	−0.63	0.80	0.83
44											0.91		
45												0.78	0.79
46													0.94
47													

$n = 17$

No. of variables = 13

similarly studied, both invertebrate and vertebrate. The hypothesis which underlies a ρ-F analysis may now be stated and then applied to the present study.

The factors which underlie intercorrelated groups of osteometric measurements include (1) size, (2) functional, and (3) inherited, but not necessarily functional, factors which we shall call developmental factors. When the effect of size has been removed, the interpretation of an individual correlation and hence of a group is based on the following:

$$\rho = F\{\alpha \text{ Function} + \beta \text{ Development} + \gamma \text{ Residual}\}$$

We seek to interpret a group in terms of this function by evaluating the coefficients $\alpha\beta\gamma$, and hence the contribution of these factors, from *a priori* knowledge. Hence the term "ρ-F" where ρ is the population correlation coefficient and F indicates the equation above. The *a priori* knowledge is found in detailed studies of both bones and soft anatomy of modern animals, and of nearest living analogues of extinct animals.

Turning to the present study, we may isolate tentatively the following factors:

1. *Over-all size factor* (discussed earlier).

2. *Masticatory functional factor*. This is shown in figure where measurements of palatal length, diastema length on both upper and lower jaws, and mandible length are seen to form an array around a core composed of the three teeth measurements and the height of the coronoid process.

3. *Optic functional factor*. This isolated basic pair is composed of an orbital dimension and the facio-cranial angle. Because of the small number of variables in this group, clear cut assignment of a factor is not possible. To the writers the two measurements suggest the function of "seeing."

4. *Unassigned basic pair*. This is composed of the length of nasal bone and width of occipital condyle. In the ρ-F analysis a situation like this may be treated as follows: since no clear functional aspect is suggested by these two measurements, assignment to either development (nonfunctional but inherited characteristics) or residual, used when either function or development, does not offer satisfactory results. In any case, a total of fourteen measurements is by no means adequate for a full study of both skull and jaws.

Analyses of the type described above have been applied to a number of animal species invertebrate, fossil, and extant. (See E. C. Olson, 1953.)[1] A particularly promising aspect of this approach has been the detailed analysis of evolutionary series, in which factors isolated through ρ-F

[1] E. C. Olson, 1953, Integrating factors in amphibian skulls, *Jour. Geol.* 61: 557–568.

analysis are traced through time within and between populations. An index of total morphological integration I_ρ was developed for this purpose (Olson and Miller, 1958, *ibid.*). In studies of degree of association of morphological measurements it has been found that in some instances the proportions are highly correlated; e.g., the pentremite calyx. In other cases as in the skull of Sciurus niger, Olson and Miller (1958, *ibid.*), regions exhibit high intercorrelation, whereas other regions do not. In addition certain proportions are highly correlated with others in widely separated regions, regardless of topological affinity.

In order to compare regions within animals or total morphology between species a single unifying measurement of the morphological integration was devised. It is called the index of integration I_ρ

$$I_\rho \stackrel{\text{def.}}{=} \frac{4(B_{0;\rho})^2}{K_\rho(n^2 - n)^2}, \quad \text{when } B_{0;\rho} \geq 1$$

$$I_\rho = 0, \qquad\qquad \text{when } B_{0;\rho} = 0$$

where $B_{0;\rho}$ = the number of observed bonds, evaluated for a selected lower limit of ρ for the measurements under analysis. Thus $B_{0;0.95}$ is the number of bonds evaluated at the level $\rho \geq 0.95$ when all the measurements have been correlated in all possible ways with each other.

K_ρ = the number of noncontained[1] ρ groups evaluated for a selected level of ρ. The term bond is utilized to express the correlation between a pair of proportions. If the level of correlation is preset at $\rho \geq 0.95$, then any pair whose correlation satisfies this requirement is bonded; any pair whose correlation is less is not bonded. The term "bond" is thus synonomous with that of "link" as used in this chapter.

In summary the ρ-F approach has made some progress along two lines of paleontological interest.

1. Establishment of detailed and sensitive relations between morphology and development. These relations are suggestive of genotype-phenotype cause and effect in hard-part anatomy, which is what the paleontologist has to work with.

2. Treatment of the total animal and its changes through evolutionary time sequence.

CLUSTER ANALYSIS OF *EQUIS HEMONIUS HEMONIUS* BY THE CORRELATION PROFILE METHOD

The first step in the profile method is to construct profiles of the various measurements formed by plotting the correlation coefficients for any single

[1] A noncontained ρ group is a group of measures bonded in all possible ways, and which is not contained in a larger ρ group.

measurement with all others, and compare the resulting profile with profiles found in a similar way for all the *other measurements*.

The "method of significant differences" has been devised by the writers for preliminary formation of profile clusters. It starts with replacing all r entries in the matrix of Table 13.2 by Z entries, Table 13.4, where Z is the following transformation: $Z = \frac{1}{2} \ln (1 + r)/(1 - r)$. These values are readily found in Fisher and Yates, or R. A. Fisher (1946), p. 210[1]. The statistic[2] $\dfrac{Z_1 - Z_2}{\sqrt{(1/N_1 - 3) + (1/N_2 - 3)}}$ may be used as a standard normal deviate, where $N_1 = $ sample size for sample 1 and $N_2 = $ sample size for sample 2, Z_1, is the transformation of r_1, and Z_2 is the transformation of r_2.

Since the matrix of correlation coefficients in our context is based on a fixed sample size N, we set up a single criterion which will allow a rapid scanning of Z matrix for significant rises and falls between Z's. Then,

$$Pr\{(Z_1 - Z_2)\sqrt{(N - 3)/2} < c\} = 0.95,$$

e.g., from consideration of the statistic above, and referring to the normal tables $C \cong 1.95$. Then

$$Pr\left\{(Z_1 - Z_2) > \frac{1.95}{\sqrt{(N - 3)/2}}\right\} = 0.95$$

In this study, $N = 17$, therefore

$$Pr\{(Z_1 - Z_2) < 0.628\} = 0.95$$

The method of significant differences removes much of the subjectivity in the search for congruent profiles. Several profiles of correlation coefficients may be considered incongruent on the basis of nonsignificant and therefore meaningless rises and falls. This serious difficulty is avoided by using the significant difference criterion dependent on sample size in the comparison of Z, rather than r, profiles.

The matrix of Z entries in Table 13.4 is scanned by comparing two rows at a time until all permutations are completed. For example, row 1 and row 2 in Table 13.3 are examined for significant difference between each vertical pair. There are significant Z differences for column 35 and column 37 (using the criterion ≥ 0.60 for quick scanning). We then may say that the profiles for variables 1 and 3 *differ significantly* for variables 35 and 37 only in the complete array. The resulting preliminary profile clusters are

[1] R. A. Fisher, 1946, *Statistical methods for research workers*, Stechert & Co., New York.

[2] C. R. Rao, 1952, *Advanced statistical methods in biometric research*, John Wiley, New York.

TABLE 13.4

$Z_{xy}(Z$ Transformation of Table 13.2) for $P_r\{(Z_1 - Z_2) \leq 0.628\} = 0.10$.

	1	3	8	9	11	18	23	35	36	37	44	45	46	47
1	/	2.25	1.95	2.61	1.74	1.66	1.38	3.00	2.04	2.44	1.10	0.87	1.29	1.13
3	2.25	/	1.74	2.10	1.38	1.48	1.10	2.36	1.53	1.84	1.26	0.95	1.43	1.16
8	1.95	1.74	/	1.95	1.38	1.73	1.30	2.60	1.66	1.66	1.08	0.83	1.26	1.10
9	2.61	2.10	1.95	/	1.59	1.59	1.38	2.66	1.95	2.10	1.13	0.89	1.42	1.22
11	1.74	1.38	1.38	1.59	/	1.19	1.26	1.66	2.30	1.84	0.71	0.55	0.91	0.77
18	1.66	1.48	1.73	1.59	1.19	/	1.42	1.66	1.48	1.53	1.05	0.89	1.22	1.05
23	1.38	1.10	1.30	1.38	1.26	1.42	/	1.33	1.42	1.30	0.87	0.85	0.98	0.91
35	3.00	2.36	2.60	2.66	1.66	1.66	1.33	/	1.95	2.30	1.13	0.87	1.33	1.13
36	2.04	1.53	1.66	1.95	2.30	1.48	1.42	1.95	/	1.95	0.89	0.71	1.13	0.97
37	2.44	1.84	1.66	2.10	1.84	1.53	1.30	2.30	1.95	/	0.95	0.70	1.07	0.93
44	1.10	1.26	1.08	1.13	0.71	1.05	0.87	1.13	0.89	0.95	/	1.87	1.74	1.82
45	0.87	0.95	0.83	0.89	0.55	0.89	0.85	0.87	0.71	0.70	1.87	/	1.42	1.53
46	1.29	1.43	1.26	1.42	0.91	1.22	0.98	1.33	1.13	1.07	1.74	1.42	/	2.30
47	1.13	1.16	1.10	1.22	0.77	1.05	0.91	1.13	0.97	0.93	1.82	1.53	2.30	/

shown below. The arbitrary criterion of 2 or less disagreements (significant differences between Z) is used. Thus

Preliminary Cluster Using Significant Difference of Z's	Members
I	1–3–8–9–36–37
II	1–3–35–37
III	3–8–11–18–23
IV	3–8–11–18–36–37
V	23–46
VI	44–45–46–47

Since there are a large number of overlaps, the next step is to plot the profiles and assign members common to several clusters to a single cluster on the basis of congruence of profiles. Fig. 13.8 shows the final assignment to profile groups in which overlaps are eliminated by graphic comparisons. The profile groups are:

$$1–3–8–9–36–37$$
$$11–18–23$$
$$35$$
$$44–45–46–47$$

To be consistent with the previous development of the ρ-F type of cluster analysis, we shall transform the $r_{xy;1,15}$ (partial correlation coefficients with effect of skull length and width removed) to Z's.

This is done as before by referring to the tables for transformation of r to Z. Since we are dealing with partial correlation coefficients, the sample size n is reduced by 2, the number of variables whose effect is removed. Thus $P\{(Z_1 - Z_2) > 1.95/\sqrt{(n - 2 - 3)/2}\} = 0.95$, and the right side of the inequality becomes 0.796.

Scanning the Z matrix of Table 13.5, the following groups are found, which are substantiated by subsequent plotting (Fig. 13.2).

Preliminary Clusters Using Significant Difference of Z's	Members
I	8–9–18–23–35
II	11–23–36–37
III	44–45–46–47

Interpretation of the correlation profile clusters or groups requires some sort of "in context" rationale. In this study various measures of the skull and jaws are used. They are all expected to interact with each other to some degree. That is, most of the measurements are functionally required to vary within restricted limits in order that the animal survive. Examination of

TABLE 13.5

$Z_{xy:1,15}$ (Z Transformation of Table 13.3) for $P\{Z_1 - Z_2 > 0.796\} = 0.90$

	3	8	9	11	18	23	35	36	37	44	45	46	47
3	/			−0.76		−0.91		0.50	−0.41	0.54		0.48	
8		/			0.49		0.58					0.43	
9			/									0.43	0.49
11	−0.76			/				1.16		−0.93	−0.76	−0.65	
18		0.49			/		0.59						
23	−0.91					/							
35		0.58			0.59		/						
36	0.50			1.16				/		−0.62	−0.44		
37	−0.41								/	−0.53	−0.74	−0.71	−0.73
44	0.54			−0.93				−0.62	0.53	/	1.53	1.10	1.19
45				−0.76				−0.44	−0.74	1.53	/	1.05	1.07
46	0.48	0.43	0.43	−0.65					−0.71	1.10	1.05	/	1.74
47			0.49						−0.73	1.19	1.07	1.74	/

the group including 44, 45, 46, 47 indicates that they all *react* as a unit with other measurements although they need not be highly correlated with each other. We may thus tentatively regard a profile group as evidence of *joint reaction* with all other measurements, whereas the ρ-F type of group is evidence of interaction of its members.

We may now combine the two types of cluster analysis by seeking a type of group with a high degree of correlation among its members, which is also a correlation profile group reacting as a unit with the other measurements. Such a dual group is illustrated in this study by the *Masticatory group* including measures 44, 45, 46, 47. Not only do they form a highly intercorrelated cluster but also a correlation profile cluster.

It seems to the writers that further investigation along the lines just described may prove quite fruitful in further sharpening and isolating factors in osteometric analysis as well as in other disciplines where factor analysis is used.

A paper of general interest in the context of this section is Björn, Kurtén, 1953, On the variation and population dynamics of fossil and recent mammal populations, *Acta Zool. Fennica* 76: 1–122. It includes a general discussion of correlation analysis, calculation of correlation coefficients in mammalian dentition, and a comparison with models based on genetic considerations. It discusses "correlation fields"—essentially a graphic summation of the correlation matrix of morphological characteristics done by contouring the correlation matrix. The form of the correlation field appears to depend on the way the characteristics are ordered in the margins of the matrix, the ordering being based on zoological criteria (e.g., anatomical proximity). It is suggested that these graphic summations of the correlation matrix are related to Butler's (1937)[1] morphogenetic fields, and to Huxley's (1932)[2] growth fields and growth gradients, at least in principle.

THE "SHOTGUN" METHOD

An Analysis of the Interaction of Quantitative Variables in the Absence of Specific Hypotheses or Strong *a priori* Expectation[3]

Use of modern analogues in the study of ancient environments or geological processes is a logical and desirable practice. Often, however, misgivings arise as to the extent of error in the analogue. If one is

---

[1] P. M. Butler, 1937, Studies of the mammalian dentition, I. The teeth of Centetes ecaudatus and its allies, *Proc. Zool. Soc. London*, Ser. B. pp. 107ff.

[2] J. Huxley, 1932, *Problems of relative growth*, Methuen and Co., London.

[3] The following section is based on a paper given at the symposium on Statistics in Geology, Los Angeles G.S.A. meetings, 1954, and R. L. Miller, 1954, An Analysis of the interaction of quantitative variables in a modern environment of sedimentation, *Bull. G.S.A.*, 65: 12, part 2; 1285.

willing to assume a meaningful uniformitarianism in the particular problem, the misgivings tend to focus, at least in part, on the complexity of the situation and the great number of variables involved but not controlled. In particular, the unrestricted use of any single measurable variable is sometimes suspect in terms of its possible interaction with a large number of other measurable variables when causal relations are sought.

The Problem

The general problem we shall discuss is that of investigation of the interaction of large numbers of variables. The basis will be a study done on 19 variables in a contemporary marine environment including both biological and physical measurements.

In particular, an attempt was made to assess dependence-independence relationships between the variables. The term "shotgun" is suggested because no formal design is used for the statistical analysis; on the contrary, the procedure of setting up a hypothesis and subsequently designing a series of statistical tests for various alternatives is deliberately avoided. In place of this is used the philosophy that we should consider all possible

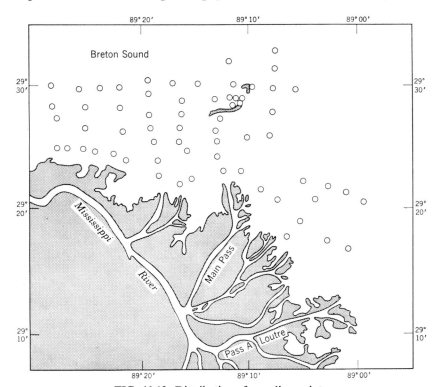

FIG. 13.10. Distribution of sampling points.

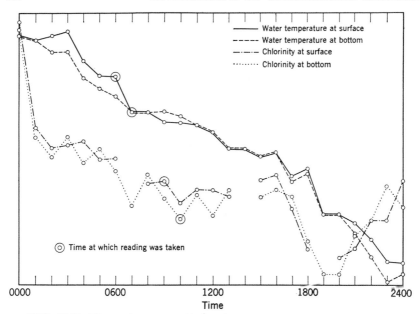

FIG. 13.11. Fluctuations at one station for several variables, 24-hour period.

Intercorrelations, and ignore *a priori* knowledge so as to not to "bias" the study, making interpretations only after the analysis is completed.

In following this procedure, certain major difficulties became immediately apparent in the problem at hand.

1. *Time-dependent fluctuations and trends.* The data collected at each sample point Fig. 13.10 were not taken at a given instant. Variable *A* at a given sample point may have been recorded several hours after variable *B* from the same sample point. Thus, the variation peculiar to a given variable during a single diurnal as well as a tidal cycle is introduced but not accounted for. Figure 13.11 indicates the situation. Variation in water temperature and chlorinity for a 24-hour period at one station is shown by the four time series. Suppose that the sampling at this station began at 0600 hours for water temperature at the surface, and bottom chlorinity was taken at 1000 hours. The circles show the relation between time and the value of the variables when the samples were recorded. In addition to the variation introduced in this way, the sampling stations were in themselves sampled on different days, so that seasonal fluctuations were also introduced.

2. *Form of the frequency distributions.* A blanket assumption of normality in this study seems to be specifically prohibited. It is true that transformations have a tendency to introduce symmetry, at least to several

TABLE 13.6

I Physical Factors

1. Water temperature (surface)
2. Water temperature (bottom)
3. Depth
4. Air temperature

5. Transparency
6. Current strength surface
7. Current strength bottom

II Chemical Factors

1. Chlorinity of surface water
2. Chlorinity of bottom water
3. pH at top of short core in the sediment

4. pH at bottom of the core

III Biological Factors

1. Foraminifera. Number of species
2. Foraminifera. Number of individuals
3. Macro-invertebrates. Number of species

4. Macro-invertebrates. Number of individuals

IV Sediment Size Parameters

1. Md_ϕ = median size of sediment particles in ϕ units.
2. σ_ϕ = standard deviation of the sediment particle frequency distribution.

3. α_ϕ = degree of asymmetry of the sediment particle frequency distribution.

of the variables, but in others, polymodality is an inherent characteristic. Furthermore, in the population sense, the frequency distribution for many variables is not known.

3. Specific tests for independence or degree of dependence are in the probability sense, not in the causal sense, i.e., in the absence of strong *a priori* knowledge, correlation is not evidence of causation. In fact, the tests which will be applied in the strict sense measure only degree of correlation or lack of correlation. As Cramer (1946) states: "Two uncorrelated variables are not necessarily independent."[1]

Items 1 and 3 above will be referred to again in the conclusion. Item 2 is taken up in the following section on statistical analysis.

The Data

The data consist of 18 numerically measured variables collected in the spring and fall of 1953 at each of a number of stations in the near shore area just east of the Louisiana Delta. The number of measurements range from 54 for certain of the variables to 28 for others. The data were made available by the American Petroleum Institute, A.P.I. Project #51,

[1] H. Cramer, 1946, *Mathematical methods of statistics*, Princeton University Press, Princeton, New Jersey, pp. 278–279.

F. P. Shepard, Director, Scripps Institution of Oceanography. This section is to be regarded as a general discussion in the context of this book, that is, statistical methodology in geology. Responsibility in what follows is entirely that of the authors.

Table 13.6 lists the variables used in the study. Figure 13.10 shows the location of the sample points from which the data were collected.

The Statistical Analysis

The statistical approach involves computing estimates of population correlation coefficients from sample sizes ranging from 28 to 54 for each of the 18 variables. The 18 variables are to be correlated with each other in all possible ways. Then examination is made of the resulting correlation matrix for (1) groups of highly intercorrelated variables, and (2) patterns of independence among the variables (correlations not significantly different from zero).

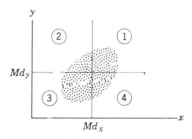

FIG. 13.12. Scatter diagram divided into quadrants.

It is felt that assumption of normality is not justified for most of the variables. Therefore, the various nonparametric measurements of degree of associa-tion are investigated. For sample, sizes ranging from 25 to 60 ranking methods (see discussion of the rank correlation Chapter 14) offer considerable labor. Therefore, the Blomqvist (1950)[1] form of the tetrachoic test was chosen. The "tetrachoic" or "four-corner" test for association is easy to apply and is based on examination of scatter diagrams. The basic reasoning is quite direct. If a bivariate scattergram for x, y is divided into four quadrants by the lines $x = $ median x and $y = $ median y, the expectation under the null hypothesis of independence or no association would be an equal distribution of points in the four quadrants.

There are several methods for evaluating degree of departure from equal distribution of points in the probability sense. See, for example, the description of the method in Dixon and Massey (1951)[2]; Mosteller (1946)[3] for more complete curves and a full discussion; and Olmstead and Tukey (1947)[4] for further discussion.

[1] N. Blomqvist, 1950, On a measure of dependence between two random variables, *Annals Math. Stats.* 21: 4; 593–600.

[2] W. J. Dixon, and F. J. Massey, 1951, *Introduction to statistical analysis*, McGraw-Hill, New York.

[3] F. Mosteller, 1946, On some useful inefficient statistics, *Annals Math. Stats.* 17: 377ff.

[4] P. S. Olmstead and J. W. Tukey, 1947, A corner test for association, *Annals Math. Stats.* 18: 495–513.

Blomqvist's methods are preferred because they appear to be better suited for small samples. A description of the specific tests follows:

I. *Test for independence* (*in the probability sense*)

Step 1. Compute n_1 which is the total number of points in quadrants 1 and 3 using the convention of Fig. 13.12. Compute also $2K$ which is the largest even number in the sample size.

Step 2. Blomquist has probability values tabled for sample sizes 4 to 50. For larger sample sizes a normal approximation is given. We enter the table with the statement $P\{|n_1 - k| \geq v\}$ = value in the body of the table, where the abscissa is $2K$, the largest even number in the sample size and the ordinate is v, the observed difference between n_1 and K. Thus the probability that n_1 could deviate from K by as much or more than v is given in the table. For example, under the null hypothesis of independence, consider the following example: there are 41 points in the sample; quadrants 1 and 3 contain 18 and quadrants 2 and 4 contain 23. Then $n_1 = 18$ and $2K = 40$. We have from the tables $P\{|18\text{–}20| \geq 2\} = 0.752$. In words, the probability that $n_1 = 18$ could deviate from $K = 20$ by as much or more than 2 is 0.752, if x and y are "independent" in the population. We conclude that x and y are, independent.

II. *Estimation of the population correlation coefficient*

We test the hypothesis that $|q| = |q_0|$ against the alternatives that $|q|$ is lower; and reject the hypothesis that $|q| = |q_0|$ when $|q'| < C$, where

$|q|$ = estimate of correlation in absolute terms

$|q_0|$ = desired level of correlation

$|q'|$ = sample correlation value

$= \dfrac{n_1 - n_2}{n_1 + n_2}$ $\begin{cases} \text{where as before, } n_1 = \text{number of points in quadrants} \\ 1, 3, \text{ and } n_2 = \text{number of points in quadrants 2, 4.} \end{cases}$

The following gives the development of confidence intervals, and was kindly suggested by W. C. Kruskal, University of Chicago, Department of Statistics. Set $P_{|q_0|}\{-c \leq q' \leq c\} = \alpha$ where α is level of confidence; then

$$P_{|q_0|}\{-c \leq q' \leq c\} = P_{|q_0|}\left(\frac{-c - |q_0|}{\sqrt{\dfrac{1 - q_0^2}{n}}} \leq \frac{q' - |q_0|}{\sqrt{\dfrac{1 - q_0^2}{n}}} \leq \frac{c - |q_0|}{\sqrt{\dfrac{1 - q_0^2}{n}}} \right)$$

$$\approx \Phi\left(\frac{c - |q_0|}{\sqrt{\dfrac{1 - q_0^2}{n}}} \right) - \Phi\left(\frac{-c - |q_0|}{\sqrt{\dfrac{1 - q_0^2}{n}}} \right)$$

where $\Phi(\ )$ represents the unit-normal cumulative form. See Chapter 4.

To solve for c, set the approximation above equal to α. The second term is ordinarily negligible and may be neglected.

Then
$$\Phi\left(\frac{c - |q_0|}{\sqrt{\dfrac{1 - |q_0|^2}{n}}}\right) = \alpha$$

and
$$\frac{c - |q_0|}{\sqrt{\dfrac{1 - |q_0|^2}{n}}} = \Phi^{-1}(\alpha)$$

where Φ^{-1} is the inverse function. Finally

$$c = -\sqrt{\frac{1 - |q_0|^2}{n}}\,\Phi^{-1}(\alpha) + |q_0|$$

For example, set the desired correlation level $|q|$ at 0.8 and α at 0.05. Then for sample size of 25 what is c?

$$c = \left(-\sqrt{\frac{1 - 0.64}{25}}\right)1.645 + 0.8 = 0.6026$$

and we reject $|q| = |0.8|$ when $|q'| < 0.6026$ for sample size of 25.

The Results

Figure 13.13 represents the correlation matrix. A zero is entered if the tests show statistical independence (zero correlation). Two levels of dependence are used.

The first is high dependence (correlation in which the criterion is set at $|\rho| \geq 0.70$ for α of 0.003. This is denoted by H in Fig. 13.13. The second is weak or low dependence set at $0 < |\rho| < 0.70$ and denoted by an L. Figures 13.14, 13.15 show the results arranged in an arbitrary fashion. One could choose other ways of displaying the results; however in any case, something similar to Fig. 13.13 would form the basis in our present context.

Examination of Fig. 13.14 and Fig. 13.15 show many interesting relationships. Certain measurements appear as highly interdependent. Some associations are expected, others are unexpected. There is also to be noted a rather striking number of independent variables where one might expect at least weak association. The various results will not be interpreted specifically since this is not within the scope of this book.

DISCUSSION

The "shotgun" method as illustrated in the foregoing offers a mechanically simple device for the reduction of a large mass of data. The

	ϕ_α	ϕ_D	Md_ϕ	Macro. No.	Macro. Species	Foraminifera Number	Foraminifera Species	pH Bottom	pH Top	Chlorinity (Bottom)	Chlorinity (Surface)	Current Strength (Bottom)	Current Strength (Surface)	Transparency	Air Temp.	Depth	Water Temp. (Bottom)	Water Temp. (Surface)
Water temp. (surface)	O	O	O	O	O	O	O	O	O	H	L	O	O	L	H	L	H	
Water temp. (bottom)	O	O	O	O	O	O	O	O	O	H	O	O	O	L	L	H		
Depth	O	O	O	O	O	O	O	O	O	H	O	O	O	O	H			
Air temp.	L	O	O	O	O	O	O	O	O	H	O	O	O	L				
Transparency	O	O	O	O	O	O	O	O	O	L	L	L	O					
Current strength (surface)	O	O	O	O	O	O	O	O	O	L	O	O						
Current strength (bottom)	O	O	O	H	O	O	O	O	O	O	H							
Chlorinity (surface)	O	O	H	O	H	O	O	O	O	O								
Chlorinity (bottom)	O	O	O	O	O	O	O	O	O									
pH Top	O	H	H	O	L	O	O	L										
pH Bottom	H	H	H	L	H	O	H											
Foraminifera species	H	O	O	O	O	O												
Foraminifera number	O	O	O	O	O													
Macro. species	O	L	H	H														
Macro. no.	O	O	O															
Md_ϕ	O	H																
σ_ϕ	O																	
α_ϕ																		

FIG. 13.13. Intercorrelations of the 18 variables, O means independence, H means high association, $|\rho| \geq 0.70$, and L means low association, $0 < |\rho| < 0.70$

Biological Measures versus Physical Factors

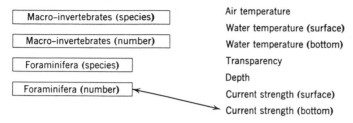

Sediment Size Measures versus Chemical and Physical Factors ·

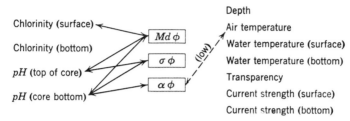

Biological Measures versus Chemical Factors and Sediment Size Measures

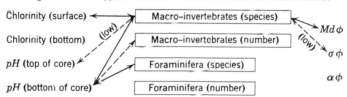

FIG. 13.14. Dependence-independence interrelationships.

number of variables may be quite large under this approach, particularly if high speed computer facilities are available. (In such a case methods more suitable for programming than the Berquist method are available.) The intercorrelation matrix is only one of many possible ways to reduce the data.

In the writers' opinion the pros and cons of the "shotgun" method are as follows. It is possible to deduce "factors" in a preliminary fashion by looking at the resulting groups of inter-correlated variables, such as shown in Figs. 13.14 and 13.15. Relationships may be hinted at which are unexpected,

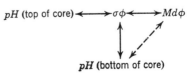

FIG. 13.15. High linear dependence ($\longrightarrow = \rho \geq 0.90$, risk of 0.003) ($- - - = \rho \geq 0.70$)

and possible explanations for these suggested, i.e., by the presence of other variables linked to only some members of a group.

However, care should be taken not to read more into a study of this kind than is justified. At best it should be used as a first approximation, and as a guide to further statistical investigation. Where strong *a priori* knowledge and expectation are present (for example, on the physical mechanisms which lead to an expectation of high or low intercorrelation), interpretation of the correlation matrix without further tests is we feel on the firmest ground. See pp. 309–310.

In this example *a priori* knowledge and expectation of interaction are spotty (both physical and biological variables are considered), and time-dependent fluctuations and trends affect the samples. Accordingly, suggested relationships should be used to form hypothesis, followed by statistical tests of these hypotheses, before any conclusions are drawn.

chapter 14

One-Dimensional Trends (Excluding Time-Series)

In this chapter one-dimensional trends are considered. We shall define this term, and discuss tests for its presence or absence. That is, ordered sequences of numbers will be examined in various ways to ascertain whether the order of elements in a sequence is about what one would expect from a random permutation. If the hypothesis of random ordering is rejected (on a probability basis), we conclude that a "trend" is present. Ordered sequences are thus classified as random, or as exhibiting a trend.

A trend is defined as any type of regularity in an ordered sequence of numbers or elements. Any ordered sequence of numbers or elements other than random shall be designated as a trend.

In particular, random fluctuations around a horizontal line such as the median line are considered not to exhibit a trend. Conversely, random fluctuations around a nonhorizontal straight line, or higher order curve, imply trend in the sequence in the sense of the line or curve. The above refers to the underlying probability mechanism, inferred from the observed (sample) sequence and *a priori* information.

The tests described and illustrated in this chapter fall into three categories.

1. In the first category we consider a count of either "turning points" or "runs up and down" in the sequence, and base the tests on the number of turning points or runs up or down, relative to the number of individual elements in the sequence. Figure 14.1 illustrates these two terms. Shown is an ordered sequence of numbers with a number of rises and falls. "Turning points" are shown at t_i and t_j, and could thus be described as peaks and troughs. Turning points may be defined as points immediately preceded and followed by points which are both higher or both lower. A "run up" is shown at r_1 and a "run down" is shown at r_2. Thus a run up

325

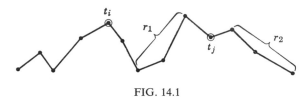

FIG. 14.1

is a sequence of ordered points, each of which is greater than the preceding one, and a run down is a sequence of ordered points, each of which is less than the preceding one.

2. The second category of tests primarily involves a dichotomizing process. For example, one may rewrite a sequence of numbers as a sequence of + and − elements, depending on whether the individual value fell above or below the median value. The tests hold for any dichotomizing process, and criteria other than the median may be used. The result is a sequence consisting of two classes of elements indistinguishable within the classes. The following illustrates such a sequence: $++-++-----$ $+-+$. The properties of such a sequence which will be useful in the following discussion include the total number of elements in the sequence, the number of elements in each of the two categories, and the number of "runs." *A run is here defined as a sequence of one or more like elements, preceded and followed by different elements.* In Fig. 14.1, there are 12 elements, 6 of which are + and 6 −, and there are 7 runs.

The dichotomizing procedure is used where it is necessary and geologically meaningful to transform a sequence of numbers or observations into two classes of indistinguishable objects. However, a great number of situations also exist where the dichotomy is naturally present and does not need to be introduced by a device such as the median. An example of such a sequence is to be found in the color of a series of finely laminated shales. We may assign the term light or dark (e.g., depending on the amount of carbonaceous matter present) and ask whether the observed sequence $LDLDDLLDLLLLD$ of light and dark laminae up the section exhibits a regularity or trend or, on the other hand, whether the sequence consists of a random arrangement of L's and D's.

Finally, we shall test for random order in sequences containing more than two classes of indistinguishable objects. The example given in a later part of this chapter involves a natural trichotomy consisting of three distinct lithologic types.

3. The third category consists of an application of Spearman's rank correlation method. In this case we test for random order, but have a specific alternative in mind. In particular, we test directly for a specific type of trend, that of linear increase or decrease. In addition to reference

as to source or more complete description of individual tests, references to other tests will be made in appropriate places.

An alternative measure of ordinal association to Spearman's ρ is Kendall's τ. Spearman's ρ and Kendall's τ do not measure precisely the same population quantities, but either one would be useful in the present context. For a discussion of the relative merits of ρ versus τ see Kruskal (1958).[1] Spearman's ρ is described in Spearman (1904)[2] and Kendall's τ in Kendall (1938).[3] General discussions and history of ordinal measures of association are given in Kruskal, *ibid.* See also Kendall (1955).[4]

DESCRIPTION AND DISCUSSION OF THE TESTS

The following discussion presents a fundamental theorem for the distribution of runs, the reasoning which underlies it, and a proof of the theorem. Before entering into this discussion we shall consider the term "run." Consider a sequence of two different kinds of elements such as $+$ and $-$, arranged in the order in which they appear: $+ + - - + - + + + + - +$. The term run was defined earlier as a succession of one or more like elements. Thus in the sequence just given there are 7 runs, including 4 runs of $+$ and 3 runs of $-$. We seek a probability distribution of the number of runs (u) for a given number of elements and given proportions of $+$ to $-$ signs in the sequence. In the sequence just given, there are $n_1 = 8(+)$ elements and $n_2 = 4(-)$ elements, a total of 12 elements. The probability distribution $P(u)$ will tell us the probability that 7 runs could have come from a random arrangement of 12 elements consisting of $8 +$ and $4 -$ entries. If the probability is high, this means that the number of ways of getting 7 runs from 12 plus and minus signs is high relative to the total number of ways of arranging 12 plus and minus signs. If the number of runs is exceptionally low, we propose to reject the hypothesis of random fluctuations of $+$ and $-$ elements. If, on the other hand, the number of runs is *exceptionally* high, we also reject the hypothesis of randomness.

THEOREM 14.1.[5] *Consider the various permutations of n_1 observations of one*

[1] W. H. Kruskal, 1958, Ordinal measures of association, *Jour. Am. Stat. Assoc.* 53: 814–861.

[2] C. Spearman, 1904, The proof and measurement of association between two things, *Am. Jour. Psych.* 5: 72–101.

[3] M. G. Kendall, 1938, A new measure of rank correlation, *Biometrika* 30: 81–93.

[4] M. G. Kendall, 1955, *Rank correlation methods*, Chas. Griffin, London, and Hafner, New York, 2nd ed.

[5] The statement of the theorem and the derivation is based on discussions in Hoel, 1947, pp. 180, 181, and Feller, 1950, pp. 52, 53, and 56–58. P. G. Hoel, 1947, *Introduction to mathematical statistics*, John Wiley, New York. W. Feller, 1950, *An introduction to probability theory and its applications*, Vol. 1. John Wiley, New York.

kind and n_2 observations of a second kind, where all the permutations are equally likely. Let $P(u)$ be the probability that such an arrangement contains exactly u runs. Then for u even-valued,

$$P(u) = 2 \frac{(n_1 - 1)! \, (n_2 - 1)! \, n_1! \, n_2!}{\left(\dfrac{u}{2} - 1\right)! \, \left(\dfrac{u}{2} - 1\right)! \, \left(n_1 - \dfrac{u}{2}\right)! \, \left(n_2 - \dfrac{u}{2}\right)! \, N!} \qquad (14.1)$$

where, $n_1 + n_2 = N$

and for u odd,

$$P(u) = \frac{(n_1 - 1)! \, (n_2 - 1)! \, n_1! \, n_2!}{\left(\dfrac{u - 1}{2}\right)! \, \left(\dfrac{u - 3}{2}\right)! \, N!}$$

$$\times \left[\frac{1}{\left(n_1 - \dfrac{u + 1}{2}\right)! \, \left(n_2 - \dfrac{u - 1}{2}\right)!} + \frac{1}{\left(n_1 - \dfrac{u - 1}{2}\right)! \, \left(n_2 - \dfrac{u + 1}{2}\right)!} \right]$$

$$(14.2)$$

Derivation

The derivation involves a counting procedure. That is, we must, for a sequence of N elements count the number of ways of arranging $n_1(+)$ elements and $n_2(-)$ elements into u runs, and compare it with the total number of ways of arranging the $+$ and $-$ elements. By virtue of our dichotomizing process (such as using the median to assign a $(+)$ or $(-)$ to the individual elements) we will have either u runs (u even) or $u + 1$ runs. We shall derive the case, u even.

If u is even, the number of runs of $(+)$ will be equal to the number of runs of $(-)$. If u is the number of runs, there will be $u/2$ runs of $(+)$ and $u/2$ runs of $(-)$. We shall count the number of ways of arranging n_1 ($+$'s) into $u/2$ runs. For convenience, think of the runs as compartments, and observe the bars or partitions which form the compartments. For example, $/+++/++/+/$. Note that (1) the first and last partitions are fixed in position and need not be counted; since $u/2 + 1$ partitions are needed to form the $u/2$ compartments, we are thus concerned only with $(u/2 + 1) - 2$ or $u/2 - 1$ partitions.

(2) The number of partitions between the $n_1(+)$ elements is $n_1 - 1$. We now ask how many ways are there of distributing $u/2 - 1$ partitions among the $n_1 - 1$ places. ($n_1 \geq u/2$, i.e., no more than one partition to a space, since we do not consider empty compartments.) The required number of ways is expressed by the combinatorial formula $\displaystyle \binom{n_1 - 1}{(u/2) - 1}$.

A similar procedure for the $(-)$ elements results in the combinatorial formula $\binom{n_2 - 1}{(u/2) - 1}$. We now proceed to put together the results of the counting in order to complete the numerator of $P(u)$.

For each of the ways of arranging the $(+)$ elements, there are $\binom{n_2 - 1}{(u/2) - 1}$ ways of arranging the $-$ elements. To count the total ways including both $(+)$ and $(-)$ elements, we have $\binom{n_1 - 1}{(u/2) - 1}\binom{n_2 - 1}{(u/2) - 1}$.

Finally the runs must alternate, so that either sign may be the first run. This doubles the total count. The completed result for the numerator is
$$2\binom{n_1 - 1}{(u/2) - 1}\binom{n_2 - 1}{(u/2) - 1}.$$

The equation for $P(u)$ may now be stated in words as the ratio of the number of ways of arranging n_1 of one kind of indistinguishable objects and n_2 of a second kind into u runs to the total number of ways of arranging the two kinds of objects. The second member of the ratio is counted by considering the number of ways in which n_1 things may be selected from $(n_1 + n_2) = N$ things which is the combinatorial formula $\binom{N}{n_1}$.

Our ratio may be written in the form[1]

$$P(u) = \frac{2\binom{n_1 - 1}{(u/2) - 1}\binom{n_2 - 1}{(u/2) - 1}}{\binom{N}{n_1}}$$

$$= 2\left[\frac{(n_1 - 1)!}{\left(\frac{u}{2} - 1\right)!\left(n_1 - \frac{u}{2} - 1 + 1\right)!} \cdot \frac{(n_2 - 1)!}{\left(\frac{u}{2} - 1\right)!\left(n_2 - \frac{u}{2} - 1 + 1\right)!}\right.$$

$$\left. \cdot \frac{n_1! \, n_2!}{N!}\right]$$

$$= \frac{2(n_1 - 1)! \, (n_2 - 1)! \, n_1! \, n_2!}{\left(\frac{u}{2} - 1\right)!\left(\frac{u}{2} - 1\right)!\left(n_1 - \frac{u}{2}\right)!\left(n_2 - \frac{u}{2}\right)! \, N!}$$

which is the form given in Theorem 14.1, eq. 14.1.
The derivation for u odd proceeds in the same manner.

[1] See also S. S. Wilks, 1943, *Mathematical statistics*, Princeton Univ. Press, Princeton, New Jersey, Chapter 10.

The Normal Approximation to the Probability Distribution Function $P(u)$ for a Sequence of Elements Consisting of n_1 of One Kind and n_2 of a Second Kind

Computation of values of $P(u)$ becomes laborious if n_1 and n_2 are not small. This is partly because of the factorial entries. The distribution of $P(u)$ approaches normality as the size of the sequence $N = (n_1 + n_2)$ approaches infinity. For practical purposes the normal approximation may be used for n_1 and n_2 both greater than 10. We then have

$$E(u) = \frac{2n_1n_2}{n_1 + n_2} + 1 \quad \text{and} \quad V(u) = \frac{2n_1n_2(2n_1n_2 - n_1 - n_2)}{(n_1 + n_2)^2(n_1 + n_2 - 1)}$$

$$P(u) \approx N\left[\frac{2n_1n_2}{n_1 + n_2} + 1, \frac{2n_1n_2(2n_1n_2 - n_1 - n_2)}{(n_1 + n_2)^2(n_1 + n_2 - 1)}\right] \tag{14.3}$$

For expository purposes we shall derive[1] $E(u)$. Consider the following sequence: $-+-++$. The spaces between runs are referred to as transition points. In this sequence there are 4 runs, 4 spaces between elements, and 3 transition points as on p. 328. $E(p_i)$ is the probability that the ith space is a transition point. To evaluate $E(p_i)$ a counting procedure is used. The probability that the third element in a sequence of 5 elements, with 3 $(+)$ and 2 $(-)$ elements is a $(+)$, is 3/5, and that the fourth element is a $(-)$, given the third element is a $(+)$, is 2/4 since one of the 5 places is already filled. On the other hand, the probability that the third element is a $(-)$ is 2/5, and the fourth element a $(+)$ is 3/4. Since the elements in random permutations are independent, the joint probability [third element $(+)$ *and* fourth element $(-)$] is equal to 3/5 × 2/4. We add this to the alternative joint probability [third element $(-)$ *and* fourth element $(+)$], which is 2/5 × 3/4. Thus $E(p_i)$ in our numerical example is 3/5 × 2/4 + 2/5 × 3/4.

This example will now be generalized. Suppose there are $n_1 + $'s and $n_2 - $'s in the sequence. Then

$$E(p_i) = \frac{n_1}{n_1 + n_2} \cdot \frac{n_2}{n_1 + n_2 - 1} + \frac{n_2}{n_1 + n_2} \cdot \frac{n_1}{n_1 + n_2 - 1}$$

or

$$E(p_i) = \frac{2n_1n_2}{(n_1 + n_2)(n_1 + n_2 - 1)}$$

The expected value for all transition points shall be denoted by $E(p)$, where $E(p) = \Sigma E(p_i)$. Since the number of spaces between elements is one less than the number of elements, and since we desire to count all possible transition points, we have $\Sigma E(p_i) = (n_1 + n_2 - 1)E(p_i)$. Substituting,

---

[1] The parameters for the normal approximation to $P(u)$ and the derivation of $E(u)$ are based on discussions in Mood, 1950, p. 393[2] and Wallis, p. 150.[3]

[2] A. F. Mood, 1950, *Introduction to the theory of statistics*, McGraw-Hill, New York.

[3] W. A. Wallis, 1950, *Lecture notes on statistical inference*, Univ. of Chicago.

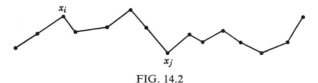

FIG. 14.2

$E(p) = 2n_1 n_2/(n_1 + n_2)$. The number of runs possible is equal to the number of elements, which in turn is one greater than the number of transition points. Therefore $E(u) = E(p + 1) = E(p) + 1$. By substituting, $E(u) = 2n_1 n_2/(n_1 + n_2) + 1$.

Turning Points and Runs Up or Down

As the number of elements N of a random permutation of unequal numbers approaches infinity, the distribution of the numbers of runs up or down (r) approaches the normal distribution. [Wallis and Roberts (1956).][1] For practical purposes, the distribution of runs $P(r)$ is considered as normal for finite N with $E(r) = (2N - 1)/3$ and $V(r) = (16N - 29)/90$.

$$P(r) \approx N\left(\frac{2N - 1}{3}, \frac{16N - 29}{90}\right) \quad (14.4)$$

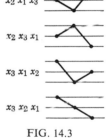

Actually this approximation holds fairly well for N as small as 10.

For expository purposes we shall present a derivation[2] of $E(r)$. Consider the ordered sequence of unequal numbers shown in Fig. 14.2. Points x_i and x_j illustrate "turning points." These turning points are immediately preceded and followed by points which are either both higher or both lower and represent the peaks and troughs of the sequence.

FIG. 14.3

In a random sequence, the probability that any consecutive set of three points provides a turning point may be found by enumeration. Suppose the numbers x_1, x_2, x_3 are all different and assume $x_1 < x_2 < x_3$, where the subscripts refer to the values, not the order. The permutations are shown in Fig. 14.3.

We focus attention on the middle point, count the number of times a turning point (t_i) appears, and then compute $E(t_i)$. $E(t_i) = \sum_{i=1}^{6} p(t_i)t_i = \frac{4}{6} = \frac{2}{3}$, since there are four turning points among the six possible

[1] W. A. Wallis and H. V. Roberts, 1956, *Statistics, a new approach*, Free Press, Glencoe, Illinois.

[2] Based on W. A. Wallis, and G. H. Moore, 1941, *ibid.*, pp. 7–12; and W. A. Wallis, 1950, *ibid.*

arrangements. In a sequence of N elements there are $N - 2$ possible sets of three consecutive elements. The reader can satisfy himself on this point by writing out a sequence and counting all possible consecutive sets of three. Thus we have

$$E(t) = \sum_{j=2}^{N-1} E(t_j) = (N - 2)\frac{2}{3}, \quad \text{and} \quad E(t) = \frac{2N - 4}{3}$$

The distribution of turning points may be expressed as normal (in the same sense as the distribution of runs up or down,) with $E(t) = (2N - 4)/3$ and $V(t) = (16N - 29)/90$.

$$P(t) \approx N\left(\frac{2N - 4}{3}, \frac{16N - 29}{90}\right)$$

(See Wallis and Moore, 1941.)[1]

The number of runs up or down is one greater than the number of turning points. This is illustrated in Fig. 14.1, where $\Sigma(t_i) = 8$ and $r = 9$. Therefore

$$E(r) = E(t + 1) = E(t) + 1$$

$$= \frac{2N - 4}{3} + 1 \qquad (14.6)$$

$$E(r) = \frac{2N - 1}{3}$$

We have thus presented a discussion of the expected values of turning points and of runs up or down. The variance is the same for both turning points and runs up or down. Thus one may count turning points and use the appropriate parameters $E(t)$ and $V(t)$ or count runs up or down and use $E(r)$ and $V(r)$. The probability result will be the same, plus unity, $P(r) = P(t + 1)$

APPLICATIONS

A series of rock samples were taken from the exposed bottom to the exposed top of the Skaergaard intrusion of iron-olivine gabbro in Greenland. (Wager and Deer, 1939.)[2] The chemical analyses by the above investigators, of certain of the sequential samples, are included in the body of Table 14.1. The table presents in sequence, from bottom to top, the analyses for 13 elements, but excludes from consideration the samples from the margins of the intrusion.

[1] W. A. Wallis and G. H. Moore, 1941, *A significance test for time-series*, Tech. Paper #1, National Bureau of Economic Research, 1819 Broadway, New York.

[2] L. R. Wager and W. A. Deer, 1939, Geological investigations in East Greenland. Pt. III, the petrology of the Skaergaard intrusion, *Meddelelser om Grønland*, Bd 105, Nr. 4.

TABLE 14.1

Sample Nos.	Layered Series								Unlaminated Layered Series		
	II 4077	III 3662	IV 3661	IVa	V 1907	VI 4145	VII 4142	VIII 1881	IX 4139	X 4137	XI 4136
SiO_2	46.37	48.15	45.65	46.90	44.81	44.61	44.13	48.27	45.19	52.13	55.30
Al_2O_3	16.82	18.02	15.08	16.55	13.96	11.70	17.88	8.58	9.37	15.87	18.32
Fe_2O_3	1.52	2.52	3.41	2.96	3.75	2.05	4.05	4.06	5.78	5.61	2.18
FeO	10.44	9.50	14.86	12.18	16.66	22.68	26.63	22.89	23.77	11.17	7.47
MgO	9.61	5.25	6.35	5.80	5.54	1.71	0.25	1.21	0.43	1.11	0.21
CaO	11.29	10.17	9.18	9.67	8.53	8.71	10.03	7.42	9.05	5.80	8.20
Na_2O	2.45	3.46	2.48	2.97	3.35	2.95	2.15	2.65	2.43	3.63	6.01
K_2O	0.20	0.14	0.28	0.21	0.33	0.35	0.47	0.34	0.49	1.38	0.78
H_2O^+	0.29	0.20	0.22	0.21	0.34	0.22	0.30	1.13	0.57	0.86	0.41
H_2O^-	0.09	0.02	0.08	0.05	0.19	0.20	0.19	0.37	0.31	0.25	0.06
TiO_2	0.79	2.64	2.59	2.61	2.55	2.43	2.48	2.20	1.67	1.14	0.94
MnO	0.09	0.12	0.15	0.14	0.17	0.21	0.48	0.26	0.32	0.30	0.09
P_2O_5	0.06	0.05	0.08	0.06	0.08	1.85	1.61	0.65	0.91	0.70	0.42

We shall now proceed to analyze the data for trend versus random ordering, and suggest tests for a specific kind of trend where an alternative to the hypothesis of randomness appears warranted.

Test for Random Order

The data for each chemical element is dichotomized into a sequence of n_1 (+) numerical elements and n_2 (−) elements, by assigning a (+) to values above the median value and a (−) to values below the median. The sequences of (+) and (−) numerical elements and the values for n_1, n_2, and u, the number of runs, is given in Table 14.2. Since the size of the sequences is very small (11), the normal approximation is not used, and $P(u)$ is calculated directly from Eqs. 14.1, 14.2 on p. 328. The results are

TABLE 14.2

	Median	Sequence	n_1 (+)	n_2 (−)	(u)	Computed $P(u)$	Spearman's ρ values
SiO_2	46.37	+ − + − − − + + − + +	5	5	7	0.190	0.290
Al_2O_3	15.87	+ + − + − − + − − +	5	5	7	0.190	−0.155
Fe_2O_3	3.41	− − − + − + + + + −	5	5	5	0.190	0.527
FeO	14.86	− − − + + + + + − −	5	5	3	0.032*	0.200
MgO	1.71	+ + + + + − − − − −	5	5	2	0.008*	−0.881
CaO	9.05	+ + + + − − + − − −	5	5	4	0.127	−0.782
Na_2O	2.95	− + − + + − − − + +	5	5	6	0.286	0.245
K_2O	0.34	− − − − − + + + + +	5	5	2	0.008*	0.946
H_2O^+	0.30	− − − − + − + + + +	5	5	4	0.127	0.770
H_2O^-	0.19	− − − − + + + − −	3	6	3	0.164	0.530
TiO_2	2.43	− + + + + + − − − −	5	5	3	0.032	−0.482
MnO	0.17	− − − − + + + + + −	5	5	3	0.032*	0.475
P_2O_5	0.42	− − − − − + + + + +	5	5	2	0.008*	0.673

NOTE. (1) That value in the sequences of Table 14.1 which corresponds to the median is omitted from the (+, −) assignments of Table 14.2. Thus with H_2O^- there are two 0.19 entries corresponding to the median of 0.19. (2) Using a level of significance of 0.025 for the lower tail, and 0.025 for the upper tail, we reject the hypothesis of random fluctuation if $P(u) \leq 0.50$. Starred entries in $P(u)$ column indicate the sequence is "probably not random."

shown in the next to last column of Table 14.2. Figure 14.3 shows a sequential graph of each set of analyses, and should be referred to when the reader considers Table 14.2. Before discussing the results, we shall proceed to a more specific test. Examination of Fig. 14.4 shows that certain of the chemical elements exhibit a distinctly linear appearance, either increasing or decreasing, e.g., MgO shows a decreasing pattern, and K_2O an increasing one. We shall now apply a specific test for regular increasing or decreasing sequences. (Since the columns must sum to 100% and the orders of magnitude for the various elements are consistent, there is a dependence between rows. Although the individual tests discussed in the following pages are probably valid, a positive correlation does exist. Some joint test might be more appropriate for the present example.)

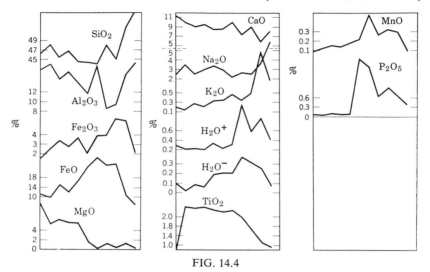

FIG. 14.4

SUGGESTED READING

A. B. Vistelius, 1957, Separation of the Hemanian beds by quantitative, mineralogical petrographic and chemical bases, *Mineralogical Soc. of U.S.S.R. Bull.* Applies theory of runs to separation of beds.

R. L. Miller and E. C. Olson, 1955, The statistical stability of quantitative properties as a fundamental criterion for the study of environments, *Jour. Geol.* 63. Uses sign test for runs to determine trend in sediment size in portion of Mississippi River.

USE OF SPEARMAN'S RANK CORRELATION COEFFICIENT

Essentially the test which is now used computes the correlation between an observed sequence and a regular rising sequence of integers. We shall illustrate the test in detail by applying it to the sequence for SiO_2. (See Table 14.2 and Fig. 14.4.) There are 11 entries, so we compare pair for pair the ranks of the SiO_2 sequence with the sequence of integers from 1 through 11 arranged in regularly increasing order.

Increasing order	1	2	3	4	5	6	7	8	9	10	11	
SiO_2 rank	6	8	5	7	3	2	1	9	4	10	11	
d (= differences)	-5	-6	-2	-3	2	4	6	-1	5	0	0	$\Sigma d = 0$

$$\rho = 1 - \frac{6 \sum d^2}{n^3 - n} = 1 - \frac{936}{1320} = 0.2901$$

The correlation of 0.2901 gives no strong evidence of upward trend.

Spearman's rank correlation coefficient ρ ranges from -1 to 1 so that high positive correlation would indicate the possibility of upward trend, whereas high negative correlation would indicate the possibility of downward trend.

The Spearman measure of degree of association has been applied to all the sequences, and the results are given in the form of the value of Spearman's ρ in the last column of Table 14.2.

DISCUSSION

The results of the runs test are given in the form of probability values which state the likelihood that the observed arrangement of s and $-s$ could have arisen by random permutations. A star after the probability entry indicates that the probability sequence is "probably not random." According to our earlier definition we say that in these cases a "trend" occurs. Six of the elements exhibit a random order and six show a trend.

Now compare these results with the Spearman rank correlation values. We shall divide the sequences into two groups, those which show trend and those which do not. In the group showing trend, MgO exhibits a regular decrease, whereas K_2O and P_2O_5 exhibit a regular increase. FeO, TiO_2, and MnO give no clear evidence of regular increase or decrease, but examination of Fig. 14.4 indicates a rise followed by a fall in all three cases. The results of the two tests (runs test and Spearman's test) appear to be consistent as far as linear trends occur. Spearman's test will not serve for nonlinear trends.

Consider now the second group of sequences, those which appear to have random order according to the tests. SiO_2, Al_2O_3, Fe_2O_3, and Na_2O show no clear evidence of regular rise or fall in their respective ρ values. However, CaO and H_2O^+, although showing no trend according to the runs test, do exhibit an appearance of decrease in the first case and regular increase in the second case, according to Spearman's test. This creates a dilemma. Which test are we to believe? In the writer's opinion, such cases should be looked upon as presenting no clear-cut results. Since the sequence sizes are small, patterns which are somewhat regular in appearance can give high probability of being random. For further discussion of this point, see the summary at the end of this section.

Actually, where linear trends are of interest, the runs test is weaker than the Spearman test. The runs up or down analysis may give results more consistent with the Spearman test.

SUGGESTED READING

R. G. Johnson, 1960, Models and methods for the analysis of mode of formation of fossil assemblages, *Bull. G.S.A.* 71: 1075–1086. Applies the rank correlation method to combinations of nine variables including percentage of fossil fragments, median size if fossils, coefficient of sediment sorting.

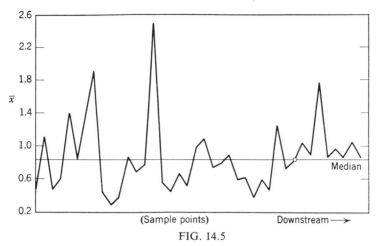

FIG. 14.5

APPLICATION OF DICHOTOMIZING PROCESS TO PRODUCE A SEQUENCE OF $n_1 + n_2$ ELEMENTS, WHEN $n_1 + n_2$ IS LARGE

A sequence of values of a particular variable may be more easily handled when N is large by the use of the normal approximation to $P(u)$. The following example illustrates the procedure.

A series of values for average sediment size was collected at downstream intervals in the main channel of the Mississippi River by Lugn (1927). Figure 14.5 shows a graph of the average sediment size from Davenport, Iowa to the entry of the Illinois River. Examination of Fig. 14.5 indicates no obvious trend. We shall proceed to test this observation by dichotomizing the data into two kinds of independent elements by computing the median and assigning a $+$ to values above the median and a $-$ to values below the median. The ordering of the sequence is preserved. There are 16 runs, 40 elements, of which 20 are plus and 20 are minus. We now test the hypothesis that the observed arrangement of 40 plus and minus elements has resulted from a random permutation. If the number of runs is smaller than would be expected from a random permutation, we suspect the existence of a "trend." If the number of runs is larger than would be expected, we could suspect the existence of a (cyclic) trend of regularly rising and falling subsequences of elements. Tables for checking the hypothesis at 0.025 probability level for significantly large number of runs and also for significantly small number of runs are available[2] for n_1, n_2 up

[1] A. L. Lugn, 1927, Sedimentation in the Mississippi River, *Augustana Lib. Publ.* No. 11: 1–104.

[2] It is not, however, necessary to use the median for the purpose of dichotomizing the data. Some other meaningful scheme will work just as well. (Hoel, 1947, p. 180, *ibid.*) This is providing choice of dichotomy is based on *a priori* reasons and not on examination of the data.

to 20 and for $n_1 = n_2$ up to 100, where n_1 and n_2 are the numbers of the + and − elements. In this case $n_1 = n_2 = 20$ since the median was used to dichotomize the data.[1] We find on consulting the tables that for $n_1 = n_2 = 20$ and $u = 16$ the hypothesis of randomness is accepted as satisfying the arbitrary 0.025 level of significance.

The 0.025 level is arbitrary and we shall therefore now compute an estimate of the exact probability by using the normal approximation.

$$E(u) = \frac{2n_1n_2}{n_1 + n_2} + 1 = \frac{2(20^2)}{40} + 1 = 21$$

$$V(u) = \frac{2n_1n_2(2n_1n_2 - n_1 - n_2)}{(n_1 + n_2)^2(n_1 + n_2 - 1)} = \frac{800(800 - 40)}{1600(39)} = 9.74$$

$$z = \frac{u - E(u)}{\sqrt{V(u)}} = \frac{16 - 21}{3.121} = -1.602$$

Reference to the cumulative tables of the normal distribution shows that the probability that the observed sequence fluctuates randomly about the median is 0.056. This is not a decisively large (or small) probability value on which to base a decision. We shall therefore test further.

Examination of Fig. 14.5 indicates a possibility of a regular rise and fall. We shall therefore test the sequence once again, this time for randomness by counting the number of turning points. (t) is 29, and $N = 40$. Using the normal approximation for $P(t)$ we have,

$$E(t) = \frac{2N - 4}{3} = 25.33$$

$$\text{var}(t) = \frac{16N - 29}{90} = 6.788$$

$$z = \frac{t - E(t)}{\sqrt{V(t)}} = \frac{29 - 25.33}{2.605} = 1.332$$

Reference to the cumulative tables of the normal distribution indicates acceptance of the hypothesis of randomness of rises and falls with probability of 0.0918 that such a sequence could be generated by random arrangement of rises and falls about the median line.

Considering the results of the runs test and the turning point test together, the writers are inclined to reject the possibility of trend for the full sequence. An *a priori* expectation of local trends, due, for example, to

[1] W. J. Dixon and F. J. Massey, *Introduction to statistical analysis*, McGraw-Hill, New York.

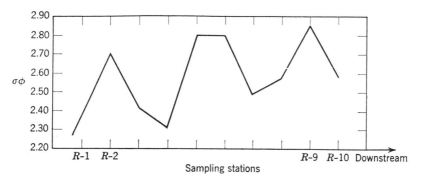

FIG. 14.6. Plot of sorting ($\sigma\phi$) values for a sequence of observations down Bear Butte Creek, South Dakota.

large sediment-laden streams entering the Mississippi, may introduce the possibility of a meaningful study of subsequences of the preceding data.

An example of trend analysis along a traverse by inspection rather than formal methods, based, however, on detailed sampling, is C. S. Wimberley, 1955, Marine sediments north of Scripps submarine canyon, La Jolla, *Jour. Sed. Petrol.* 25: 24-37. Regression analysis is used rather than "trend analysis" in a study by C. C. Matson, and R. L. Folk, 1958, Differentiation of beach, dune and aeolian flat environments by size analysis, Mustang Island, Texas, *Jour. Sed. Petrol.* 28: 211–226. That is, properties such as skewness and kurtosis are plotted against each other rather than each separately against distance along a traverse. The results are used to differentiate beach, dune, and aeolian flat environments.

APPLICATIONS WHEN $n_1 + n_2$ IS SMALL

The following illustrates the suggested treatment for a small sequence of sediment size analyses which complements the previous discussion. We shall examine a sequence of observations of sorting (σ_ϕ) of sediment collected at intervals downstream in Bear Butte Creek in South Dakota (Plumley, 1948).[1] A plot of these data, Fig. 14.6 indicates the possibility of an upward trend even though the individual values rise and fall to a considerable degree. In addition there is an apparent regularity to the successive rises and falls of the sorting values. Two hypotheses will be set up. The first is that the distribution of + and − elements in the sequence is random; if the hypothesis is rejected we suspect a trend. The second hypothesis is that the number of turning points is no greater or less than

[1] W. J. Plumley, 1948, Black Hills terrace gravels: a study in sediment transport, *Jour. Geol.* 56: 526–577.

would be expected in a random distribution. If this hypothesis is shown false and the number of turning points is high, we may suspect a cyclic phenomena, e.g., a regular rise and fall of the ordered data.[1]

The tests will be made in the order the hypotheses are proposed.

Runs Test

The values are dichotomized into $(+)$ and $(-)$ elements by the median. Since the number of elements in the sequence is small ($N = 10$), the normal approximation cannot be used and $P(u)$ is computed directly. The sequence $- + - - + + + - - + +$ furnishes us with the following information: $u = 6, N = 10, n_1 = n_2 = 5$. Therefore $P(u) = 2 \left[\dfrac{4! \, 4! \, 5! \, 5!}{2! \, 2! \, 2! \, 2! \, 10!} \right] \cong$ 0.1428 and we conclude that the probability that the array of $(+)$ and $(-)$ elements is sufficiently high to justify accepting the hypothesis of randomness. Since there was an appearance of a periodic rise and fall, the second test for the hypothesis of randomness will be based on the number of turning points. We have defined a turning point to be a point which is either higher or lower than the two points which immediately precede and follow it in a sequence.

In this example, $t = 5$ and $N = 10$; therefore

$$E(t) = \frac{2N - 4}{3} = 5.33$$

$$V(t) = \frac{16N - 29}{90} = 1.455$$

$$z = \frac{t - E(t)}{\sqrt{V(t)}} = 0.273$$

which gives for probability of randomness the value 0.393. We conclude that relative to a sample size of 10 the 5 turning points do not give evidence of a regular rise and fall.

The sample value r's for Spearman's ρ as a test for an upward linear trend is $r_s = 0.500$ which we consider to be a marginal value. However, this does suggest the possibility of a cycle superimposed on a linear trend sloping from lower left to upper right in Fig. 14.6, and this is supported by the appearance of the graph.[2] A suggested procedure for the linear trend is to fit a straight line to the data by least squares, and test goodness-of-fit as for a regression equation. If this hurdle is successfully passed, then re-application of the runs test around the regression line may be made. If

---

[1] M. G. Kendall, 1955, *Rank correlation methods*, Chas. Griffin, London.

[2] Although in theory (see footnote p. 337) the dichotomizing line for the runs test should not be based on inspection of the sample data, in practice, this is often done.

the number of rises and falls around the regression line (as the dichotomizing mechanism) is larger than expected under the random hypothesis (one-tail test), there is some evidence favoring cycles superimposed over a nonhorizontal linear trend.

Runs of Greater Than Two Kinds of Independent Elements

Suppose for purposes of illustration, a student of Pleistocene geology has taken a series of till samples in the following manner. At intervals of approximately one mile (depending on exposure) a linear sequence of 20 samples of about a cubic foot each of glacially deposited sediment is collected. We shall assume that the sampling traverse roughly lies on the position of the axis of the former lobe of ice. Each cubic foot of sediment is examined for pebbles. The dominant (most numerous) rock type in a single sample is listed as either limestone (L), shale (S), or crystalline (C). The results are as follows.

Station	1	2	3	4	5	6	7	8	9	10	11	12	13	14	15	16	17	18	19	20
Dominant lithology	L	L	S	L	S	X	X	X	X	S	L	L	S	S	S	S	S	L	L	X

The number of runs = 10, number of $L = 7$, $S = 8$, $X = 5$. We now proceed to test whether the arrangement of the three kinds of elements is random. The equations are given without derivation and are taken from W. A. Wallis and G. H. Moore, 1941, *ibid.* and adapted to this problem.

$$E(u_3) = \frac{2(LS + LX + SX)}{(L + S + X)} + 1 = \frac{2(7.8 + 7.5 + 8.5)}{(7 + 8 + 5)} + 1 = 14.1$$

$$V(u_3) = \frac{[2(LS + LX + SX)]^2}{(L + S + X)^2(L + S + X - 1)}$$

$$- \frac{2(LS + LX + SX) + 6LSX}{(L + S + X)(L + S + X - 1)} = 3.922$$

$$z = \frac{u_3 - E(u_3)}{\sqrt{V(u_3)}} = 2.070$$

From the cumulative tables of the normal distribution, the probability of getting as few runs as 10 when the 20 entries represent a random permutation of three kinds of elements is 0.019. The hypothesis of randomness is rejected. An examination of the distribution of the L, S, and X entries appears to show a clustering effect. Further investigation seems indicated, perhaps along the lines of correlating clustering to bed rock source. A more detailed sampling scheme, in the light of the result of the test, would probably be of value. Treatment by "nearest neighbor" techniques as described in Chapter 16 may be also of value.

A word of caution is appropriate here. Although the statistical test has rejected the hypothesis of randomness, the test has not in itself favored any of the many alternative hypotheses which could have been set up to describe the observed sequence. The use of the term "clustering" in the previous paragraph was subjective. In the writer's opinion, the safest conclusion to draw is that further (but more specific) investigation should be undertaken.

SUMMARY

It is important to recognize that the runs and turning point tests are tests of *random order*. When the geologist considers applying one or another of the tests described here, he must be certain that the order in which the elements appear in the sequence is a geologically meaningful one. We shall confine the discussion of time-ordered sequences to a later section. The order may occur by virtue of the field sampling, such as a traverse, or may be introduced into data such as is illustrated in the stream length versus azimuth discussion.

As the reader has seen, we choose the particular test of random order on the basis of some suspected alternative to random order, but we do not actually demonstrate the validity of that particular alternative versus any of the many other alternatives possible! For a discussion of the logical implications of this procedure, see Kendall (1948), pp. 135, 136.[1]

Finally, we arbitrarily define the term "trend" to mean a *regularity in the order* as opposed to random order. This regularity is not specified and includes regular rises and falls in the sequence as well as a linear increase

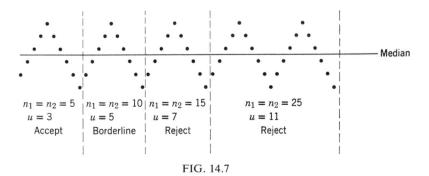

FIG. 14.7

[1] M. G. Kendall, 1948, *The advanced theory of statistics*, Vol. II, Chas. Griffin, London.

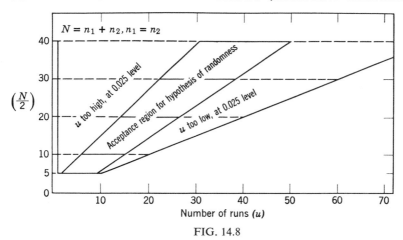

FIG. 14.8

or decrease, in addition to parabolic or exponential "trends." To choose among the various types of trends, where random order has been rejected, requires further analysis, e.g., curve fitting.

The results of applying the runs test should be treated with caution, particularly in small sequences. Figure 14.7 shows a schematic sequence of regularly rising and falling groups of elements. The median is drawn as shown, and we shall assume that no two numbers are exactly alike and that all differences among numbers are larger than analytical error. We shall now apply the runs test to increasingly large subsequences, using the 0.025 level of significance. Starting from the first element in the ordered sequence, consider the first 10 elements. A single rise and a single fall are shown, which gives every evidence to the eye of regularity. Applying the runs test we have $- - + + + + + - - -$, where $n_1 = n_2 = 5$ and $u = 3$. At the 0.025 level we *accept* the hypothesis of randomness! Consider now the subsequence from the first to the twentieth entry. Again striking regularity is apparent, but for $n_1 = n_2 = 10$ and $u = 5$ the result is on the borderline between randomness and regularity. However, an analysis of the subsequence from the first element to the thirtieth results in a *rejection* of the hypothesis of randomness at the 0.025 level for $n_1 = n_2 = 15$ and $u = 7$, as our observation would lead us to expect.

Figure 14.8 should make clear that the apparent regularity of the sequence is weighed against the *length* of the sequence, illustrating that increasing sample size increases the power of the test. The ordinate gives value of $n_1 = n_2$, and the abscissa the number of runs. The 0.025 level for lower limit of the number of runs and the 0.025 level for the upper limit mark the region of acceptance of the null hypothesis of random order for various levels of $n_1 = n_2$. It can be seen that when $n_1 = n_2$ is small, a large proportion of the possible number of runs falls in the interval of acceptance of random order. However, as $n_1 = n_2$ increases, a decreasing proportion of the possible number of runs falls in the interval of acceptance of random order.

In many cases, a geologist may not wish to draw a final conclusion from the runs test for the first subsequence of Fig. 14.7. On the other hand, the computation of $P(u)$ does exactly what it purports to do; namely, it states that the number of ways of arriving at the arrangement of 5 +'s and 5 −'s into three runs, as exhibited in the first subsequence, is *large* relative to the total number of permutations of 5 +'s and 5 −'s.

However, the writers feel that if the geologist keeps the following in mind, the runs test is nevertheless a very useful and easily applied tool.

1. Maintains a clear understanding of the meaning of the runs test.
2. Exercises caution in application to very small sequences.
3. Understands the limitations of the test.
4. Has some *a priori* expectation of results.

A further difficulty in interpretation that illustrates a limitation of the test arises in terms of order of magnitude of differences between entries. Assume for this discussion that all differences shown in Fig. 14.9 are real in that they are not due to experimental error or rounding.

The first sequence is accepted as random by using the runs test with $n_1 = n_2 = 9$ and $u = 10$. By the dichotomizing process, the second sequence is identical with the first in that the (+'s) and (−'s) occupy the

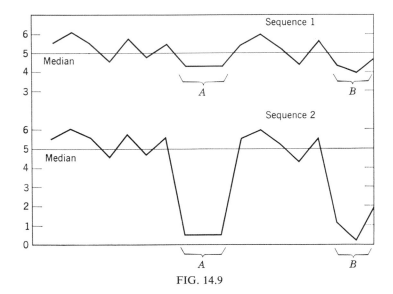

FIG. 14.9

same positions. However, once again the geologist would certainly consider as striking and important the triplets marked *A* and *B* in sequence 1. The second sequence differs from the first only by changing the order of magnitude of differences in the *A* and *B*; the *relative* rises and falls are unchanged. The user should realize that in a case such as is illustrated here the runs test does not take into account the *magnitude* of differences.

The following procedure is suggested for analysis of data for trend.

1. Apply the appropriate runs on turning point test to the data.

2. Alternatively apply Spearman's rank correlation method for cases where linear trend is of interest, or apply Kendall's τ.

3. In case the hypothesis of randomness is rejected in (1), or a high correlation coefficient r_s is found in (2), then curve fitting by least squares methods may be useful. However, in theory at least the choice of curve to fit should be based on *a priori* expectations rather than examination of the sample data.

4. The goodness-of-fit of the selected curve should be measured, e.g., by χ^2 test.

5. Subsequently, runs tests around the fitted curve as a dichotomizing mechanism may be indicated.

chapter 15

Time Series

A time series is a sequence of observations ordered with respect to time. Since time series have been of interest in many fields of inquiry over a long period, there is available a lengthy literature and numerous analytical techniques.

It is convenient to divide time series into two classes for this discussion.

CLASS I

A value of chronological time is available for each observation. The time unit need not be fixed. Thus the time value may be in units of millions of years at one extreme or of microseconds at another.

CLASS II

No accurate or reliable time unit is available. The series is legitimately a "time-series" only because there is a meaningful ordering in a time sense. That is, we are able to say that the ith observation preceded the jth observation in the ordered sequence $1, 2, \cdots, i, j, \cdots$, but cannot measure the elapsed time between i and j. Thus an ordinal scale is used.

A very large number of situations in geology fall into the second class. In a Paleozoic stratigraphic section, for example, there is, in our present state of knowledge, information available for a "relative time series" only. We may measure thickness of bed or sedimentation unit, and form an ordered sequence of thicknesses. We cannot, however, attach chronological time to each measurement. A similar situation arises for most paleontological problems. All of this leads to the generalization that most time series of "historical" geology are at present "relative time-series." Age dating methods are under much study and several have already proved to be successful in various dating problems, e.g., carbon-dating methods, potassium/argon and uranium/lead ratios. The difficulty in dating methods in the present context, however, appears to be in time *units*. The older the rock the greater the "error" of a given date. An essential point to consider here is that the time unit which should be used depends on the problem, but the time unit cannot at any point be smaller than the maximum error inherent in the dating method at that same point in time.

The purposes of examining time-series of geologic interest may include a search for cycles, a trend, or prediction. The meaning of the term "cycle" in a geological sense, e.g., must be considered with some care. A "cyclothem" or repetitive sequence of beds of both marine and continental origin[1] is a cycle just as much as the regular rise and fall of sunspot intensity, or of average temperature by years. However, in the case of the cyclothem absolute chronological dates for each observation are not available. (We do not here consider the additional difficulty of placing scattered outcrops in their proper chronological sequence.)

Varve deposits present us with another example. If we assume that the alternate light and dark layers represent seasonal lake deposits so that to each pair there is attached a unit of one year, then the problem falls in Class I. If, on the other hand, the varves represent individual irregularly spaced events such as heavy rains with subsequent deposition, followed by dry periods, the problem falls in Class II.

A SHORT DISCUSSION OF TIME SERIES ANALYSIS

Kendall (1948) describes time series in detail. His discussion presupposes, however, that the observations occur at regular time intervals. The following section is based in large part on Kendall and is presented to acquaint the reader with some of the varied classical approaches to time series analysis.

Time series may be and usually are decomposed into three parts: (1) a trend, (2) cycles, and (3) "random" component. A particular series may or may not consist of all three components.

Several definitions are necessary at this point.

Seasonal effect is a regular fluctuation or rise and fall which is due to some natural cyclic occurrence, independent of the variable under investigation. Obvious examples are the yearly temperature cycles, daily tidal cycles, and reproductive cycles in animals. Both Kendall (1948)[2] and Wallis and Roberts (1956)[3] warn that isolation and subsequent elimination of this effect should be done only where the *a priori* knowledge is strong and clear cut.

Kendall suggests that "seasonal effect" may be eliminated or removed from a time series by proper choice of time interval. Thus the effect of

---

[1] J. M. Weller, 1930, Cyclical sedimentation of the Pennsylvanian period and its significance, *Jour. Geol.* 38: 97–135.

[2] M. G. Kendall, 1948, *The advanced theory of statistics*, Vol. II, Mapleton House, Brooklyn 4, New York.

[3] W. A. Wallis and H. V. Roberts, 1956, *Statistics, a new approach*, The Free Press, Glencoe, Illinois.

tide in a time series of still water levels in Cape Cod Bay may be eliminated by choosing a twelve-hour period for the observations. We shall return to this subject later.

Trend is a rather ambiguous term. Kendall believes that a smooth, broad motion over a long period of time (relative to the length of the series) is indicative of a trend. The key here is the phrase, *relative to the length of the series*. When the series is terminated before we study it, such as a stratigraphic column, or a progression of fossil species through time, the preceding definition is useful. Otherwise, Kendall suggests that we think of slow movements and quick movements rather than trends or oscillations.

Trends may be determined by fitting a polynomial to the data with a resultant smoothing effect. If the series is very irregular, a high degree polynomial may be needed, involving a great deal of labor. Moving averages are used in various techniques directed toward a more objective polynomial fit to the data. The moving average is taken up and applied in an example later.

Trend elimination is accomplished by subtracting the trend, as described by a polynomial, from the time series.

A *stationary time series* has the property of being without trend, either by lacking it in the original data or because of removal. If it is established that a time series is stationary, we may then consider cyclic effects. Once seasonal effects are removed, e.g., as already discussed, Fourier analysis or harmonic analysis[1,2] is widely used to represent regular rises and falls as being due to the sum of cyclic components. Another application of Fourier analysis, in this case to a geological problem, is A. B. Vistelius, (1947).[3]

REFERENCES ON TREND ANALYSIS

Paul Lorenz, 1935, Annual survey of statistical technique: trends and seasonal variations, *Econometrica* 3: 456–471. A general discussion of the meaning of the terms, *trend* and *seasonal variation*, with an extensive bibliography.

Norbert Wiener, 1949, *Extrapolation interpolation and smoothing of stationary time series*, Technology Press, M.I.T., and John Wiley, New York. Combines the methods of statistics, and communication engineering, into a unified approach to time series by use of Fourier techniques.

S. Chapman and J. Bartels, *Geomagnetism*, Vol. II, *analysis of the data and physical theories*, Oxford University Press, London. Includes a variety of time series with analysis and physical interpretation, in geophysics. Chapter XVI is of general interest in time series analysis.

[1] N. Weiner, 1930, Generalised harmonic analysis, *Acta Math.* 55, 117.

[2] R. A. Fisher, 1929, Tests of significance in harmonic analysis, *Proc. Roy. Soc.* A, 125: 54.

[3] A. B. Vistelius, 1947, *Simple types of problems in the mathematical treatment of lithological observations*, Symposium No. 1, All Union Inst. of Oil Geology, U.S.S.R.

ADDITIONAL APPLICATIONS OF TREND ANALYSIS METHODS IN TIME SERIES

H. Korn, 1938, *Schichtung und absolute zeit U.S.V.* Neues Jahrb. f. Min., *Geol. Pal.* Abt. A, Bd. 74, Heft 1, pp. 51–166. Uses smoothing in upper Devonian, lower Carboniferous bed thicknesses on a geologic time axis, followed by Fourier analysis for periodicity.

A. B. Vistelius, 1961, Sedimentation time trend functions and their applications for correlation of sedimentary deposits, *Jour. Geol.* Vol. 69 (in press). A method is described for investigation of possible time trends in sedimentation. The trend is expressed by the general equation $y = u(t) + \epsilon(t)$, where y is the bed composition, t is either time or thickness of bed, $u(t)$ is the systematic trend component of the sedimentation and $\epsilon(t)$ is the random component of the process. The systematic trend is emphasized and the random component reduced by a smoothing process. Many geological examples are given.

A phenomenon present to some degree in most time series is termed *serial correlation* or *autocorrelation*. Instead of correlation in the usual sense where changes in dependent variable depend on changes in the independent variable, we refer to correlation between members of a series where changes in the dependent variable are not accounted for by the independent variable. Consider, e.g., the forward velocity of a suspended sediment particle under unidirectional current flow. If at a particular time the velocity is above the mean, it is likely that at just the previous moment, as well as a moment later, the velocity will also be above the mean. In this very real sense successive points on a time series may not be independent of each other. Serial correlation thus introduces difficulties into time series analysis, and must be taken into account.

The degree of serial correlation can be computed for a time series by using the serial correlation coefficient as described in Kendall (1948), section 30.12, p. 402.[1] It is, however, a very laborious procedure. See also Pope (1953).[2]

TWO EXAMPLES OF AUTOCORRELATION ANALYSIS APPLIED TO GEOLOGICAL PROBLEMS

A. B. Vistelius, 1949, On mechanical relationships in strata formation, *Dokl. Akad Nayk Trans.* 65:4, in which autocorrelation is applied to the study of sequences of bed thickness. Three correlograms are obtained: Jurassic of Dagestan, Cretaceous of Georgia, and Tertiary of Baku.

A. B. Vistelius, 1952, *On the Kirmakinian suite of eastern Azerbijian 1. Basis of the lithologic boundaries.* Conditional probabilities for sequences of oil-bearing beds of Baku are investigated. Applications are made of products of probabilities, Markov matrices, and autocorrelation. Another paper in this general context is A. B. Vistelius, 1949, The

[1] M. G. Kendall, 1948, *The advanced theory of statistics*, Mapleton House, Brooklyn 4, New York.

[2] J. A. Pope, 1953, Errors in the estimation of serial correlations, *Nature* 172: 4382; 778.

question of the mechanics of strata formation, *Dokl. Akad. Nayk. Trans.* 65: 2. The rhythmical sequence of beds in the Cretaceous of Novorsijsk (Black Sea) is studied with the aid of "Markov Chains."

A UTILITARIAN POINT OF VIEW

The writers feel that the philosophy presented by Wallis and Roberts (1956) more closely approximates their own view on time series analysis in geological problems, unless the analyst is an expert. Time series must be treated with great caution. An attempt to extract cycles or trends by various analytical techniques, but without an *a priori* model based on the natural situation, is very dangerous. The following procedures are suggested with the caution that the intuitive grasp of the subject by the investigator should be the final arbitrator. Results of this sequence of tests should be used as suggestive of the direction for further exploration of the natural structure which underlies that particular time series.

APPLICATION

Since it is the writers' contention that any formal time series analysis in geology should be undertaken with as strong as possible grasp of the physical situation underlying the series, the examples used in the following discussion will be hypothetical, rather than drawn from published data on problems which the writers have not worked on.

Suppose that two deep sea cores were taken several hundred miles apart in the center of an ocean basin. These cores will be designated core No. 1 and core No. 2 in what follows. It is assumed that there are no

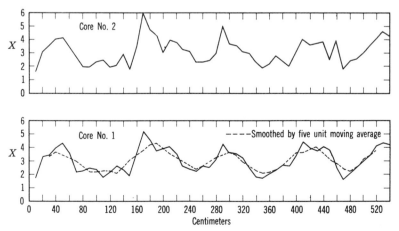

FIG. 15.1. Variation of some variable x with depth equals time in two deep sea cores.

nearby islands or mainland, and we shall make the further assumption that sedimentation has proceeded at an undisturbed and constant rate through the period of time represented by the length of the cores. This will enable us to reasonably substitute a unit of time for a unit of length of core. A measurement of some property of the sediment is taken every 10 cm from the bottom to the top of the core. The values of the measured property for core No. 1 are given in Table 15.1, where length in centimeters is understood to be equivalent to time. Both cores are shown graphically in Fig. 15.1. Note that this time series is to be considered free from "trend" and in the notation of this section is a stationary time series.

Test Whether the Series Differs Significantly from Randomness

It is not difficult to be misled by the appearance of a time series, and to declare that a particular trend or cycle is exhibited. Visual inspection of time series is not a safe basis from which to draw conclusions. The first step in analysis of a series should be a test of the null hypothesis that the rises and falls are random. A practical, easily applied test is the runs test discussed earlier in this chapter.

The present form of the runs test is taken from Wallis and Roberts (1956) and is applied to core No. 1. Could we expect the observed number of runs of plus and minus signs to have been generated by a random arrangement? In Table 15.1 the median was used to assign a plus or minus sign to each observation. The number of runs is 10, and there are $n_1 = 27$ (+) signs $n_2 = 27$ (−) signs. Next, a standard normal variable is formed

$$K = \frac{(r + 1/2) - M}{\sigma}$$

where $M_r = 2n_1n_2/n + 1$ and $\sigma_r = \sqrt{\dfrac{2n_1n_2(2n_1n_2 - n)}{n^2(n - 1)}}$, where $n = n_1 + n_2$

is thus put in the convenient computing form

$$K = \frac{n(r - 1/2) - 2n_1n_2}{\sqrt{\dfrac{2n_1n_2(2n_1n_2 - n)}{n - 1}}}$$

For core No. 1, $\quad K = \dfrac{36(9.5) - 1458}{\sqrt{38,623}} = -5.65.$

Thus the observed number of runs (10) is 5.65 standard deviations lower than the expected number of runs (27) under the hypothesis of randomness. We conclude that core No. 1 does not consist of purely random fluctuations and proceed with the analysis. It should be noted that a high serial

TABLE 15.1

Distance along Core in cm	x	Using Md = 2.95	For Smoothing Purposes Only Five Unit Moving Average		Seasonal Cycle Four Unit Moving Average		Deviation (Obs. Value) − (Moving Average)	Time Series Corrected for Seasonal Cycle
			Total	Average	Total	Average		
10	1.9	−						2.31
20	3.4	+						3.41
30	3.5	+	17.2	3.44	12.8	3.20	0.30	3.13
40	4.0	+	18.9	3.78	15.3	3.82	0.18	4.02
50	4.4	+	17.7	3.54	15.5	3.87	0.53	4.81
60	3.6	+	16.5	3.30	14.2	3.55	0.05	3.61
70	2.2	−	15.0	3.00	12.5	3.12	−0.92	1.83
80	2.3	−	13.0	2.60	10.6	2.65	−0.35	2.32
90	2.5	−	11.2	2.24	9.4	2.35	0.15	2.91
100	2.4	−	11.1	2.22	9.0	2.25	0.15	2.41
110	1.8	−	11.5	2.30	8.8	2.20	−0.40	1.43
120	2.1	−	11.4	2.28	9.0	2.25	−0.15	2.12
130	2.7	−	10.9	2.18	9.0	2.25	0.45	3.11
140	2.4	−	12.7	2.54	9.1	2.27	0.13	2.41
150	1.9	−	15.9	3.18	10.6	2.65	−0.75	1.53
160	3.6	+	17.7	3.54	13.2	3.30	0.30	3.62
170	5.3	+	19.1	3.82	15.3	3.82	1.48	5.71
180	4.5	+	21.1	4.22	17.2	4.30	0.20	4.51
190	3.8	+	21.6	4.32	17.5	4.37	−0.57	3.43

200	3.9	+	19.9	3.98	16.3	4.07	−0.17	3.92
210	4.1	+	17.8	3.56	15.4	3.85	0.25	4.51
220	3.6	+	16.4	3.28	14.0	3.50	0.10	3.61
230	2.4	−	14.7	2.94	12.5	3.12	−0.72	2.03
240	2.4	−	13.2	2.64	10.6	2.65	−0.25	2.42
250	2.2	−	12.1	2.42	9.5	2.40	−0.20	2.61
260	2.6	−	12.8	2.56	9.7	2.42	0.18	2.61
270	2.5	−	14.7	2.94	10.4	2.60	−0.10	2.13
280	3.1	+	16.1	3.22	12.5	3.12	−0.02	3.12
290	4.3	+	17.0	3.40	13.5	3.37	0.93	4.71
300	3.6	+	17.8	3.56	14.5	3.62	−0.02	3.61
310	3.5	+	17.1	3.42	14.7	3.67	−0.17	3.13
320	3.3	+	14.6	2.92	12.8	3.20	0.10	3.32
330	2.4	+	12.7	2.54	11.0	2.75	−0.35	2.81
340	1.8	−	11.2	2.24	9.2	2.30	−0.50	1.81
350	1.7	−	10.5	2.10	7.9	1.97	−0.27	1.33
360	2.0	−	10.7	2.14	8.1	2.02	−0.02	2.02
370	2.6	−	11.4	2.28	8.9	2.22	0.38	3.01
380	2.6	−	13.0	2.60	9.7	2.42	0.18	2.61
390	2.5	−	15.4	3.08	11.0	2.75	−0.25	2.13
400	3.3	+	17.7	3.54	12.8	3.20	0.10	3.32
410	4.4	+	17.8	3.56	14.1	3.52	0.88	4.81
420	3.9	+	19.3	3.86	15.3	3.82	0.08	3.91
430	3.7	+	19.8	3.96	16.0	4.00	−0.30	3.33
440	4.0	+	17.8	3.56	15.4	3.85	0.15	4.02
450	3.8		15.5	3.10	13.9	3.47	0.33	4.21

TABLE 15.1 (continued)

Distance along Core in cm	x	Using Md = 2.95	For Smoothing Purposes Only Five Unit Moving Average		Seasonal Cycle Four Unit Moving Average		Deviation (Obs. Value) − (Moving Average)	Time Series Corrected for Seasonal Cycle
			Total	Average	Total	Average		
460	2.4	−	13.8	2.76	11.8	2.95	−0.55	2.41
470	1.6	−	12.2	2.44	9.8	2.45	−0.85	1.23
480	2.0	−	11.2	2.24	8.4	2.10	−0.10	2.02
490	2.4	−	12.1	2.42	8.8	2.20	0.20	2.81
500	2.8	−	14.6	2.92	10.5	2.62	0.18	2.81
510	3.3	+	16.9	3.38	12.6	3.15	0.15	2.93
520	4.1	+	18.7	3.74	14.5	3.62	0.48	4.12
530	4.3	+			15.9	3.97	0.33	4.71
540	4.2	+						4.21

$r = 10$: $n_1^+ = n_2^- = 27$

correlation would lead to a high probability that the runs test will reject the hypothesis of randomness.

If the series is not "random," one might proceed either to smoothing as the final step, or if the situation warrants, go instead to further analysis and continue through removing effect of seasonal fluctuation, test for hypothetical cycle, and correlation, as appropriate.

Smoothing by Moving Averages

The smoothing of a time series by moving averages should be regarded as a descriptive rather than an analytical technique. Not only do moving averages tend to mask highs and lows which may be important but there is also a tendency to displace or shift peaks and valleys. See, e.g., Fig. 15.1. A moving average is generated by adding several preceding points and several following points to a given point in the series. This sum is called a *moving total*. Thus a five-point moving average consists of the value at the point plus the values of the two preceding points and the two following points. The 5 are then shifted down the column one unit, and the process repeated; e.g., in Table 15.1 column 4 for point 3, enter sum of points 1, 2, 3, 4, 5 opposite point 3, for point 4 enter sum of points 2, 3, 4, 5, 6 opposite point 4, etc. The column of moving totals in Table 15.1 is then converted to moving averages in column 5 by dividing each moving total by 5. The results are plotted in Fig. 15.1.

SUGGESTED READING

A. B. Vistelius, 1957, The regional litho-stratigraphy and conditions of formation of the productive beds of the southeastern Caucausus, *Trans. Leningrad Naturalist Soc.* Vol. 69, pt. 2. Uses still another method for smoothing. He utilizes a sine function to smooth numerical lithologic characteristics. The resulting function is used for stratigraphic analysis.

Removing the Effects of a Seasonal Fluctuation

A seasonal fluctuation may be regarded as a cyclic phenomenon which is clearly recognized as occurring regularly in a natural situation and which reasonably can be expected to affect the particular time series under study. Thus in many situations the yearly climatic cycle may affect time series. The term seasonal does not, however, restrict this type of cycle to one which has a one-year period. For example, the twelve-hour tidal cycle in the oceans falls into this category as does certain physiological cycles in biological problems.

In our present example we shall assume that on *a priori* grounds a well-established "four element" cycle is involved. By this we mean, in terms of the length-time unit of this deep sea core, a cycle exists whose period (e.g., from peak to peak) is four points long on the time series.

Wallis and Roberts (1956) discuss two methods which may be used to "correct" or "adjust" a time series for the effect of a seasonal fluctuation. Both introduce a correction which is applied to a given element in a cycle by averaging the values for that element over repeated cycles. The *difference method* described here is best used where the seasonal effects are

TABLE 15.2

Computation of Average Unit Deviations in a Four Unit Cycle

	1st		2nd		3rd		4th
Distance along Core	Deviation	Distance	Deviation	Distance	Deviation	Distance	Deviation
30	0.30	40	0.18	50	0.53	60	0.05
70	−0.92	80	−0.35	90	0.15	100	0.15
110	−0.40	120	−0.15	130	0.45	140	0.13
150	−0.75	160	0.30	170	1.48	180	0.20
190	−0.57	200	−0.17	210	0.25	220	0.10
230	−0.72	240	−0.25	250	−0.20	260	0.18
270	−0.10	280	−0.02	290	0.93	300	−0.02
310	−0.17	320	0.10	330	−0.35	340	−0.50
350	−0.27	360	−0.02	370	0.38	380	0.18
390	−0.25	400	0.10	410	0.88	420	0.08
430	−0.30	440	0.15	450	0.33	460	−0.55
470	−0.85	480	−0.10	490	0.20	500	0.18
510	0.15	520	0.48	530	0.33	540	
Totals	−4.85		+0.25		+5.36		+0.18
Average	−0.373		0.019		0.412		0.014
	−0.37		0.02		0.41		0.01

considered independent of the time series level. That is, a correction is the same for the element in the cycle no matter whether the series is high or low at that point.

Since we have suggested a four element seasonal cycle, the first step in the procedure requires computations of a four unit moving average. The moving total is placed opposite the third of the four entries (see Table 15.1), and then corresponding moving averages are computed in column 7.

Next the deviations (time series entry minus moving average) are entered in column 8. As shown in Table 15.2, we collect like elements from the successive cycles and enter the corresponding deviations in the proper element column. The deviation in a column is once more summed and divided by the number of entries, giving an average deviation for each element in the seasonal cycle as shown at the bottom of Table 15.2.

The cycle corrections for the four unit seasonal cycle are −0.37 for the first element in the cycle, +0.02 for the second, +0.41 for the third, and +0.01 for the last element. These corrections are now applied to the original series; starting with the first element at 30 cm we have a correction

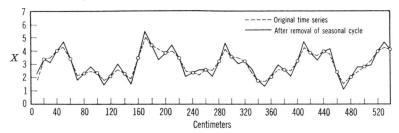

FIG. 15.2. Extraction of seasonal cycle from original time series from a deep sea core.

of $3.50 - 0.37 = 3.13$. The resulting "corrected" series is plotted in Fig. 15.2.

The second method is similar in the first steps but utilizes a ratio of moving average to observed value. Then, for like elements as before, the entries are summed over all cycles and an average ratio in the form of a percentage, is computed for each element. These average ratios are called *seasonal indices*, and are used to "correct" or "adjust" the original data.

The "ratio to moving average method" is most useful where the seasonal index is dependent on the level of the time series.

ADDITIONAL REFERENCE ON SEASONAL CYCLES

Horst Mendershausen, 1937, Annual survey of statistical technique: Methods of computing and eliminating changing seasonal fluctuations, *Econometrica* 5: 234–262. A detailed discussion of analysis and eliminating seasonal fluctuations. Divides methods into several classes and gives references under these subdivisions.

Test for Hypothetical Cycle after Adjustment for a Seasonal Cycle Has Been Made

Inspection of Fig. 15.2 and *a priori* information lead us to suspect a large-scale cycle of a 120 cm period with peaks at about 50, 170, 290, 410, and 530 cm respectively. We shall proceed to test for the reality of this proposed regularity in the time series by using a method described by McEwen (1949).[1] In this paper McEwen suggests that we add like elements of successive cycles and look at the resulting averages. In the illustrative example the hypothetical cycle that we wish to test consists of 12 entries. In Fig. 15.2 beginning with the peak the first of the hypothetical cycles begins at 50 cm and ends 160 cm. The second cycle begins at 170 cm and ends 280 cm, etc. For example, the second element in the first cycle is 3.61 at 60 cm, the second element in the second cycle is 4.51 at 180 cm. These are collected in Table 15.3. Inspection of the averages

[1] G. F. McEwen, (1949), *The reality of regularities indicated in sequences of observations*, Proceedings of the Berkeley Symposium on Mathematical Statistics and Probability. University of California Press, Berkeley and Los Angeles.

TABLE 15.3

Time Series

Element in the Cycle

	1¹	2	3	4	5	6	7	8	9	10	11	12	
1st cycle	4.81	3.61	1.83	2.32	2.91	2.41	1.43	2.12	3.11	2.41	1.53	3·62	
2nd cycle	5.71	4.51	3.43	3.92	4.51	3.61	2.03	2.42	2.61	2.61	2.13	3.12	
3rd cycle	4.71	3.61	3.13	3.32	2.81	1.81	1.33	2.02	3.01	2.61	2.13	3.32	
4th cycle	4.81	3.91	3.33	4.02	4.21	2.41	1.23	2.02	2.81	2.81	2.93	4.12	
Total	20.04	15.64	11.72	13.58	14.44	10.24	6.02	8.58	11.54	10.44	8.72	14.18	145.14
Mean	5.01	3.91	2.93	3.40	3.61	2.56	1.51	2.15	2.89	2.61	2.18	3.55	

¹ Beginning at 50 cm and ending at 530 cm in order to include full hypothetical cycles only.

indicates an initial high followed by a regular drop, then a second low peak, and finally an upswing. McEwen suggests that we test for the reality of this regularity by an analysis of variance. We shall use the simple one-way analysis of variance described in Chapter 7 (see Table 7.12.) to test the null hypothesis that the means are equal. The elements in the cycles

TABLE 15.4

Analysis of Variances

Source of Variation	D.F.	Sum of Squares	Mean Square	Test of Hypotheses: All 12 Mean are Equal
Among means	$12 - 1 = 11$	39.025^1	3.55	$F''_{36} = \dfrac{3.55}{0.30} = 11.8^2$
Within means	$12(4 - 1) = 36$	10.708	0.30	
Total	47			

Among means

$$\frac{(20.04)^2 + \cdots + (14.18)^2}{4} - \frac{(145.14)^2}{48} = 477.892 - 438.867 = 39.025$$

Within means

$$\text{Difference between below and above} = 49.733 - 39.025$$

Total

$$(4.81)^2 + \cdots + (4.12)^2 - \frac{(145.14)^2}{48} = 488.600 - 438.867 = 49.733$$

[1] Computed following outline in Table 7.18.
[2] Significant at 0.001 level i.e., $F''_{360.05} \cong 2.9$

are summarized in Table 15.3; the analysis of variance is in Table 15.4. From Table 15.4 it is apparent that the hypothesis of equal means is rejected. There is a "real" difference between the means.

This does not, however, tell us that we have uniquely discovered or established the existence of a cycle. In fact, to the eye at least, further decomposition of the time series, involving the apparent secondary peaks, seems indicated. The results of this test as in the previous discussion indicate the possibility of a 12 element cycle, and is suggestive of further investigations in the context of the natural situation which formed the basis for this particular series. Two further steps seem appropriate. First, reanalyze the data for a shorter cycle. Second, reexamine the natural situation; possibly design a more detailed sampling scheme including more closely spaced data in the original locality and adding additional localities.

A Situation Where the Test for Reality of a Cycle Could Be Applied

A formation exposed to a thickness of 3000 meters near the coast of Southern California consists of a layered sequence which contains

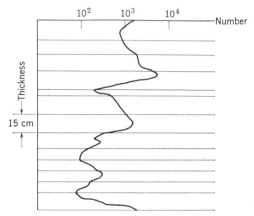

FIG. 15.3. Graph of the numerical distribution of planktonic foraminifera by sedimentation units. The vertical axis represents the sequence of sedimentation units as a stratigraphic section with the youngest deposit on top. The horizontal axis represents the number of foraminifera per sedimentation unit.

abundant planktonic foraminifera in fossil form. The average thickness of the layers is 15 cm. The lithology is described as a fine sandy shale, but it is not possible to distinguish a lateral trend either in sediment size or abundance of planktonic foraminifera within the layers. The rate of deposition is a factor of interest in interpretation of the history of deposition of the formation. Detailed examination leads to the designation of the layers as sedimentation units, i.e., each deposited under essentially uniform conditions.

A disagreement in interpretation arises. Two hypotheses are proposed for the sedimentation rate.

1. The layers represent uniform deposition in a marine basin in fairly deep water, with vertical settling of sediment to the bottom. On general principles, an estimate of rate of sedimentation of 20 cm per 1000 years gives a fairly large time estimate for the total deposit. This is the first hypothesis.

2. The relative abundance of planktonic foraminifera by layers indicates the possibility of a cyclic phenomenon. Ecologic considerations suggest the possibility of interpreting the apparent cycle as a regular two- or three-year population increase followed by a decrease. Since the peaks occur about every third layer, this would indicate a much lower rate of deposition. This is the second hypothesis.

A test for the reality of the several year cycle would appear to be useful here. In addition, supposing that the test results are negative, a test for trend versus random fluctuations might yield useful information.

CORRELATION BETWEEN TIME SERIES

Burnaby (1953)[1] describes a method for testing the hypothesis that two time series are unrelated. The cross difference product E is defined as

$$E_{r,r+1} = (p_r - q_{r+1})(q_r - p_{r+1}); \qquad r < r + 1 \quad \text{(in ordering)}$$

where $p_1, p_2 \cdots p_r \cdots$ and $q_1, q_2 \cdots q_r \cdots$ represent two time series. Mean $E = (1/n)(E_{1,2} + E_{3,4} + \cdots)$ is positive if corresponding p and q terms differ less from each other than from their neighbors in the same series. The reader may verify this by setting up hypothetical series. In practice for moderately large samples, a simplification is introduced by inspection and the counting of plus, minus, and zero signs for the E's. A χ^2 test may then be used. The null hypothesis for a pair of time series with only chance agreement between pairs is that the number of plus and minus signs is equal. (See Chapter 6, Eqs. 6.10 and 6.11.) This rapid method is applied by Burnaby to two series of varves; it is illustrated in the following example where the deep sea core analyzed earlier is now compared with a second core taken several hundred miles away but in the same deep sea basin.

The χ^2 test results are given in Table 15.5. Note how the quick tabulation of signs is made by using two columns, the first to contain the sign of the cross difference for each member of a pair, the second to contain the sign of the product. The writers have found that in tabulating long time series this method reduces error.

We conclude from the χ^2 test that the similarity between the two series is not due to chance. An interesting application made by Burnaby to varves opens up a more general class of problems. In the example of the cores above the two cores were already matched pair for pair since both had the same number of elements. Let us now consider a situation where two time series not necessarily of equal length are available and *the problem is to match them in such a way that the agreement is better than that expected by chance.* Examples of situations like this include two varve series with no common reference point such as described by Burnaby, or two stratigraphic series, or once again a pair of cores. The property considered may be thickness, average size of particle, percentage of a trace element, etc. The matching may be made visually and then tested as before. However, if the level of significance is P_n in the test of the null hypothesis, then the true level of significance must be multiplied by the number of alternative ways of matching the series so that $P_t = NP_n$.

[1] T. P. Burnaby, 1953, A suggested alternative to the correlation coefficient for testing the significance of agreement between pairs of time series and its application to geological data, *Nature* 172: 210.

TABLE 15.5

Distance along Core in cm	Core No. 1	Core No. 2	Cross Difference		Sign
10	1.9	1.7	−	−	+
20	3.4	3.2			
30	3.5	3.6	−	−	+
40	4.0	4.1			
50	4.4	4.2	+	+	+
60	3.6	3.5			
70	2.2	2.0	+	−	−
80	2.3	2.0			
90	2.5	2.4	0	0	0
100	2.4	2.5			
110	1.8	2.0	−	−	+
120	2.1	2.1			
130	2.7	3.0	−	+	−
140	2.4	3.1			
150	1.9	1.8	−	−	+
160	3.6	3.5			
170	5.3	6.0	+	+	+
180	4.5	4.8			
190	3.8	4.4	+	+	+
200	3.9	3.0			
210	4.1	4.0	+	+	+
220	3.6	3.9			
230	2.4	3.3	−	+	−
240	2.4	3.2			
250	2.2	2.3	−	−	+
260	2.6	2.3			
270	2.5	2.4	−	−	+
280	3.1	3.0			
290	4.3	5.1	+	+	+
300	3.6	3.7			
310	3.5	3.6	+	+	+
320	3.3	3.1			
330	2.4	3.0	+	+	+
340	1.8	2.3			
350	1.7	1.9	−	−	+
360	2.0	2.1			
370	2.6	2.8	+	+	+
380	2.6	2.4			
390	2.5	2.0	−	−	+
400	3.3	3.0			
410	4.4	4.0	+	+	+
420	3.9	3.6			
430	3.7	3.7	−	−	+
440	4.0	3.8			
450	3.8	2.5	−	+	−
460	2.4	3.9			
470	1.6	1.8	−	−	+
480	2.0	2.4			
490	2.4	2.5	−	−	+
500	2.8	2.9			
510	3.3	3.5	−	−	+
520	4.1	4.0			
530	4.4	4.6	+	+	+
540	4.2	4.3			

Cross difference $= (p_r - q_{r+1})(q_r - p_{r+1})$
$q_r = r$th entry in core No. 2, $p_r =$ corresponding entry in core No. 1.

$$\chi^2 = \frac{(22 - 13)^2}{13} + \frac{(4 - 13)^2}{13} = 12.46$$

$\chi^2_{0.995} = 7.88$ for 1 d.f.

Summary: 22(+), 4(−), 1(0).

For example, series A of a sequence of graded bedding has 200 recognizable beds, whereas series B has 74. There are 127 alternative ways of matching the full series B with series A. In general, if the number of elements in the larger series is denoted by N_l and in the smaller by N_s, then the corrected level of significance may be rewritten as

$$P_t = [(N_l - N_s) + 1]P_n$$

The assumptions required in the test for correlation between time series is that the pair of time series has approximately the same mean and variance. Burnaby suggests that a linear transformation will meet this difficulty.

SUGGESTED REFERENCES IN THE CONTEXT OF THE CHAPTER

G. H. Orcutt and S. F. James, 1948, Testing the significance of correlation between time series, *Biometrika* 35: 397–413. Presents a model for time series, then gives empirical distributions of correlations, which can be used for testing correlation between a pair of time series. Many references.

E. Groba, 1958, Methodische Schwierigkeiten bei der Untersuchung Literaler Sedimente, *Geol. Rundschau Band* 47, Heft 1, 24–28. Discusses the general problem of taking time synchronous samples in littoral studies.

M. H. Quenouille, 1952, *Associated measurements*. Academic Press, New York, Chapter 11, Time Series Analysis.

SUMMARY

It appears that application of time series analysis to geological problems is essentially an untapped field of investigation. Except for Burnaby's paper on correlation between two time series referred to earlier, and some work on varves and tree-rings in late quaternary (Korn's paper and Vistelius' work, see p. 349), there has been to the authors' knowledge virtually no work published. This observation extends to the more sophisticated and generalized areas of stochastic processes. See, for example, Bartlett (1955),[1] Doob (1953),[2] Feller (1950).[3]

PAPERS OF GEOLOGICAL INTEREST IN WHICH TIME SERIES ARE UTILIZED BUT NO FORMAL ANALYSIS APPLIED

Ralph Yalkovsky, 1957, The relationship between paleotemperature and carbonate content in a deep-sea core, *Jour. Geol.* 65:5; 480–495. Includes chemical analysis for 11 elements in a sequential arrangement on a deep sea core. Assuming fairly constant rate of sedimentation a number of time series are thus given.

Cesare Emiliani, 1955, Pleistocene temperatures, *Jour. Geol.* 63: 6; 538–571. A number of time series based on core (deep sea) measurements of paleotemperatures.

[1] M. S. Bartlett, 1955, *Stochastic Processes*. Cambridge Univ. Press, London.

[2] J. L. Doob, 1953, *Stochastic Processes*. John Wiley, New York.

[3] W. Feller, 1950, *An introduction to probability theory and its applications*, Vol. I, John Wiley, New York.

A. Carozzi, 1951, Rythmes de Sedimentation dans le Cretace Helvetique, *Geologische Rundschau*, 39: 177–195. Several properties of sedimentary rocks are given as time series in an excellent paper.

W. D. Bruckner, 1953, *Jour. Sed. Petrol.* 23:4; 235–237. Cyclic calcareous sedimentation as an index of climatic variations in the past.

M. Sauramo, 1954, Das Ratsel des Ancylussees, *Geologische Rundschau*, 42: 197–232. Time series based on pollen analysis.

Ernst Antevs, 1938, *Rainfall and tree growth in the Great Basin*, American Geographical Society Spec. Publication 21; also under Carnegie Inst. of Wash., pub. No. 469. As title indicates it discusses the natural situation, gives graphical time series also smoothed and treated in various ways; some formal time-series analysis.

Consideration should be given to the possibility that most phenomena occurring over geological time intervals involving millions of years are episodic rather than periodic; that is, that phenomena reoccur, or intensity varies, but not in the sense of a regular period between peaks. It is tempting to speculate that the phenomena of mountain-building and major glaciations, for example, are subject to a regularity through time, hence periodic; and we need only hit on the right analytic combination, such as some time series method, to be able to describe quantitatively such major geologic time-dependent sequences.

chapter **16**

Distribution of Points in a Plane and Higher Dimensions: Discussion of Models, Tests, and Applications

This section is primarily concerned with a survey and discussion of some tests for randomness of the distribution of points in a plane although extensions to higher dimensions are given. Also included is some discussion of the distribution of points on a line. Two specific alternatives to randomness are considered: (1) uniform distributions where the points tend to be dispersed with respect to each other and (2) clustering where the points tend to occur in clumps. Since we use the term "random distribution of points in a plane," it is necessary that a definition of this term be given and consistently followed throughout the discussion. The plane is stressed because its dimensionality is applicable to a wide array of geological problems.

The word *random* is used in the discussion of planar distributions of points with the following meaning,[1] although extension to higher dimensions follows readily from the subsequent discussion.

1. In a random distribution of points over a plane, any point has an equal probability of occurring at any position on that plane.

2. A small subdivision of the plane has as much chance of containing a point as any other small subdivision of the same size.

3. The position of a point on the plane is no way influenced by the position of any other point.

[1] P. J. Clark and F. C. Evans, 1954, Distance to nearest neighbor, as a measure of spatial relationships in populations, *Ecology* 35: 445–453.

Care should be taken in specifying the extent of the area to be considered, since it is possible that a certain area may have a random distribution of points, but a much larger region containing the first area may be nonrandom.

Mathematical models for certain situations are also presented, as well as derivations for several of the models as an aid in understanding them. Before going into the various models, it will be helpful to define several additional terms which are used repeatedly throughout this section. Curtis and McIntosh (1950) give a detailed review of various measures used by plant ecologists to analyze distribution of points over a plane. Several of these measures seem to be of general applicability to geologic problems. The following terms have been selected for generality and usefulness from those listed in this paper:

1. *Density:* $D = \dfrac{\text{Total number of points}}{\text{Total area}}$. D is thus an expression of the number of points per unit area.
2. *Mean area:* mean area $= 1/D$.
3. *Quadrat:* the sampling unit (usually a square).

Curtis and McIntosh (*ibid.*)[1] also discuss the problem of what size of quadrat to select for analysis of a given region. They suggest that an optimum quadrat size should be twice as large as the mean area of the region. This size is thus dependent on both the number of points and on the area of the region. We may write this suggestion more concisely. Since mean area $= 1/D$ and $D = \dfrac{\text{Total number of points}}{\text{Total area}}$, optimum quadrat size is $\dfrac{2(\text{Total area})}{\text{Total number of points}}$. The question of optimum quadrat size is taken up again at the end of this section and the preceding expression applied to a real situation.

THE POISSON MODEL

The Poisson distribution has been presented and derived in Chapter 2. We shall describe a model which leads to the Poisson distribution and has wide application and importance in natural phenomena.[2] Although

---

[1] J. T. Curtis and R. P. McIntosh, 1950, see p. 379 for full reference. See also J. G. Skellam, 1955, Quadrat sampling from the mathematical standpoint, *Proc. Linnean Soc. London*, Session 165, 1952–53, Pt. 2.

[2] The following discussion of the Poisson model for distribution of points in one, two, and higher dimensions is based on W. Feller, 1950, *An Introduction to probability theory and its applications*, John Wiley, p. 116ff.

intervals on a line is used as illustration, the principle is applicable to higher dimensions.

Suppose an interval of unit dimension is divided into equal subintervals of length $1/n$. There will then be n of these subintervals. We shall now consider the distribution of points in the entire interval in the following manner: either a subinterval is empty or it contains a point. If the subintervals are small enough, the likelihood of several points in a subinterval becomes negligible. The probability of a point in a subinterval shall be denoted by p_n, and we stipulate that the probability of a point in a subinterval is not affected by the presence or absence of a point in any other subinterval. Furthermore, p_n is the same for all subintervals since the subintervals are equal. The conditions described satisfy the requirements of the binomial distribution, and the following statement can be made: the probability of exactly k points in the total unit interval is given by the binomial distribution, $b(k; n, p_n)$. It can be shown that under certain restrictions if the expected value of the binomial $np \to \lambda$, then $b(k; n, p_n)$ can be restated as $b(k; n, \lambda/n)$, which approaches the Poisson distribution, $p(k; \lambda)$. We may now say that the probability of exactly k points in a unit interval is $p(k; \lambda) = e^{-\lambda}(\lambda^k/k!)$, $k = 0, 1, \quad , n$. With the unit interval subdivided into n equal subintervals of length $1/n$, the total length of the unit interval is $1/n + 1/n + \cdots + 1/n = n \cdot 1/n = 1$. Suppose we use an interval of length t instead of a unit interval. There are thus nt subintervals, and when we reason and sum as above, the total length of the interval is t. $\left(\sum_{1}^{nt}\left(\frac{1}{n}\right) = t.\right)$ Then the parameter λ, which represents the density of points in the Poisson model and which has the relation $np_n \to \lambda$ in the Poisson approximation to the binomial, becomes $(nt)p_n \to \lambda t$.

We can now say that the probability of finding exactly k points in a fixed interval of length t is given by the Poisson distribution.

$$p(k; \lambda t) = e^{-\lambda t}\frac{(\lambda t)^k}{k!} \qquad (16.1)$$

This model (16.1) has two basic assumptions:

1. If the interval is small, the probability of finding more than one point in the interval is small compared to the length of the interval.

2. The intervals are mutually independent in the sense that one cannot deduce the number of points in an interval from knowledge of any other interval.

For practical applications of this model we must now show that the parameter λt can also be approximated[1] by T/N, where T is the total

[1] For another approach to the estimation of the parameters λt see exercise No. 7, Chapter 3.

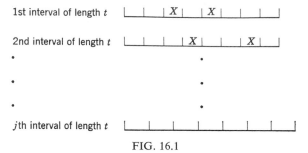

FIG. 16.1

number of points in N separate intervals, each of fixed length t. We shall count the number of points which occur in each of the N repeated intervals of individual length t. Fig. 16.1 illustrates the counting procedure.

N_i is the number of intervals each of length t containing i points. $N_0 + N_1 + N_2 + \cdots + N_k = N$. Let T be the total number of points. Then

$$0N_0 + 1N_1 + 2N_2 + \cdots + iN_i + \cdots + KN_k = T$$

T may be written as $T = \sum\limits_{i=0}^{k} [i(N_i)]$, $i = 0, 1, 2, \cdots, k$, where k is maximum number of points observed in any of the intervals.

$i(N_i)$ is the total number of points summed over all subintervals containing N_i points. The averge number of points in an interval may be thought of as the total number of points divided by the total number of intervals. This is expressed as T/N. By the law of large numbers,[1] when N, the number of intervals, is very large, the probability of exactly i points in each of N intervals of length t can be approximated

$$N \approx N \cdot p(i; \lambda t) = N \cdot e^{-\lambda t} \frac{(\lambda t)^i}{i!}$$

The total number of points previously expressed as

$$T = 0 \cdot N_0 + 1N_1 + 2N_2 + \cdots + iN_i + \cdots$$

can be substituted term for term by the Poisson distribution,

$$T \approx N[0 \cdot p(0, \lambda t) + 1 \cdot p(1, \lambda t) + 2 \cdot p(2, \lambda t) + \cdots i \cdot p(i, \lambda t) + \cdots]$$

or

$$T \approx N \left(e^{-\lambda t} \frac{(\lambda t)^1}{1!} + 2e^{-\lambda t} \frac{(\lambda t)^2}{2!} + \cdots + ie^{-\lambda t} \frac{(\lambda t)^i}{i!} + \cdots \right)$$

[1] See Feller, 1950, *ibid.*

Rearranging terms,

$$T \approx Ne^{-\lambda t}\lambda t\left(1 + \lambda t + \frac{(\lambda t)^2}{2!} + \cdots + \frac{(\lambda t)^i}{i!} + \cdots\right)$$

But by Taylor expansion,

$$e^{\lambda t} = 1 + \lambda t + \frac{(\lambda t)^2}{2!} + \cdots$$

Substituting,

$$T \approx Ne^{-\lambda t}\lambda t\, e^{\lambda t} = N\lambda t$$

Collecting and rearranging, $\lambda t \approx T/N$.

Both T and N can be obtained from observational data. It is thus possible to compare the Poisson model with actual situations, since we get can an estimate of λt.

Tests of Fit to the Poisson Distribution

Clapham (1936)[1] uses the ratio of μ^2/μ_1' as an index of fit, where $\mu_2 = \sigma^2$ (variance) and $\mu_1' = \mu$ (mean).[2] For the Poisson distribution, the ratio μ_2/μ_1' is equal to unity. If the ratio exceeds unity, the points (over a plane, for example) are considered more widely dispersed than in a random distribution. If the ratio is less than unity, the points are considered less widely dispersed than in a random distribution (a clustering effect). Since practical applications deal in terms of a sample of points rather than the whole population, the parameters μ_2 and μ_1' are estimated. $\dfrac{\sum\limits_{i=0}^{k}(x_i' - \bar{x})^2}{\bar{x}(n-1)}$ (where n is total number of points) is the estimator of μ_2/μ_1'.

Unfortunately, this very convenient ratio is not independent of the size of quadrat.[3] (The quadrat refers to the usually square sampling unit used in analysis of the distribution of points over a plane in applied problems, particularly plant ecology.) Evans (1952)[3] discussed the alteration of the shape of the frequency distribution due to change in quadrat size. As the quadrat is increased in size it is more likely to contain many points; conversely it is less likely to contain no points. Thus as quadrat size increases, the number of quadrats containing no point or just one point decreases, but because of the concurrent drop in the quadrat number, Evans pointed

[1] A. R. Clapham, 1936, Over dispersion in grassland communities and the use of statistical methods in plant ecology. *Jour. Ecology* 24: 232–251.

[2] See pp. 43, 44, Chapter 3 for discussion of notation μ, μ', etc.

[3] F. C. Evans, 1952, The influence of size of quadrat on the distributional patterns of plant populations. *Contr. Lab. Vert. Biol.* No. 54, Ann Arbor, Michigan.

J. G. Skellam, 1952, Studies in statistical ecology. *I. Spatial pattern, Biometrika*, Vol. 39, Pts. 3, 4; 346–362.

out that the relative frequency in these classes actually increased, and at the same time the upper tail of the frequency distribution lengthened (toward more per quadrat). (See Fig. 16.2.)

The Index of Dispersion

R. A. Fisher[1] proposed a method of comparison of data with the Poisson distribution which he calls the index of dispersion. The statistic given below is treated as a χ^2 variable with $(N - 1)$ degrees of freedom.

$$\sum_{i=0}^{k} \frac{[f_i(x_i - x)]^2}{\bar{x}} \quad \text{(in sample notation)}$$

where $x_i = 0, 1, 2, \cdots, k$, and f_i is the number of quadrats containing x_i points. $N = \Sigma f_i$ and $\bar{x} = \Sigma f_i x_i / N$. The index may be written in the following convenient form

$$\frac{\sum f_i x_i^2 - \bar{x} \sum f_i x_i}{\bar{x}} \quad \text{(for sample data)}$$

In a more recent paper, Fisher (1950)[2] discusses the difficulties involved if x is small and the classes few in number. In such cases, the evidence of deviation from the Poisson distribution may be based to a great degree on those class intervals whose expected frequencies are less than 5. This introduces doubt as to the validity of the index of dispersion in such cases. Although Fisher does not consider the difficulty as serious,[3] he discusses refinements when class expectations are small.

Conventional χ^2 fit by classes

The χ^2 fit by conventional methods, of an observed frequency distribution to the Poisson distribution, is subject to the same difficulties (expected values in the classes in the tail of the distribution much less than 5). As Fisher (1950) points out, if grouping of classes to bring up the expected value is carried out extensively, the χ^2 test is made unduly insensitive, and the strong evidence really provided by the individual classes is ignored.

The following illustrates the procedure. The generalized Poisson is $p(x) = e^{-\lambda}[(\lambda)^x/x!]$ and we estimate λ by $\bar{x}$. Substituting, we have, $e^{-\bar{x}}[(\bar{x})^x/x!]$. However, in this form we get the expected proportion or percentage for given x, and so we multiply by the sample size n to get the

[1] R. A. Fisher, 1925, *Statistical methods for research workers*, G. E. Stechert, New York. (See p. 59, 10th ed. 1946.)

[2] R. A. Fisher, 1950, Significance of deviations from expectation in a Poisson series, *Biometrics* 6: 17–24.

[3] See also Lancaster, 1952, *Biometrika* 39: 419–421.

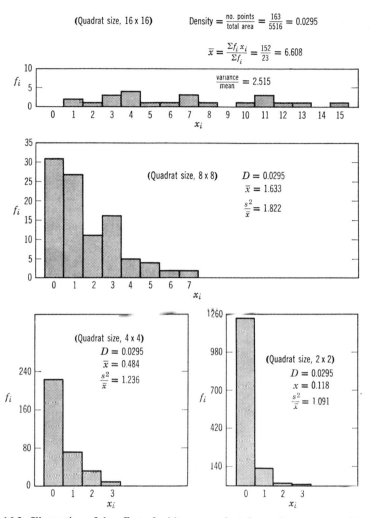

FIG. 16.2. Illustration of the effect of arbitrary quadrat size on the measures of density, x and ratio of variance to mean. Data from the distribution of *Lystrocanthus* spines at a particular level in the Mecca shale (Fig. 16.8).

expected frequency. The terms in the Poisson sequence then become $n(\bar{x})^x/e^{\bar{x}}x!$ for given x. Computing procedure is handled by putting the above ratio into log form.

$$\log\left\{\frac{[n(\bar{x})^x]}{[e^{\bar{x}}(x!)]}\right\} = (\log n + x \log \bar{x}) - [\log (x!) + \bar{x} \log e]$$

$$= \log \text{ expected value for class } x \text{ (see Fig. 16.13)}$$

x	Observed Frequency	log Expected Frequency	Expected (antilog of Previous Column) (Observed) − (Expected)	$\dfrac{(\text{Observed-Expected})^2}{\text{Expected}}$
0	n_0	$\log n - x \log e$		
1	n_1	$\log n_1 + 1 (\log x) - \log (1!) + x \log e$		
2	n_2	$\log n_2 + 2 (\log x) - \log (2!) + x \log e$		
3	n_3	$\log n_3 + 3 (\log x) - \log (3!) + x \log e$		
.		.		
.		.		
.		.		
k	n^k			

$$N = \text{number of classes } (X\text{'s}) \qquad \sum_{i=1}^{n} n_i = n = \Sigma f_i$$

$$\text{where } x = \frac{\Sigma f_i x_i}{\Sigma f_i} \qquad\qquad \Sigma\left[\frac{(\text{Observed-Expected})^2}{\text{Expected}}\right] = \chi^2$$

FIG 16.3.

NOTE. In general, the number of degrees of freedom are the number of class minus the number of linear restraints minus 1. Here the estimate $\bar{x}$ is the only restraint that is, in the Poisson this is 1; $\lambda = E(x) = \text{var}(x)$; thus d.f. $= N - 1 - 1 = N - 2$. See Chapter 6, p. 117.

DEPENDENCE OF POINTS AND "CONTAGIOUS" DISTRIBUTIONS

In many situations in nature, the Poisson model does not directly apply. If the criterion of independence of the individual points or of the individual sampling units (such as a quadrat) is not satisfied, the distribution of points should not *a priori* be expected to fit the Poisson model. For example, clustering of the points due to mutual attraction of some sort introduces the term "contagious distributions." Several models have been proposed for such a situation. Two of these in general use, particularly in plant ecology, seem readily applicable to geological problems.

Neyman Type A Contagious Distribution

This model is proposed by J. Neyman (1939).[1] The term "contagious" is used to describe a class of distributions in which there is a natural tendency toward clumping or clustering of the points, and was discussed by Polya (1931).[2] The equation takes the following form, e.g., the probability that the number of points in a square is exactly 2:

$$P(x = 2) = e^{-m_1(1 - e^{-m_2})} \frac{m_2^2}{2!} (m_1^2 e^{-2m_2} + m_1 e^{-m_2})$$

where m_1 and m_2 are two parameters, the former representing the number of clusters per sampling unit or quadrat, and the latter representing the number of individual points per cluster. Thomson (1952)[3] describes in detail a method for applying the model to emprical problems. In this paper polynomials are employed to compute the various terms in Neyman's equation. Shenton (1949)[4] has described still another solution for application of Neyman's model by the use of the method of maximum likelihood.

Thomas' "Double Poisson" Model

We now consider a more complex situation in which the Poisson model is involved. Assume an area over which a number of points are randomly distributed, but in addition assume that with each of these points a random number of other points are associated, i.e., another Poisson distribution. We have thus to consider two interacting distributions, that of the randomly distributed points and that of the points associated with each of

[1] J. Neyman, 1939, On a new class of contagious distributions applicable in entomology and bacteriology, *Annals math. Stats.* X: 35–37.

[2] G. Polya, 1931, *Sur quelques points de la théorie des probabilities*, Annales de l'Institut Henri Poincaré, 1: 117–182.

[3] G. W. Thomson, 1952, Measures of plant aggregation based on contagious distribution, *Contrib. Lab. Vert. Bil.* Ann Arbor, Michigan, No. 53.

[4] L. R. Shenton, 1949, On the efficiency of the method of moments and Neymans Type A distribution, *Biometrika* 36: 450–54.

them. Suppose the area is divided into small squares. Thomas (1949)[1] proposes a model which enables one to compute the probability that a given square contains 0, 1, 2, $\cdots$ points. The equation is

$$P(k \text{ points in a small square, or quadrat}) = \sum_{r=1}^{k} \frac{m^r e^{-m}}{r!} \frac{(r\lambda)^{k-r} e^{-r\lambda}}{(k-r)!}$$

where m is the parameter equal to average number of "clusters" per quadrat. λ is the parameter equal to one less than the mean number of plants per cluster.

Thomson (1952) has also presented a detailed method for solution of the "double Poisson" series for application to empirical problems. As in his solution to Neyman's Type A contagious distribution, he applies polynomials to simplify the required calculations.

According to Skellam (1952)[2] models of this type are not genuinely applicable if the clusters are not compact or if the process extends over a period of time such that successive additions of points are noted. This somewhat limits the applications of contagious distributions of the type just described in those geological studies where time changes are considered.

Skellam (1952, *ibid.* pp. 353–354) describes a model which takes into account cases where aggregates or cluster are not compact and where the quadrat is small by comparison. He has also proposed (pp. 347–358) a model which is applicable to patterns arising by processes operating over a period of time.

Evans (1952)[3] points out with a numerical example that a distribution may vary radically from a Poisson series and still have the variance exactly equal to the mean. Skellam (*ibid.*) also notes the difficulties of quadrat size. The interpretation of Evans' statement above, as given by Thomson (*ibid.*), is that although disagreement of the ratio of mean to variance from that expected in a Poisson distribution does indicate some degree of departure from a random distribution, the converse does not hold. That is, the close approach of the ratio of the mean to the variance, to the value unity, does not necessarily imply a Poisson distribution.

The *density* is independent of quadrat size if expresssed as the number of individuals per unit area (as defined on p. 366) but is directly proportional to quadrat size if defined as the number of individuals per quadrat.

The *frequency distribution* is also affected by quadrat size. (See earlier discussion and Fig. 16.2.) Evans (*ibid.*) suggests that a replicate analysis

[1] M. Thomas, 1949, A generalization of Poisson's binomial limit for use in ecology, *Biometrika* 36:18–25.

[2] J. G. Skellam, 1952, Studies in statistical ecology. I. Spatial pattern, *Biometrika* Vol. 39, Pts. 3, 4; 346–362.

[3] F. C. Evans, 1952, The influence of size of quadrat on the distributional patterns of plant populations. *Contr. Lab. Vert. Biol.* Ann Arbor, Michigan, No. 54.

of the region using different sized quadrats may be used to estimate the relative degree of departure of the distribution of points from a random distribution. His proposed method uses the various sizes of quadrat to plot a series of points of density against frequency of occurrence. A curve fit to these points is compared visually with a curve showing the relation of density to frequency in a theoretical random distribution. The theoretical curve is computed from the equation $F = 100 (1 - e^{-D})$, [Clapham (1936)],[1] where F is frequency and D is density. Although this approach seems to the writers to be one which would give very useful results, it is laborious, and at this time of writing, presents a qualitative rather than a quantitative final result.

ILLUSTRATIVE APPLICATION OF SOME OF THE TESTS FOR FIT TO POISSON

The following examples are taken from analysis of the distribution of particulate matter in the Mecca shale of Pennsylvanian age [Miller (1956)].[2] The χ^2 test of goodness-of-fit of a sample frequency distribution to the Poisson was made on a sample of 163 *Lystrooanthus* fin-spines distributed over an area of about 5×6 meters. The data given in Table 16.1 are

TABLE 16.1
Distribution of Number of Spines per Quadrat

No. of Spines Observed in a Quadrat	No. of Quadrats
(x_i)	(f_i)
0	31
1	27
2	11
3	16
4	5
5	4
6	2
7	2
	$98 = \Sigma f_i$

[1] A. R. Clapham, 1936, Over-dispersion in grassland communities and the use of statistical methods in plant ecology, *Jour. Ecology* 24: 232–251.

[2] R. L. Miller, 1956, Speculation on water currents in a black shale environment, by use of orientation and dispersion of fossil fragments, *Trans. Am. Geophys. Union*, 37: 354-355.

based on an optimum quadrat size computed according to Curtis and McIntosh (1950). (See introduction to this chapter and Fig. 16.2.) The same data as given in Table 16.1 are used in several tests.

Table 16.2 shows the application of the computing form for Poisson goodness-of-fit test, as described in Fig. 16.3 and p. 370. The last three classes are combined in the expected column. Customary procedure suggests that all classes whose expected frequencies are less than 5 be combined with the adjacent upper class (or classes) until the sum is greater than or equal to 5. However, as Fisher points out (see p. 370 of this chapter) this may lead to an important loss of information. We have compromised to the extent of summing all classes after the last class whose expected value exceeds 5 as shown in Table 16.2.

Since there are six classes remaining after summing of the last three, the degrees of freedom are $6 - 2 = 4$. A sample of 98 subsamples (quadrats) (from a Poisson distribution) will have a $\chi^2_{\text{4d.f.}}$ deviation as large as 14.86 only five times in a thousand.[1] In this example, the $\chi_{\text{4d.f.}}$ deviation is 38.10. We therefore reject the hypothesis that the sample came from a Poisson population on the grounds that is it an extremely improbable event.

Since a Poisson distribution represents a random distribution of points (in this case, over a plane), we may be justified in stating that the Lystrocanthus spines are not randomly distributed. Alternative interpretations are not available from the above test. Before discussing this further, we shall reexamine the data of Table 16.1 by applying two other tests described on pp. 370ff.

Application of Fisher's "Index of Dispersion"

$$\text{Index of dispersion, } (I_D) = \frac{\sum_{i=0}^{k} f_i x_i^2 - \bar{x} \sum_{i=0}^{k} f_i x_i}{\bar{x}}, \qquad i = 0, 1, \cdots, k$$

$$\sum f_i x_i = 163, \quad \sum f_i x_i^2 = 565, \quad \bar{X} = \frac{\sum_{i=0}^{k} f_i x_i}{\sum_{i=0}^{k} f_i} = \frac{163}{98} = 1.663$$

Therefore

$$I_D = \frac{565 - 1.663(163)}{1.663} = 176.75$$

$\chi^2 = 176.75$ and degrees of freedom $= 98 - 1 = 97$.

A $\chi^2_{\text{97d.f.}}$ value of 125.0 may be expected only five times in a thousand for samples of 98 drawn from a Poisson population. Since the observed

---

[1] Thus, $P\{\chi_4^2 \leq 14.86\} \approx 99.5\%$ or $P\{\chi_4^2 \geq 14.86\} \approx 0.5\%$.

TABLE 16.2

χ^2 Test for Goodness-of-Fit to the Poisson Distribution for the Dispersal of Lystrocanthus Spines

Classes	Observed Frequency	Expected Frequency	Observed-Expected	(Observed-Expected)²
Number of Points Observed in a Quadrat (X_i)	Number of Quadrats Containing X_i Points (f_i)	Computed from Poisson		Expected
0	31	18.58	12.42	8.30
1	27	30.83	−3.83	0.48
2	11	25.70	−14.70	8.41
3	16	14.24	1.76	0.22
4	5	5.92	−0.92	0.85
5	4	1.97 ⎫	7.38	20.55
6	2	0.55 ⎬		
7	2	0.13 ⎭		
d.f. = 4	$98 = \sum\limits_{i=0}^{7} f_i$	97.92		$38.10 = X^2$

NOTE. Computations in the above table follow the form given in Fig. 16.3. $\bar{X} = \dfrac{\sum X_i f_i}{\sum f_i} = \dfrac{163}{98} = 1.663$, $\quad n = \sum f_i = 98$, $N = 6$, after combining classes, d.f. $= N - 2 = 4$.

$\chi^2_{\text{97d.f.}}$ value above is 176.75, we reject the hypothesis that the sample was drawn from a Poisson population, and hence the hypothesis of randomness. Note that no alternative hypothesis is considered in Fisher's index. (See p. 370.)

Application of the Ratio of the Mean to the Variance (Clapham's Ratio)[1]

A property of the Poisson distribution is that the ratio of the mean to the variance equals unity. An intuitively appealing test for goodness-of-fit-to the Poisson distribution would seem to be to test the ratio of the sample mean to the sample variance, as discussed on p. 369. Furthermore, the result may offer a relative test of alternative hypotheses. If the ratio of mean to variance exceeds unity, a rough inference may be drawn that a clustering effect is present. If, on the other hand, the ratio is less than unity, the inference is that there is a regular dispersion of points such that individual points tend to "repel" each other.

1. Suppose the variance is small relative to the mean. This implies that on the average the quadrats contain about the same number of points; hence a regular dispersal of points over the plane. The ratio in this case would be less than one.

2. Suppose the variance is large relative to the mean. This implies that the number of points varies widely from quadrat to quadrat; hence a clustering effect. Here the ratio would be greater than one.

We now apply the ratio test to the data of Table 16.1. Using the sample estimator of $\mu_2/\mu_1{}^1$ we have

$$\frac{\sum\limits_{i=1}^{n}(x_i - \bar{x})^2}{\bar{x}(n-1)} = \frac{\sum f_i x_i{}^2 - \bar{x}\sum f_i x_i}{\bar{x}(\sum f_i - 1)} = 1.822$$

where

$$\bar{x} = \frac{\sum\limits_{i=1}^{n} f_i x_i}{\sum f_i} = 1.663$$

and this result may be interpreted as saying that not only is the hypothesis of randomness rejected, but the alternative hypothesis of clustering is favored over the other alternative, that of mutual dispersion.

However, as discussed on p. 374 the size of quadrat chosen as sampling unit has a marked effect on the results. Figure 16.2 shows the results in the form of frequency distributions and gives the values of density, mean,

[1] This ratio is similar in form to Fisher's 'index of dispersion,' but is treated somewhat differently in the following discussion.

and the ratio of mean to variance for four different quadrat sizes. The four quadrat sizes used were in units of area, 8 × 8 (the optimum size according to Curtis and McIntosh,[1,2]), 16 × 16, 4 × 4, and 2 × 2 taken from Fig. 16.2. Note the marked effect of quadrat size on frequency distribution form, average number of points per quadrat, and finally, on the ratio of variance to mean. It would appear that if no restrictions were placed on quadrat size that one could suitably change the value of the ratio from very close to one implying randomness, to very much larger than one implying clustering, on the same data merely by adjusting the size of the quadrat.

How shall one judge whether the diversity of the value of the ratio from unity in either direction is sufficiently large to favor an alternative hypothesis? Application of Fisher's index as a χ^2 test of goodness-of-fit to the Poisson appears to provide the most direct answer to the question. We now turn to quite a different approach.

THE "NEAREST NEIGHBOR" TECHNIQUE: THE REFLEXIVE RELATION BETWEEN POINTS IN SPATIAL DISTRIBUTIONS

Another approach to the analysis of spatial distributions which avoids the difficulties inherent in quadrat sampling is based on direct consideration of the spatial relationship of the individual points to each other. In what follows, we will confine the discussion to points in a plane. A method will be described in the latter part of this section which can be readily extended to higher dimensional distributions.

---

[1] Curtis and McIntosh base their proposal on the computed relationship between the properties of density and frequency and quadrat size, (where frequency is defined to be

$$\frac{\text{Number of quadrats containing points}}{\text{Total number of quadrats}}$$

The expected relationship among these three variables is based on the random distribution of points over a plane and follows a mathematical model proposed by Preston (1948).[3] The proposal for optimum quadrat size is the result of a compromise in an effort to gain maximum accuracy in the prediction of a number of properties useful to plant ecologists, including frequency. It is found that a quadrat size which is twice the mean area results in a "frequency" of 86% or less. Because of the complex relationships of the various properties of interest a frequency value much higher than 86% results in minimum accuracy in prediction of such properties as density.

Our present concern, however, is not with maximum accuracy for the various properties which Curtis and McIntosh discuss. It is rather with the size of quadrat which will give reliable results in application of the ratio of variance to mean, or in testing the fit to a Poisson by Fisher's index of dispersion or χ^2 fit by class intervals.

[2] J. T. Curtis and R. P. McIntosh, 1950, The interrelations of certain analytic and synthetic phytosociological characters, *Ecology* 31: 434–455.

[3] F. W. Preston, 1948, The commonness, and rarity, of species, *Ecology* 29: 254–283.

Derivation of the Probability Distribution of the "Nearest Neighbor"

The derivation given here is based on discussion by several writers, in particular, Skellam (1952),[1] Moore (1954),[2] and Clark and Evans (1954, 1955).[3]

Consider a collection of points, fixed with respect to some appropriate cartesian coordinate system. A point is selected at random in a region of interest, and the distance between it and its nearest neighbor is recorded. This process is repeated a number of times with a resulting distribution of distances, which are representative of the spatial relationships of points in that region.

Let ρ = mean density of the observed distribution (mean density is defined earlier in this chapter as the number of individuals per unit area, or

$$\frac{\text{Total number of points}}{\text{Total area}}$$

Let r = the distance in any specified units from a given individual to its nearest neighbor.

For a random distribution of points on a plane, the probability that a randomly chosen unit area will contain exactly x points is the Poisson function

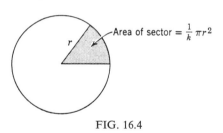

Area of sector $= \frac{1}{k}\pi r^2$

$$P(x) = e^{-\lambda}\frac{(\lambda)^x}{x!} \quad (16.2)$$

where the parameter λ is the mean density.

Suppose we consider the unit area to be a sector of a circle of radius r, formed by dividing the circle into k equal sectors.

FIG. 16.4

If ρ is the number of individuals per unit area, or mean density per unit area, then $\rho k^{-1}\pi r^2$ is the mean density per sector (unit area). This is equal to λ. Substituting in equation 16.2, the probability of finding exactly x points in a sector of area $k^{-1}\pi r^2$ is

$$P(x) = e^{-\rho\pi k^{-1}r^2}\frac{(\rho\pi k^{-1}r^2)^x}{x!}$$

Similarly the probability that no points will be contained in this sector is

$$P(0) = e^{-\rho k^{-1}\pi r^2}$$

[1] Skellam, 1952, *ibid.*

[2] P. J. Moore, 1954, Spacing in plant populations, *Ecology* 35: 222–227.

[3] P. J. Clark and F. C. Evans, 1954, Distance to nearest neighbor as a measure of spatial relationship in populations, *Ecology* 35: 445–453.

———, 1955, On some aspects of spatial pattern in biological populations, *Science* 121: 397–398.

By referring to Fig. 16.4, the probability that the sector will contain no point within a distance r is equivalent to the probability that the sector contains no point. Thus we have the proportion of distances within the sector to the nearest neighbor from the point at the center greater than or equal to the distance r. Also, the probability that the sector contains one or more points is one minus the probability that the sector contains no points. But this is equivalent to the probability that the sector will contain a point at a distance less than or equal to r. Thus we have the proportion of distances of nearest neighbor less than or equal to the distance r. This may be expressed as

$$1 - e^{-\rho k^{-1}\pi r^2} = P(r)$$

If r is allowed to vary, the rate of change of the function $P(r)$ with respect to r gives the probability distribution of r.

$$\frac{dP(r)}{d(r)} = e^{-\rho k^{-1}\pi r^2} 2\rho k^{-1}\pi r$$

or

$$dP(r) = 2\rho k^{-1}\pi r e^{-\rho k^{-1}\pi r^2}\, dr$$

The mean or expected value of r is found by applying the general equation for $E(r)$ which is $\int_0^\infty r g(r)\, dr$, and in this instance is

$$E(r) = \int_0^\infty 2\rho\pi k^{-1} r^2 e^{-\rho\pi k^{-1} r^2}\, dr$$

$$= \frac{\sqrt{k}}{2\sqrt{\rho}} \tag{16.3}$$

The variance of r is found from the relationship $E(r^2) - E(r)^2$.

$$E(r^2) = \int_0^\infty r^2 g(r)\, dr$$

$$= \int_0^\infty 2\rho\pi k^{-1} r^3 e^{-\pi k^{-1} r^2}\, dr$$

$$= \frac{k}{\rho\pi}$$

Therefore,

$$\text{var }(r) = \frac{k}{\rho\pi} - \frac{k}{4\rho} = \frac{(4 - \pi)k}{4\pi\rho} \tag{16.4}$$

Extension of Nearest Neighbor Concept to "nth Nearest Neighbor"; the Property of Reflexivity

A natural extension of the nearest neighbor to a randomly selected point is to the successive nearest neighbors, the second nearest neighbor, the

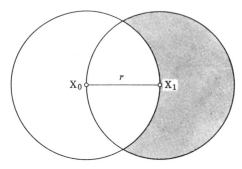

FIG. 16.5

third nearest neighbor, etc. The following discussion is based on a paper by Clark (1956).[1]

Consider a plane in which the points are distributed and choose one of these. Designate this point as X_0. Designate the nearest neighbor to X_0 as X_1. If X_0 is the nearest neighbor to X_1 and X_1 is the nearest neighbor to X_0, then the two points have a reflexive relation. Suppose we continue to designate points around X_0 in their order of *nearness*. If X_1 is the nearest neighbor of X_0, the next nearest neighbor is X_2, the third nearest neighbor is X_3, etc. The definition of reflexive neighbors is now extended to the nth nearest neighbor. If the nth nearest neighbor is reflexive for X_0, then by definition X_n is nearer X_0 than any other point except $X_1, X_2, \cdots, X_{n-1}$, which are the successive nearest neighbors to X_0 in order of nearness.

Clark has tabled the expected proportion of individuals for which the relations of the nth nearest neighbor is reflexive in an infinite randomly distributed population over a plane. The derivation of the expected proportion in an infinite random population, of reflexive pairs of the type X_0, X_1, is given here. This is done so that the reader may better understand the mathematical model on which the test is based. The following derivation is adapted from Clark and Evans (1955).[2]

Suppose we focus attention on two individual points X_0 and X_1 in a population of average density ρ. The population consists of points distributed at random in a plane; in short, the circumstances are just as in the previous discussion of the derivation of the frequency distribution of the distances between randomly distributed points and their first-nearest neighbors.

We may regard the two points as centers of intersecting circles of radius r as illustrated in Fig. 16.5. The probability that X_1 is the nearest neighbor

[1] P. J. Clark, 1956, Grouping in spatial distributions, *Science* 123: 3192; 373–374.
[2] P. J. Clark and F. C. Evans, 1955, On some aspects of spatial pattern in biological populations, *Science* 121: 397–398.

of X_0 is equivalent to the assumption that the circle with X_0 as center contains no other points. Referring back to p. 381 of this section, we find that the probability that a sector of size $1/k$ of a circle of radius r which contains no other points is $dP(r) = 2\rho\pi k^{-1}re^{-\rho k^{-1}\pi r^2}\,dr$. If we consider the area of the whole circle rather than a sector of area $1/k$ of the area of the circle, we then have,

$$dP(r) = 2\rho\pi re^{-\rho\pi r^2}\,dr$$

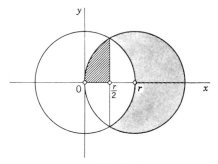

FIG. 16.6

Now, given that X_1 is the nearest neighbor of X_0, the probability that X_0 is also the nearest neighbor of X_1 is equal to the probability that the part of the circle X_1 not contained in circle X_0 has no other points in it. This is the shaded area in Fig. 16.6. The area of this portion is $r^2\,(\pi/3 + \sqrt{3}/2)$ and may be found as follows:

From the symmetry of the figure as illustrated it can be seen that the area of the crosshatched portion whose base is from 0 to r is exactly one-fourth of the total portion of the circle intersected by the circle to the left. Thus the area of shaded portion is πr^2 minus four times the area of the crosshatched portion

$$\pi r^2 - 4\int_0^{r/2}\sqrt{r^2 - (x - r)^2}\,dx = r^2\left(\frac{\pi}{3} + \frac{\sqrt{3}}{2}\right)$$

Since ρ is the mean density of the region, the Poisson parameter λ becomes $\rho r^2(\pi/3 + \sqrt{3}/2)$. Substituting in the Poisson equation,

$$P(x) = e^{-\lambda}\frac{\lambda^x}{x!}$$

we have

$$P(0) = \exp\left[-\rho r^2\left(\frac{\pi}{3} + \frac{\sqrt{3}}{2}\right)\right] \tag{16.5}$$

which is the probability that X_0 is the nearest neighbor of X_1 given that X_1 is the nearest neighbor of X_0.

Finally the probability that X_0 is nearest neighbor of X_1 and X_1 is nearest neighbor of X_0 is the product of the two individual probabilities.

The proportion P of the population, for which the relation of nearest neighbor is reflexive, is the integral from $r = 0$ to $r = \infty$ of the joint probability.

$$P = \int_0^\infty 2\rho\pi r e^{-\rho\pi r^2} \exp\left[-\rho r^2\left(\frac{\pi}{3} + \frac{\sqrt{3}}{2}\right)\right] dr$$

$$= \int_0^\infty 2\rho\pi r \exp\left[-\rho r^2\left(\frac{4\pi}{3} + \frac{\sqrt{3}}{2}\right)\right] dr$$

$$= \exp\left[-\rho r^2\left(\frac{4\pi}{3} + \frac{\sqrt{3}}{2}\right)\right] \frac{\pi}{\frac{4\pi}{3} + \frac{\sqrt{3}}{2}}\Bigg|_0^\infty = \frac{6\pi}{8\pi + 3\sqrt{3}}$$

Clark (1956) gives the generalization to k dimensions of the probability distribution of the distance r to the nth nearest neighbor.[1]

$$_kP_n = \left[\frac{\frac{1}{2}\Gamma\left(\frac{k+1}{2}\right)}{\Gamma\left(\frac{k+1}{2}\right) - \pi^{1/2}\Gamma\left(\frac{k}{2}+1\right)\int_{1/2}^1 (1-x^2)^{(k-1)/2}\,dx}\right]^n \qquad (16.6)$$

where k is the dimensionality, and the power n is equal to the nth nearest neighbor, X_n to X_0, the initial point. $_kP_n$ gives the expected proportion of points in an infinite random distribution for which the relation of the nth nearest neighbor to X_0 is reflexive.

Thus in the derivation for the plane we have $k = 2$. Substituting in Equation (16.6)

$$_2P_n = \left[\frac{\frac{1}{2}\Gamma(\frac{3}{2})}{\Gamma(\frac{3}{2}) - \frac{\Gamma(2)}{\pi}\int_{1/2}^1 (1-x^2)^{1/2}\,dx}\right]^n \qquad (16.7)$$

Since

$$\Gamma(\tfrac{3}{2}) = \tfrac{1}{2}\sqrt{\pi}, \quad \Gamma(2) = 1 \quad \text{and} \quad \int_{1/2}^1 (1-x^2)^{1/2}\,dx = \frac{\pi}{6} - \frac{\sqrt{3}}{8},$$

$$_2P_n = \left[\frac{\dfrac{\sqrt{\pi}}{4}}{\dfrac{\sqrt{\pi}}{2} - \dfrac{1}{\sqrt{\pi}}\left(\dfrac{\pi}{6} - \dfrac{\sqrt{3}}{8}\right)}\right]^n = \left(\frac{6\pi}{8\pi + 3^{3/2}}\right)^n \qquad (16.8)$$

[1] The generalization is based on the probability distribution of the distance r to the nth nearest neighbor for a random distribution with density ρ in two dimensions, as presented by M. Morisita, 1954, *Mem. Fac. Sci.*, Kyushu Univ., Ser. E., 1: 187ff.

and for first nearest neighbor $[6\pi/(8\pi + 3)]^{3/2} = 0.6215$, for second nearest neighbor $[6\pi/(8\pi + 3^{3/2})]^2 = 0.3863$, etc.

Expected proportions for random distributions in an infinite population are given for the 1st through the 21st nearest neighbor for one-, two-, and

TABLE 16.3

Proportions of Individuals in an ∞ Random Population for Which the Relation of nth Nearest Neighbor Is Reflexive

nth Nearest Neighbor	One Dimension	Two Dimensions	Three Dimensions
1	0.6666	0.6215	0.5926
2	0.4444	0.3863	0.3512
3	0.2963	0.2401	0.2081
4	0.1975	0.1492	0.1233
5	0.1317	0.0927	0.0731
6	0.0878	0.0576	0.0433
7	0.0585	0.0358	0.0257
8	0.0390	0.0223	0.0152
9	0.0260	0.0138	0.0090
10	0.0173	0.0086	0.0053
11	0.0116	0.0053	0.0032
12	0.0077	0.0033	0.0019
13	0.0051	0.0021	0.0011
14	0.0034	0.0013	0.0007
15	0.0023	0.0008	0.0004
16	0.0015	0.0005	0.0002
17	0.0010	0.0003	0.0002
18	0.0007	0.0002	0.0001
19	0.0005	0.0001	0.0000
20	0.0003	0.0001	0.0000
21	0.0002	0.0000	0.0000

NOTE. In the above table, the values for two dimensions are taken directly from Clark (1956), and the values for one and three dimensions are computed directly from Clark's general equation (see Eq (16.6)), which for one dimension reduces to $_1P_n = (2/3)^n$ and for three dimensions reduces to $_3P_n = (16/27)^n$.

three-dimensional cases in Table 16.3. This table can be utilized for comparison with small samples to test whether the tendency for isolation of groups of points is greater, equal to, or less than expected in a random distribution. The computing chart (Fig. 16.7) illustrates a way in which the sample proportions may be computed.

If the observed proportions are consistantly higher than the expected random proportions, there is a tendency for isolation greater than would be expected in a random distribution over the plane—thus a clustering effect. If the observed proportions are consistently less than the expected random proportions, there is a tendency for mutual dispersion of points. The form in Fig. 16.7 will serve equally well for other dimensions, provided the values in the bottom row, entitled "expected proportion if random," is changed to the correct set of values.

The reflexive property of points in a plane is applied to the distribution of *Lystrocanthus* spines (see Fig. 16.8) used in discussing quadrat-based methods. (See Fig. 16.2.) However, a different stratigraphic level is used in this case. Following the procedure suggested, the results are given in Table 16.4. Comparison of the two bottom rows are made by entering a plus sign if observed is greater than expected, and a minus sign for the converse. We conclude in this example that the observed proportions are consistently higher than the expected, and therefore there is a tendency toward clustering among the *Lystrocanthus* spines.

ADDITIONAL REFERENCES ON NEAREST NEIGHBOR TECHNIQUE

R. G. Johnson, *Mode of formation of the marine fossil assemblages of the Pleistocene Millerton formation of California.* Applies nearest neighbor technique to the linear case, with an interest in the dispersion of fossils in horizontal bedding plane exposures. Some relation is found between the dispersion pattern and modal sediment size.

R. G. Johnson, 1959, *Spatial distribution of Phoronopsis viridis Hilton,* Science 129:1221ff, used first nearest neighbor in a plane in a test for proportion of reflexives. The study was done on several samples of marine intertidal invertebrates and the proportions of reflexives compared by χ^2.

Dice (1952)[1] investigated the spatial interrelationship of points on a plane in the following interesting way. A point is selected at random and the distance from this point to the nearest neighbor in each of six sextants around the point is recorded. Frequency distributions of artificial distributions of (1) randomly distributed points and (2) clusters, form standards. Dice then compares the frequency distributions of several natural populations to determine a tendency toward clustering versus a tendency toward randomness. The suggestion is made that departures from randomness be made by measuring skewness and kurtosis of the frequency distributions.

Moore (1954)[2] points out that the distances to nearest neighbor in the six sextants are unfortunately not independent of each other, and assesment of the form of distribution when clumping is present is difficult.

[1] L. R. Dice, 1952, *Measure of the spacing between individuals within a population. Contrib. Lab. Vert. Biol.,* Univ. of Michigan, No. 55.

[2] P. J. Moore, 1954, *ibid.*

Randomly Selected			Nearest Neighbor		
Point X_0	X_1	X_2	X_3	$\cdots$	X_{21}
First point					
Second point			Enter an r if reflexive		
.			property is satisfied		
.			between $X_0 X_i$, and		
.			enter a zero if not.		
nth point					
Observed proportion in sample of size N	$\dfrac{\Sigma r_{x_1 x_0}}{N}$	$\dfrac{\Sigma r_{x_2 x_0}}{N}$	$\dfrac{\Sigma r_{x_3 x_0}}{N}$	$\cdots$	$\dfrac{\Sigma r_{x_n x_0}}{N}$
Expected proportion if random	0.6215	0.3863	0.2401		0.0000

FIG. 16.7 Computing chart.

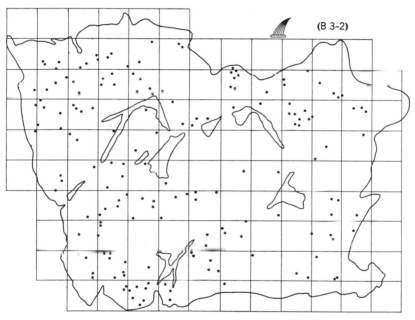

(B 3-2)

FIG. 16.8. The planar distribution of *Lystrocanthus* spines at a particular stratigraphic level in the Mecca shale of Pennsylvanian age is illustrated to scale by points. The total area in arbitrary units is 5516 after correcting for gaps in the deposit. Curtis and McIntosh suggest the optimum size of quadrat to be $\dfrac{2(\text{total area})}{\text{Total no. of points}}$ or $\dfrac{2(5516)}{163} =$ 67.67 square units. This is approximated closely by an 8 × 8 unit quadrat. In the second trial (quadrat twice as large), several difficulties arose. The larger quadrat size resulted in marginal quadrats being only fractionally occupied by shale. An arbitrary rule was established that unless a quadrat was at least 50% occupied, it was not counted. This resulted in a loss of information and magnified the effect of where the quadrats were placed, relative to the irregular outline of the deposit.

TABLE 16.4

Randomly selected Point X_0	Nearest Neighbor												
	X_1	X_2	X_3	X_4	X_5	X_6	X_7	X_8	X_9	X_{10}	X_{11}	X_{12}	X_{13}
1st Point	r	0	0	0	0	r	0	0	r	0	0	0	0
2nd point	r	r	0	0	r	0	0	0	0	r	0	0	0
. . .													
89th Point	0	0	0	r	0	0	0	0	0	0	0	0	0
Sum of r's for the ith Nearest Neighbor	59	27	33	22	7	11	1	5	3	7	5	1	1
Observed Proportion	0.663	0.303	0.370	0.247	0.078	0.121	0.011	0.056	0.034	0.078	0.056	0.011	0.011
Expected Proportion	0.621	0.386	0.240	0.149	0.093	0.058	0.036	0.022	0.014	0.009	0.005	0.003	0.002
	+	−	+	+	−	+	−	+	+	+	+	+	+

A point is selected randomly and designated as X_0. Its reflexive properties with the first through the thirteenth nearest neighbors is entered in the table. This completes the first row of entries under the row-designation, "1st Point." An r is entered to indicate a reflexive relation of the X_0 with X_1 and X_6 and X_9. All other neighbors are nonreflexive and zeros are entered. Next, a second point is selected and designated X_0, and the process is repeated. This was done for 89 points in the *Lystrocanthus* spine example. The procedure follows that given in Fig. 16.7.

SUMMARY

The nearest neighbor reflexive model and subsequent test as developed by Clark seem to the writers to possess several important advantages over most other tests of the spatial distribution of points. These advantages are:

1. The model and the test are independent of the size of quadrat instead distances between the points themselves are considered.

2. Specific alternatives to the hypothesis of randomness are offered, as in the quadrat-size dependent ratio of mean to variance.

3. It is possible to test for tendencies to form specific-sized clumps, such as pairs or triplets, etc.

At the present time there are several disadvantages, which are, however, outweighed by the following advantages:

1. The lack of an over-all significance test for comparison of observed with expected when the hypothesis to be tested is randomness versus the alternatives clustering, or mutual dispersion.

2. The procedure of measurement of distances is rather tedious compared to counting points in a quadrat.

chapter 17

Some Statistical Approaches to Mapping Problems

The title and subject matter of this chapter have been somewhat arbitrarily brought together. However, it serves as a convenient device for topics and papers which are related in varying degrees under the chapter title.

In the present period of exploration of various combinations of statistical analysis and mapping in geological contexts, a considerable number of pertinent papers have appeared. Many of these will be referred to in the following pages, and additions, extentions, and new suggestions are also included. Attention is given to two major subdivisions which are not mutually exclusive:

1. Various quantitative methods which lead to a map as the final product.

2. Statistical methods intended as aids in analysis and interpretation of maps. The term map is not confined to geographical co-ordinates over some portion of the earth's surface although much of the discussion does fall in that category.

The chapter begins with discussion of graphic methods for mapping a single dependent variable against a pair of coordinate variables, continues to regression methods and analysis of variance models, and finally to systems involving the mapping of many components.

We deal with isometric maps in several of the sections. Literally isometric means equal measure. The term is used here to include maps consisting of two coordinate variables x and y and a dependent variable Z whose value at any point $x_1 y_1$ is intended to represent the true value at that point on the map surface.

Customarily, it is assumed that Z is measured without serious error, and that a three-dimensional surface may be represented by passing lines or contours through equal values of Z. In practice, interpolation between observed values of Z is used in drawing the contour lines. A scattering of measured Z values forms the basis for the interpolation. This introduces a subjectivity to the method, in that the final product is looked upon as a continuous surface, but is based on interpolation between points, often irregularly distributed.

As first stated, the coordinate variables x and y need not be map coordinates in the geographical sense. For example, Krumbein (1959)[1] uses trend surface analysis (discussed in this chapter) to analyze the relation between wet and dry grain sizes as a function of the coordinates percent moisture and geometric mean diameter.

GRAPHIC AND ARITHMETIC SMOOTHING TECHNIQUES

Profile Method

This is a systematized graphic way of smoothing out local irregularities in a contour map so that only the broad underlying trend remains. The first step is to superimpose a grid over the contour map. Then a profile corresponding to each east-west line of the grid is constructed directly

---

[1] W. C. Krumbein, 1959, The sorting out of geological variables illustrated by regression analysis etc., *Jour. Sed. Petrol.* 29: 4; 575–587. A. B. Vistelius, 1947, *ibid.* constructs an isopleth* map of correlation coefficients. W. C. Krumbein and E. Aberdeen, 1937, The sediments of Borataria Bay, *Jour. Sed. Petrol.* 7: 3–17 maps statistical parameters such as mean and standard deviation of sediment size over the bottom of a bay on the margin of the Mississippi delta. R. C. Anderson, 1955, Pebble lithology of the Marseilles till sheet in Northeastern Ill., *Jour. Geol.* 63: 228–243 use cartesian grid sampling methods, but utilizes χ^2 test of homogeneity for comparison of striae and facets among different rock types.

* To the best of our knowledge isopleth maps have not been extensively used or their statistical aspects discussed, in the geological literature. Isopleth maps include percentage and ratio maps where for each value of a variable z there are x, y, map co-ordinates as above, but in which the variable z is generated by such devices as centroids or moving averages. An example of an isopleth map based on a ratio is the number of oil wells per section, or the estimated thickness of sandstone per unit area in a facie map, or the surface area of manganese nodules per unit area of sea floor. Discussion and definitions for isopleth maps are to be found in Mackay (1951)[2] and Schmid and MacConnell, (1955).[3]

In drawing contours on maps the subjective element is greater in isopleth than in isometric maps. As Mackay points out, a "topographic sense" is a reliable guide in an isometric map. In isopleth maps one deals with ratios for areas in which the point used for contouring is not an observed value but an arbitrary device i.e., a centroid or moving average per unit area. In these instances a "topographic sense" is less likely to be developed.

[2] J. Mackay, 1951, Some problems and techniques in isopleth mapping, *Economic Geography* 27: 1; 1–9.

[3] C. F. Schmid and E. H. MacConnell, 1955, Basic problems, techniques, and theory of isopleth mapping, *Jour. Am. Stet. Assoc.* 50: 220–239.

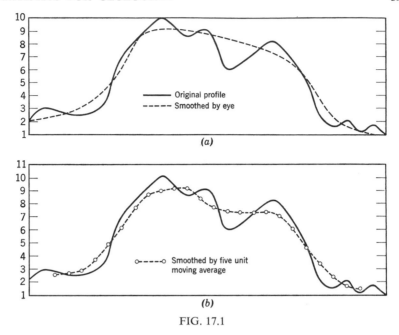

FIG. 17.1

from the contour map. Similarly, profiles for each of the north-south lines are constructed. The number of profiles are, of course, determined by the fineness of the grid. The grid size is a matter of judgment.

Each profile is then smoothed by eye as described by Krumbein (1956).[1] (See also Fig. 17.1.) He states that although degree of smoothing is subjective, an attempt should be made to reduce the number of inflection points to a minimum.

After all profiles have been smoothed, the intersections of the east-west and north-south sets of profiles must be matched. Then the new set of values taken from the smoothed profiles at the grid points (the intersection points) are plotted and the data are contoured. In addition to the resulting "regional" trend map, a map of the residual or local effect can be constructed. This is done by taking the difference at the grid intersection points between the smoothed and original profiles. These differences, which may be plus, minus, or zero, are plotted, and then contoured to form the residual or local effect map. See Figs. 1, 2, 3 in Krumbein (1956), and discussion in the next section of this chapter.

A suggestion is made by the authors that the subjective element of smoothing by eye could be reduced by using moving averages on the

---

[1] W. C. Krumbein, 1956, Regional and local components in facies maps, *Bull. Am Assoc. Petrol. Geol.* 40: 2163–2194.

individual profiles. In this way the data for the residual map would also be available by the same operation. To illustrate, a sample profile is shown in Fig. 17.1a over which a smoothed line has been drawn by eye. Figure

TABLE 17.1
Data for Constructing Smoothed Profile Using Five Unit
Moving Averages

Original Observation	Σ	Moving Average	Residual
2.0			
3.0			
2.8	12.9	2.58	0.22
2.5	13.7	2.74	−0.24
2.6	14.7	2.94	−0.34
2.8	18.9	3.78	−0.93
4.0	24.4	4.87	−0.87
7.0	30.8	6.15	0.85
8.0	38.0	7.60	0.40
9.0	43.2	8.64	0.36
10.0	44.7	8.93	1.07
9.2	45.7	9.12	0.08
8.5	45.3	9.06	−0.56
9.0	41.3	8.26	0.74
8.6	38.6	7.70	0.90
6.0	37.3	7.45	−1.45
6.5	36.5	7.30	−0.80
7.2	35.9	7.17	0.03
8.2	36.4	7.28	0.92
8.0	34.9	6.98	1.02
6.5	29.7	5.98	0.52
5.0	23.0	4.60	0.40
2.0	17.2	3.42	−1.42
1.5	11.9	2.38	−0.88
2.2	8.7	1.74	0.46
1.2	7.7	1.54	−0.34
1.8			
1.0			

17.1b shows the same profile smoothed by a five unit moving average. There seems little real difference between the two results other than the underlying difference in degree of subjectivity. Table 17.1 illustrates the computing scheme for the first ten points. The first column gives the actual profile data; the second, sums for successive groups of 5 points; the third, the averages which are plotted to form the smoothed profile; and the fourth column gives the residuals or difference between observed entry and moving average, with sign preserved.

APPLICATIONS OF SMOOTHING TECHNIQUES

M. A. Romanova, 1957, Geology of the upper part of red beds of the Tscheleken peninsula, *Trans. Leningrad Soc. Natur.* 69: 116–125, uses smoothing of observations of geological variables such as chemical composition, mineral content, against thickness of strata as the independent variable, and P. E. Potter, The petrology and origin of the Lafayette gravel part I: Mineralogy and petrology, *Jour. Geol.* 63: 1–35, utilizes moving averages over a plane, as well as *t*-tests and standard error of the median, in a mapping problem.

REGRESSION SURFACES

We differentiate regression surfaces from graphic and arithmetic smoothing methods in mapping on the basis that in the former an equational statement is available, whereas in the latter it is not. Clearly, if the worker desires only an approximate smoothing of the map data for further ease of interpretation there is little point in going through the admittedly laborious procedure of computing a regression surface by whatever method available. Indeed, the argument of subjectivity versus objectivity has in our experience little validity in that the surfaces generated by the regression methods are little different in appearance from those found by graphic methods. In this case, in fact, the marginal group of methods, such as abbreviated regression method or expected value method, must be treated with greater caution than either direct graphic or full regression methods, for they do not take into account trends not parallel to the sampling grid.

In summary, then, the regression methods are "analytic" and result in an equation as well as a map. When there is a need for the equation in further investigation, as well as the map, then regression methods are justified. An additional advantage in some problems, is the availability of an "error" band about the regression surface.

The geological literature at present appears to contain few discussions and applications of regression surfaces. In two of the papers a principle or concept is presented along with methodology and application of regression surfaces.

Response Surface

The concept of the "response-surface" was discussed by Box (1954)[1] in a problem involving statistical analysis of chemical data. Krumbein (1956)[2] has reapplied the term to analysis of facies maps. Thus the surface represented by the map is thought of as a *"response surface generated by*

[1] G. E. P. Box, 1954, The exploration and exploration of response surfaces, some general considerations and examples, *Biometrics* 10: 16–60.

[2] W. C. Krumbein, 1956, Regional and local components in facies maps, *Bull. Am. Assoc. Petr., Geol.* 40: 9; 2163–2194.

the geologic factors controlling depositional, tectonic, and erosional processes that developed the composition and geometry of the rock body." In the following discussions several additional terms introduced to the geologic literature by Krumbein are also used. The "response surface" may be thought of as composed of local and regional effects. The term "regional effect" is to be considered equivalent to the term "trend-map" introduced by Miller (1956).[1] These terms refer to the underlying smoothed surface from which local fluctuations, perturbations, or "noise" has been removed. The "local effects" or "residual" of Krumbein is equivalent to the "error-term" of Miller. In both cases this is the difference between the original contoured surfaces and the fitted or computed surfaces at data points.

Krumbein also constructs maps of the residual data and suggests possible interpretations of the "residual maps" as well as the "regional" or "trend-maps." A difficulty at present appears to be that the form of the "residual" map is very much dependent on the method used to get the "regional effect" or "trend-map." See, for example, Figs. 3, 5, and 6, pp. 2170–2177 in Krumbein's paper. There, the same original map is analyzed in three different ways, and the resulting regional and residual maps are compared. The regional maps are strikingly similar for all three methods, but the residual map obtained by the profile method is quite different from the residual maps obtained by the abbreviated regression method and the expected value method (see Figs. 3, 5, 6, in Krumbein, 1956).

Trend Mapping

Local irregularities often obscure rather than clarify any attempt to extract a diagnostic pattern from a particular region. Thus a "trend" is sought which adequately represents the distribution of the particular parameter of interest over a geographical region in which samples have been made, and which eliminates the effect of purely local irregularities or "noise." The simplest type of trend in such a situation is a plane (we are here dealing with three dimensions, the two map coordinates, and a third dimension representing various values of the variable). A plane is too great a simplification for many situations, e.g., the distribution of sediment size on the continental shelf. Nevertheless, as a first approximation a plane does represent a simple gradient of the distribution of values. Least squares methods are immediately available for fitting a plane and for further refinements in determining trend. When irregularities are large, higher degree polynomials are needed. Such a surface can be expressed

---

[1] R. L. Miller, 1956, Trend surfaces: their application to analysis and description of environments of sedimentation, *Jour. Geol.* 64: 425–446.

analytically and points for contouring computed from the resulting equation. The points then form the basis for contouring the computed surface. Ambiguity in contouring is eliminated because as many close-spaced points as required can be obtained from the equation.

Grant (1957)[1] defines trend formally as a function of x, and y (the map coordinates) that describes the behavior of a dependent variable independently of experiment, e.g., field data. He then proceeds to describe the least squares method in the form similar to that given in Durbin and Kendall (1951)[2] in which $t(x,y)$ is estimated from observations T_i. The values of the function t differ from the observed values T at each data point by a residual whose expected value over all observations is zero. (See discussion in Chapter 8.) His trend, then, is similar to the earlier discussion in this chapter, a polynomial of best fit to the observed data.

REGRESSION METHODS

The analysis of maps by the use of regression surfaces is conveniently divided into two groups, those which require data spaced over regular intervals as in a grid and those which use irregularly spaced data directly.

Methods Using a Grid

Geophysical investigators have published a considerable number of papers on this subject. Certain types of geophysical data lend itself to this treatment. Simpson (1954)[3] describes a method adapted for the high speed computor. Oldham and Sutherland (1955)[4] describe a method using orthogonal polynomials.[5] See DeLury, (1950)[6] for discussion and tables for use with orthogonal polynomials. Krumbein (1956)[7] describes two methods in some detail in a general discussion of statistical techniques applied to facies map analysis. The first is called the *abbreviated regression*

[1] F. Grant, 1957, A Problem in the analysis of geophysical data, *Geophysics* 22: 309–344.

[2] J. Durbin and M. G. Kendall, 1951, On the method of least squares, *Biometrika* 38.

[3] S. M. Simpson, 1954, Least squares polynomial fitting to gravitational data, and density plotting by digital computors, *Geophysics* 19; 2: 255–269.

[4] C. H. G. Oldham, and D. B. Sutherland, 1955, Orthogonal polynomials: their use in estimating the regional effect. *Geophysics* 20; 2; 295–306.

[5] The discussion in this book is intended for those branches in the earth sciences where application of quantitative analysis is not so highly developed as in geophysics. We shall therefore follow the practice of either referring to or reapplying methods already developed in geophysics wherever it seems appropriate. We similarly draw freely on appropriate discussions in other disciplines such as biometrics and psychometrics.

[6] D. B. DeLury, 1950, *Values and integrals of the orthogonal polynomials up to* $n = 26$, University of Toronto Press, Toronto, Canada.

[7] W. C. Krumbein, 1956, *ibid.*

method. In this case cross product terms in the polynomials are omitted. As a result the computations are not too laborious, and may be performed on a desk model electric calculator. In regions where the trend is not parallel to the arbitrary grid the abbreviated regression method is not recommended.

The second method is based on the complete polynomial including cross product terms. However, in this case, Krumbein is able to show in his example by a preliminary analysis of variance of the original map that only certain cross terms are important contributors, which thus shortens the computational labor.

Grant (1957)[1] gives a detailed discussion and analysis of the application of orthogonal polynomial methods to mapping problems, as well as alternative methodology when the points are not evenly distributed.

An application of orthogonal polynomials is given by A. B. Vistelius, 1958, *On the spectral brightness of sand-silt rock of the Aptian, Aban and Slnomian of the Caspian region*, Symposium on Geol. Work in the Caspian, Issue 1. Lab. Aeromethods, Leningrad. He studies spectral brightness of sand samples with the aid of a photometer. The statistical analysis utilizes orthogonal polynomials to show that the "spectral brightness" is related to conditions of sedimentation.

A predominant number of the different kinds of maps of geological interest do not have actual data available at regularly spaced intervals such as a grid. In Krumbein's paper (1956) the examples he uses include clastic ratios and sand thicknesses. In both cases it is necessary to interpolate from contours in order to acquire data located at regular intervals rather than at the irregularly spaced actual observations. Krumbein recognizes this difficulty as a weakness, but suggests the possibility of a statistical method as described in Goulden (1952, p. 318)[2] to get these missing values. However, he goes on to say that interpolation from contour-map is not unlike a graphic equivalent of more formal statistical methods.

Least squares methods lose their optimum properties as soon as points are used other than the original set at which the actual measurements were made. However, with respect to a good fit of a known surface by a polynomial, least squares on a regular grid may be better than least squares on an irregular grid of uneven density.

Another approach to this problem suggests itself. It is to depart entirely from the grid-based computational methods and instead to compute the regression surface directly from the irregularly spaced data of the original map. We now proceed to a discussion of these methods.

[1] F. Grant, 1957, *ibid.*
[2] C. H. Goulden, 1952, *Methods of statistical analysis*, John Wiley, New York, p. 318.

Methods Not Requiring Grid-Spacing for Original Data

The principle involved is simply to use least squares methods for finding the coefficients for a polynomial of the form

$$X_M = a + bx_2 + cx_3 + dx_2x_3 + ex_2^2 + fx_3^2 + gx_2x_3^2 + hx_2^2x_3 + \cdots,$$

where M is some measurement of interest, X_M is the dependent variable, and x_2, x_3 are the map coordinates. This is a direct approach and does not require any set spacing or grid for the original data. Grant (1957),[1] for example, discusses the advantages of polynomial fitting over smoothing and grid methods. The immediate problem in this approach is the great labor involved for polynomials of degree higher than cubic. The method usually used is to develop the normal equations[2] and to solve simultaneously for the coefficients.[3] However, the number of normal equations and thus unknown coefficients become large very quickly as the level of the polynomial is raised, and the worker is faced with the problem of solving very large determinants. For work with a hand computor, therefore, the labor is prohibitive. For example, for a cubic there are 10 coefficients requiring the solution of (10×10) determinants; for a quartic there are 15 coefficients requiring the solution of 15 by 15 determinants. The use of orthogonal polynomials is not so laborious, but requires a grid spacing of data points, although one can orthogonalize the polynomials for particular points.

To the best of our knowledge three alternatives are described in the literature of the earth sciences for an attack on this problem.

1. The first is described by Gilchrist and Cressman (1954)[4] and applied to meteorological data. A method is given in this paper where an objective transition is made from irregularly spaced field data to a fixed final grid. In this same context, Grant (1957) also discusses the transition from irregularly spaced points to a grid form. With objective grid data in hand, one could then proceed to the convenient method of orthogonal polynomials as used in several of the techniques discussed in (1) above. The final step utilizes high speed computor techniques.

2. To solve determinants directly by using electronic high speed computors. This was done in a study of the relation between dynamics and sediment patterns in the surf zone by Miller and Zeigler (1958).[5]

[1] F. Grant, 1957, *ibid.*

[2] See, for example, A. Hald, 1952, *Statistical Theory with Engineering Applications*, pp. 638 to 645; John Wiley, New York

[3] See Chapter 10 for further comments.

[4] B. Gilchrist and G. P. Cressman, 1954, An experiment in objective analysis, *Tellus*, 6: 4.

[5] R. L. Miller and J. Zeigler, 1958, A model relating dynamics and sediment pattern, etc., *Jour. Geol.* 66: 4; 417–441.

In this case cubic and quartic polynomials with all cross terms were computed on AVIDAC, a high speed digital computor at Argonne National Laboratories and also by the I.B.M. 650 electronic computor. The resulting surfaces were plotted as "trend maps."

Whitten (1959)[1] analyzed properties of the Donegal granite in Ireland by nonorthogonal methods, and in addition to examining and interpreting several lower order polynomial surfaces, he pays special attention to the residual data, which he also mapped. He interprets the residual maps as "ghost stratigraphy" or relics of pregranitization metasediments. His polynomials were computed by high speed computor techniques.

Krumbein (1959)[2] reviews the literature in trend-mapping as related to geological problems and discusses further the approach of analyzing not only successive orders of polynomial surfaces but also the construction and analysis of residual surfaces. He describes a program for computing polynomial surfaces on the I.B.M. 650 high speed electronic computor.

There is no doubt that the use of electronic high speed computors will become more and more widely used in geological problems as knowledge of their potential is made available. Crystallographers have used utilized high speed computor methods, particularly in Fourier methods of fitting, for some time. See, for example, Vand and Pepinsky (1953).[3] For another application of high speed computor methods in the earth sciences see Chapter 10.

3. The third method is given here in detail because it offers an opportunity for those who do not have high speed computor facilities available to compute an approximation to the least squares regression surface by using only a desk model electric calculator. This method was applied to a study of the relation between the wave and current system and sediment size and sorting parameters in a near shore region at La Jolla, California by Miller (1956, *ibid.*).

We shall consider as an illustrative example of the third method a contemporary near-shore marine area in which samples of bottom sediment have been collected. [Inman (1953)].[4] For each sample the median size of sediment has been recorded. Figure 17.2 shows the distribution of

[1] E. H. T. Whitten, 1959, Composition trends in a granite; modal variation and ghost stratigraphy in part of the Donegal granite, Eire, *Jour. Geophys. Research* 64: 835–849.

[2] W. C. Krumbein, 1959, Trend surface analysis of contour-type maps with irregular control-point spacing, *Jour. Geophys. Research* 64: 823–834.

[3] V. Vand and R. Pepinsky, 1953, *The statistical approach to X-ray structure analysis*, X-ray and Crystal Anal. Lab. Dept. Physics, Pennsylvania State Univ. State College, Pennsylvania.

[4] D. L. Inman, 1953, *A real and seasonal variations in beach and nearshore sediments at La Jolla, California*, U.S. Beach Erosion Board, Tech. memo 34.

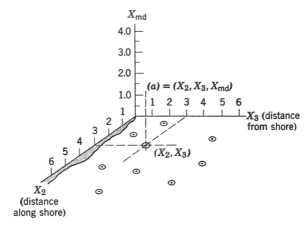

FIG. 17.2. The coordinates are as follows: X_2 is distance along shore, X_3 is distance from the shore, and X_{md} is median sediment size in phi units. Suppose that at sampling location $X_2 = 3$ and $X_3 = 3$, and the value of median sediment size is 2.5. Then the point a is located in space by reading up parallel to the X_{md} axis for a distance of 2.5.

the sampling points and gives the coordinates to be used throughout the rest of this discussion.

If we visualize the placing of points in space similar to a in Fig. 17.2 for each sampling point in the region under study, we then have a distribution of points which form the basis for the contouring of trend patterns. The first step in computation involves the fitting of a plane of best fit to these points. The plane may be regarded as a first approximation to the

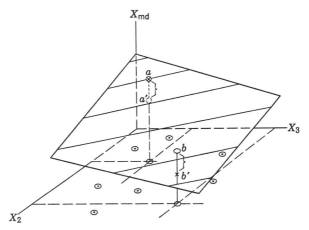

FIG. 17.3. Plane of best fit to the three-dimensional data. Observed value a lies below its computed counterpart a' on the plane, and observed value b lies above its computed counterpart b' on the plane.

trend pattern. We desire to find a plane which is the "best fit" to the points in the sense that the sum of the squares of the differences between each observed value and its counterpart on the computed plane are a minimum. This is illustrated in Fig. 17.3. Note that point a lies below its counterpart a' on the computed plane and that point b lies above its counterpart b' on the computed plane. If we consider an irregular distribution of values of md for the various sample points of the illustration, it is obvious that a plane cannot pass directly through all of them. We thus seek that plane so tilted in space that the sum of the squares of the "errors" in fit, $(a - a')^2 + (b - b')^2 + \cdots$, etc., are at a minimum. An excellent flow sheet for computing the plane of best fit by least squares is given in Croxton and Cowden (1946, pp. 748 and 757).[1]

We now proceed to complete the first approximation to a surface of best fit. The next step involves the computation of a value $Z = (X_{md} - X_{md}^{plane})$ for each observed value of X_{md}, where

X_{md} represents the dependent variable X_M of the polynomial referred to above. The subscript md refers to the median sediment size measured at each of a number of points on the $X_1 X_2$ plane, or map.

$X_{md}^{plane} =$ the computed value on the plane,

$X_{md}^{plane} = a + bx_2 + cx_3$.

Then, for arbitrarily selected class intervals along the X_3 axis, we sum over X_2. Now, for each slab parallel to the X_2, X_{md} plane, compute a single value

$$\bar{Z}_i = \sum_{s=1}^{n_i} \frac{Z_{\Delta_i X_3}}{n_i}$$

where n_i is the number of Z's in the ith slab, and the subscript $\Delta_i X_3$ is ith class interval on the X_3 axis. Figure 17.4 illustrates this procedure.

Summary points $(\bar{Z}_{\Delta_i X_3}$, midpoint $\Delta_i X_3)$ are plotted on the X_{md}, X_3 plane as deviations from the net regression line, which is defined as

$$X_{md}^{net\ regr} = a + bX_2 + c(\bar{X}_3)$$

By a similar procedure, analogous points are plotted on the X_{md}, X_2 plane, as shown in Fig. 17.5. Curves are then drawn by eye to give as good a fit as possible to the summary points on both the X_{md}, X_3 and the X_{md}, X_2 plane. If we indicate the curve on the X_{md}, X_3 plane as $F'(X_2)$, we then have a first approximation surface, which may be expressed as follows:

$$X'_{md} = a + F'(X_3) + F'(X_2)$$

[1] F. E. Croxton, and D. J. Cowden, 1946, *Applied general statistics*, Prentice-Hall, New Jersey.

where

$$a = \bar{X}_{md} - \frac{\sum\limits_{j=1}^{n} [F'(X_{2j}) + F'(X_{3j})]}{n}$$

$$\bar{X}_{md} = \frac{\sum\limits_{j=1}^{n} (X_{md})_j}{n}, \qquad n = \text{total sample size}$$

The first approximation to a surface is now completed. The polynomial is not expressed analytically, since we proposed to proceed to a second approximation directly from the graphs of $F'(X_3)$ and $F'(X_2)$.

The second-approximation trend surface proceeds as follows. Once again the "errors" are computed, this time reading directly from the graphs of Fig. 17.5. For each observed value of X_{md} a new value X'_{md} is computed from the equation $X'_{md} = a + F'(X_3) + F'(X_2)$ where the individual values of $F'(X_2)$ and $F'(X_1)$ are read from the sketched curves. We expect that the sum of absolute values of terms $|X_{md} - X'_{md}| = Z'$ will be less than the previous sum $|X_{md} - X^{plane}_{md}| = Z$, since we have graphically improved the "fit" by introducing a curved surface instead of a plane. Figure 17.6 illustrates this. Note that the way the surface will curve depends upon high and low regions of values of the observed points of md.

As before, slabs whose width is determined by the arbitrarily selected class interval on the X_3 axis are averaged to arrive at a Z_i' for each slab.

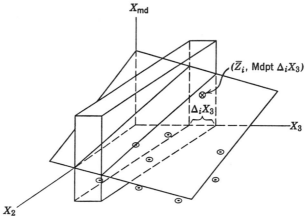

FIG. 17.4. Illustration of the geometrical relationships involved in computing the points ($\bar{Z}_i$, Mdpt $\Delta_i X_3$) plotted on the X_{md}, X_3 plane. The width of the slab is determined by the width of the interval $\Delta_i X_3$ on the X_3 axis. All points $Z = (X_{md} - X^{plane}_{md})$ which fall in the slab, then contribute to the average for the ith slab, namely, $\bar{Z}_i$.

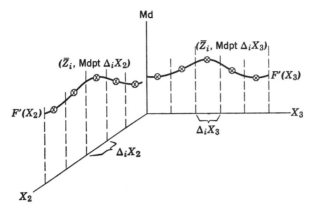

FIG. 17.5. Each point on the X_{md}, X_3 plane computed as illustrated in Fig. 17.4 represents an averaging for that slab. A similar procedure is followed for the X_{md}, X_2 plane. Curves are then drawn by eye through the points as shown here. These curves are then denoted by $F'(X_2)$ and $F'(X_3)$.

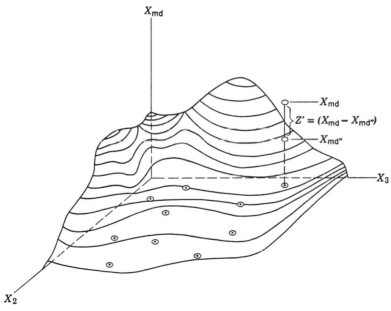

FIG. 17.6. A curved surface representing a second-approximation trend pattern. The effect of high and low clusters of points is illustrated by high and low regions on the surface. $Z' = (X_{md} - X'_{md})$ illustrates the difference between an individual observed point and its computed counterpart on the surface.

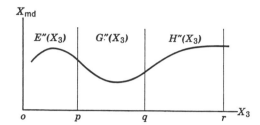

FIG. 17.7. Illustration of the arbitrary partitioning of a function into segments of second degree or lower.

As before, summary points ($\bar{Z}'_{\Delta_i X_3}$, midpoint $\Delta_i X_3$) are plotted on the X_{md}, X_3 plane and also on the X_{md}, X_2 plane.

We have now completed the graphic procedure for a second-approximation trend surface of best fit. The last step is to fit curves to the points ($Z_{\Delta_i X_3}$, midpoint $\Delta_i X_3$) on the X_{md}, X_3 plane and similarly on the X_{md}, X_2 plane. However, actually to plot the surface in its second-approximation form, an analytical statement of the new curves $F''(X_2)$ and $F''(X_3)$ is needed. The following discussion covers the method.

COMPUTATION OF THE EMPIRICAL FUNCTIONS

We desire to work out an empirical function from the sketched curves which were discussed previously. In order to reduce the labor and also the possibility of error in computation, the following method is used:

1. We shall apply the method of averages to equations of no higher than second degree by partitioning the curve under study into subdivisions containing no more than one bend point (see Figs. 17.7 and 17.8). $E''(X_3)$ is thus defined over the range o to p, $G''(X_3)$ over the range p to q, and $H''(X_3)$ over the range q to r.

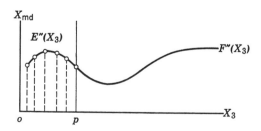

FIG. 17.8. Illustration of selected points for empirical curve-fitting for segment of $F''(X_3)$ from o to p on X_3 axis.

2. Six[1] points are read from the first partition of the empirical curve and are substituted in the working second-degree equation, $X_{md} = a + bX_3 + cX_3^2$, resulting in six separate observation equations. Consecutive pairs of equations are then added to form three equations in three unknowns.

3. The unknowns, which are the coefficients, a, b, and c, are solved by using determinants.

In this way the function $F''(X_3)$ has been expressed in terms of successive functions which range over consecutive parts of $F''(X_3)$

$$F''(X_3) = E''(X_3)]_o^p, \quad G''(X_3)]_p^q, \quad H''(X_3)]_q^r$$

and

$$I''(X_2) = I''(X_2)]_o^l, \quad K''(X_2)]_l^m, \quad L'(X_2)]_m^n$$

Computation of values for purposes of contouring the final trend surfaces are made from the equation

$$X''_{md} = a'' + F''(X_3) + I''(X_2)$$

where

$$a'' = X_{md} - \frac{\sum_{j=1}^{n} [F''(X_{3i}) + I''(X_{2i})]}{n}, \quad n = \text{total sample size}$$

and $F''(X_3)$ and $I''(X_2)$ are computed from the previous equations.

THE MOSAIC METHOD; DISCUSSION

Although the numerical illustration of the method as given in Miller, 1956 *ibid.* divides the region into four subregions, each fit by a second order or lower polynomial, the proposition is general and may be applied to a number of subregions over a map. In this way the surface may be thought of as a "mosaic" in which each subregion may be analyzed separately, and also a single expression for the surface may be obtained over the entire region.

Discontinuities may in theory be quite appreciable at the edges of the subregions under the "mosaic method," but in practice useful surfaces, considered as approximations only, have been obtained. The extent of discontinuities depends in part on the evenness and closeness of the distribution of points of observation, which in turn is reflected in the accuracy of graphic methods.

A difficulty involves extrapolation versus interpolation. How closely should the points be spaced for "reliable" results? Suppose, for example, that a geographically large section of a basin actively receiving sediments has been sampled, but with sample points much farther apart than in

---

[1] The number six is arbitrary and chosen for convenience.

Inman's study[1] (*ibid.*) (see, for example, Stetson, 1953).[2] Will trend contouring be justified? Accuracy of interpolation between sample points by any method of trend contouring is obviously a function of the spacing as well as the number of sample points. Situations where the sample points are dense in part of a geographical region and sparse in another part are special cases of this difficulty.

Extrapolation beyond the edges of the sampled area presents still another facet of the same difficulty. How far out beyond the edges of the area of control points can a trend surface be extended? As Hald (1952, p. 545)[3] points out, "Extrapolation implies an element of uncertainty which cannot be statistically evaluated." Unless sufficient empirical knowledge is available on which to base an educated guess as to the form the function should take beyond the region spanned by the sample points, extrapolation is a very dubious procedure.

FABRIC DIAGRAMS

The statistical analysis of fabric diagrams (which may be regarded as maps of either two- or three-dimensional orientation of a measurable axis in a suitable coordinate system) is reviewed by Chayes (1949).[4] The following is based on Chayes' discussion.

In the two-dimensional case, χ^2 methods are used to compare observed data with, for example, an isotropic model in which equal frequencies are expected in each of an arbitrary number of equal azimuth subdivisions.

The Schmidt rose diagram (Schmidt, 1918)[5] is an alternative to the histogram presentation form. As in the usual compass rose diagrams, the azimuth is arbitrarily subdivided into wedges of equal size representing class intervals. Radii bisecting each class interval and proportional in length to the frequency in that class are constructed, and the end points connected to make the final graph. By using the gaussian error curve (normal curve) Schmidt was able to construct theoretical rose diagrams for various degrees of departure from the isotropic case. In this way a graphic comparison could be made with observed compass rose diagrams.

[1] D. L. Inman, 1953, *ibid.*

[2] H. C. Stetson, 1953, *The sediments of the western Gulf of Mexico. Pt. I*, Papers in Phys. Ocean. and Meterol., Vol. 12, No. 4. Mass. Inst. Tech. and Woods Hole Oceanographic Inst.

[3] A. Hald, 1952, *Statistical Theory with Engineering Applications*, pp. 545–546, John Wiley, New York.

[4] F. Chayes, 1949, Chapters 22, 23 in *Structural Petrology of Deformed Rocks*, by H. W. Fairbairn Addison-Wesley Press, Cambridge, Mass.

[5] W. Schmidt, 1918, *Statistische Methoden beim Gefugestudium kristalliner Schiefer*, Sitz, Kaiserl. Akad. Wiss Wien, Math-Nat. Kl. Abt. 1, 126, pp. 515ff.

In the three-dimensional case Chayes gives a model and bases discussion on tests of this hypothesis, and alternatives to the model given in the following:

Model of three-dimensional isotropism. *In an indefinitely large sample the lattice or grain dimensions are so distributed that equal frequencies are found on equal areas of the reference sphere.*

Winchell (1937)[1] uses a Schmidt net to get observed frequencies, and then a χ^2 test to compare with expected frequencies under the hypothesis given above.

The Winchell "general test" (Winchell, 1937, *ibid.*) approaches the problem from a different point of view. The universe is redefined as a large number of small samples, each reduced to a point diagram on a Schmidt net. This point diagram is then viewed as subdivided into a number of very small squares so that on the average the number of points in a square will be quite small. Then the Poisson model is used, and it is possible to calculate the probability that 0, 1, 2, $\cdots$ points will be found in a square. The theoretical expectations under this model are then compared with observed frequencies by χ^2. See discussion in Chapter 16 on the Poisson model.

Chayes (1946)[2] suggests that correlation methods may be useful for assessing degree of preferred orientation, and will be more sensitive to recognizable preferred orientations, which would be classified as isotropic under the Winchell general test.

He calls attention to the analysis of haemocytometer counts by Student (1907).[3] In order to test whether there was any local lack of homogeneity (anisotropism) in the distribution of blood cells over an area, the area was divided into squares. The number of cells (points) in a given square was determined, as well as the number in each of the four squares nearest to the given square. This resulted in four pairs of observations. Repeating the procedure for each square in turn gave a number of paired observations four times the number of squares in the grid over the area. The expectation is that local inhomogeneity would result in a significant positive correlation between the frequencies in the cells and those in the four nearest neighbors. Chayes adapts this procedure, stating that a local inhomogeneity strong enough to yield a significant positive correlation may be interpreted as evidence of preferred orientation in the parent fabric.

---

[1] H. Winchell, 1937, New method of interpretation of petrofabric diagrams. *Amer. Mineral.* 22: 15–36.

[2] F. Chayes, 1946, Application of the coefficient of correlation to fabric diagrams. *Trans. Am. Geophys. Union*, 27:400ff.

[3] "Student," 1907, On the error of counting with a haemocytometer. *Biometrika* 5 : 351ff.

A review of tests of significance of preferred orientation in three-dimensional fabric diagrams was made by Flinn (1958)[1] who expressed dissatisfaction with the various tests, and proposed instead that comparison be made directly between the actual rock fabric diagrams and artificially constructed random diagrams. A method of contouring is described which is intended to facilitate comparisons.

Two additional papers on this subject are H. J. Pincus, 1951, Statistical methods applied to the study of rock fractures, *Bull. G. S. A.* 62: 81–130. He includes a sampling scheme, frequency distributions of strike and dip, used for graphic analysis only. Relevant to this topic is the introduction of a rectangular method of plotting points, which is compared to the Schmidt net, and an analysis of point diagram data by the Poisson exponential binomial limit (using Molina's tables[2]). He refers to his application as the A test and compares it with Winchell's method (1937, *ibid.*) and Chayes' correlation coefficient application (1949, *ibid.*). Essentially the Poisson function is used to test for departures from isotropicity.

A. B. Vistelius, 1953, On treatment of microstructure diagrams, *Mineralogical Society of U.S.S.R. Bull*: Series 2, part 82, no. 4, discusses various methods of the investigation of three-dimensional diagrams. He suggests that the Schmidt method is in contradiction with the principle of additivity of probabilities. Vistelius' proposes a new method based on χ^2 with many degrees of freedom. The same topic is further discussed in A. B. Vistelius, 1957, On the statistics of microstructure diagrams, *Mineralogical Society of U.S.S.R. Bull.* part 86.

GENERAL ORIENTATION PROBLEMS

A detailed paper summarizing principles and applications in geology of orientation analysis is given by H. J. Pincus, 1953, The analysis of aggregates of orientation data in the earth sciences, *Jour. Geol.* 61: 482–509 (Special Statistics Issue I). Included is a historical development of the subject, and an annotated bibliography on applications.

Since 1953 several contributions have been made to the models and tests for orientation, and a number of applications have been published. In what follows, a number of more recent papers are listed as an extension to Pincus' reference list.

J. C. Griffiths and M. A. Rosenfeld, 1953, A further test of dimensional orientation of quartz grains in Bradford Sand, *Am. Jour. Sci.* 251: 192–214. The inclination of long axes of quartz grains is measured in thin section and related to the maximum permeability direction in the Bradford Sand. Statistical analysis of orientation is briefly discussed and the efficiency of analysis of variance and of experimental design is emphasized.

Z. V. Jizba, 1953, Mean and standard deviation of certain geologic data; a discussion, *Am. Jour. Sci.* 251: 899–906. The applicability of standard statistical analysis to some geologic problems is questioned. Examples show that when the origin for data can be

[1] D. Flinn, 1958, On tests of significance of preferred orientation in three-dimensional fabric diagrams, *Jour. Geol.* 66: 5; 526–539.

[2] E. C. Molina, 1947, *The Poisson exponential binomial limit*, D. Van Nostrand Co., New York.

arbitrarily chosen, the means and standard deviations are invalid. In such cases where no natural base line is available and the origin arbitrarily chosen, two investigators may arrive at different conclusions using the same data.

F. Chayes, 1954, Effect of change of origin on mean and variance of two-dimensional fabrics, *Am. Jour. Sci.* 252: 567–570. The mean and variance of two-dimensional cyclical data are sensitive to the choice of origin, as pointed out by Jizba. The strength of this effect, and the mean from which the variance will be minimized, can be determined prior to calculation of the variance.

J. Hospers, 1955, Rock magnetism and polar wandering, *Jour. Geol.* 63: 59–74. Includes three-dimensional orientation analysis of data on direction of magnetization of lava flows. The analysis is based on methods proposed by R. A. Fisher, 1953, Dispersion on a sphere, *Proc. Roy. Soc. London, Ser. A*, 217: 295–305.

J. R. Curray, 1956a, An analysis of two-dimensional orientation data, *Jour. Geol.* 64: 117–131. Curray describes a test of significance of difference between an empirical orientation distribution and a random distribution. Comparisons with chi square and *F*-tests appear to favor the present test in certain cases. A second part of the paper deals with goodness-of-fit tests of several models to empirical sand grain orientation data. The best fit appears to be a circular normal distribution and one obtained by wrapping a normal distribution around the center point on polar coordinates.

H. J. Pincus, 1956, Some vector and arithmetic operations on two-dimensional orientation variates with applications to geological data, *Jour. Geol.* 64: 533–557. An extension of one aspect of Pincus' earlier paper (1953) using vector methods.

J. R. Curray, 1956b, Dimensional grain orientation studies of recent coastal sands, *Bull. AAPG* 40: 2440–2456. Application of the method of analysis described in Curray's 1956a paper to recent sands along the Gulf Coast on both a regional and a local bases.

P. W. Harrison, 1957, New techniques for three-dimensional fabric analysis of till and englacial debris containing particles from 3 to 40 mm in size, *Jour. Geol.* 65: 98–105. Includes description and application of a χ^2 test devised by Tukey (unpublished) for orientation analysis. A flow sheet for ease of computation is devised by Harrison and J. Rusnak and presented in this paper.

G. A. Rusnak, 1957a, The orientation of sand grains under conditions of "unidirectional" fluid flow. 1. Theory and experiment. *Jour. Geol.* 65: 384–409. Application of Tukey's χ^2 orientation test to sand grain data collected under controlled fluid flow in a laboratory flame and compared with river bottom data.

G. A. Rusnak, 1957b, A fabric and petrologic study of the Pleasantview Sandstone, *Jour. Sed. Petrol.* 27: 41–55. Tukey's test for orientation is applied to consolidated rock fabric and conclusions drawn to environment of deposition.

D. Durand and J. A. Greenwood, 1958, Modifications of the Rayleigh test for uniformity in analysis of two-dimensional orientation data. *Jour. Geol.* 66: 229–238. Includes a critical review of the Rayleigh test for uniform orientation as used by Curray (1956a, b). Modifications include correction for small sample size, 180° versus 360° azimuth, proposal of a new statistic V^1 which is a best test for uniformity. The appendix discusses the relation between the Rayleigh test and the Tukey test.

ANALYSIS OF VARIANCE APPLIED TO MAPPING

A large number of mathematical models of analysis of variance have been described in the literature. Some have been discussed in Chapter 7. Other designs as well as examples from a variety of disciplines may be obtained from the references cited at the end of that chapter. The examples which follow fall in the general category of mapping problems and hence are included in this chapter rather than in the chapter on analysis of variance. The procedures described in Chapter 7 serves adequately for the examples presented, even though the original sources may have neither formally stated the problems nor computed the statistics in the identical manner.

SELECTIVE SORTING IN A LAKE MICHIGAN GRAVEL BAR

Krumbein and Miller (1953)[1] divided a 50-foot long Lake Michigan gravel bar into five segments. In each segment five samples of 20 pebbles each were collected at random in the 16 to 32 mm class. The number of

TABLE 17.2
Chert Pebbles in Gravel Bar along Beach North of Wilmette, Illinois[1]

6	7	2	6	5
2	9	8	8	7
5	8	8	10	9
6	6	4	8	3
6	5	10	9	6
25	35	32	41	30

[1] Data show number of pebbles per sample of 20 at five randomized localities in each of five segments.

chert pebbles in each sample of 20 was counted and recorded. The object was to see whether selective transportation introduced any significant differences in chert-pebble concentration along the bar. The data are shown in Table 17.2, where the columns represent the number of chert pebbles in the five samples collected in each bar segment.

REFERENCES

W. J. Dixon and F. J. Massey, 1951, *Introduction to statistical analysis*, McGraw-Hill Book Co., New York.

G. W. Snedecor, 1946, *Statistical methods*, 4th ed., Collegiate Press, Ames, Iowa.

R. A. Fisher, 1949, *Statistical methods for research workers*, Oliver and Boyd, London.

L. C. H. Tippett, 1950, *Technological applications of statistics*, John Wiley, New York.

———, 1952, *Methods of statistics*, John Wiley, New York.

W. G. Cochran and G. M. Cox, 1950, *Experimental designs*, John Wiley, New York.

C. H. Goulden, 1952, *Methods of statistical analysis*, John Wiley, New York.

[1] W. C. Krumbein, and R. L. Miller, 1953, Design of experiments for statistical analysis of geological data, *Jour. Geol.* 61: 510–532; by permission of Univ. of Chicago Press. (The problems in this section are based on this work.)

By virtue of the sampling program and the discussion in Chapter 7, it is apparent that this experimental procedure will fit the Model I analysis of variance as outlined in Tables 7.12 and 7.18. Thus the hypothesis of interest is that the population means of the five different segments of the bar are identical. The computations are obtained in the manner outlined in Table 7.18 and are summarized in Table 17.3. Since $F\begin{bmatrix} 4 \\ 20 \end{bmatrix}_{0.05} = 2.87$ as obtained from F tables is greater than the computed F in Table 17.3,

TABLE 17.3

Analysis of Variance of Chert Pebbles in Beach Gravel Bar

Source	D.F.	Sum of Squares	Variance	F
Among groups	4	28.2	7.05	1.50 N.S.
Within groups	20	94.0	4.70	—
Total	24	122.2	—	—

$$F\begin{bmatrix} 4 \\ 20 \end{bmatrix}_{0.05} = 2.87$$

we accept our null hypothesis of equal means. From a geological point of view this is interpreted as meaning there has been no selective sorting with respect to chert-pebbles. For further discussion of a similar application to facies mapping see Krumbein (1955).[1]

SAMPLING GRIDS AND THE TWO-WAY ANALYSIS OF VARIANCE

The simplest model for the two-way form of analysis of variance is the comparison of row and column variances. A sedimentary design could involve collecting a series of samples on a grid, one axis of which extends in the direction of sediment transport and the other is normal to it.

Without Replication

The sampling grid may be used to study local or regional changes in sedimentary attributes. Consider a complex of stream deposits ranging from predominant gravel to mainly sand along a stream valley some tens of miles long. This long-distance or "regional" change is complicated by local variations, such as sand and gravel pockets and other features, which may locally be great enough to mask the regional trend. The purpose of the study is to discern the regional trend with a minimum effect of local disturbances.

[1] W. C. Krumbein, 1955, Statistical analysis of facies maps, *Jour. Geol.* 63: 453–470.

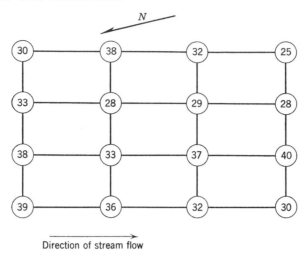

FIG. 17.9

To overcome the local variations, it is decided to collect a series of very closely spaced samples on a grid at each mile point, average the grid data, and use the average to discern the regional trend. A sample is taken at each grid point, and some operation is performed on it (particle size, shape, or lithologic analysis, porosity, water content, etc.). The numerical value for each sample is then entered in its proper cell position in the grid. The statistical question is whether this group of numbers may be considered as homogeneous, i.e., whether it represents a single local population or whether the spread is great enough to introduce regional changes, which may be thought of as changes in the population.

The number entered in a cell commonly represents a single observation on the sample, as when the porosity of the rock is determined. However, in particle-size analysis, the mean particle size may be used, which represents an average of observations on many grains. In the latter case the law of large numbers applies, and it is apparently legitimate to use either single values or average values in the cells. There may be some restrictions on this usage, however.

Figure 17.9 represents a sample grid from Arroyo Seco, Los Angeles County, California, in which the number of granodiorite pebbles in each of 16 samples of 100 pebbles is listed. The grid spacing was arbitrarily selected as 25 feet along the valley and 15 feet across. The number of granodiorite pebbles at each grid point is shown in the figure. The samples were collected for another purpose, but the data serve to illustrate this problem.

Two factors of variation are present, one due to the main downstream current and the other related to the cross-fluctuations in the currents. These processes may produce different "natural treatments" by which the composition of the deposits may be changed. The appropriate analysis of variance model compares the row and column effects with the "residual" or interaction variance attributable to random variations occurring independently of row and column differences.

If it is found that no significant variations occur along or across the valley within the grid on some preselected level of significance, it may be

TABLE 17.4

Analysis of Variance of Arroyo Seco Granodiorite Pebbles[1]
(From Krumbein and Miller, 1953)

Source of Variation	D.F.	Sum of Squares	Variance	F
Among columns	3	39.5	13.17	<1 NS
Among rows	3	131.5	43.88	2.84 NS
Residual	9	139.0	15.44	—
Total	15	310.0	—	—

[1] Data in Fig 17 9 $F\left[\begin{array}{c}3\\9\end{array}\right]_{0.05} = 4.26$

assumed that the observed variations among the individual samples are due to random error. On the other hand, if significant variations occur between rows or columns, one may suspect that the grid is too large and thus brings part of the regional trend into the local samples. However, the statistical test allows for no specific alternatives to the hypothesis.

The statistical hypothesis set up for any given experiment in this case is that the means are homogeneous both along and across the valley. The experimental design is summarized in Table 7.14.

The computations for this model are those outlined in Table 7.19 and summarized in Table 17.4.

As Table 17.4 shows, the F values for columns and rows are not significant, indicating that the means are homogeneous. In short, it is safe to average the 16 samples and enter them as a single point in the regional study.

In this connection, however, the meaning of the residual variation requires some discussion. Broadly speaking, the residual variance is the random, uncontrolled variance within the population plus some other factors in the study which were not included in the experimental design. In the instance given, it is assumed that there is no serious laboratory error involved in the analysis and that the (row x column) interaction i.e., the residual variance is unimportant.

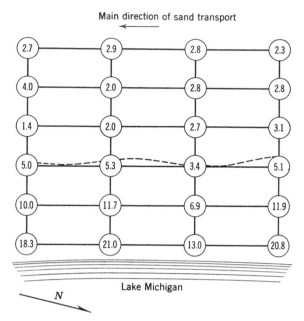

Main direction of sand transport

2.7	2.9	2.8	2.3
4.0	2.0	2.8	2.8
1.4	2.0	2.7	3.1
5.0	5.3	3.4	5.1
10.0	11.7	6.9	11.9
18.3	21.0	13.0	20.8

Lake Michigan

N

FIG. 17.10. (From Krumbein and Miller, 1953, *ibid.*, pp. 515 and 517.)

If the variance ratio had been significant in either the columns or the rows, a smaller grid would have been more appropriate. It is to be noted that this experiment applies only to the population of granodiorite pebbles; for some other attribute the rates of change may be greater or less. The general problem of sampling sediments may require a number of such studies in different deposits to develop sharper concepts of population changes in sediments. The topic of variability among various deposits was discussed by Krumbein (1934)[1] and by Griffiths (1953),[2] the latter in connection with analysis of variance for sampling errors.

In some instances sampling grids definitely include significant changes in the population. This is illustrated in Fig. 17.10 which shows the natural moisture content of freshly collected Lake Michigan beach samples at Wilmette, Illinois, collected on a grid from the water line inland. The example is used because it is evident by inspection that a marked variation occurs between rows (across-beach), although the variation between columns (along-beach) does not appear to be strong. Table 17.5 shows the analysis of variance of the complete sample set. The between-column

[1] W. C. Krumbein, 1934, The probable error of sampling sediments for mechanical analysis, *Am. Jour. Sci.* 227: 204–214.

[2] J. C. Griffiths, 1953, Estimation of error in grain size analysis, *Jour. Sed. Petrol.* 23: 75–84.

TABLE 17.5

Analysis of Variance of Moisture Content of Beach Samples[1]
(From Krumbein and Miller, 1953, *ibid.*)

Source of Variation	D.F.	Sum of Squares	Variance	F
Between columns	3	21.46	7.15	2.53 NS
Between rows	5	798.45	159.69	56.43
Residual	15	42.46	2.83	—
Total	23	862.37	—	—

$$F\begin{bmatrix} 3 \\ 15 \end{bmatrix}_{0.05} = 3.29; \quad F\begin{bmatrix} 5 \\ 15 \end{bmatrix}_{0.01} = 4.56.$$

[1] Data in Fig. 17.10.

variance is not significant, but the between-row variance is highly significant.

The geological complication in this sampling grid is that it straddles the beach berm. On the lakeward side, waves wash across the beach to the berm line, but only during storms do they extend beyond the seasonal berm. By splitting the grid along the berm line and considering only the upper half of Fig. 17.10, which provides four columns and three rows, the analysis of variance yields the values shown in Table 17.6. Here the cross beach variance (rows) has decreased, and there is no significant variation in either direction among the samples. A similar process for the lakeward samples would show that significant row variances are still present in the lakeward half of the grid.

For the moisture-content population of the sand experience suggests that an appropriate sampling grid may well be fairly large landward of the berm and very small on the lakeward side. On the other hand, other sedimentary attributes, such as particle roundness, may or may not show similar variances in relation to the berm line. In designing beach-sampling

TABLE 17.6

Analysis of Variance of Moisture Content of Beach Samples[1]
(From Krumbein and Miller, 1953, *ibid.*)

Source of Variation	D.F.	Sum of Squares	Variance	F
Among columns	3	0.43	0.143	<1 NS
Among rows	2	0.73	0.365	<1 NS
Residual	6	3.52	0.586	—
Total	11	4.68	—	—

[1] Data in upper half of Fig. 17.10.

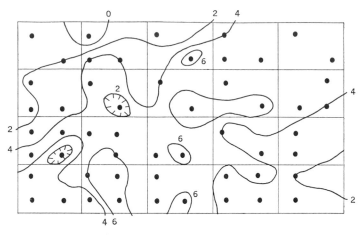

FIG. 17.11. Number of sands map. Contours represent the number of discrete sands in the Arnold zone. (From Fig. 2, p. 458, W. C. Krumbein, *Statistical Analysis of Facies Maps*, 1955, *Jour, Geol*, 63:5.

programs, therefore, one needs to give consideration to the properties being studied as well as to the parts of the beach being sampled. Cochran (1953)[1] also mentions randomizing samples within the grid cells as well as collecting them at systematic points.

With Replication

Applications of the two-factor basic form with multiple cell entries (replication) is made by Krumbein (1955, *ibid.*) in analyzing the areal variation of the number of sands in the Arnold zone, in Carter County, Oklahoma.

Figure 17.11 (Krumbein)[2] shows the arrangement of wells within "cells" subdividing the region of interest. From each well by electric log methods, the number of sands were counted and entered in an analogous position as in Table 17.7. Since the raw data represented counts of sands in which small numbers were used, the variance within cells was "stabilized" [Kempthorne (1952, p. 153)][3] by the square root transformation. See also Krumbein and Miller (1954).[4] Table 17.8 shows a summary and results of the analysis. The decision in this case is that no trend is evidenced over the region studied. Krumbein, in turn, interprets this to suggest that there were uniform geologic controls through time in the Arnold zone.

[1] W. G. Cochran, 1953, *Sampling techniques*, John Wiley, New York.

[2] Krumbein, 1955, *ibid.*

[3] See Table 7.21.

[4] W. C. Krumbein and R. L. Miller, 1954, A note on transformations of data for analysis of variance, *Jour. of Geol.* 62: 192–193.

TABLE 17.7
Number of Sands in Arnold Zone[1]

Raw Data					Square Root Transformed Data				
1	4	1	3	4	1.00	2.00	1.00	1.73	2.00
2	4	6	4	4	1.41	2.00	2.45	2.00	2.00
2	5	4	4	4	1.41	2.37	2.00	2.00	2.00
3	1	6	6	5	1.73	1.00	2.45	2.45	2.37
		etc					etc		

[1] Page 459, Krumbein, 1955, *ibid.*

The Problem of Unequal Numbers of Observations Per Cell

In the foregoing discussion examples were given or referred to in which the mechanics of analysis was based on an equal number of observations per cell. In many cases involving field studies, particularly where large areas are concerned, it is not possible to adjust the size of the sample grid to include equal numbers of observations for each areal subdivision (or cell). Outcrops may be concentrated in part of the region and sparse in another part. In subsurface studies data from bore holes tend to occur in clumps rather than evenly spaced intervals.

Only two ways are available for taking this difficulty into account, without abandoning the analysis of variance techniques.

1. A simple and straightforward suggestion is to fill in gaps in the areal distribution of data by contouring the region and interpolating for the missing values.[1] Clearly this is subjective, and based on the assumption that nothing very unusual actually exists in the blank regions. This is,

TABLE 17.8
Analysis of Variance of Number of Sands in the Arnold Zone[1]

Source	Sum of Squares	D.F.	Mean Square	F
Between cols.	1.0138	4	0.2534	1.41 NS
Between rows	0.5337	3	0.1779	<1 NS
$C \times R$ interaction	1.8982	12	0.1582	<1 NS
Subtotal	3.4457	19		
Residual	3.5953	20	0.1798	
Total	7.0410	39		

[1] Krumbein, 1955, *ibid.*

[1] W. C. Krumbein and R. L. Miller, 1953, Design of experiments for statistical analysis of geological data, *Jour. Geol.* 61: 510–532.

however, a question of judgment, and should be based on as much *a priori* information as can be brought to bear.

2. A second method of treatment involves computing the "effective" sample size. Olson and Potter (1954)[1] give this method in some detail with a numerical example applied to crossbedding. Another way to compute "effective" sample size is given in Snedecor (1946, p. 241);[2] Kempthorne (1952, pp. 103–110)[3] gives generalized equations with proofs.

A critical discussion of statistical treatment of crossbedding analysis is given by W. Niehoff, 1958, *Die Primar Gerichten Sedimentstruktunen, etc. Geologische Rundschau,* Band 47, Heft 1, 252–321. He presents a qualitative approach for reducing diagonal bedding in folded rocks.

ANALYSIS OF VARIANCE WITH "NESTED SAMPLING"; HIERARCHAL METHODS APPLIED TO MAPPING

Within the last few years statistical analysis of geological properties distributed on a regional basis have been facilitated by the application of sampling designs which have been referred to variously as nested, hierarchial, or multilevel. In these designs the purpose is to cover the large region as representatively as possible and at the same time to pay due attention to local variation. Usually the region is subdivided into relatively few highest level areas of equal size. Each of these highest level areas may then be subdivided in a number of smaller regions. Now several of the smaller regions in the single highest level area are chosen in some way to represent all the subdivisions in this area for sampling purposes. This process may be repeated until finally a smallest geologically meaningful level is reached.

For example, in a study of stratigraphic variability Potter and Siever (1955)[4] designed the sampling as follows:

1. Nine "supertownships" (one supertownship = 3 × 3 townships). This forms the highest level.
2. Two townships per supertownship.
3. Two sections per township.
4. Two wells per section.

In this way regional coverage was insured without neglecting local variability. In addition estimates of variation at each sampling level are

[1] J. S. Olson and P. E. Potter, 1954, Variance components of cross-bedding direction in some basal Pennsylvanian sandstone. *Jour. Geol.* 62: 26–47.

[2] G. W. Snedecor, 1946, *Statistical methods,* Ames, Iowa, Iowa State College Press.

[3] O. Kempthorne, 1952, *The design and analysis of experiments,* John Wiley, New York.

[4] P. E. Potter and R. Siever, 1955, A comparative study of upper Chester and lower Pennsylvanian stratigraphic variability, *Jour. Geol.* 63: 429–451.

available for geologic interpretation. Figure 3, p. 438 (Potter and Siever, 1955)[1] from this paper illustrates the design.

One of the earliest papers to apply the technique of nested sampling to geologic problems, with subsequent analysis of variance, is that of Olson and Potter (1954).[2] In this instance attention was focused on crossbedding in two sandstones of Pennsylvanian age. The nested sequence of sampling was as follows:

1. A series of townships or ranges in the outcrop region. This is the highest level.
2. Several sections in the same township or range.
3. One or more exposures in the same or adjacent square mile sections.
4. A variable number of sedimentation units per each exposure.
5. Duplicate bedding planes within the same sedimentation unit.

The result of such a sampling design together with analysis of variance was a map of cross-bedding directions in which local average directions and variation around these averages (confidence limits) was available as well as average directions and variations at higher levels. See figure on p. 65 from the companion paper by Potter and Olson 1954,[3] Other papers utilizing this technique for mapping purposes include a study of areal variation In radioactivity of shale Krumbein and Slack (1956),[4] a further study of cross-bedding Potter and Siever (1956)[5] and a general discussion of facies map analysis by Krumbein (1956).[6] Krumbein and Tukey (1956)[7] use a hierarchal sampling scheme, and a form of analysis of variance in an analysis of multicomponent systems. This paper is discussed in the section on multicomponent systems.

APPLICATIONS IN PROBLEMS IN GEOMORPHOLOGY

Strahler (1956)[8] describes two parameters considered useful in mapping problems in geomorphology, and discusses statistical analysis of the results.

[1] Potter and Siever, 1955, *ibid.*

[2] J. S. Olson and P. E. Potter, 1954, Variance components of cross-bedding direction in some basal Pennsylvanian sandstones of the Eastern Interior Basin: Statistical Methods, *Jour. Geol.* 62: 26–49.

[3] P. E. Potter and J. S. Olson, 1954, Variance components, etc., Geological application. *Jour. Geol.* 62: 50–73.

[4] W. C. Krumbein and H. A. Slack, 1956, Statistical analysis of low level radioactivity of Pennsylvanian black fissile shale in Illinois, *Geol. Soc. Am. Bull.* 67: 739–762.

[5] P. E. Potter and R. Siever, 1956, Sources of Basal Pennsylvanian Sediments in the Eastern Interior Basin: 1. Cross-bedding, *Jour. Geol.* 64: 225–244.

[6] W. C. Krumbein, 1956, Statistical analysis of facies maps, *Jour. Geol.* 63: 452–470.

[7] W. C. Krumbein and J. W. Tukey, 1956, Multivariate analysis of mineralogic lithologic and chemical composition of rock bodies, *Jour. Sed. Petrol.* 36:4; 322–337.

[8] A. N. Strahler, 1956, Quantitative slope analysis, *Bull. G.S.A.* 67: 571–596.

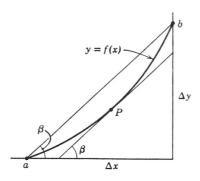

FIG. 17.12. (From A. N. Strahler, *Bull.* *Geol. Soc. Am.*, 1956, p. 576.)

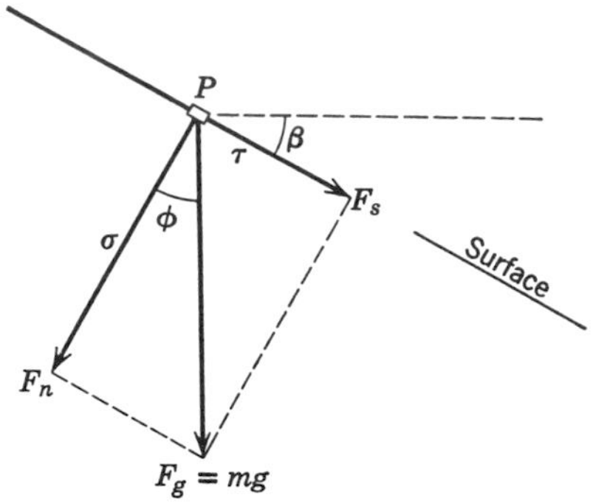

FIG. 17.13. (From Strahler, 1956, p. 577, Fig. 5.)

Several descriptive parameters of ground surface slope are described. Ground surface slope is an important geomorphic property and influences soil flow, soil creep, and runoff.

The first parameter is the slope tangent. If the ground surface slope is considered to be the curve $y = f(x)$ in Fig. 17.12, then the trigonometric tangent of the straight line a, b over a small segment of $f(x)$ is $\Delta y / \Delta x$. In the limit $\Delta y / \Delta x$ becomes the first derivative of $f(x)$ at the point P. This conclusion is based on the mean value theorem, which states that if a, b are on the curve of a continuous function $y = f(x)$, and the slope of a straight line through a, b is $\Delta y / \Delta x$, at least one point P exists on $f(x)$, where $a \leqslant P \leqslant b$, such that the slope of the tangent at P denoted by dy/dx, is equal to $\Delta y / \Delta x$.

An isotangent map may be constructed by approximating the above procedure at a number of points on a contour map or in the field. The isotangent map will be contoured for equal tangents rather than equal elevation. Strahler suggests that the isotangent map may also be termed a "first derivative" or "rate of change" map.

The second parameter is the trigonometric sine. Point P (Fig. 17.13) represents a rock or soil particle on the sloping surface, which makes an angle β with the horizontal. The gravity force vector F_g may be resolved into its components F_n, normal to the slope, and F_s parallel to the slope. F_n is denoted by σ and has according to Strahler "a directly proportional effect on the friction of the particle with the surface." F_s denoted by τ is the direction of movement of the particle along the slope producing shear between the particle and the surface. Examination of Fig. 17.13 shows that ϕ equals angle β. Thus if the sine of the angle between sloping surface and horizontal surface at a given point is denoted by β the following geometric relation is evident: $\sin \beta = \sin \phi = F_s / F_g$.

An isosine map may then be made by contouring areas of equal sin β. It may be interpreted as a map of the distribution of that component of F_g which contributes to the downslope forces; however, the isosine map is basically identical to the isotangent map. It appears to the authors that further discussion of the physical meaning of the isosine map would be desirable. Hacker (1940)[1] also considers the forces on a particle on a ground slope. However, he comes to the conclusion that the four factors determining the stability of a rock mass are; the inclination of the surface of smallest cohesion, the cohesion, the coefficient of friction, and the inclination of slope. Thus both Strahler and Hacker measure the same angle, but Hacker comes to the conclusion that the weight of the rock mass is not a determining factor, "since downward pull and friction increase at the same rate with the weight of rock mass."

Strahler proceeds to a statistical analysis of slope. He obtains slope frequency distributions from isotangent or isosine maps by measuring the area between successive contours with a polar planimeter. The histograms are in the form of percent of total area, and thus analogous to the percent by weight histograms of sediment size analysis. Strahler assumes that the percent of total area histogram represents the total population form, and thus is able to treat the mean, variance, and standard deviation as the population parameters μ, σ^2, and σ rather than as sample statistics $\bar{x}$, s^2, and s. He reasons that the total area is involved and therefore an approximation (depending on accuracy of measurements) to the slope population is achieved. It should be pointed out that this conclusion is valid only for the particular region studied.

Strahler also describes the random coordinate method of sampling a region, for his slope analysis (see Krumbein and Miller, 1953[2] for further discussion and Krumbein, 1953).[3] Strahler proceeds to utilize the population histogram based on areas from isotangent maps as follows. Using the randomized point sampling methods, he is able to compare results of sample statistics $\bar{x}$ and s^2 for various sample sizes with the approximate population area-based parameters from the same region, which is determined by using a planimeter. In this way it becomes possible to estimate adequate sample sizes for using the random point sampling method in preparing isotangent and isosinal maps. This results in a considerable saving of time, since a sample so large as 1000 points is still far less labor than the planimeter-area method. Other extensions such as

[1] W. Hacker, Overloading as a motor of mass movement, *Annals of Assoc. of Am. Geogr.* 20:4; 271–276.

[2] W. C. Krumbein and R. L. Miller, 1953, Design of experiments for statistical analysis of geological data, *Jour. Geol.* 61:6; 510–522.

[3] W. C. Krumbein, 1953, Statistical designs for sampling beach sand, *Trans, A.G.U.* 34:6; 857–867.

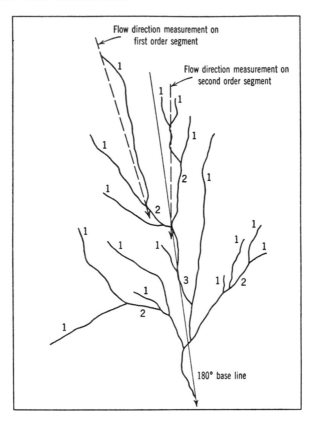

FIG. 17.14. Flow direction measurements on a youthful dendritic basin. (After Shykind, 1956.)

power of the test analysis suggest themselves to the reader. Other applications include comparison by χ^2 of population slope parameters from several field regions as well as an interesting application of operator variation applied to the point sampling method for samples of 100 and for two operators. The conclusion in the latter instance was that operator variance (at least in the case of the two operators) induced no significant differences in sample means.

A second study was done in 1956 by Shykind[1] in which submarine canyons were compared statistically with subærial drainage basins. In this paper he maintained that if one considers small enough units, the dendritic pattern forms a building block for all other basin forms. The

---

[1] E. B. Shykind, 1956, *Quantitative studies in geomorphology: subaerial and submarine erosional environments*, Unpublished doctoral dissertation, University of Chicago, Chicago, Illinois, also Abstract, same title, *Bull. GSA* 56: 1235-36.

various geometric properties of a dendritic pattern are discussed, including the symmetry properties. Shykind then proposes a parameter which is called the flow-direction frequency distribution, and considers in particular the flow-direction frequency distribution of all stream segments within a basin.

The azimuth of flow direction for a given stream segment is obtained by taking the angle between a straight line from upstream end to downstream end and a base line. The axis of symmetry of a dendritic basin is considered (Strahler 1954),[1] in principle at least, as a proper base line. For practical considerations the base line (denoted as 180° in a full azimuth) is established to be the straight line connecting the mouth of the major stream segment with its upstream termination. (See Fig. 17.14.)

Shykind then proceeds to make the following definition: if the stream segments are "randomly oriented" within a basin, the pattern is termed dendritic. Departures from randomness indicate nondendritic patterns. This statement is amplified by two statistical hypotheses:

1. Stream segment orientations ordered according to length fluctuate randomly around the direction of the master stream segment, if dendritic patterns are considered.

2. Channel lengths ordered with respect to orientation of flow direction fluctuate randomly around median channel length if dendritic patterns are considered.

The statistical analysis uses is that of the runs test. (See Chapter 14.) Comparison of a symmetric dendritic pattern of Aneth 3, Utah Quadrangle) with an asymmetric pattern (Aneth 5 Utah) gave the following results:

	Symmetric dendritic Aneth 3, Utah Quad.	Asymmetric Aneth 5, Utah Quad.
Orientation around the 180° axis of symmetry, ordered with respect to length	Random[1]	Nonrandom
Length around the median ordered with respect to orientation	Random	Random

[1] Results obtained using the Strahler stream-ordering method.

The flow-direction measurement was considered further by the following test. A comparison of the frequency distribution of orientation of stream segments as determined by an arbitrary ordering system is made with the

[1] A. N. Strahler, 1954, Statistical Analysis in Geomorphic Research, *Jour. Geol.* 62:1.

frequency distribution formed by measuring the orientation of small segments of fixed length directly without regard to an ordering system. The test area was that of a third order basin taken from Schumm (1954)[1] at Perth Amboy, New Jersey.

The distribution of 483 oriented segments of arbitrary length was compared with the distribution of 62 oriented segments, obtained when an ordering system was used. The Kolmogorov-Smirnov statistic was applied since it is nonparametric, and compares total sample frequency distributions rather than descriptive statistics such as average or variance.[2] It was found that the two frequency distributions did not differ significantly, and Shykind concluded that the flow-direction measurement can be based on the much less laborious segment lengths based on an ordering system.

MULTICOMPONENT SYSTEMS

A class of mapping problems which arises in geology is that which involves admixtures of three or more components expressed as percentages or proportions whose total adds to 100%.

The familiar ternary diagram used by petrologists, e.g., for three component systems, is a representative of this class. Mertie (1948, 1949)[3,4] extends the procedure to tetrahedrons and finally to as many as seven variables. Krumbein (1954)[5] investigates properties of the tetrahedron as a facies mapping device. In this paper, the discussion essentially deals with a nonorthogonal coordinate system as a convenient method for plotting four or less variables.

The preceding papers suggest an area of investigation which is new to the geological literature. It seems likely that geometries based on nonorthogonal coordinate systems will prove not only more convenient but also may bring out relationships not otherwise suspected in various geological problems. In particular, subsequent statistical analysis may be facilitated.

Krumbein and Tukey (1956, *ibid.*) describe a method of analysis intended for problems in areal variation in composition, although application can

---

[1] S. A. Schumm, 1954, *Evolution of drainage systems and slopes in Badlands at Perth Amboy, New Jersey*, Office of Naval Research Doc., Tech. Rep. No. 8.

[2] An application of the flow-direction measurement was made by Shykind in a comparison of four submarine canyons, with a collection of twentyone subaerial basins. The similarity of the submarine canyons to one or more of the subaerial patterns suggests at least a partial history of subaerial erosion for the submarine canyons.

[3] J. B. Mertie, 1948, Charting five, six and seven variables on hypertetrahedal faces, *Am. Mineral.* 33: 324–336.

[4] ———— 1949, Charting five and six variables on the bounding tetrahedra of hypertetrahedra, *Am. Mineral.* 34: 706–716.

[5] W. C. Krumbein, 1954, The tetrehedron as a facies mapping device, *Jour. Sed. Petrol.* 24: 3–19.

be made to a number of other types of problems. The method is designed to handle any number of components expressed as percentages whose total adds to 100%. Attention is focused on questions involving homogeneity versus heterogeneity at various areal levels from local to regional.

Data intended for comparing large and small scale effects are collected using a hierarchal sampling scheme. (See section on analysis of variance applied to mapping.) A geologically interesting category is selected and the percentage of each member of the category is recorded at each sampling point. For example, a suite of heavy minerals may form a category, and each sample point over some region is analyzed for percentage of each of seven heavy mineral species forming the components or types in the category.

The model enables one to approximate a multivariate problem by univariate methods. The statistical model is described in the appendix. A one-way nested sampling design is combined with a one-way listing of the components or types to form a two-way table. Attention is focused on the interactions, and in the examples studied, the main effects of the variables are irrelevant. A preliminary step involves transformation of the original percentage data by the arc sin square root transformation. For example, in complete chemical analysis of rocks the interest may lie in the trace elements. A log transformation may then be used to "weight" the percentages. However, Krumbein (1957)[1] suggests that when the percentage range is large, e.g., both trace and major elements in the original data, the arc sin transformation is best. See Chapter 7, pp. 175–177, for further discussion of transformations.

Particular care must be taken in the sampling design and initial selection of variables as well as subsequent interpretation of the various steps in the analysis. Thus it appears that optimum results in this method are more likely to be obtained by one who has had some experience in application of analysis of variance or has the opportunity to confer with a statistician.

Application of Information Theory

We now turn to a paper by Pelto (1954)[2] in which information theory is applied to mapping multicomponent systems. In this paper two proposals are made for the mapping of many components. In what follows, we focus attention on the second of these, an entropy-like function, defined by Shannon (1949)[2] to be

$$H = -\sum_i p_i \log p_i,$$

[1] W. C. Krumbein, 1957, Comparison of percentage and ratio data in facies mapping, *Jour. Sed. Petrol.* 27: 296–297.

[2] C. R. Pelto, 1954, Mapping of multicomponent systems, *Jour. Geol.* 62:5, 501–511.

(where p_i is the percentage of the ith component, and $\sum_i p_i = 100\%$,) which with the addition of a constant is equivalent in form to the definition of entropy

$$S = -k \sum_i f_i \log f_i,$$

where f_i is the probability of a system being in cell i of its phase space, and k is Boltzmann's constant, as used in thermodynamics. However, in the present context the term entropy is used to represent uncertainty. For the reader who wishes to explore further the geological possibilities in the field of communication theory or information theory, the following are recommended:

C. E. Shannon, and W. Weaver, 1949, *The mathematical theory of communication*, Univ. of Illinois Press, Urbana. N. Weiner, 1948, *Cybernetics*, John Wiley, New York. D. K. C. McDonald, 1952, Information theory and its application to taxonomy, *Jour. Applied Physics* 23; 529–531.

Further references are given in Pelto's paper. As Pelto points out, since entropy is a measure of uncertainty it appears to be useful for mapping multicomponent systems. Thus zones of high entropy (or lack of information) form natural barriers between invironmental regions where the information available is high. In a situation where, say, five components are recorded at each of a number of sampling points on a map it is reasonable to conclude that the minimum "information" gained is where the five components are represented in equal proportion. Since no one component predominates, it is not possible to classify that point on the map in terms of any one or several of the components.

On the other hand, maximum "information" is gained when one of the components is 100% and the other four are each zero.

Pelto introduces the term *relative entropy*, which is defined as the ratio of the actual entropy to the maximum entropy which can be obtained for the number of components under consideration

$$100H_r = \frac{-100 \sum_{i=1}^{N} p_i \ln p_i}{H_m}$$

where p_i is the proportion of the ith component in an N-component system, and H_m, the maximum possible entropy, is

$$H_m = -\sum \frac{1}{N} \ln \frac{1}{N} = \ln N$$

Thus in the case of the number of components $N = 5$

$$H_m = -5(0.20 \ln 0.20) \simeq 1.608$$

Then $100 \, H_r$ which is relative entropy expressed as a percentage is at a maximum;

$$100H_r = \frac{-100 \sum\limits_{i=1}^{5} (0.20) \ln p_i}{-\sum\limits_{i=1}^{5} (0.20) \ln p_i} = 100 \text{ in percent}$$

and for minimum, where one component is 100% and the other four zero,

$$100H_r = \frac{-100(1.00 \ln 1.00 + 0 \ln 0 + \cdots + 0 \ln 0)}{1.608} = 0 \text{ in percent}$$

A table for quick computation of entropy values has been constructed by the writers. Only slide rule accuracy is used throughout. (See Table 17.9.)

APPLICATION OF THE RELATIVE ENTROPY MAP TO AN ENVIRONMENTAL STUDY

The procedure is illustrated by the present writers. A relative entropy map is constructed from data given in an ecological study of foraminifera in San Antonio Bay [Parker, Phleger, and Peirson (1953)].[1] Only a portion of their region is used in the present case. Parker, et al. on the basis of a large number of samples, subdivide the observed species of Foraminifera into seven biofacies. Table 17.10 shows the members of the various biofacies which were found in San Antonio Bay and a portion of Matagorda Island. Members of the various biofacies which were found in other areas of the total region are not given here. An eighth category includes the remaining species found in San Antonio Bay and a portion of Matatogorda Island which were not assigned to a particular biofacies. This category is termed "not diagnostic."

We thus have an eight-component system and proceed to construct a relative entropy map. Table 17.11 shows the data for several sampling stations and the details of computation. All values of the quantity $(-p \ln p)$ were found by reference to Table 17.9 which is accurate to two places. However, the use of natural log tables is almost as quick.

Altogether the data from 122 sample stations were used in the present example. Figure 17.15 shows the portion of the total region studied by Parker et al. which is used here and based on Fig. 1, p. 2, of their publication, entitled *Location of Stations*. The relative entropy contours are given as well as the location of the stations in our present relative entropy map. Regions of high relative entropy ($>50\%$) are shaded and regions of

[1] F. L. Parker, F. B. Phleger and J. F. Peirson, 1953, *Ecology of foraminifera from San Antonio Bay and environs, Southwest Texas*. Spec. Publ. No. 2, Cushman Foundation for Foraminiferal Research.

TABLE 17.9

Table for Calculation of Entropy

p	$-p \ln p$
0.001	0.007
0.002	0.012
0.003	0.017
0.004	0.022
0.005	0.027
0.006	0.031
0.007	0.035
0.008	0.038
0.009	0.042

p	$-p \ln p$	p	$-p \ln p$
0.01	0.046	0.50	0.346
0.02	0.084	0.51	0.344
0.03	0.106	0.52	0.340
0.04	0.129	0.53	0.336
0.05	0.150	0.54	0.334
0.06	0.168	0.55	0.329
0.07	0.186	0.56	0.325
0.08	0.202	0.57	0.320
0.09	0.216	0.58	0.316
0.10	0.230	0.59	0.312
0.11	0.243	0.60	0.307
0.12	0.254	0.61	0.302
0.13	0.265	0.62	0.297
0.14	0.275	0.63	0.291
0.15	0.285	0.64	0.286
0.16	0.293	0.65	0.280
0.17	0.301	0.66	0.274
0.18	0.309	0.67	0.268
0.19	0.315	0.68	0.261
0.20	0.322	0.69	0.256
0.21	0.328	0.70	0.250
0.22	0.333	0.71	0.243
0.23	0.340	0.72	0.236
0.24	0.342	0.73	0.230
0.25	0.346	0.74	0.223
0.26	0.350	0.75	0.216
0.27	0.353	0.76	0.208
0.28	0.357	0.77	0.200
0.29	0.359	0.78	0.194
0.30	0.361	0.79	0.186
0.31	0.364	0.80	0.178
0.32	0.365	0.81	0.170
0.33	0.366	0.82	0.162
0.34	0.366	0.83	0.152
0.35	0.3675	0.84	0.147
0.36	0.368	0.85	0.139
0.37	0.370	0.86	0.126
0.38	0.368	0.87	0.121
0.39	0.3675	0.88	0.113
0.40	0.366	0.89	0.102
0.41	0.366	0.90	0.094
0.42	0.364	0.91	0.086
0.43	0.364	0.92	0.077
0.44	0.361	0.93	0.067
0.45	0.360	0.94	0.058
0.46	0.356	0.95	0.050
0.47	0.355	0.96	0.039
0.48	0.354	0.97	0.029
0.49	0.350	0.98	0.019
		0.99	0.010

(0.32 through 0.41 are bracketed together with value 0.37)

H_m (maximum entropy)	
Number of components	H_m
3	1.0986
4	1.3863
5	1.608
6	1.795
7	1.943
8	2.076
9	2.187
10	2.303

TABLE 17.10

Marsh	Bay	Open Gulf	Bay But Not Upper S. A. Bay	Beach	Gulf Bay	Not Diagnostic
Ammoastuta inepta	Ammobaculites dilatus	Bolivina lowmani	Discorbis floridana	Quinqueloculina seminulum	Bolivina striatula	Ammoscalaria pseudospiralis
Arenoparrella mexicana	A salsus and variants	Cibicidina strattoni	Elphidium discoidale	Q. wiesheri	Elphidium sp. cf. E Koeboeense	Elphidium gunteri
Miliammina fusca	A sp A	Elphidium advenum	E incertum mexicanum	Q. sp. cf. Q. compta	Elphidium poeyanum	E. matagordanum
Trochammina macrescens	A sp B	Gaudryina exilis	Quinqueloculina cultrata		"Rotalia" beccarii A	Massilina protea
Matagorda Marsh	Elphidium delicatulum	Massilina peruviana	Q funafutiensis		"R" beccarii B	Quinqueloculina poeyana
	E. galvestonensis	Nonionella atlantica	Triloculinella obliquinoda		Triloculina sidebottomi	Q. rhodiensis
Discorinopsis aguayoi	E. sp. cf. E. tumidum	Reussella atlantica				"Rotalia" beccarii C.
Triloculina fiterrei meningori	Palmerinella palmerae	Textularia sp. cf. T. majori				Trochammina inflata
		Bigenerina irregularis				
River		Quinqueloculina lamarckiana				
Proteonina lagenaria						
Urnulina compressa						

TABLE 17.11
Biofacies

Station	Marsh	River	Bay	Open Gulf	Upper San Antonio Bay	Beach	Gulf Bay	Not Diagnostic	$100 \sum p_i \ln p_i$	100 hr
#60	2.0	0	85.0	0	0	2.0	9.0	2.0	60.7	29.2
#58	5.0	0	35.6	2.0	5.0	0.6	16.0	34.0	144.2	69.3

The entries above were obtained by the authors from total population tables given by Parker et al. for all individual species found at a given station. They combined those species into biofacies from tables to form the total percent entries shown here. The specimens listed by Parker et al. as being smaller than 0.149 mm contained some immature forms not clearly assignable to species, and were thus not used here.

Steps in computation. (1) Compute $0.02 \ln 0.02 = -0.084$ and similarly for all entries in station No. 60. Multiplying the sum of these by 100 gives the value 60.7. (2) For eight components the maximum entropy $H_m = -8(0.125 \ln 0.125) = 2.076$

$$(3) \ 100 \, H_r = \frac{-100 \, (0.02 \ln 0.02 + 0 \ln 0 + 0.85 \ln 0.85 + \cdots)}{2.076} = \frac{60.7}{2.08} = 29.2$$

Thus in station No. 60 the relative entropy is very low, and the dominant biofacies is *Bay* with 85% of the total population. Station No. 58 in contrast has a high relative entropy with no dominant biofacies present.

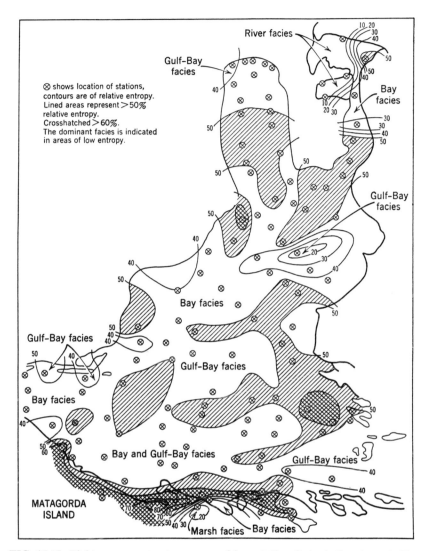

FIG. 17.15. Eight-component entropy map of foraminifera facies in San Antonio Bay, Texas.

⊗ shows location of stations, contours are of relative entropy. Lined areas represent >50% relative entropy; crosshatched >60%. The dominant facies is indicated in areas of low entropy.

entropy higher than 60% are crosshatched. Since these high relative entropy areas represent a considerable degree of uncertainty, they are interpreted to form natural dividing zones between the low entropy zones where one or two biofacies predominate. The lowest entropy zones are then "environments." For example, the upper right portion of the map shows several very low entropy zones in which the river biofacies predominates. Others show Gulf-Bay as the dominant member, and the bottom center of the map shows a concentration of marsh biofacies. Several interesting points stand out.

1. In general, the relative entropy map agrees well with the published interpretation of this area by Parker, Phleger, and Pierson.

2. *Environments as clear cut regions with a neat margin around the edge do not appear to exist here in a geographical sense.* Indeed the concept of "environment" as a definite zone does not appear to serve in this case at all. There are to be sure parts of the bay where the transition from high to low entropy is rapid such as at the marsh center and the river center. More generally, however, the pattern appears to be patchy and sinuous and typically quite gradual, rather than abrupt, in transition.

3. The elongated narrow high entropy zone at the botttom of the map corresponds well geographically with the transition from San Antonio Bay to Matagorda Island, thus lending credence to the proposal that a high entropy zone be regarded as a natural barrier between environments.

4. Parker et al. suggest a loose correlation of bottom sediment type with biofacies. A detailed study of this kind would be greatly facilitated by superimposing the relative entropy map of biofacies over a sediment distribution map. Similar comparisons could be made with salinity and temperature distributions. Other geological applications of the relative entropy map will occur to the interested reader. We now turn to consideration of sediment distribution maps in terms of entropy functions

Relative Entropy as a Measure of "Areal Sorting" in Sediments

Another application of the relative entropy function H_r is in measuring the degree of "areal sorting" of sediment sizes in the sense of a map. In

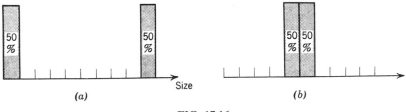

FIG. 17.16

this case H_r is treated as a descriptive parameter on which contour maps may be based.

We shall define areal sorting in the following example to be the distribution of percent by weight of sediment sizes over a predetermined range of size class intervals and expressed in terms of relative entropy. The range of class intervals is fixed by the largest and smallest sizes[1] observed in the region, and is held constant throughout the computations. Size classes which are empty but within the predetermined range are included as zero entries.[2] This includes empty class intervals, both internal and external, to the maximum and minimum filled classes at any one example point.

Such a measure of areal sorting is convenient, e.g., if one wishes to determine the way sediment sizes are distributed by physical process over a region relative to the number of size class which could have been occupied by a percentage of sediment.

Some of the properties of H_r are advantageous for such an application.

1. The range of values is from (0) for best sorting to (1) for poorest sorting. Maximum H_r is obtained when the percentages are equally distributed among all possible size classes. Minimum H_r is obtained when all the percentage is concentrated in one size class.

---

[1] Within the practical range of the mechanical device used for size analysis.

[2] Careful consideration, in context with the problem at hand, appears to be necessary in the treatment of the number of classes. If the interest lies in asking how the sediment size percentages are distributed among a fixed maximum number of size classes, we are essentially comparing points with points over an area. If the interest is focused on changes at a single point, then the number of classes should vary with the number of filled classes but including interval zero classes. In either case certain difficulties appear.

Suppose in theory, only 2 classes of a possible 10 are occupied. Then the value of H_r is the same for the following two extremes, if a fixed number of classes is used (Fig. 17.16).

If 10 classes are used in computing H_r for (a) above and 2 classes for (b) a more realistic result is obtained. In practice, however, within the size ranges considered in this problem, the above situation (a) is unlikely to occur in nature.

On the other hand, if H_r is computed on the basis of the number of occupied classes (but including zero internal classes), the following situation arises not only in theory but commonly in nature. Two frequency distributions are shown in Fig. 17.17. In (a) 8 size classes are occupied by a percentage of sediment. Arbitrary numbers are assigned to the midpoints of the classes for convenience in computation. (b) shows a frequency distribution in which 4 classes are occupied. The percentages are given in both cases by a number in the "bars."

From most points of view, (b) is considered to be much better "sorted" than (a). The variance in (a) is 0.818 and in (b) is 0.454. The dimensionless coefficient of variation V shows a similar result. However, if the number of size classes used in computing H_{max} is 8 in the one case and 4 in the other, we have the unsatisfactory result that H_r for (a) is 0.747 and for (b) is 0.736—very nearly the same. On the other hand, if a common base is used for the number of size classes, say 8, then H_r for (b) drops to 0.454 which gives a more reasonable comparison with (a) at $H_r = 0.747$.

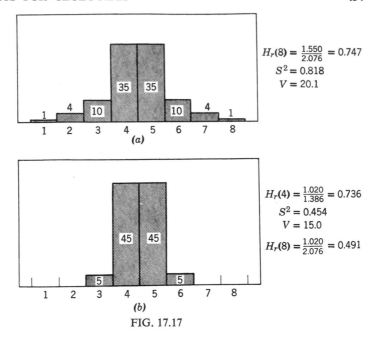

$H_r(8) = \frac{1.550}{2.076} = 0.747$

$S^2 = 0.818$

$V = 20.1$

(a)

$H_r(4) = \frac{1.020}{1.386} = 0.736$

$S^2 = 0.454$

$V = 15.0$

$H_r(8) = \frac{1.020}{2.076} = 0.491$

(b)

FIG. 17.17

2. The parameter is dimensionless. It does not depend on the average size of sediment.

3. It is very easy to calculate.

A detailed analytic comparison of H_r with the variance for a given sediment size frequency distribution would seem to be of general statistical interest. We shall, however, present here two contour maps of the same region, one giving contours of the standard deviation of sediment size in millimeters, and the second showing the contours of H_r. An example of the computation is given in Table 17.12.

The region investigated is on the south end of Lake Michigan in the Indiana Dunes State Park. A rectangular grid was laid down so that dune, back shore, berm, foreshore, step, and breaker zones were included. Thus a wide variety of dynamic situations were contained within a rectangle of 120 by 60 feet. Figure 17.18 shows the location of the sampling points, the dynamic zones, and the topography. The sieve analyses, topography, and a major portion of the field sampling were done by N. Coleman of the University of Chicago. Figure 17.19 shows the contour map of the standard deviation in millimeter units illustrating some common difficulties arising when the standard deviation is mapped. Local irregularities obscure underlying patterns or trends. Since the coarse material is concentrated in the breaker zone and foreshore, the size-dependent standard deviation

TABLE 17.12

Examples of Computation of H_r Values

Grain-size in millimeters	Sample A		Sample B	
	% by gram weight	p_i	% by gram weight	p_i
>15.850				
15.850 − 11.100			2.265	0.084
11.100 − 7.925			1.909	0.084
7.925 − 5.613			2.201	0.084
5.613 − 3.962			4.338	0.129
3.962 − 2.794			4.350	0.129
2.794 − 1.981			3.591	0.129
1.981 − 1.397			4.660	0.150
1.397 − 1.000			5.004	0.150
1.000 − 0.701	0.024	−	7.106	0.186
0.701 − 0.500	0.341	0.017	13.297	0.265
0.500 − 0.350	7.320	0.186	22.284	0.333
0.350 − 0.250	37.040	0.370	18.611	0.315
0.250 − 0.175	49.951	0.350	9.197	0.216
0.175 − 0.125	4.616	0.150	0.589	0.031
0.125 − 0.088	0.523	0.027	0.233	0.012
0.088 − 0.061	0.073	0.007	0.029	−
<0.061	0.048	−	0.005	−
		$\Sigma p_i = 1.107$		$\Sigma p_i = 2.297$

Sample A

$$S = \sqrt{\frac{9.875 - 9.140}{99}} = 0.086$$

$$\bar{X} = 0.30 \text{ mm}$$

$$H_r = \frac{1.107}{2.904} = 0.381$$

Sample B

$$S = \sqrt{\frac{1228.890 - 320.440}{99}}$$
$$= 3.120$$

$$\bar{X} = 1.79 \text{ mm}$$

$$H_r = \frac{2.297}{2.904} = 0.791$$

The p_i entries for each percentage are taken from Table 17.9 and recorded in the columns headed p_i for samples A and B. The computation of the standard deviation for each sample is also shown. Sample A was taken from the upper dune area, contrasting with sample B from the breaker zone. Note that $H_{\max} = 2.904$ is based on 18 class intervals, the largest number found at any sampling point in the region shown in Fig. 17.18. Computation of $H_{\max}$ is given in the previous section. In this case, it is $H_m = -18 (0.055 \ln 0.055) \simeq 2.904$.

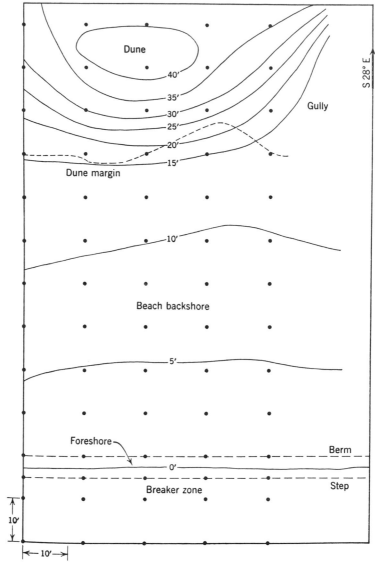

FIG. 17.18

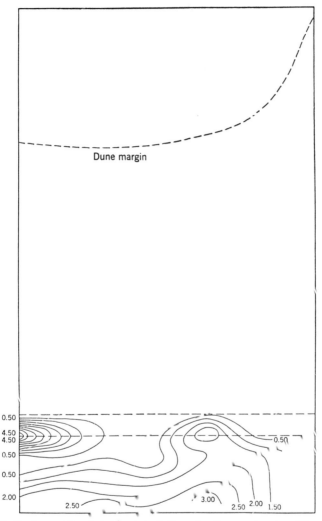

FIG. 17.19. Contour map of standard deviation of sediment sizes in millimeter units, contour interval 0.50.

Contours also tend to concentrate in the same region, irrespective of the dynamic effects. Conversely, variation is obscured in the backshore and dune regions where the average sizes are smaller.

The map of areal sorting based on the relative entropy function is shown in Fig. 17.20. The relevant data are given in Table 17.12. Since it is not size dependent, areal variation is brought out in the backshore and dune regions and smoothed out in the breaker zone and foreshore.

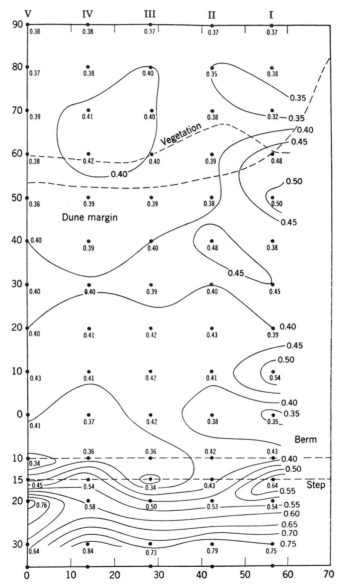

FIG. 17.20. Relative entropy map, 18 size classes, contour interval 0.05.

Interpretation is facilitated in this case. An improvement of sorting in a shoreward direction is noted in the breaker zone, consistent with observations in a number of other localities (Miller and Zeigler, 1958 *ibid.*). Marked irregularities in areal sorting along the right-hand margin of the map in the back shore may be interpreted tentatively as local concentration reflecting rain wash in a line with the gulley adjacent to the dune (see Fig. 17.18).

The interpretations given are subjective. However, the writers feel that sufficient contrast between H_r and standard deviation maps have been shown to warrant the suggestion of H_r as a measure of areal sorting, particularly in problems such as the one described. It is to be noted that in cases when the compartments (size class in the present case) have a meaningful ordering, H_r is insensitive to such important effects as polymodality, as is also the variance. In such cases, perhaps the best solution is to seek *additional* parameters on the basis that no single parameter is sufficient to describe fully the situation.

appendix A

Differentiation of a Collection of Fossils

Statistical analysis deals primarily, but not exclusively, with numbers. Suppose we start, however, with number-data. Experience and reasoning have shown (probably a dangerous statement) that careful measurements of morphological characteristics are most useful in the lowest taxonomic levels. Presence or absence of one or a combination of morphological characters form the basis for differentiation at higher taxonomic levels.

Let us suppose the problem at hand to be the following: A rich and diverse find of fossil remains has been made. The biostratigraphic context will not be considered here. The taxonomic affinities are such that at least three new genera and a much larger number of new species seem likely to be established. We shall assume for simplicity that all the individuals can be assigned to a single family on the basis of clearly recognizable gross morphological characteristics. Since the discussion has to do with the quantitative approach, we shall proceed to discuss the problem from this point of view.

WHAT TO MEASURE

We deal primarily with osteometry or, in the case of invertebrates, preservable hard parts. However, by suitable selection of the measurements, soft part anatomy can be indirectly taken into account. For example, a measurement from origin to insertion of a muscle, a measurement of the distance between several foramina through which nerves pass.

Selection of the measurements in a taxonomic problem may be based on any one of the following three points of view:

1. Measure everything that can be measured with no selection based on *a priori* knowledge.

The underlying philosophy here is that if no selection of measurements is made, unsuspected relationships will be brought out in the subsequent analysis of the data.

Obvious impracticality of this approach is the huge number of resulting characters. Even assuming that the sheer labor of the analysis is not overwhelming, there would be great difficulty in interpretation.

2. Measure only those parts of the fossil to which at least a tentative morphological interpretation can be attached. The interpretation may be in terms of function in which hard and soft parts interact; or of adaptive changes in hard parts which have become established independent of the soft anatomy.

    (*a*) The immediate implication of the first class of measurements above is that as detailed as possible knowledge of the soft anatomy (nerves, muscles, circulatory and digestive systems) should be acquired *before* selection of the measurements. This approach cannot be applied as successfully to animals where the soft anatomy is to a great degree independent of the hard parts as in Foraminifera.

    (*b*) The recognition of adaptive characters which are confined to the hard parts and do not reflect a functional interaction with the soft anatomy is a difficult thing. In long extinct forms with no near modern analogues, an "educated guess' is usually the best interpretation that can be made. Here the *a priori* knowledge of the paleontologist must be brought to bear as a basis for selection of measurable parts.

For example, let us suppose that two tentative species of *Chonetes*, the Paleozooic Brachiopod, are under consideration. Several prominent and persistent spines are noted along the hinge line in both cases. In addition, both tentative species have a highly variable series of projections on the outer surface of the valves. We shall assume that no reasonable relationship can be established with the irretrievably lost soft anatomy in either case. If the variability in form of the prominent spines from individual to individual is low *within* each group, adaptive significance is a possibility. Measurement and statistical comparison between the two groups may in such a case be worthwhile. In the case of the projections on the surface of the valves varying markedly from individual to individual, interpretation of quantitative analysis would be difficult.

3. Choose those characters which have been found useful in taxonomic differentiation of nearest related forms.[1]

The basis for selection and rejection of such measurements is basically a combination of 1 and 2 above. An immediately apparent difficulty with this approach lies in the danger of overlooking informative measurements

---

[1] For example, see C. D. Michener and R. R. Sokal, 1957, A quantitative approach to a problem in classification, *Evolution*, XI: 130–162.

which have either been overlooked by taxonomists on the nearest related forms, or which are not present on the nearest related forms.

In summary, there seems to be at present no general approach which will guarantee thorough coverage of the hard parts and is at the same time practical. The writers advocate strongly the second approach for two reasons. In most cases it will include within its scope the measurements described in the third approach, and at the same time offers a basis for selecting the most useful measurements from the much larger number suggested in the first approach. In addition a sound basis is established for important problems other than taxonomic assignment. The weakness of this approach lies in the possible exclusion of measurements which may turn out to be of great importance but which are not interpretable beforehand.

REPEATABILITY

Linear measurements should be taken only between points which can be precisely located in such a way that any one else will measure the same distance. Thus the description of a measurement on a vertebrate skull from suture to suture is not sufficiently precise; wherever possible linear measurements must be located with respect to points not lines. The degree of accuracy depends in part on the kind of measurement made. However, a further consideration is the number of significant places in the units of measurement. We have used the following rule of thumb: measure to the finest subdivision marked on the measuring device. If the measurement is less than half the distance between the finest subdivisions, assign to the lower value; if more than half, assign to the higher value.[1] As in the rounding of numbers, the important thing here is to arbitrarily select a convention and then use it consistently.

There has been no published work to the writers' knowledge on operator variation[2] in paleobiometric problems. It seems quite likely, however, that certain kinds of hard part measurements are more prone to operator variation than others.

DISCUSSION OF KINDS OF HARD PART MEASUREMENTS, EXAMPLES

The following list is not intended to be complete.

1. *Linear measurements.* Squirrel skull. (see Olson and Miller, 1958, *ibid.*)

[1] Where the measurement is exactly half the finest subdivision a useful convention is round upward if the digit preceding the five is odd, and downward if the preceding digit is even.

[2] See Chapter 7, p. 181 for applications and references.

2. *Counts.* Number of costae on brachiopod *spirifer pennatus*; counting on dorsal side from fold margin. See also Table A.1. Fig. A.1.

3. *Angles.* Angle between hinge line and margin of ventral sinus in *spirifer pennatus.* See also Table A.1, Fig. A.1.

4. *Area.* External area of frontal bone, e.g., by planimetry.

5. *Volume.* For example, squirrel cranium. Cranial capacity by filling with seed.

6. *Sphericity.* The degree of approach of a brachiopod to a sphere. An example of a detailed series of measurements is given in the Pentramite calyx. See Fig. A.1 and Table A.1.

Returning briefly to the problem at hand, we set as a basic premise the following:

The smallest recognizable taxonomic unit will be that in which individuals are not statistically significantly different from one another for all morphological characters considered. (Exceptions are molt stages, and morphogrowth stages such as in foraminifera.)

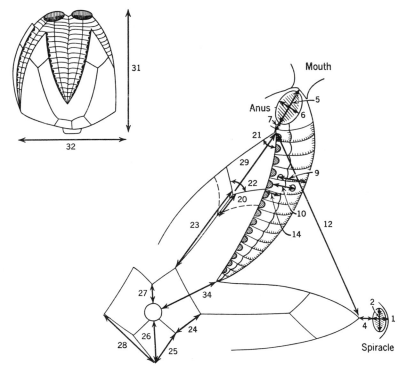

FIG. A.1. Diagrammatic plan view, of *Pentremites* showing measurements used in various quantitative studies of this form. See Table A.1 for description of measurements corresponding to the numbers in the figure. (Not all the measurements, listed in Table A.1 are shown here.)

These smallest units will form the building blocks of which higher taxonomic units will be erected. No genetic significance is attached to this unit designation. For an introductory discussion of the pros and cons of

TABLE A.1

Measures of Pentremites

(After Olson and Miller, 1958)

Measure	Description
1	Outer edge of spiracle to margin of oral opening
2	Width of spiracle
3	Distance between two spiracles
4	Exposed tip of deltoid plate to oral opening along line bisecting spiracle
5	Outer edge of anal opening to margin of oral opening
6	Width of anal opening
7	Exposed tip of deltoid plate to outer edge of anal opening
8	Length of ambulacral groove
9	Length of food groove
10	Length of respiratory groove
11	Distance between adjacent ambulacral ridges
12	Width of ambulacrum measured between tips of adjacent deltoid plates
14	Width of side plate
15	Width of lancet plates
20	Length of deltoid plate covered by radial plates
21	Angle of deltoid plate made by two sides at apex
22	Angle between sides of radial plates as base of (exposed) deltoid
23	Length of interradial suture
24	Length of radial-basal suture adjacent to azygous plate
25	Length of radial-azygous plate suture
26	Length of azygous plate from center of base to distal apex of azygous
27	Length of interbasal suture
28	Width between proximal corners of radials on azygous basal side
29	Length of exposed portion of deltoid
30	Width of deltoid plate from tips of lateral margins of paired radials
31	Total length of calyx
32	Maximum width of calyx
34	Base of ambulacrum to base of calyx
35	Number of side plates

morphological species see Neville George, 1954, *Science Progress* 42; 222–228.

The next basic premise is now introduced. *Each individual represents a sample of one from some unknown statistical population.* At this point a discussion of the terms *statistical population* and *biological population* is needed.

The term biological population has been used to describe a coherent collection of individual animals. For example, a species may be considered as a biological population in that members may interbreed only with each other to produce viable offspring. Subdivisions of species have been described as populations when there exists some physical barrier forming the basis for a geographical differentiation. Even more subtle differences have been used. Indeed, the use of the term population ranges from a strict genetic basis to presence or absence of a single character, or to geographical isolation such as ridges on a volcanic island.

The biometrician starts with the same basis. A population is a collection of objects with one or more common attributes. However, the biometrician goes further. For convenience, the set of numbers generated by recording some common attribute for each individual member is also referred to as a population. This abstraction allows for the use of such concepts as the population distribution function, population parameters, etc., in a convenient manner. The above is readily extended into simultaneous treatment of several attributes. This second premise sets the stage for erection of statistical hypotheses followed by suitable tests. (A review of the definition and concept of the statistical population, (see index) is advisable at this point.) The problem falls into two natural subdivisions: the setting up of paleontological hypotheses, followed by rephrasing of all or a part of the paleontological hypothesis, in precise statistical language and the choice of a suitable statistical test.

The paleontological hypothesis: *that the tentative assignment of individuals to groups is a correct one.*

1. A very reasonable approach is to depend on the general knowledge and skill of the paleontologist and subjectively arrange the individuals into groups based on degree of similarity.

2. Another approach would be to deliberately select group-forming characteristics, i.e., characteristics whose variability is distributed among the individuals so that they serve to divide the individuals into groups with the following property: the variability is small *within* the tentative groups and large *between* them. This was done by T. S. Westoll,[1] e.g., who examined histograms of ratio of thickness to length of a Permian Brachiopod and used the resulting shapes of the histograms as a basis for analysis. He interpreted the biomodality as a case of sexual dimorphism rather than a species difference. The use of only one characteristic at a time would

[1] T. S. Westoll, 1950, Some aspects of growth studies in fossils, *Proc. Roy. Soc.* B 137, 490–509.

severely limit the search for a *formal* procedure in the setting of tentative groups or categories. Thus in (1), an expert will often use a *combination* of characters, shape, etc., as a basis for decision. Treatment of a single characteristic at a time introduces an artificiality to the paleontological hypothesis even though the subsequent statistical hypotheses may then be quite easily formulated and tested.

appendix **B**

Models for Fossil Populations

The nature of the populations to be treated forms an appropriate first topic in this discussion. The population to be treated in this context consists of the smallest homogeneous collection of *fossils* that can be established. It includes within its scope all members of a biological population which have been preserved and which exist at the present time as fossils. The collector samples this population at field localities. From the samples, inferences are drawn, not about the biological population which supplied the animals before death and subsequent preservation, but about that population consisting of all fossilized and presently existing individuals.

In this context, Olson (1956)[1] has pointed out that the inferential step utilizing statistics from the *fossil sample* to the parent biological population is often very difficult because of preferential preservation in which the smallest (youngest) individuals are less likely to be fossilized, and to accidents of preservation where for a given shape certain sizes will tend to become broken. In some cases Olson has shown that the inferential step from *fossil sample* to *parent biological population* is not justified at all.

Olson develops a model for the parent biological population by graphically combining size as a function of time (Olson, Fig. B.1) and frequency as a function of time (Olson, Fig. B.2). See also Kurten (1953.)[2] The choice of distribution function in both cases is based on biological expectations. Thus there are several expected shapes of distribution functions for size as a function of time, e.g., slow growth, rapid growth, exponential growth (Fig. B.1); the several expected distributions for frequency as a function of time (age) include low early mortality with high litter rate, slowly increasing mortality, etc. This is done for a single generation with the assumption that stability has been reached and successive generations will

---

[1] A general discussion of biometrics is given in J. B. S. Haldane, 1956, Biometry, *Sankhya* 16:3; 207–214.

[2] Björn Kurten, 1953 (*ibid.*), *Population dynamics*, part II, pp. 46–118.

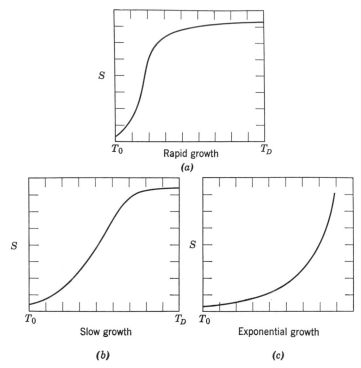

FIG. B.1. The three types of growth curves used for analyses leading to size-frequency distributions of various universes, UB. T_0, time of natality (or time of appearance of first preservable parts); T_D, time of maximum life-span in species; S, size, based on a gross measure.

will not alter the form of the functions. The final result of this combination gives the expected size-frequency distribution form for the parent biological population which Olson refers to as U_B. (Olson, Fig. B.3) shows the resulting form of the expected size-frequency distribution for the parent biological population (U_B) for the combination of slow growth and low early mortality. He would not under most circumstances expect such a distribution to be preserved in the fossil state. On the other hand, such a distribution cannot be inferred from a sample of individual fossils collected in the field except in very unlikely physical situations where even the smallest are preserved in their proper frequencies. The writers feel that Olson has drawn attention to certain fundamental considerations underlying a problem which has long plagued paleontologists, particularly those who wish to apply statistical methods. The general problem is that of *selective sampling* first applied by nature to the original population, and second applied by the collector to those samples made available by nature.

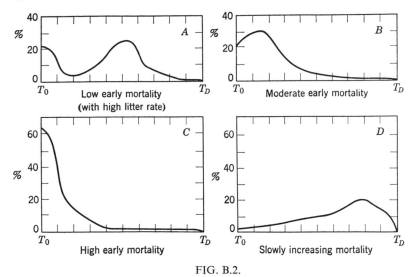

FIG. B.2.

However, given that these difficulties exist, further exploration of the philosophy and operating procedure in application of statistical methods to size frequency distributions should be of some interest. We shall focus attention on the fossil population and the physical conditions of transportation, deposition, and subsequent diagenesis which act on varying degrees on all fossils. The following cases will be considered.

CASE I. LIFE HABITAT ASSEMBLAGE

Loosely defined, this term implies that the assemblage of fossils under consideration died and were buried essentially in the places they occupied during life. It is not possible to apply the definition precisely since all

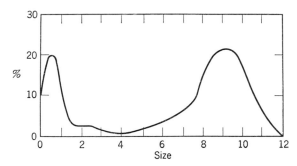

FIG. B.3. Figures B.1, B.2, and B.3 reprinted from E. C. Olson, 1957, Size-frequency distributions in samples of extinct organisms, *Jour. Geol.*, 65: 309–333.

degrees of difference exist in the movement undergone by an animal from the time it dies to the time it is observed in its fossil state by the paleontologist.

CASE II. TRANSPORTED, NONLIFE HABITAT ASSEMBLAGE

This term includes all members of an assemblage of fossils which have been transported after death from their life habitats and redeposited, (e.g., by currents) and buried in other places.

Difficulties are immediately apparent if one attempts to restrict occupation of life-habitat to definite boundaries. Thus a free swimming or free floating marine organism could be deposited in either a life-habitat or nonlife-habitat assemblage of bottom dwelling animals. The life habitat of such a form may include what would with time become a widely diverse collection of marine sedimentary deposits. Similarly, a wide ranging land-carnivore could include in his life-habitat a widely diverse collection of subaerial deposits.

We shall introduce at this time consideration of the environment of deposition including both sediment and animals. Detailed analysis and differentiation of environments of deposition is a field of study which is by no means well understood, and in many aspects is relatively new.

In view of the present state of knowledge on environments of deposition the following must be considered as suggestive only:

1. If the environments of deposition are essentially similar in those physical properties which affect transportation and burial,

2. If the lithology and subsequent *observable* geologic history of the deposits are similar,

3. If *observable* diagenetic effects do not markedly differ, e.g., solution; secondary replacement, e.g., silicification,

4. If the geologic time differences are not greatly different;
then it may be quite reasonable to compare samples from different localities satisfying these criteria.

The argument which underlies the above is that *subsets of a single parent biological population when subjected to a similar geologic history as outlined above will tend on the average to undergo about the same change in form of the frequency distribution, i.e., from* the parent biological population to the subsequent fossil population. Consider the following scheme: The parent biological population exists over a period of time and is analogous to an open system in that members are constantly introduced to it at birth and members are constantly removed from it at death. Although this process may reasonably be looked at as essentially continuous we shall for convenience view the removal of members as happening as large-scale

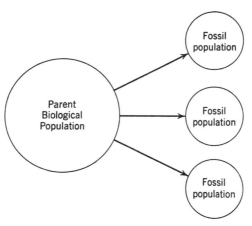

FIG. B.4

discontinuous events, or "macro-quanta." The rationale for this is that as the paleontologist sees the field samples, they represent drawings from fossil populations which are discrete in both time and space. (See Fig. B.4.) Thus the parent biological population at a particular locality during a particular time period produces a subpopulation of dead individuals, subject to transportation, burial, and diagenesis. As the physical conditions in this locality change, the animals may be transported from various distances, then deposited and subjected to a new set of diagenetic changes. The problem here is to place the fossil localities in relationships to each other and to the fossil population in such a way as to allow for meaningful paleontological sample-population hypotheses.

A number of situations can be visualized. Figures B.5 and B.6 illustrate two of these. See Miller and Olson (1955)[1] and R. G. Johnson (1960)[2] for further discussion.

We shall now discuss several possible general models for the *fossil* population which will deal in the context of this chapter with statistical or quantitative treatment. These models deal only with one characteristic at a time in order to be consistent with the univariate treatment in the present discussion.

CLASS I

This includes all fossil populations in which the paleontologist is willing to assume that the form of the frequency distribution is normal, (for

[1] R. L. Miller and E. C. Olson, 1955, The statistical stability of quantitative properties as a fundamental criterion for the study of environments, *Jour. Geol.* 63, No. 4, pp. 376–387.

[2] R. G. Johnson, 1960, Models and methods for analysis of the mode of formation of fossil assemblages, *Bull G.S.A.* 71: 1075–1086.

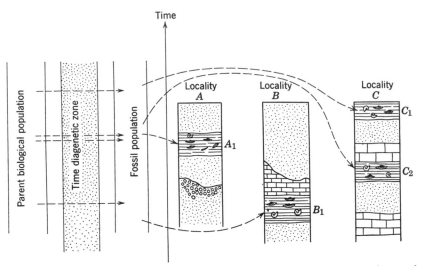

FIG. B.5. The relation between parent biological population, fossil population, and fossil localities. A_1, B_1, C_1, C_2 represent samples from the fossil population, which in turn, is a subset of the biological population. Both parent biological population and fossil population are continuous in time but not in place.

Paleontological hypothesis: sample $A_1 B_1 C_1 C_2$ (all of which arise from similar lithologies and appear not to have been transported) have been drawn from a single population (fossil) and contain the full ontogenetic range.

Statistical hypothesis: for example, the sample means are not significantly different; the variances do not differ significantly.

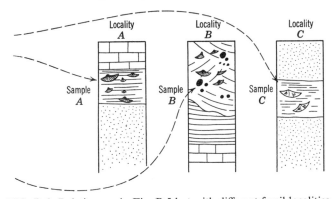

FIG. B.6. Relations as in Fig. B.5 but with different fossil localities.

Paleontological hypothesis: sample A is in shale and represents the full ontogenetic range. The individuals are unbroken and appear not to have been transported. Sample B contains broken and whole specimens of large size in sandy conglomerate where selective sorting and active transportation have taken place. Sample C is in badly weathered shale. Solution blurring and pitting have taken place. Only large specimens are found.

Statistical hypothesis: stages of means and variances; null hypotheses as in legend, Fig. B.5.

452

example, single ontogenetic stages or the fossilized remains of certain life habitat assemblages). Also included in this class are those whose frequency distributions do not widely depart from the normal form, e.g., nearly symmetrical distributions. General considerations for the fossil population of Class I consists of the following:

1. A given characteristic is univariate normal; the several characteristics of interest are distributed as a multivariate normal distribution.
2. An average, μ; or averages $\mu_1 \mu_2 \cdots$.
3. A measure of variation around the average, σ^2; or variances σ_1^2, $\sigma_2^2 \cdots$.
4. Tolerance limits.
5. Coefficients of variation, $V_1, V_2 \cdots$.

Since we do not have the fossil population available, we seek a best estimate in each case of the population parameters listed above in terms of the corresponding sample statistics. Where several samples are available of what in terms of the previous discussion forms a coherent fossil population the estimates are correspondingly improved.

In all cases, the estimates of the population parameters should be given with the corresponding standard errors so that evidence of the relative accuracy of the estimate is available.

The possibility of building up "best estimates" of population parameters for various species, as more information comes in from further discoveries, is worth considering. Aside from obvious time and locality difficulties, problems of fundamental importance and interest to the paleobiometrician such as relative rates of evolution, modes of evolution, are hampered by the necessity of comparing long series of isolated samples with concomittant sample techniques in the statistical treatment.

Extension from the basis given above may then be facilitated. More sophisticated statistical analyses such as linear discriminant function applications, D^2 analysis, and factor analysis, e.g., ρF analysis, may then be applied.

In line with the present topic of models for the univariate case, a discussion of application of sequential analysis to discrimination of species, with both practical and theoretical possibilities, is to be found in B. Burma (1953),[1] An application of sequential analysis to the comparison of growth stages and growth series, *Jour. Geol.* 61 : 6; 533–543. In an earlier paper by Burma (1948)[1] a general discussion of the univariate case is given and is recommended to the interested reader.

[1] B. H. Burma, 1948, Some aspects of the theory and practice of quantitative paleontology, *Jour. Paleon.* 22: 725–761.

CLASS II

This class includes those fossil populations in which the paleontologist has sufficient *a priori* reasons to exclude normal or near-normal probability distribution functions as appropriate.

1. The paleontologist finds that an appropriate transformation to normal form will enable him to proceed as in Class I, e.g., log or arc sin transformations (see index).

2. The paleontologist is unwilling to assume any form for the distribution.

In such cases as (2) nonparametric tests, in which the form of the distribution is not specified, may be used. Nonparametric comparison of means, computation of correlation, sign tests, and comparison of sample cumulative frequency distributions are all available and taken up in other parts of the book (see index). Most nonparametric tests with the exception of χ^2 are fairly new, and paleobiometric literature contains at present few applications. Those known to the authors at the time of writing are: An application of the sign test to an ordered sequence of coefficients of variability on Oreodonts by R. Bader (1956, *ibid.*), An application of the Kolmogorov-Smirnov test to a comparison of size-frequency distributions in a species of invertebrate from two different local environments, R. L. Miller and E. C. Olson (1955), and The statistical stability of quantitative properties as a fundamental criterion for the study of environments, *Jour. Geol.*, 63: 4; 376–387. An application of K–S test to the comparison of certain characters in three major groups of snakes is made by R. G. Johnson, 1956, Origin and evolution of the venomous snakes, *Evolution* X: 1; 56–65, and χ^2 tests are applied to the study of interspecific associations in fossil assemblages, by R. G. Johnson, 1961, Interspecific association in Pennsylvanian fossil assemblages of Western Illinois, *Jour. Geol.* (in press).

Because knowledge of the form of the population distribution function is not needed, the writers believe that nonparametric statistical inference will continue to gain in importance in paleobiometrics.

A summary of European progress up to 1954 on applied statistics in the paleontological species problem is given in George T. Neville, 1954, Fossil species, *Sci. Progress.* XLII: 166; 220–228. C. Emiliani, 1950, *L'analisi statistics applicate alle popolezioii di organismi*, Milano, pp. 1–11, illustrates the use of statistical methods to organic populations. The statistical analysis is used to give an "exact" definition of ecotypes.

F Distribution

Consider the distribution of the ratio

$$z = \frac{x_1/n_1}{x_2/n_2}$$

where x_1 and x_2 are independent and distributed as chi-square with n_1 and n_2 degrees of freedom respectively. Now x_1 is distributed as

$$f(x_1) = \frac{1}{\left(\dfrac{n_1 - 2}{2}\right)! \, 2^{n_1/2}} \, x_1^{(n_1/2)-1} e^{-x_1/2} \qquad x_1 > 0 \qquad \text{(C.1)}$$

The distribution of the variable

$$y_1 = \frac{x_1}{n_1}$$

may be found as follows:

$$y_1 = \frac{x_1}{n_1}$$

$$dy_1 = \frac{dx_1}{n_1}$$

Now substitute for x_1 in (C.1) and obtain

$$\int_0^\infty \frac{(y_1 n_1)^{(n_1/2)-1} e^{-n_1 y_1/2} n_1}{\left(\dfrac{n_1 - 2}{2}\right)! \, 2^{n_1/2}} \, dy_1 = \int_0^\infty \left[\frac{y_1^{(n_1/2)-1} e^{-n_1 y_1/2}}{\left(\dfrac{n_1 - 2}{2}\right)! \left(\dfrac{2}{n_1}\right)^{n_1/2}} \right] dy_1 \qquad \text{(C.2)}$$

The terms under the bracket, under the integrand, is the gamma distribution with $\beta = 2/n_1$ and $\alpha = (n_1 - 2)/2$. Hence, the value of the integral in

(C.2) is one and the probability density function of y is the term under the bracket, namely,

$$f(y_1) = \frac{y_1^{(n_1/2)-1} e^{-n_1 y_1/2}}{\left(\dfrac{n_1-2}{2}\right)! \left(\dfrac{2}{n_1}\right)^{n_1/2}} \qquad y_1 > 0$$

Similarly $y_2 = x_2/n_2$ is distributed as

$$f(y_2) = \frac{y_2^{(n_2/2)-1} e^{-n_2 y_2/2}}{\left(\dfrac{n_2-2}{2}\right)! \left(\dfrac{2}{n_2}\right)^{n_2/2}} \qquad y_2 > 0$$

The joint distribution of y_1 and y_2 is by the assumption of independence

$$g(y_1, y_2) = f(y_1)f(y_2) = \left[\frac{y_1^{(n_1/2)-1} y_2^{(n_1/2)-1} \exp\left[-\dfrac{(n_2 y_2 + n_1 y_1)}{2}\right]}{\left(\dfrac{n_1-2}{2}\right)! \left(\dfrac{n_2-2}{2}\right)! \left(\dfrac{2}{n_1}\right)^{n_1/2} \left(\dfrac{2}{n_2}\right)^{n_2/2}} \right]$$

We may now return to our problem of investigating the distribution of the variable $z = \dfrac{x_1/n_1}{x_2/n_2} = y_1/y_2$. We know

$$\int_0^\infty \int_0^\infty g(y_1\ y_2)\, dy_1\, dy_2 = 1$$

Now substitute for y_1 in terms of y_2 at the same time performing the transformation

$$z = \frac{y_1}{y_2} \qquad v = y_1$$

Here the Jacobian of transformation is y_2/z. We thus obtain

$$\int_z \int_{y_2} \frac{z^{(n_1/2)-1} y_2^{(n_1/2 + n_2/2)-1} \exp\left[-\dfrac{y_2}{2}(n_2 + n_1 z)\right] n_1^{n_1/2} n_2^{n_2/2}}{\left(\dfrac{n_1-2}{2}\right)! \left(\dfrac{n_2-2}{2}\right)! \, 2^{(n_1+n_2)/2}}\, dy_2\, dz$$

$$\int_z \int_{y_2} \frac{n_1^{n_1/2} n_2^{n_2/2} z^{(n_1/2)-1} y_2^{\frac{1}{2}(n_1+n_2-2)} \exp\left[-\dfrac{y_2}{2}(n_2 + n_1 z)\right]}{\left(\dfrac{n_1-2}{2}\right)! \left(\dfrac{n_2-2}{2}\right)! \, 2^{(n_1+n_2)/2}}\, dy_2\, dz$$

Let $w = y_2(n_2 + n_1 z)$, then $dw = (n_2 + n_1 z)\, dy_2$ and thus

$$\int_z \int_{w=0} \frac{n_1^{n_1/2} n_2^{n_2/2} z^{(n_1/2)-1} w^{\frac{1}{2}(n_1+n_2-2)} e^{-w/2}}{\left(\dfrac{n_1-2}{2}\right)! \left(\dfrac{n_2-2}{2}\right)! \, (n_2 + n_1 z)^{\frac{1}{2}(n_1+n_2-2)+1} 2^{(n_1+n_2)/2}}\, dw\, dz$$

Multiplying numerator and denominator by $[(n_1 + n_2 - 2)/2]!$ We obtain

$$\int_z \frac{n_1^{n_1/2} n_2^{n_2/2} z^{(n_1/2)-1} \left(\frac{n_1 + n_2 - 2}{2} \right)!}{\left(\frac{n_1 - 2}{2} \right)! \left(\frac{n_2 - 2}{2} \right)! (n_2 + n_1 z)^{(n_1+n_2)/2}} dz$$

$$\times \int_w \frac{w^{\frac{1}{2}(n_1+n_2-2)} e^{-w/2}}{\left(\frac{n_1 + n_2 - 2}{2} \right)! \, 2^{(n_1+n_2)/2}} dw$$

The terms under the extreme right integral sign are a gamma distribution with $\beta = 2$, $\alpha = (n_1 + n_2 - 2)/2$.

Hence the distribution of the variable $z = y_1/y_2$ is

$$g(z) = \frac{n_1^{n_1/2} n_2^{n_2/2} z^{(n_1/2)-1} \left(\frac{n_1 + n_2 - 2}{2} \right)!}{\left(\frac{n_1 - 2}{2} \right)! \left(\frac{n_2 - 2}{2} \right)! (n_2 + n_1 z)^{(n_1+n_2)/2}} \qquad z > 0 \qquad \text{(C.3)}$$

Any variable distributed as (C.3) is said to have the F distribution with degrees of freedom equal to the degrees of freedom of the numerator and denominator; in this case z is said to be distributed as F with n_1 and n_2 degrees of freedom.

$$z \text{ is } F\left(\frac{n_1}{n_2} \right)$$

appendix D

Chi-square Distribution

DERIVATION OF χ^2 DISTRIBUTION

Let us consider the probability density function of the random variable x which is $N(0,1)$. x is distributed as

$$f(x) = \frac{1}{(2\pi)^{\frac{1}{2}}} e^{-x^2/2} \qquad -\infty < x < \infty \qquad (D.1)$$

What is the distribution of the random variable $z = x^2$? We know

$$\frac{1}{(2\pi)^{\frac{1}{2}}} \int_{-\infty}^{\infty} e^{-x^2/2} \, dx = 1 \qquad (D.2)$$

and

$$dz = 2x \, dx = 2\sqrt{z} \, dx \qquad (D.3)$$

Substituting for x in (D.1) and changing the limits of integration we obtain

$$\frac{1}{(2\pi)^{\frac{1}{2}}} \int_{0}^{\infty} \frac{e^{-z/2}}{2\sqrt{z}} \, dz \qquad 0 \le z < \infty \qquad (D.4)$$

To obtain the pdf of z we evaluate this integral as

$$\frac{1}{(2\pi)^{\frac{1}{2}}} \int_{0}^{\infty} \frac{e^{-z/2}}{2\sqrt{z}} \, dz = \frac{1}{2}$$

Therefore, the pdf of $z = x^2$ is

$$g(z) = \frac{1}{(2\pi)^{\frac{1}{2}}} \frac{e^{-z/2}}{\sqrt{z}} \qquad 0 \le z < \infty \qquad (D.5)$$

$$g(z) = 0 \text{ otherwise.}$$

458

Consider the moment generating function associated with $g(z)$, namely,

$$Ee^{tz} = \int_0^\infty \frac{1}{(2\pi)^{1/2}} \frac{e^{-(z/2 - tz)}}{\sqrt{z}} \, dz$$

$$= \int_0^\infty \frac{1}{(2\pi)^{1/2}} \frac{e^{-(z/2)(1-2t)}}{z^{1/2}} \, dz$$

Referring to the *Handbook of chemistry and physics*[1] we obtain

$$m(t) = (1 - 2t)^{-1/2} \tag{D.6}$$

This, however, is the moment generating function of the gamma distribution

$$h(x) = \frac{1}{\alpha! \, \beta^{\alpha+1}} x^\alpha e^{-x/\beta} \qquad x > 0$$

$$= 0 \qquad \text{otherwise}$$

where

$$m(t) = (1 - \beta t)^{-(\alpha+1)}$$

$$\alpha = -\tfrac{1}{2}$$

$$\beta = 2$$

Therefore, the variable $z = x^2$ is distributed in a gamma distribution with parameters $-\tfrac{1}{2}$, 2.

We are now prepared to consider the moment generating function of the random variable chi-square.

$$\chi^2 = \sum_{i=1}^n x_i^2 = \sum_{i=1}^n z_i$$

The moment generating function of χ^2 is of the form

$$E[e^{t\chi^2}] = E\left[\exp\left(t \sum_{i=1}^n z_i \right) \right] \tag{D.7}$$

The p.d.f. of every z_i is, from (D.5)

$$g(z_i) = \frac{1}{(2\pi)^{1/2}} \frac{e^{-z_i/2}}{\sqrt{z_i}} \, dz_i \qquad i = 1, \cdots, n$$

$$0 \le z_i < \infty \tag{D.8}$$

$$= 0 \quad \text{otherwise}$$

Further let us assume that each z_i is independent in a statistical sense (see Chapter 1 pp. 13–15).

[1] C. D. Hodgman, 1956, *Handbook of chemistry and physics*, p. 275, equation 429, thirty-eighth edition, Chemical Rubber Publishing Co., Cleveland, Ohio.

Thus (D.7), upon expansion, becomes

$$E\left[\exp\left(t\sum_{i=1}^{n}z_i\right)\right] = E\{\exp\left[t(z_1 + z_2 + \cdots + z_n)\right]\}$$
$$= E[\exp\left(tz_1 + tz_2 + \cdots + tz_n\right)]$$
$$= E(e^{tz_1}e^{tz_2}\cdots e^{tz_n}) \tag{D.9}$$

By virtue of independence, (D.8) may be rewritten as

$$Ee^{tz_1}Ee^{tz_2}\cdots Ee^{tz_n}$$

By (D.8), however, any z_i has as its moment generating function Ee^{tz_i}, which by (E.7) is $m(t) = (1 - 2t)^{-\frac{1}{2}}$. Thus, the moment generating function of χ^2 is

$$E[e^{t\chi^2}] = (1 - 2t)^{-\frac{1}{2}}(1 - 2t)^{-\frac{1}{2}}\cdots(1 - 2t)^{-\frac{1}{2}} = (1 - 2t)^{-n/2} \tag{D.10}$$

This is clearly the moment generating function of a gamma distribution with

$$\alpha = \frac{n - 2}{2}$$

and $$\beta = 2$$

Hence, χ^2, consisting of the sum of squares n independently distributed variables each $N(0,1)$, referred to as χ^2 with n degrees of freedom, i.e., χ_n^2, is distributed as

$$f(\chi_n^2) = \frac{1}{\left(\dfrac{n-2}{2}\right)!}\frac{1}{2^{n/2}}(\chi_n^2)^{(n-2)/2}e^{-\chi_n^2/2} \qquad \text{for } \chi_2 > 0$$

$$= 0 \quad \text{otherwise}$$

Mean and Variance of χ_n^2 where $\chi_n^2 > 0$

From (D.10) we find

$$m'(t) = 2n/2(1 - 2t)^{-(n/2)-1}$$
$$m'(0) = n = \mu_1'$$
$$m''(t) = 2\left(\frac{n}{2} + 1\right)n(1 - 2t)^{-(n/2)-2}$$
$$m''(0) = 2\left(\frac{n}{2} + 1\right)n$$
$$= n(n + 2) = \mu_2'$$
$$\mu_2 = \mu_2' - (\mu_1')^2 = n(n + 2) - n^2 = 2n$$

Hence,

$$E[\chi^2_{(n)}] = m'(t = 0) = n$$
$$\text{var } \chi_n{}^2 = \mu_2 = \mu_2' - (\mu_1')^2$$
$$= n(n + 2) - n^2 = 2n$$

Thus a chi-square distributed variable with n degrees of freedom has a mean value of n and a variance of twice as much, $2n$.

E

Cumulative Chi-Square Distribution

The cumulative chi-square distribution is written as

$$F(\chi_n{}^2) = \int_0^{\chi^2} \frac{1}{\left(\dfrac{n-2}{2}\right)! \, 2^{n/2}} \, (\chi_n{}^2)^{(n-2)/2} e^{-\chi_n{}^2/2} \, d\chi_n{}^2$$

Here $F(\chi_n{}^2)$ is a function of n, the degrees of freedom. Thus for a given n

$$P\{b \le \chi_n{}^2 \le a\} = \alpha = F\{a\} - F\{b\} = \alpha$$
$$= P\{\chi_n{}^2 \le a\} - P\{\chi_n{}^2 \le b\}$$

Hence to compute the probability of any event distributed as $\chi^2_{(n)}$ we must know a, b, and n. Conveniently enough the chi-square cumulative distribution has been tabulated in many places. In this instance any probability value of $\chi^2_{(n)}$ may be obtained by entering the tables at the appropriate number of degrees of freedom. On the other hand, if a desired chi-square value is needed, one enters the table for the respective degrees of freedom, then proceeds to obtain a particular chi-square for the desired probability. Caution must be taken before entering the chi-square, or for that matter, any tables of the cumulative function to see what values have been entered in the tables, i.e.,

$$\int_0^{\chi_n{}^2} \frac{1}{\left(\dfrac{n-2}{2}\right)!} \frac{1}{2^{n/2}} (\chi_n{}^2)^{(n-2)/2} e^{-\chi_n{}^2/2} \, d\chi_n{}^2 = F(\chi_n{}^2)$$

or

$$1 - \int_0^{\chi_n{}^2} f(\chi_n{}^2) \, d\chi_n{}^2 = \int_{\chi_n{}^2}^{\infty} f(\chi_n{}^2) \, d\chi_n{}^2$$

the latter being

$$1 - F(\chi_n{}^2)$$

and the former being

$$F(\chi_n{}^2)$$

appendix F

The Addition Theorem For Chi-Square Distribution

The property of the addition of chi-square distributed variables is extremely useful when we deal, for example, with the analysis of variance. With this brief motivation we shall first examine the pdf of the variable

$$v = \chi^2_{(n_1)} + \chi^2_{(n_2)}$$

where

$$\chi^2_{n_1} = \sum_{i=1}^{n_1} x_i{}^2$$

and

$$\chi^2_{n_2} = \sum_{i=1}^{n_2} x_i{}^2$$

where x_i's are $N(0,1)$

and $\chi^2{}_{n_1}$, $\chi_{n_2}{}^2$ are independent in the statistical sense. The moment generating function of v is

$$m(t) = E \exp tv = E \exp t(\chi^2_{n_1} + \chi^2_{n_2}) = E \exp (t\chi^2_{n_1} + t\chi^2_{n_2})$$

By independence

$$E \exp t\chi^2_{n_1} \exp t\chi^2_{n_2} = E \exp t\chi^2_{n_1} E \exp t\chi^2_{n_2}$$

is clearly $(1 - 2t)^{-n_1/2} (1 - 2t)^{-n_2/2}$. Combining terms we obtain

$$(1 - 2t)^{-(n_1 + n_2)/2}$$

Letting $n_1 + n_2 = n$ we find $m(t) = (1 - 2t)^{-n/2}$, which is the moment generating function of the $\chi_n{}^2$ distribution. Hence if $\chi^2_{n_1}$ and $\chi^2_{n_2}$ are independent χ^2's with n_1 and n_2 degrees of freedom respectively, then their sum is distributed as $\chi_n{}^2$. The following generalization may then be made. If $\chi^2_{n_1}$ and $\chi^2_{n_2}$ are independent chi-square variables distributed with $n_1 + n_2 = n$ d.f. their sum $\chi^2_{n_1} + \chi^2_{n_2}$ is distributed as $\chi^2_{(n)}$ with n d.f.

appendix G

The Kolmogorov-Smirnov Statistic; Charts for 0.95 and 0.99 Confidence regions[1]

The Kolmogorov-Smirnov statistic[1] can be used to test the hypothesis that two sample-cumulative-frequency distributions were drawn from populations having the same distribution. The solution depends on a graphic procedure to determine d_n (the maximum vertical deviation measured directly from the graph between two sample-cumulative-frequency distributions). If the statistic d_n exceeds a fixed value obtained from tables,[2] then at a given probability level the two frequency distributions are considered to have been drawn from different populations.

The test has several advantages. It is easy to use and the procedure is graphic; thus the computations are reduced to a minimum. A large number of samples can be tested against each other on the same plot. The test is nonparametric, no assumptions need be made about the form of the population-frequency distribution. The writers consider this to be of particular importance in many geologic problems. The assumption of normality is not only often not justified in view of the lack of information, but theoretical considerations often require markedly non-normal distributions. Finally, the test is not subject to the very small sample limitation of χ^2, e.g., the minimum of 5 for the theoretical frequency in each class interval.

[1] Several applications of the Kolmogorov-Smirnov statistic have been made to geological problems: R. L. Miller, and E. C. Olson, 1955, The statistical stability of quantitative properties as a fundamental criterion for the study of environments, *Jour. Geol.* 63: 376–387 and E. T. Degens, E. G. Williams, and M. I. Keith, 1957, Environmental studies of Carboniferous sediments. I. Geochemical criteria for differentiating marine from fresh water shales, *Bull. A.A.P.G.* 41: 2427–2455.

[2] A brief discussion of the test and tables for d_n is found in Dixon and Massey, 1951, pp. 256–257.

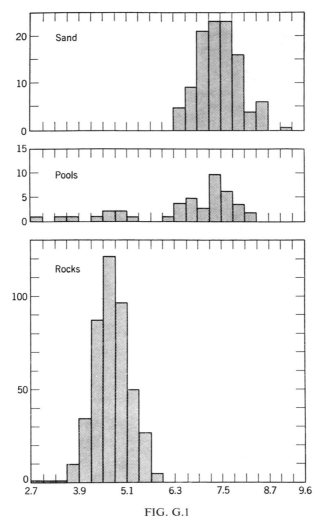

FIG. G.1

The following example will serve to illustrate the procedure. The data shown in histogram form, Fig. G.1, display the frequency distribution of a size measure on Mytilus in each of three subenvironments. We desire to test the hypothesis that these three sample-frequency distributions were drawn from populations having the same frequency distribution. The three cumulative-sample-frequency distributions are plotted on the same graph (see Fig. G.2). Note that (1) because of differences in sample size, different scales are used, and (2) because of large size of two of the samples, a grouping into class intervals is made. The class intervals in this case are

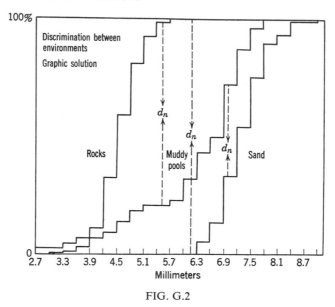

FIG. G.2

0.3 mm as shown along the abscissa. The ordinate is divided into units which correspond to the sample size. For example, the subdivision of the ordinate from 0 to 100% for rocks is 431 units, and for pools, 45 units, which are approximately $9\frac{1}{2}$ times as large as the units for rocks.

TABLE G.1

Results of Application of Kolmogorov-Smirnov Test to Comparison of Sample-Size-Frequency Distributions[1] of Live Mytilus Collected from Three Different Environments[2]

Sand vs. Muddy Pools	Sand vs. Rocks	Muddy Pools vs. Rocks
$d_n = 0.3933$	$d_n = 1.00$	$d_n = 0.777$
Signif. $_{.05} = 0.2407$	Signif. $_{0.05} = 0.1469$	Signif. $_{0.05} = 0.2122$
Conclusion: different	Conclusion: different	Conclusion: different

[1] Sample sizes: muddy pools = 45; sand = 105; rocks = 431.
[2] Collection by Richard Bader, near Bar Harbor, Maine.

The maximum vertical deviations (d_n) between the several environments are indicated on the graph. Note that d_n between sand and rocks is 100%. Table G.1 summarizes the results. For comparison, the table includes the minimum deviation required at the 0.05 level (signif.$_{0.05}$), to say that a given pair of samples are drawn from two separate populations.

0.95 AND 0.99 CONFIDENCE REGIONS FOR THE KOLMOGOROV-SMIRNOV TEST FOR SAMPLE SIZES OF 2 TO 300

Use of the Charts (Figs. G.3 and G.4)

The discussion below illustrates how the charts are used for comparison of an observed cumulative step-function with a completely specified cumulative frequency distribution function, $F(x)$. In this illustration we shall use the 0.99 level of significance.

1. The null hypothesis is that $F(x)$ is the correct population cumulative frequency distribution for the observed sample cumulative step-function.

2. For given sample size N, read from the abscissa directly to the 0.99 curve and over to $\epsilon_{N,0.99}$ on the ordinate.

3. The value of $\epsilon_{N,0.99}$ so obtained is a number such that $\mathrm{Pr.}\{D_N < \epsilon_{N,0.99}\}$ = 0.99. If the observed maximum discrepancy (D_N) exceeds the number $\epsilon_{N,0.99}$, the null hypothesis is rejected on the grounds that 99% of the time in repeated sampling we would not expect so large a discrepancy between a step-function for a sample of given population and the population cumulative frequency distribution function.

The charts have also been used for comparison of the cumulative step-functions of two independent samples of sizes n_1 and n_2.

1. The null hypothesis is that the two continuous population cumulative distributions from which the samples were drawn, are the same. Thus if the observed maximum discrepancy between the two sample cumulative step-functions is significantly large, the null hypothesis is rejected.

2. Compute the number $n_1 n_2/(n_1 + n_2)$, which is then read directly as N on the abscissa of the appropriate chart. For comparison of two samples, use of the ratio is correct asymptotically. [See Smirnov (1948).]

Table G.2 gives comparison of results with several other methods. The three methods compared are (1) an exact method given by Massey (1951), also discussed in Goodman (1954), (2) an approximation based on Kolmogorov's asymptotic equation, Smirnov (1948), and (3) the approximation to the exact values given by Birnbaum (1952) as discussed above. The table gives comparative values for $\epsilon_{n_1 n_2;0.95}$ and $\epsilon_{n_1 n_2;0.99}$, where $\mathrm{Pr.}\{D_{n_1 n_2} < \epsilon_{n_1 n_2;0.95}\} = 0.95$ and $\mathrm{Pr.}\{D_{n_1 n_2} < \epsilon_{n_1 n_2;0.99}\} = 0.99$, and $D_{n_1 n_2}$ is the maximum observed discrepancy between two sample cumulative step-functions of sample sizes n_1 and n_2. In the table, $\epsilon_{n_1 n_2;0.95}$ and $\epsilon_{n_1 n_2;0.99}$ represent exact values taken from Massey's tables; $\hat{\epsilon}_{n_1 n_2;0.95}$ and $\hat{\epsilon}_{n_1 n_2;0.99}$, represent approximate values read from the curves given in the present charts; $K_{n_1 n_2;0.95}$ and $K_{n_1 n_2;0.99}$ are approximate values computed from the table given in Smirnov (1948).

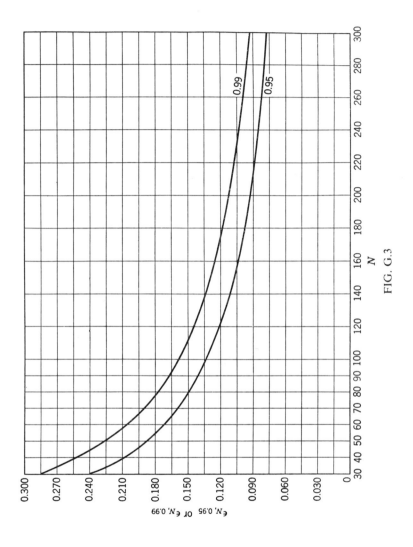

FIG. G.3

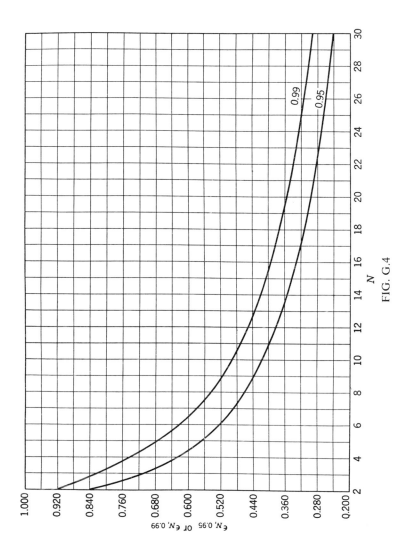

FIG. G.4

It is recommended that these charts (Figs. G.3, G.4) be used whenever extreme accuracy is not required.

TABLE G.2

Comparison of Results Using Approximation Given in Paper With Exact Values and Smirnov's Approximation (for Sample Sizes $n_1 = n_2$)

$n_1 = n_2$	$\epsilon_{n_1 n_2; 0.95}$	$\hat{\epsilon}_{n_1 n_2; 0.95}$	$K_{n_1 n_2; 0.95}$
7	0.714	0.668	0.730
10	0.600	0.566	0.607
22	0.409	0.394	0.410
33	0.333	0.326	0.334
39	0.308	0.300	0.308
	$\epsilon_{n_1 n_2; 0.99}$	$\hat{\epsilon}_{n_1 n_2; 0.99}$	$K_{n_1 n_2; 0.99}$
7	0.857	0.784	0.870
10	0.700	0.676	0.728
13	0.615	0.556	0.638
16	0.562	0.542	0.576
20	0.500	0.490	0.515
27	0.444	0.426	0.443

REFERENCES

Z. W. Birnbaum, 1952, Numerical tabulation of the distribution of Kolmogorov's statistic for finite samples sizes, *J. Amer. Stats. Assoc.* 47: 425–441.

L. A. Goodman, 1954, Kolmogorov-Smirnov tests for psychological research, *Psychological Bull.* 51: 160–168.

N. Smirnov, 1948; Table for estimating the goodness of fit of empirical distributions, *Annals Math. Stats.* 19: 279–81.

F. J. Massey, 1951, Distribution of maximum deviation between two sample cumulative step functions, *Annals Math. Stats.* 22: 125ff.

Author Index

Subject Index